LIFE AND
PATTERNS OF ORDER

LIFE AND PATTERNS OF ORDER

THOMAS A. STEYAERT
Diablo Valley College
Pleasant Hill, California

McGRAW-HILL BOOK COMPANY
New York, St. Louis, San Francisco,
Düsseldorf, Johannesburg, Kuala Lumpur,
London, Mexico, Montreal,
New Delhi, Panama, Rio de Janeiro,
Singapore, Sydney, Toronto

LIFE AND
PATTERNS OF ORDER

*Library of Congress Catalog Card
Number 70-129492*

07–061340–0

'34567890   VHVH   798765432

This book was set in Optima by
Progressive Typographers,
and printed on permanent paper
and bound by Von Hoffmann Press, Inc.
The designer was J. Paul Kirouac;
the drawings were done by
Del Gatto/Bego. The photo editor was
Mary Ann Akmakjian.
The editors were James R. Young,
Hiag Akmakjian, Jeremy Robinson, and
Ellen Simon.
Peter D. Guilmette supervised
production.

ACKNOWLEDGMENTS

Quote for opening of Chapter Two,
page 13:
"The Idea of Order at Key West."
Copyright 1936 and renewed 1964 by
Holly Stevens Stephenson. Reprinted
from *The Collected Poems of Wallace
Stevens* by permission of Alfred A.
Knopf, Inc.

Quote on page 25:
From W. Bateson: "Mendel's
Principles of Heredity" published by
Cambridge University Press—copyright
date 1909. By permission of the
publisher.

Table 3.1 on page 43:
From *Elements of Biology* by P. B.
Weisz. Copyright © 1961, 1965,
1969 by McGraw-Hill, Inc. Used
with permission of McGraw-Hill Book
Company.
Quote for opening of Chapter Four,
page 71:
From "Miss T" by Walter de la Mare.
Used with permission of The Literary
Trustees of Walter de la Mare and
The Society of Authors.
Table 9.1 on page 182:
From *Biology* by W. L. Smallwood
and E. R. Green. Copyright 1968
by Silver Burdett. Used by permission.
Figure 14.1 on page 294:
From *Life: An Introduction to Biology,*
2nd Edition, by George Gaylord
Simpson and William S. Beck, © 1957,
1965 by Harcourt Brace Jovanovich and
reproduced with their permission.
Adapted from *Principles of Animal
Ecology,* Allee et al., Philadelphia,
Saunders, 1949. After A. Leopold,
Wisconsin Conservation Department
Publication No. 321 (1943), with
permission; after Gause.
Figure 14.3 on page 296:
From *Life: An Introduction to Biology,*
2nd Edition, by George Gaylord
Simpson and William S. Beck, © 1957,
1965 by Harcourt Brace Jovanovich
and reproduced with their permission.
Adapted from *Principles of Animal*

Ecology, Allee et al.,
Philadelphia, Saunders, 1949. After
A. Leopold, Wisconsin Conservation
Department Publication No. 321
(1943), with permission.
Figure 14.6 on page 299:
From *Life: An Introduction to Biology,*
2nd Edition, by George Gaylord
Simpson and William S. Beck, © 1957,
1965 by Harcourt Brace Jovanovich and
reproduced with their permission.
Adapted from *Principles of Animal
Ecology,* Allee et al., Philadelphia,
Saunders, 1949. Adapted from D. A.
MacLulich, University of Toronto
Biological Series No. 43, 1937.

Figure 16.6 on page 354:
From *Life: An Introduction to Biology,*
2nd Edition, by George Gaylord
Simpson and William S. Beck, © 1957,
1965 by Harcourt Brace Jovanovich and
reproduced with their permission.
Adapted from *Principles of Animal
Ecology,* Allee et al., Philadelphia,
Saunders, 1949. Adapted with
permission from Lack: *Darwin's
Finches,* Cambridge, Cambridge
University Press, 1947.

Table 20.1 on page 439:
From *The Science of Biology* by P. B.
Weisz. Copyright © 1959, 1963,
1967 by McGraw-Hill, Inc. Used
with permission of McGraw-Hill Book
Company.

This book is intended for use in one-semester or one-quarter courses in introductory biology. It attempts to convey adventures of inquiry as well as discovered knowledge and insights of biology to college freshmen who are not planning to make biology their major. The material has been chosen for its relevance to the personal life of the student as well as to other courses in a general education or liberal arts program.

Clarity of expression is sought in this text by keeping technical words to a minimum and language lively. Discussions are constantly related to pervading themes, thus drawing the book into a perceivable whole.

The text is organized into six parts. Part 1 looks at biology as a search for patterns of order in the living world and describes how scientists in the past have developed generalizations about heredity, evolution, and the cell as the basic unit of life. Parts 2 to 4 cover metabolism, growth and reproduction, and homeostasis as the three major characteristics of living things. All levels of organization are brought into the discussion of each of these three major functions. Metabolism, for example, is presented in the context of feeding relationships in ecosystems as well as photosynthesis and respiration in cells. Homeostasis is presented as the order found in systems from atoms to oceans. Heredity is described as the physical means by which this order is inherited and perpetuated.

Some instructors may be concerned by the placing of Mendel and his laws in a historical context in Chapter 2 and emphasizing neither in Chapter 8. I can only say that experience has demonstrated that these laws are not necessary for an understanding of genetics in this century. Undue emphasis on the work of Mendel may distract the student from the real issue, namely, the behavior of chromosomes and the genes they contain.

Human growth and development is not emphasized in Chapter 10 but is delayed until Chapter 12. This organization is based on the assumption that it is more conducive to understanding if only one type of embryo, in this case the extensively studied amphibian, is emphasized and all variations on this theme arbitrarily ignored. Studies with cell and tissue cultures are then taken up and it is emphasized that the generalizations learned in this study of growth and development in cells and tissues in culture and in the intact amphibian embryo are applicable in large part to these same processes in all vertebrates and, to a lesser degree, in invertebrates.

Human growth and development is discussed in Chapter 12 as an excellent example of homeostasis. The interactions between sense receptors and nerves, hormones and endocrine glands, and the behavior of an individual as embryo or as father or mother not only exemplifies homeostatic feedback mechanisms but it is also knowledge of paramount importance to students and the world's population.

Part 5 consists of a discussion of the genetic and environmental components of the process of evolution as well as the patterns of diversity in microbes, plants, and animals that are its product. Part 6 discusses the evolution of man as a primate who has evolved not only a mind but also the ability to alter and jeopardize all the ecosystems of the world. Stress is placed upon man as a functional component of ecosystems, a part of nature and apart from nature, and the only organism capable of deciding the future course of his evolution.

With this content and approach this book should permit close integration with the social sciences. Chapter 1 presents the diverse ways that different disciplines look at the world before launching into the biological point of view. Genetics of man is presented in Chapters 8 and 9, and the role of heredity and environment is included in Chapter 10. Population biology and animal behavior are extensively described in Chapters 13 to 15, and social and cultural evolution are emphasized in Chapters 16, 21, and 22. Birth control is described in Chapter 12 and debated in Chapter 22.

Whenever possible, the example used for reference or expansion of an idea is man, but the book is not a watered-down anatomy or physiology text. Although it includes some simple discussions of cell specialization and internal organization and function, it goes into detail on human physiology only in reference to the nervous, endocrine, and reproductive systems. This detail is necessary to support the discussions of homeostasis and reproduction, two topics of great interest to the student and vital to the future of the world.

Ecology is not handled in a separate chapter but is a constant theme to which all discussions are related and placed in perspective. Similarly, evolution is not a separate chapter at the beginning, where it would not be understood, or at the end, where it would not aid in the understanding of the preceding material. Instead, it is constantly brought into discussions throughout the text and explained in detail only after genetic and environmental components are understood.

The most significant feature of the book is its emphasis on man in an ecological perspective. A plea for ecological responsibility is placed in the last chapter. Having read and understood the preceding chapters, the student can consider these ecological arguments from a rational point of view and reach conclusions with the help of empirical evidence.

At the end of each chapter the Suggestions for Further Reading have been selected on the basis of scientific merit and suitability for a college freshman just beginning biology. *Scientific American* offprints have not been listed because they are so well known to teachers, who can decide whether to make them available.

Review Questions included at the end of each chapter may be used as assignments or for self-testing. Most questions serve to review the material in the chapters.

An extensive glossary with definitions of technical terms and Greek and Latin roots is provided.

The text is accompanied by a study guide.

I should like to acknowledge the suggestions made so freely by the students who used this text in its early manuscript forms. Their patience, interest, and enthusiasm provided great encouragement.

With humility I acknowledge the support, encouragement, humor, and constructive criticisms of my colleagues at Diablo Valley College, in particular those who have used the manuscript as a text since its inception in 1965.

During the early stages of development of this text Cebern S. Jones was my typist, whom I should like to thank. In the final stages my typist and publisher of preliminary editions was June S. Castle, whom I wish to thank, together with her husband Elias, and their family for the dedication and professional excellence they demonstrated. I would also like to acknowledge and thank Cheryl Beal for typing the Study Guide and the Instructor's Manual which supplement this text.

During the evolution of this book the forces of natural selection as well as variation were aided immensely by reviews of the manuscript in either partial or complete form, and I would like to express my gratitude to these reviewers for their invaluable contribution, particularly Eric Davidson, Daniel Koblick, W. M. Laetsch, John Palmer, and Stephen Wolfe.

THOMAS A. STEYAERT

Part 1
The Search
for Patterns of Order

The world of living things often appears as a chaos of unrelated events. The various disciplines of knowledge attempt to construct patterns to explain these events. Several men in the last century developed generalizations about heredity, evolution, and the cell as the basic unit of life. Their ideas formed the foundations upon which the modern patterns of order in biology are based.

The sea.   (*Courtesy of M. Chapman.*)

Chapter 1
Perceiving Order in the Living World

*Being alive: hissing waves
rustling like wind-blown leaves
of summer trees at night.*

Kurokawa

Man is a unique animal in that
he searches for order in the
world he lives in. Looking
through the chaos of seemingly
unrelated events, he tries to
perceive their inherent patterns
of order. By interpreting these
patterns in a rational framework he attempts to understand
all life around him.

THE SEARCH FOR ORDER
DISCIPLINES: FIELDS OF STUDY

There are many ways in which man attempts to understand the organization of the universe, the world, and himself. Areas of study and investigation range from the level of the atom to the mind of men, from interactions between atoms to interactions between minds. The purpose of man's labors in the various fields of study, or *disciplines,* is to understand the universe and man's place in it (see Figure 1.1).

THEORIES AND UNDERSTANDING DATA

What does "understand" really mean? Generally, it means becoming familiar enough with an event to be able to *predict* its outcome. Familiarity is developed by sensing and perceiving the various elements of an event. These elements may be fitted together, or synthesized, into a generalization, a *theory,* which can be taken as symbolizing the sequence of causes which produced that event, and under similar conditions events similar to it will result.

THEORETICAL MODELS

Man's knowledge consists of theoretical *models* which he and his predecessors have constructed as explanations of natural phenomena. Models, like theories, are superimposed by man on nature, and because they are based on current knowledge, they must be flexible and subject to change. Models accepted as explanations in one age or culture are not necessarily accepted by a later period of time or another culture. Theoretical models are formed in many different ways, but the methods generally involve two basic classes of mental process: (1) *Deduction* is the logical process of drawing new conclusions from a set of assumptions or *premises,* and (2) *induction* is the process of reasoning from the specific to the general, from an individual fact or facts to a generalization, a theoretical model proposing to describe all similar events.

FIGURE 1.1 Knowledge is acquired through various fields of study called *disciplines*. This figure places the major disciplines side by side to show how each one is intimately related to the one next to it.

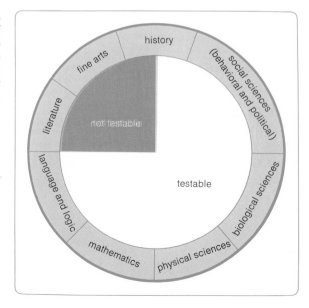

1 Existing knowledge, induction, deduction, intuition → proposed hypothesis.
2 Deduction → predictions of events which will occur if hypothesis is correct.
3 Descriptive or experimental tests reveal whether events in fact occur as predicted.
4 Hypothesis, if tests demonstrate its validity, is called a *theory.*

FIGURE 1.2 Scientific method.

Science is knowledge gained systematically and logically. Often it is said that there is a *scientific method,* a procedure followed by scientists as they pursue knowledge. Too often students picture a rigid sequence of steps that a scientist follows as he "grinds out" new theories. A better view is that the scientific method is a combination of *intuition, induction, deduction,* and *testing* (see Figure 1.2). Through intuition and inductive reasoning from what is already known the scientist constructs a tentative model proposing to describe the phenomenon he is studying. Using this model (or hypothesis) as his premise, he then makes predictions of events through deduction. Further experience shows whether the events occur as predicted.

SCIENCE AND ITS METHODS

There are two ways the predictions deduced from the model can be tested for validity, descriptive studies and experimental studies. *Descriptive studies* usually involve no significant alteration of natural conditions and consist of observations in which the normal behavior of the things being studied is determined, given the particular conditions existing at the time. On the other hand, *experimental studies* usually involve artificial manipulation of the conditions to which the organisms or materials being studied are exposed. All the factors which may affect the outcome of the experiment should ideally be known and controlled, so that only *one variable* exists, the factor being tested. The sample with the factor under investigation is referred to as the *experimental sample.* Other samples lack the factor being tested and are termed *controls.* Controls are used as a frame of reference to which the experimental samples can be compared. The ultimate object of a series of experiments is usually to establish the theoretical reliability of a generalization. In science the reliability of a theory is measured by one's ability to predict an event or observation correctly on the basis of the theory. The degree of predictability depends in part upon the amount of evidence assembled in support of the theory. The greater the similarity between the way an event was predicted to occur and the way it actually occurs in the experiment, the greater the probability that the event will occur as predicted under natural conditions in the future.

Truths and facts are the result of consensual validation of what is perceived. Human beings have a natural sensibility to hidden patterns existing within what they perceive. Some people have a more emotional response to the clues hidden in their experiences and sense a problem based upon these clues. They may proceed to the construction of theories to explain the phenomena they perceive. These people are among those we call creative, and they exist within all the disciplines of knowledge.

But there must be agreement about what is perceived, and it is this validation which yields facts and truths.

Both science and art rely upon intuition and perception. What are they? No one has yet been able to construct an acceptable explanation of how judgments are made. How the mind proceeds from general to specific or from facts to generalization is not known. It is clear, however, that how man perceives his environment with his various senses has much to do with the patterns of knowledge he constructs. This perception is limited by man's intelligence, his accumulated knowledge, the quality of his senses, the prevailing attitudes of his culture, and his relationships with what he is perceiving. To make order out of the chaos, to see patterns existing in separate events, man must recognize whether events are random or connected.

HOW DOES AN ARTIST SEARCH FOR ORDER IN THE SEA?

The disciplines collectively called the arts may convey understandings of the world that cannot be put into words. It is, for example, inherently impossible to reduce Leonardo da Vinci's Mona Lisa or one of Beethoven's symphonies to sentences with words conveying the same impressions or feelings as the originals. We can, however, read poems such as the two haiku in Figure 1.3 and perceive how different poets describe patterns of order in the sea.

HOW WOULD A SCIENTIST SEARCH FOR ORDER IN THE SEA?

Although we could talk at length about the nature of each of the various disciplines constituting the life sciences as a whole, the best way to understand their likenesses and differences is to see what the people in each discipline do. Let us consider an imaginary group of men from the life sciences and social sciences assembled at a marine laboratory. By asking each in turn to describe his field of work we shall be better able to see how a common object of concern, the ocean, can be studied from many points of view. We shall begin with the social scientists.

FIGURE 1.3 How two poets perceive the sea.

Sea
The spring sea;
all day long
undulating, down and up.
                    Buson

At Matsushima
Islands all around
with pointed pine trees.
How cool the wind sounds.
                    Shiki

The *economist* may explain that he has come to the coast to study the feasibility of producing fresh water from seawater. He might say: "The world water shortage is actually in agricultural water and not domestic water. The technical problems of removing the salt from ocean water are essentially solved, and we are now trying to decrease the cost of pumping the water inland to where most of the farmlands are. So far, we cannot afford to pump water higher than 900 feet. Beyond that the cost becomes prohibitive despite the demand."

A *psychologist* among the group of social scientists might be addressing his attention to a different aspect of the ocean. "I am studying emotional reactions to stress in men working on the ocean floor in submersible vehicles. We are concerned with the drop in level of performance by these men after being under water for several days. I am trying to isolate and identify the factors in the environment which seem to be most important in causing this change in the men's behavior. Then we can either eliminate these factors from the environment or set up a test to identify those men who are susceptible to these stresses. Perhaps we shall do both."

There are, of course, numerous other social sciences, but we must move on to the *biologists,* because their work is the theme of this book. Basically, biologists work with interactions between organisms and their environment, with organisms, or within their component units, the cells. Biologists of the first group who consider the interactions between environments and populations are termed ecologists.

An *ecologist* might say: "The growing human population must look more and more to the sea as a source of food. My research has suggested that the amount of food we can take from the sea cannot be increased indefinitely without fatally disrupting the natural balance between the different organisms living in the sea, but the interrelationships between organisms and their environment in the ocean is just beginning to be understood. Through my research here I am trying to describe the food chain of the sardine, that is, the sequence by which food and energy reach the fish. I want to know which organisms the sardine eats and which organisms those organisms eat until I understand the entire food chain down to the one-celled plants which lie at the beginning of the sequence.[1] In addition, I want to describe the cycling of minerals through this food chain from producers to consumers to decomposers and back to the producers. I shall attempt to learn something of the social behavior of the sardine to better understand the means by which they exist in cohesive groups rather than as isolated individuals. When we know more about the interactions within sardine schools and between sardines and their environment, it should be possible to find means by which man may become a more responsible consumer in the food chains of the sea as well as of the land."

A *physiologist* might say at this point. "Populations do what they do because of what organisms do. To really understand the role of sardines in the sea you must

FIGURE 1.4 Schematic drawing of a food chain for marine organisms. The shark eats cod, cod eat herring, and herring eat smaller fish and crustaceans, which eat diatoms.

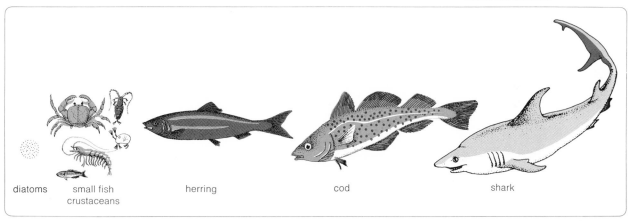

diatoms   small fish   herring   cod   shark
crustaceans

[1] A schematic drawing of a food chain for a marine organism can be seen in Figure 1.4.

understand their anatomy and physiology, the reasons for their behavior, as well as the means by which they have grown and developed to their adult size. It is also important to understand the organization of their organ systems. My research deals with the locomotion of the sardine. I am studying the means by which nerve impulses travel from the sense receptors to the brain and back out the nerves to the muscles which they cause to contract. The cause of behavioral acts like swimming is physiological, and in order to understand that behavior we must study its physiological basis as it exists in the nervous and muscular systems."

A *cell biologist* might reply: "It is clear that an organism's behavior is the result of the behavior of its cells. An organism is made of cells, or the products of cells, and every bit of work an organism does is actually done by cells. If you are to understand how a sardine swims, you must understand the structure and function of muscle cells. A muscle does work as a result of shortening, and the muscle shortens as a result of the shortening of thousands of muscle cells in it. My research here at the marine laboratory has shown that muscle cells contract because of the telescopic sliding together of ratchetlike filaments which make up most of the bulk of muscle cells. I am going to study this process more intensively by using an electron microscope, which can provide views of muscle cells magnified over 100,000 times. From these closeup pictures of muscle-cell structure I hope to develop a model of how the contractile elements actually function."

Included in our seaside group are several *biochemists,* one of whom might add: "Cells are made of molecules, and the function of the cell is ultimately the result of the behavior of these molecules. Consider a muscle cell. To understand the contraction of the filaments in a muscle cell we have to understand how the molecules of the filaments are synthesized and what causes them to function. Our problem is an investigation into the means by which particular cell proteins are formed according to the directions inherited by the cell in its chromosomes. The structure and function of an organism are based on the characteristics of its proteins. Since an organism's structure and function ultimately depends on its inherited characteristics, heredity must specify the nature of the proteins, which in turn affect the traits of the organism."

A *biophysicist* standing nearby might add: "The nature of a molecule is a result of the nature of the atoms from which it is formed. Atoms bond together to form molecules, and the type of bond varies with the type of atom. Since molecules contain various kinds of atoms, they contain various kinds of bonds. To understand molecules one must understand the forces within and between molecules and the energies stored in the bonds. My research deals with the nature of the bonds that form and break in rapid sequence while the contractile filaments of a muscle cell are sliding past each other. To determine the structure of the contractile filaments I am going to direct a beam of x-rays through a preparation of purified muscle-filament protein arranged in front of a photographic plate. The structure of the molecules will be determined from the images formed on the plate by the x-rays deflected from the

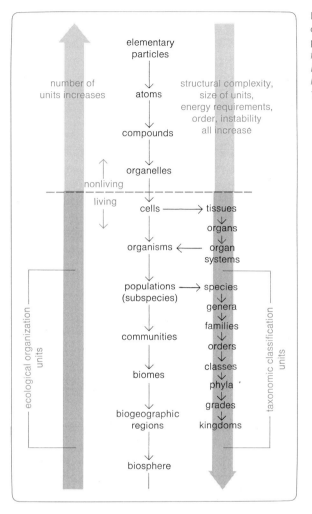

FIGURE 1.5 Hierarchy of levels of organization, from elementary particles to biosphere. *(Adapted from Paul B. Weisz, Elements of Biology, 2d ed. Copyright McGraw-Hill Book Company, 1965. Used by permission.)*

molecules. This information will make it possible to construct a model of the contractile molecules and to hypothesize about the types of bonds existing in its structure.''

Our group of scientists by the sea is hypothetical, of course, but it allows us to see how men labor in diverse ways to understand all the aspects of the same living world. Though each investigator concentrates on a particular problem, he must also be aware that other fields of study are relevant to his own; each area of investigation has bearing on many others. To understand the biology of any organism we need to know about its ecology, its organ systems, organs, tissues, cells, and molecules

HOW IS THE LIVING
WORLD ORGANIZED?

(see Figure 1.5). Various *levels of organization* can be perceived in the living world, and the study of an organism must be placed in its proper perspective: It is made up of units smaller than itself, and in turn it is part of higher levels of organization that are larger and more complex. Consider our sardine, for example; its movement, like that of any other animal, is effected by the shortening of its muscles, and in order to understand this phenomenon we must comprehend the physiological nature of muscle contraction. A complete understanding, however, demands that we know the nature of those interactions between the sardine and its environment which make it respond with a sequence of impulses cascading through its nervous and skeletal systems from sensory organs to nerve cells to muscle cells and their contractile molecular parts. The arrival of the nerve impulse at the muscle cell causes a release of chemical energy, which alters the chemical bonds in the contractile filaments and makes them telescope together. As a result the muscle cells shorten, and the muscle contracts as a whole, causing the skeletal system to be moved from one position to another. This motion may propel the sardine through the water, but it may also have further effects. For example, it could attract the attention of a shark waiting to eat the sardine.

Is any one level of organization in this sequence more important than the others? It is evident that each level of organization perceived in the natural world is integrated closely with the others. The lowest level of organization having all the characteristics we associate with life is the cell. The function of the cell, in turn, depends on complex and highly regulated interactions taking place among the molecules the cell has synthesized. Living organisms behave as they do as a result of their past experience and according to the hereditary messages carried in their cells. Though the cell is the basic unit of life, it cannot exist in a multicellular organism unless the organism provides it with nutrients. To get food, the organism must depend upon interactions with its environment, its fellow organisms, and its prey. It is clear that no one level of study, in the analysis of the living organism, can be regarded as ''more important'' than any other. Complete understanding demands a far broader scope than the knowledge encompassed in any one field.

Biology is the accumulation of knowledge about the various levels of organization in the living world, gained through the painstaking efforts of a great many investigators. The next chapter describes some of the key figures in the early days of the search for patterns of order in the living world.

REVIEW QUESTIONS
1 Contrast the means by which man searches for order in the arts and sciences.
2 What does ''to understand'' mean?
3 How are generalizations constructed?
4 What is the scientific method?
5 How is a pattern of order differentiated from randomness when an array of events is observed?

Bronowski, J.:* *Science and Human Values,* Harper Torchbooks 505, Harper & Row, Publishers, Incorporated, New York, 1959. The impact of science on ethics and human values as well as on our physical environment.

Butterfield, H.: ''The Scientific Revolution,'' *Scientific American,* September, 1960. An easy-to-read account of the growth of science since the Renaissance.

Cassidy, H. G.: *The Sciences and the Arts: A New Alliance,* Harper & Row, Publishers, Incorporated, New York, 1962. A refreshing synthesis of ideas about how the sciences and arts view the world.

Conant, J. B.: *On Understanding Science,* Yale University Press, New Haven, Conn., 1947.

Conant, J. B.: *Science and Common Sense,* Yale University Press, New Haven, Conn., 1951.

Conant, J. B.: *Modern Science and Modern Man,* Columbia University Press, New York, 1952. In Conant's three books a noted scientist and educator discusses the methods of science, the nature of scientific research, and the role of science in society.

Terman, L. M.: ''Are Scientists Different?'', *Scientific American,* January, 1955. General characteristics of scientists compared with those of nonscientists by a well-known psychologist.

SUGGESTIONS FOR
FURTHER READING

* Available in paperback.

Peas. (*Courtesy o*
M. Chapman.)

Chapter 2
Searching for Order
in the Living World

It was her voice that made
The sky acutest at its vanishing.
She measured to the hour its solitude.
She was the single artificer of the world
In which she sang. And when she sang, the sea,
Whatever self it had, became the self
That was her song, for she was maker. Then we,
As we beheld her striding there alone,
Knew that there never was a world for her
Except the one she sang and, singing, made.

Stevens

It might be said that man has always been a biologist. He has always attempted to understand the nature and habits of plants and animals he is familiar with as well as their interrelationships. We shall deal with these questions by means of the concept of *organic evolution by natural selection,* which is among the great unifying concepts in modern biology.

EVOLUTIONARY THEORY
THE GRAND SCALE OF BEING, AN EARLY THEORY OF NATURAL DIVERSITY

The development of the concept of evolution began long ago. Early attempts to explain the origin and the purpose of the diverse forms of life on earth took the form of belief in a Grand Scale of Being, also known as *scala naturae*, Chain of Being, *échelle des êtres*, Ladder of Perfection, and so on. According to this idea, which descends to us from ancient Jewish and Greek sources, God created the world so that all matter forms a continuum, a continuous sequential order from nonliving to living, with man at the top of the scale. All living things, it was thought, could be placed on this ladder so that every organism ranked either higher or lower than others. This was believed to be the Creator's plan, and learned efforts were made to find, identify, and place organisms in their proper places on the Grand Scale of Being.

Sir Thomas Browne (1605–1682)
(The Bettmann Archive.)

No adherent of the concept of the Grand Scale of Being would have questioned a decision to place the orangutan high on the ladder next to man. It was obvious that there is a great similarity between man and the great apes, and therefore it was only proper to place an animal similar to man near him on the ladder. But what was to be placed above man on the ladder? Sir Thomas Browne wrote in *Religio Medici* (1643): "There is in this Universe a Stair rising not disorderly, or in confusion but with a comely method and proportion." He pictured this Scale of Nature proceeding from minerals to lower forms of life to man and on to the angels in imperceptible degrees. Browne pictured man as existing in both physical and spiritual universes. Man was "that great and true Amphibium, whose nature is disposed to live . . . in divided and distinguished worlds."

The Scale of Being was a static concept of nature in which Creation had taken place according to a Divine Plan at a fixed time in the past. Throughout the Middle Ages in Europe this concept remained dominant. As perceived by the men of that time the pattern of order in the living world is unchanging, divinely inspired, and perfect.

AGE OF EXPLORATION

Toward the end of the Middle Ages explorers began to sail to distant islands and continents. They reported many new and strange creatures, thereby raising questions how these newly discovered organisms were to be placed in the grand scheme of things. Man understands and symbolizes with words and names. He has a need to categorize and to name, and categorization requires an understanding of the relationships among the objects being classified. The educated post-Renaissance public was fascinated with the problem of finding a pattern of order for the naming of living things, or what we would term today a system of classification.

THE CLASSIFICATION SYSTEM OF LINNAEUS

Carl von Linné was born in 1707 in Sweden and took a medical degree in Holland. In 1737 he published his *Systema Naturae*, in which he developed the convention that scientific names of animals and plants should consist of two words representing the *genus* and the *species*. The genus name indicates a generalized type consisting of organisms obviously related, such as doglike forms. The *species* name is an adjective which restricts the scientific name to a particular group of organisms in

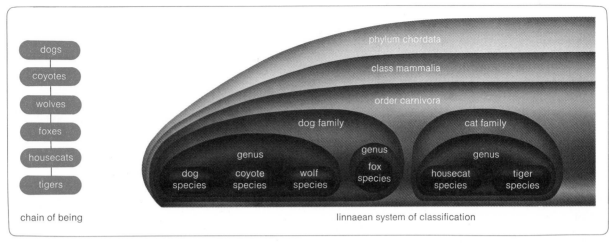

chain of being

linnaean system of classification

FIGURE 2.2 These seven groups are the major classifications in taxonomic rank. Between these groups smaller subdivisions can be added by using the prefixes *super-* and *sub-*. For example, going from phylum to class; phylum, subphylum; superclass, class.

Taxonomic rank

Kingdom
  Phylum
    Class
      Order
        Family
          Genus
            Species

nature. Thus, *Canis lupus* indicates the wolf, while *Canis familiaris* refers to the domesticated dog. Both species are included in the doglike genus, *Canis*. Domestic dogs clearly constitute a unique group of animals in nature, and they are obviously more similar to wolves than to cats. Therefore dogs are placed with wolves in the same *generic* category, thus showing their close relationship, while cats are placed in separate categories. Dogs, wolves, and cats, however, have more in common with each other than with a cow; and in the linnaean system they are grouped together in a higher, more inclusive category (see Figure 2.1). Linné organized all the living things he was familiar with into a *pattern of classification* better than any which had been suggested before; higher groups are more inclusive, lower groups less inclusive and more specific. The lowest unit of classification is the *species,* including only organisms which are very much alike. *Genus* is on the next level higher than species and contains various species whose differences are greater than the differences within a species. Genera (plural for genus) are grouped into *orders* in the linnaean system (in later years the category of *family* was introduced between genus and order) and orders into *classes* and *phyla* (plural for *phylum*). These, in turn, are combined under *kingdom,* the highest and most inclusive category (see Figure 2.2).

Linné assigned all names in Latin because that was the language of educated people in the eighteenth century. As was common among scholars, he also latinized his own name and became Carolus Linnaeus, the name by which we know him.

Linnaeus was a major influence in changing the concept of relationships among living things from the linear Chain of Being to the inclusive and exclusive groupings of his system of classification. It was no longer debated whether a dog is "higher" or "lower" than a wolf or a coyote but whether they are in the same genus and, if so, how distantly that might be related to the genus in which cats were to be placed.

Linnaeus and his successors believed that as they added the names of newly discovered and described organisms to his scheme of classification they were discovering the similarities and differences among the world's living things according to the "Creator's plan." Thus the linnaean pattern of classification was considered to be a supernatural design, a scheme which seemed to show the interrelatedness of life. The general public became fascinated with the spirit of adventure in this search to find all the organisms of Creation and to place them in their proper category. Explorers, colonists, travelers, and sea captains sent specimens and seeds back to Linnaeus, each to be endowed with a name and assigned its proper place in the "design of the Creator."

FIXITY OF SPECIES

Linnaeus and other naturalists of his day believed that there had been one act of Creation and that all modern species had been created 5,700 years earlier, just as described in Genesis, and had not changed since. Species were immutable, unchanging, fixed. The concept of *fixity of species* was entrenched as a result of his work, though Linnaeus himself eventually expressed doubt on this point. The belief that all living things had been specially created and had remained unchanged since Creation lent itself to the current dogmas of religion and science.

There remained an apparent contradiction to these dogmas, however: the *presence of variation within a species*. It was obvious that not all members of a species are identical. This variation was believed to be limited and was considered a nuisance by the person attempting to define the species. Some of the variant traits were thought to have been inherited from ancestors who had acquired them during their lifetimes. The Greek philosophers too had believed that organisms could inherit characteristics acquired by their parents.

DEGENERATION OF SPECIES

Comte Georges de Buffon
(1707–1788) *(The Bettmann
Archive.)*

Linnaeus lived at the same time as Comte Georges de Buffon, a French nobleman and great naturalist. Buffon developed a theory of *degeneration,* a concept of change in which there is "a falling away" of one type of organism into another. Buffon regarded change as a degeneration from species types originally formed by the Creator and believed that variations are due to the direct effect of the environment on organisms. Thus certain environmental variations, plus the forces of migration, geographical isolation, overcrowding, and a struggle for existence, would cause a gradual development of new forms of life. Here and there in his many writings Buffon mentioned every major factor which Darwin would use in his great synthesis 100 years later, but Buffon did not grasp the more general significance of his view, that is, the possibility of new species arising by natural means. In his old age he made wild speculations—that the pig arose as a combination of other animals, the ass was a degenerate horse, and the ape a degenerate man.

It was in the intellectual climate of hope during the French Revolutionary period that the theories of evolution of Jean Baptiste de Lamarck were announced. Lamarck believed that the products of Creation are continually being perfected and that living forms are in endless flux, a continuous *transmutation*. The direction of change, in Lamarckian theory, is always upward, due to the innate perfectionism of life until the very highest form—man—is reached. When a man dies, the materials return to the inorganic environment, to begin again at the bottom of the "ladder of life." According to Lamarck, life in its most primitive form is continuously being created anew from nonliving materials by spontaneous generation. Thus a significant general feature of Lamarckian theory was the idea that *change* occurs in living forms instead of all species being fixed and immutable. As a minor variation on his general theme of upward, progressive transmutation, Lamarck added an additional feature, one which has frequently (and erroneously) been thought of as the major element of his theory. He proposed that small, heritable deviations from the general upward evolution of all life forms would also occur due to the influence of the *environment*. Thus changes in the environment could cause adjustments in organisms by stimulating either *use* or *disuse* of organs. An organ would grow or shrink according to the *need* for it. The accumulation of characteristics *acquired* by successive generations of organisms could thus lead to new forms of life. For example, Lamarck believed that changes in the climate might cause an animal to make more extensive use of those parts of its body which are most capable of meeting the new demands. Alterations in structure and function would result from the *effort* the plant or animal would make to meet the new environmental pressures. Some of these alterations would be inherited, and with the passage of time, members of species could become unlike their ancestors. In other words, new physiological needs would initiate the heritable development of new organs or alterations of old ones. Lack of need for an organ would make it shrink or disappear. Thus, Lamarck was among those who believed that the principle of *use* and *disuse* should be applied to the popular concept of *inheritance of acquired characteristics*.

LAMARCK AND PERFECTION

Jean Baptiste de Lamarck
(1744–1829) *(The Bettmann
Archive.)*

Baron Georges Cuvier, a contemporary and an ideological antagonist of Lamarck, despised the idea of transmutation (evolutionary change) in species. He believed that the fossils then beginning to be discovered represented organisms that had lived in previous epochs. Each epoch occupied a certain geological time, each had begun with a separate special Creation, and each had ended with a catastrophe, such as a great flood. The latest catastrophe, he said, was at the time of Noah. Fossils were believed to exist in layers representing separate Creations and catastrophes. Each world of prehistoric life was better than the preceding one, the last Creation being most nearly perfect of all since it had produced man. (This concept, known as the *theory of catastrophisms,* is probably responsible for many science-fiction stories of lost worlds.) Cuvier's great achievement was to stress the relation between the

CUVIER AND CATASTROPHISMS

Baron Georges Cuvier
(1769–1832) *(The Bettmann
Archive.)*

passage of geological time and change in the form of the organisms which lived on earth, a vital element of later evolutionary theory.

Charles Darwin (1809–1882)
(The Bettmann Archive.)

In 1809, the year Lamarck published his major work, *Philosophie zoologique,* Charles Darwin was born in England. His grandfather, Erasmus Darwin (1731-1802), a physician, had been keenly interested in natural history, including the possibility of evolution. His writings contained many ideas similar to those of Lamarck though independently developed. Charles Darwin's father, also a physician, wanted young Charles to follow in his footsteps. At the age of sixteen, Charles went off to medical school, but he was repelled by the barbarity of the surgery of that age and, on his father's advice, instead took up the study of theology at Cambridge, where he also took courses in geology and natural history. He received a degree in theology, but his primary interest was the study of nature.

In 1831, the year he took his degree, the British government was outfitting a small ship, H.M.S. *Beagle* (Figure 2.3), for a 5-year voyage around the world to check time zones, map and chart coastlines and harbors, and carry out other geodetic investigations. A naturalist was needed to make observations on the geology, plants, and animals encountered during the voyage. Charles Darwin was ideally suited for this job and accepted the invitation to join. On the voyage Darwin used every opportunity to go ashore to escape his seasickness, to collect specimens, and to observe nature. He amassed a vast amount of information, and his creative mind led him to derive a new significance from his observations. For Darwin the most important phases of the voyage were in South America and the Galapagos Islands, 600 miles off the coast of Ecuador. Fascinated by the distribution of animals, Darwin made three key observations.

1   In observing living species along the eastern coast of South America he noted species which closely resembled other species several hundred miles away but which were much less similar to other related species 1,000 miles away. He perceived a pattern in which *diversity* between obviously related species *increases with distance* between localities. He wondered whether these species had been created with this distribution or whether there might be another explanation.

2   In a river bank in Argentina Darwin uncovered the fossil remains of an extinct mammal resembling modern armadillos. Concluding that the fossil and modern armadillos were related, he questioned whether the fossil glyptodont (as it is called today) might be an *ancestor* to the *modern* armadillo or, on the other hand, whether both had been created separately by special acts of Creation.

3   After studying the various forms of land birds on the Galapagos Islands Darwin was impressed with the fact that although they differed slightly from island to island, these birds bore strong similarities to each other and to several species on the west coast of South America, 600 miles away. He concluded that they were

FIGURE 2.3 Darwin's ship *Beagle* sailing around Cape Horn. *(The Bettmann Archive.)*

all finches but wondered whether each species on each island had been created specially or *whether they might have descended from a common ancestral finch* which had flown over from the mainland. He also considered how the current belief that the environment could alter the forms of organisms could explain how birds could vary so much on islands with identical conditions.

CHARLES DARWIN AND
NATURAL SELECTION

In his autobiography he reveals that: "It was evident that such facts as these, as well as many others, could only be explained on the supposition that species gradually become modified; and the subject haunted me." Such modification of species would mean that species had not been created specially just as they are found today. He had heated debates with the Captain of the *Beagle* about the advisability of a literal acceptance of Creation as described in Genesis. Finally, in 1836, the *Beagle* returned to England, and Darwin began collecting additional facts to support the general proposition that *species change and give rise to new species.*

Thomas Malthus (1766–1834)
(The Bettmann Archive.)

In 1838, Darwin read the *Essay on Population,* by Malthus, which says that the human food supply increases arithmetically (1, 2, 3, 4, 5, 6, 7, etc.) while the human population increases geometrically (1, 2, 4, 8, 16, etc.). Malthus described how growth of the human population is held in check by disease, starvation, and war.

Malthus included arguments phrased in mathematical terms and was clear and concise. Darwin realized Malthus' principle as true not only of human beings but of *all living things.* Malthus' insight fitted well with Darwin's new theory of the origin of diversity in species. This theory was based essentially upon three inductive generalizations and two deductions, which can be summarized as follows:

Generalizations from observation

1   *Organisms making up a population are not all alike. They vary, and some of this variation is inheritable.* (Look around your classroom for proof of variation within a population).

2   *There is a tendency of natural populations to overproduce.* American oysters, for example, may release over 100 million eggs in one season, a single puffball fungus may release 700 billion spores in one season, and a single codfish can lay over 6 million eggs.

3   *Natural populations do not continually increase in number, however; on the contrary, they usually stay about the same.* The ocean is not crowded with codfish, and its bays are not covered with oysters, for example.

Deductions

1   Natural populations could increase at a rapid rate to a fantastic size, but they tend to stay about the same. Therefore many organisms in a population must die in *competition* for food, space, etc. This means that there is a *struggle for existence.*

2   If a *struggle for existence* takes place between variant types in a *population,* those organisms whose variations allow the slightest advantage have the best chances for survival and will persist to reproduce their kind. The *organisms with the best adaptations will be the best reproducers,* and the population will eventually consist predominantly or exclusively of individuals bearing this trait.

Darwin was familiar with animal breeding, a process in which the breeder selects the types he wishes to persist and allows them to reproduce their kind. Recognizing that nature, in a similar way, has selected the best-fitted types for reproduction in natural populations, he called his theory *natural selection.*

Alfred Wallace (1823–1913)
(*The Bettmann Archive.*)

The next step in the scientific method would be to *test* the deductions—exactly what Darwin did. Deciding to think about his controversial pattern of continual change in the living world for a while before publishing his ideas, he attempted to anticipate every possible criticism of his theory and prepare an answer to them all. Twenty years later he had not yet completed this analysis but was forced into publication by the arrival of a letter from another naturalist, Alfred Russel Wallace, who described how he had been studying the distribution of animals among islands of the East Indies and had been struck with the presence of variation, overreproduction, and survival of the best-fitted variants. From his observations and from reading Malthus, Wallace had reached the same conclusions as Darwin, even developing the same terms to describe the process they both called *natural selection.*

Wallace's description of the same theory that Darwin had been considering for 20 years created a curious problem. Who should claim credit for the idea? It was proposed that brief abstracts from both authors be read before the Linnaean Society in London in 1858. (Neither Wallace nor Darwin was actually present at the meeting.) The only visible reaction to their papers was that one man withdrew a paper he was scheduled to read on the fixity of species. Darwin began to bring his extensive notes together as a book, *On the Origin of Species,* which was published in

1859 and sold out on the first day. The intellectual community had had a year in which to marshall their opinions, and a violent reaction to the new theories of evolution soon developed.

DARWIN'S CRITICS

Many people in different walks of life were shaken by the implications of the theory, and numerous criticisms appeared. Of all the arguments, the most rational centered around the age of the earth, the sources of variations, and the perpetuation of small variations.

Lord Kelvin, basing his logic upon a false assumption that the earth was cooling down at a certain rate, stated that the earth was only 24 million years old. This span of time was woefully inadequate for the process of natural selection and its requirement for *vast amounts of time* during which small but beneficial variations could be selected and perpetuated.

Darwin found support for his position that the earth was immensely old in Charles Lyell's *Principles of Geology*. Lyell argued that the earth had to be extremely ancient in order to account for the accumulation of the vast deposits of sedimentary rock. Lyell also attacked the theory of catastrophisms of Cuvier and his followers on the grounds that fossils are distributed continuously through rocks and not in layers coinciding with finite epochs. Today we know that the earth is over 5 billion years old, but Darwin could not refute Kelvin's arguments during his lifetime.

Charles Lyell (1797–1875)
(The Bettmann Archive.)

Equally troubling to Darwin's confidence in his own theory was his inability to explain the mechanism by which small variations, so vital to his model of natural selection, could be formed and retained in a population. Actually information was even then available to him which would have explained the mechanism. Recent evidence indicates that Darwin read papers of Gregor Mendel describing his work with the garden peas in a remote Austrian monastery. The relevance of these experiments to the general problem of heredity escaped the whole scientific world until several decades later, however, and Darwin ended his days still believing the popular notion that organisms inherit their traits through a blending of blood from both parents.

THE RISE AND FALL
OF THE DOCTRINE OF
BLENDING OF HEREDITY

ARISTOTLE'S VIEW OF HEREDITY
THROUGH PARENTAL BLOOD

Aristotle knew that every female mammal has a uterus and recognized it as the site for the development of offspring. Speculating on how the act of sexual intercourse could induce the formation of an embryo in the uterus, he found it significant that a normal woman of reproductive age menstruates each month except when she is pregnant. He reasoned that a pregnant woman does not suffer this loss of blood because the blood is needed for the formation of the embryo. According to Aristotle, the mother's blood provides the building blocks for the construction of the embryo. What part, then, does the father play? Aristotle believed that the father's role is of a higher nature, contributing not only the design for the embryo but its life. Thus according to this scheme, the mother contributes the building material and an incubator while the father provides the blueprints and the vital force.

Aristotle believed that the father's semen is formed from his blood through a process of concentration and purification and that it contains the determiners of traits. He considered that the mother contributes unadulterated blood since the female lacks the special powers of purification possessed by the male. According to this scheme, an embryo would form from the blood of each parent, but since only the father is able to contribute design, hereditary traits are inherited solely from the father!

THE BLENDING OF
HEREDITARY TRAITS

In A.D. 200 a Greek named Empedocles improved the position of females in the theory formed 500 years earlier by Aristotle by proposing that both male and female parents contribute semen, which forms directly from their body parts and is carried by blood to their gonads. He believed that male and female semen blend during sexual intercourse and the trait-determining fluids are also blended. *Traits of offspring were thought to result from a blending of fluids removed from the bloods of each parent.* This was the *blending* concept of heredity, a belief that the traits of a child are a result of a blending of all the traits of both parents.

We shall see that blood has nothing to do with heredity except to keep the parents and offspring alive. Despite the fact that blood plays no direct role in the formation of eggs and sperm, many people today still use such phrases as "blood relatives," "blood brother," "mixed bloods," "bad blood in the family," and "blood will tell."

DARWIN, BODY CELLS,
AND BLOOD

Aristotle's idea that heredity was based upon blood together with Empedocles' idea of blending of traits from both parents formed the concept of *blending of bloods* and traits, which in various forms prevailed until well into the nineteenth century. Darwin accepted the concept of hereditary blending, and his convictions were deeply influenced by it. He was challenged by a Welsh engineer named Fleeming Jenkin with the following argument. Darwin's theory of natural selection called for the appearance of small variations within populations and the perpetuation of these variations in the population if they endowed their bearer some degree of competitive success. Jenkin argued, however, that any chance variation that might arise would be lost in the following generations through mating with individuals that did not have the trait. The variant trait would simply blend in and be lost through what he called a *swamping effect*. This could be compared to paint that is continually poured from can to can. Because of constant mixing, the color in all the cans would soon become identical. A new color variant arising in one can would be blended in and lost during the following mixings. According to this argument, all organisms within a species should be identical. Since organisms are obviously not identical, Darwin came to the Lamarckian conclusion that heritable variation can be caused by differences in the environment. Since the environment would act upon all members of the population, its influences could cause the entire population to change. Darwin believed that heritable variations acquired by the entire population would not be swamped out but would be perpetuated and that all the buckets of paint would change slightly in color. To explain how this might happen, Darwin developed a new concept, which he termed *pangenesis.*

Unlike Empedocles and Lamarck, Darwin was aware that the body was made of cells. Darwin's pangenesis was a system in which environmentally stimulated *changes in body cells* could form part of the transmissible inheritance of an organism as a result of particles called *gemmules* being formed by the cells. These gemmules would act as "messengers" and would carry the "directions" for the construction of new variant cell types through the bloodstream to the testes or ovaries, where the gemmules would be incorporated into the sperm or eggs. (The functions of testes, sperm, ovaries, and eggs were well known by this time.) Darwin pictured a plan by which the reproductive material, the germ cells, would be developed anew with each generation (see Figure 2.4). Offspring, he said, assembled from particles derived from the body cells of parents, which might have been altered by the environment. By this plan, heritable variation could be induced in a population as a result of an environmental change experienced by the organisms in that population. Darwin had stepped up the pace of variation to answer Jenkin's argument, but was he correct in his concept of pangenesis? *Do gemmules actually exist? Do body cells in fact transmit heritable traits to the germ cells (eggs and sperm)?*

THE GERM-CELL THEORY

During the last three decades of the nineteenth century several concepts of basic importance to the biology of inheritance were established and had direct effects on the theory of evolution. Of primary importance was the principle of *continuity of the germ plasm,* attributable in its most general form to the great German biologist August Weismann. Weismann pointed out that the germ-cell line, that is, the sperm and eggs plus the immature cell types giving rise to sperm and eggs, are set aside from other cells early in the embryonic development. In reproduction they are passed along relatively unchanged from parent to offspring down through time. Therefore if a heritable change occurs in the *germ cells,* it could not be due to the environment acting on *body cells,* which remain separate from the germ line, but could be due only to changes in the hereditary determinants in the germ cells themselves. Weissmann believed that *germ cells come only from germ cells* and thus are not formed from particles coming from body cells by way of the bloodstream, such as Darwin's gemmules. Thus a continuity exists from germ cell to germ cell through successive generations while no such continuity exists for the body cells. We now know that Weismann's description is in general correct: In many organisms the

August Weismann (1834–1914)
(The Bettmann Archive.)

primitive germ cells are indeed separated from the future body cells at the very beginning of embryonic life, and the germ line continues to remain separate in the body of the adult. The contrast between Weismann's theory of the continuity of the germ plasm and Darwin's theory of pangenesis is summarized in Figure 2.4 (*a* and *b*).

Thus Darwin's theory of pangenesis had to be rejected as a source of variation, but this did not invalidate the theory of natural selection. There remained, however, the troublesome problems of the source of heritable variation within populations of organisms and the means by which such variation can be maintained in the population, rather than simply blending in with the dominant characters of the population like Fleeming Jenkin's variant colors of paint. But while arguments over Darwinism raged in England, some of the answers to these basic mysteries lay in the mind of an obscure monk in Brünn, in what was then Austria.

GREGOR MENDEL

In February, 1865, the Brünn Society for the Study of Natural Science gathered for their monthly meeting in the local schoolhouse. The evening's program included a reading of a paper on "Experiments in Plant Hybridization" by Gregor Mendel, a monk at the local monastery and teacher of natural sciences at the secondary school. The audience of about forty people listened quietly as Mendel described his work but left the meeting without asking a single question of the man who would eventually be ranked with Darwin as one of the great biologists of the nineteenth century. During Mendel's lifetime no one understood what he was trying to say. He sent a copy of his paper to one of the leading botanists in Europe, Karl von Nägeli, a brilliant theoretical biologist who was searching for a general key with which to interpret the relation between the heredity of an organism and the life processes carried out in its cells and tissues. Nägeli could see very little meaning in Mendel's descriptions of numbers of different types of pea plants, ratios of one type to another,

FIGURE 2.4 Two theories about the source of germ cells, the sperm and egg (Darwin's theory: black lines; Weismann's theory: yellow lines).

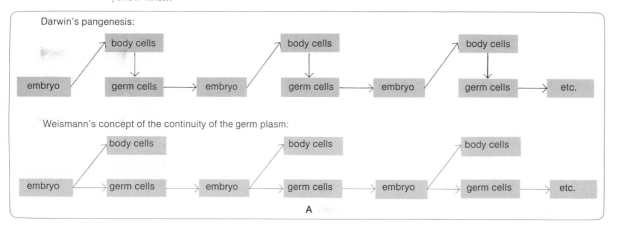

and so on. Their correspondence continued for 8 more years, but there is no indication that Nägeli ever understood the significance of what Mendel was saying.

Gregor Mendel (1822–1884)
(The Bettmann Archive.)

Mendel had spent his childhood on a farm, where he had helped his father graft fruit trees and raise bees, and he was intrigued by the problem of explaining the inheritance of the traits of organisms. Later, as a teacher, he found time to conduct experiments in a fashion that was years ahead of his time.

After assuming his teaching duties, Mendel began raising garden peas in the monastery garden and began crossing various strains. Fascinated with the remarkable regularity with which the same pattern of traits appeared each time he formed hybrids by crossing different strains of peas, he realized that no one had adequately studied the results of going one step further and *crossing the hybrids*. His motivations were clearly stated in the introduction to his famous paper:

One who surveys the work done in this field will come to the conclusion that, among the numerous experiments, not one has been carried out comprehensively enough to determine the number of different forms under which the offspring of hybrids appear, or to arrange these forms with certainty according to their separate generations, or definitely to ascertain their statistical relations. Some courage is, indeed, needed to undertake such far-reaching labors. Still, that would seem to be the only right way of ultimately achieving the solution of a problem that is of enormous importance in its bearing upon the evolutionary history of organic forms.

Mendel had been intrigued with the mechanisms of heredity for years, and in the period following his own remarkable early experiments he carefully studied Darwin's *Origin of Species*. A well-worn copy of this book with many marginal notes in Mendel's handwriting lies in the library of the monastery today. Mendel had pondered the mechanisms of heredity and its role in evolution.

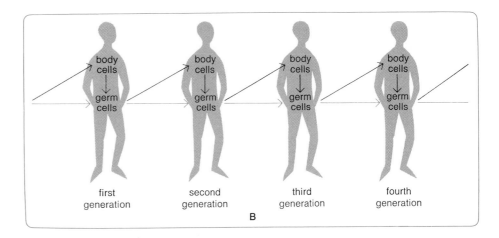

first
generation

second
generation

third
generation

fourth
generation

B

dominant   recessive

round or wrinkled seeds

yellow or green seeds

red or yellow flowers

axial or terminal flowers

inflated or constricted pods

green or yellow pods

long or dwarf stems

FIGURE 2.5 The several
characteristics of peas studied
by Mendel. *(Adapted from
William L. Smallwood and Edna
R. Green, Biology, Silver Burdett
Company, Morristown, N.J., 1968.)*

Some key decisions of Mendel's permitted him a success unknown to previous investigators. He decided to study one trait at a time, and he was fortunate in choosing a self-fertilizing organism with certain traits that are clear-cut and easily identified. He was searching for statistical certainty, possible only if subjectivity is replaced by objectivity. This can be achieved only if the traditional reliance upon ancedotes or subjective descriptions is discarded and replaced by a mathematical compilation of data collected with a minimum of interference from prejudices and preformed opinions. Mendel's success was a testament to the superiority of objective methods over the subjectivity of earlier workers.

Mendel selected the common garden pea as his experimental subject. This pea has many varieties, but after 2 years of testing he selected seven traits which were the easiest to study, since each trait had a pair of contrasting alternate forms easily differentiated from each other without any hairline or subjective decisions. The seven traits and their alternate forms are shown in Figure 2.5.

When spring arrived in 1856, the peas in Mendel's little garden were ready to blossom. Using a fine camel's-hair brush, he carefully deposited the pollen from a plant that had always produced round peas on the female part of the flower of a wrinkle-seeded plant. In similar fashion, he transferred pollen between each of the alternate forms within each of the other six traits. By crossing these alternate forms he hoped to produce hybrids.

He waited anxiously through the following weeks to see what kind of offspring would develop. Finally, the peas ripened, and he saw that all the peas from his first cross were round and none were wrinkled! And the peas with the other six traits showed the same results. One alternate form of each trait had disappeared in this first hybrid generation. He concluded that for each of the seven traits one alternate form is *dominant* over the other, the latter being *recessive. All the hybrids formed by crossing parents of different strains* (round and wrinkled, etc.) *were like the dominant parent* (see Figure 2.5 and Table 2.1).

An advocate of blending would have argued that the recessive trait had disappeared because it had blended in, but Mendel's data challenged this viewpoint. He next attempted to cross the hybrids from the first set of experiments, for example, hybrid round with hybrid round. Would the now invisible recessive traits reappear? Does wrinkledness in the seed really blend in with roundness and simply disappear? He saved the seeds and next spring planted some from each hybrid. When the vines blossomed, Mendel repeated the procedure he had used with the parents of these plants. He dusted the pollen from hybrid round-seeded plants on the flowers of another hybrid round and repeated the procedure with the other six hybrids. Again, he waited. This time the results were different, and very enlightening, for the wrinkled peas and all the other *recessive forms reappeared in some of the offspring of the original hybrids.* Since the recessive traits reappeared, they could not have been

TRAIT	ALTERNATE FORMS
1 The shape of the seed	Round in some plants, wrinkled in others
2 The color of the peas	Either yellow or green
3 The color of the flower	Either red or white
4 The position of the flower	Axial (along the stem) or terminal (at the end of the stem)
5 The shape of the ripe pods	Simple curved (inflated) or constricted between the peas
6 The color of the unripe pods	Green or yellow
7 The length of the stem	Tall or dwarf

lost by blending. Furthermore, Mendel saw that the ratio of dominant to recessive in the grandchildren was always approximately 3:1 (see Table 2.1).

Mendel doubted that a recessive trait could disappear in one generation and reappear in the following if heredity were due to blending of fluids. He interpreted his results according to a very different scheme, proposing that the dominant and recessive forms of a trait are determined by factors which cannot blend but remain separate and distinct from each other even in the hybrid condition. The hybrid can thus give rise to two kinds of germ cells, one carrying a dominant factor and one carrying a recessive factor. *Mendel had demonstrated that the mechanisms of heredity do not operate through blending.* He proposed that heredity is due to *particles* received from each parent and that the particles governing each trait are present in duplicate in each plant.

TABLE 2.1 Mendel's results in hybrid crosses involving seven traits, each having a pair of alternate forms.

TRAIT	ALTERNATE PARENTAL FORMS	F_1 FIRST GENERATION HYBRIDS	F_2: SECOND GENERATION HYBRIDS OBTAINED BY CROSSING F_1 HYBRIDS WITH EACH OTHER				
			NUMBER OF PLANTS			PERCENTAGE	
			DOMINANT*	RECESSIVE	TOTAL	DOMINANT	RECESSIVE
Seeds:	Round or wrinkled	All round	5,474	1,850	7,324	74.74	25.26
Seeds:	Yellow or green	All yellow	6,022	2,001	8,023	75.06	24.94
Flowers:	Red or white	All red	705	224	929	75.90	24.10
Flowers:	Axial or terminal	All axial	651	207	858	75.87	24.13
Pods:	Inflated or constricted	All inflated	882	299	1,181	74.68	25.32
Pods:	Green or yellow	All green	428	152	580	73.79	26.21
Stem length:	Tall or dwarf	All tall	787	277	1,064	73.96	26.04
Total			14,949	5,010	19,959	74.90	25.10

* Dominant means the form found in all F_1 hybrid plants.

Thus, by concentrating on simple contrasting characteristics Mendel was able to follow the pattern of their inheritance from parent to offspring through successive generations. *He was able to conclude that the inheritance of each trait is determined by a pair of independent elements which always remain distinct from each other.* He named this law his *law of segregation.*

Mendel now asked whether a pair of hereditary factors for one trait would blend with factors for another trait. What would happen if he studied two traits at once; for example, would the factors for seed form remain separate from the factors for seed color?

Mendel crossed peas whose seeds were round and yellow with peas whose seeds were wrinkled and green. Since round seed shape and yellow seed color are dominant, he was not surprised to see the first generation (the F_1 or first filial generation) produce all round and yellow seeds.

Mendel then crossed the F_1 round-yellow hybrids with other round-yellow hybrids. He found the expected round-yellow and wrinkled-green in the F_2 but he also found round-green and wrinkled-yellow in the following numbers and ratios of Table 2.2. Mendel knew that each of the two traits separately would have yielded a 3:1 ratio in this F_2 generation. Yet, when studied together, the ratio was 9:3:3:1. This could have happened only if the pairs of factors in each trait had asserted themselves independently. He knew that *the frequency with which two separate events occur simultaneously is the product of their separate chances.* Seed *shape* by itself would yield a ratio of 3/4 round and 1/4 wrinkled in the F_2, and seed *color* would produce a ratio of 3/4 yellow and 1/4 green in the F_2 if each trait were *studied by itself.* If the two traits were determined by two pairs of particles which assorted themselves independently, the chances for round-yellow in the F_2 should be the product of their separate chances: 3/4 × 3/4, or 9/16. The chances for the other combinations would be as shown in Table 2.3.

Since Mendel got the ratio 9:3:3:1 in the cross of peas which were hybrid for two traits, he concluded that the pairs of factors for each trait assorted themselves independently. The pair of factors for seed color assorted themselves independently from the pair of factors for the shape of the seed. He called this the *Law of independent assortment.*

In review, we see that Mendel formulated three main hypotheses:

TABLE 2.2

		RATIO	
Round-yellow	315	9	9/16
Round-green	108	3	3/16
Wrinkled-yellow	101	3	3/16
Wrinkled-green	32	1	1/16
Total	556	16	

TABLE 2.3

Separate event in F_2:		Separate event in F_2:	
Round	$3/4$	Yellow	$3/4$
Wrinkled	$1/4$	Green	$1/4$
Special events studied together in F_2:			
Round and yellow	$3/4 \times 3/4 = 9/16$		
Round and green	$3/4 \times 1/4 = 3/16$		
Wrinkled and yellow	$1/4 \times 3/4 = 3/16$		
Wrinkled and green	$1/4 \times 1/4 = 1/16$		

1 Heredity is transferred from generation to generation in a particulate form for each trait, and these particulate elements occur in pairs. An organism gets one member of the pair from the father and one from the mother. In hybrids, one member of the pair may be dominant and the other recessive. This he called the *law of dominance.*

2 *Blending does not occur* since the hereditary factors behave as particles and remain distinct from each other even when paired in an organism. The members of each pair segregate from each other during the formation of germ cells, so that the sperm and eggs formed by an organism each receive one factor of each pair. This he called the *law of segregation.*

3 Blending does not take place between different pairs of factors. A pair of factors for one trait will assort themselves independently from a pair of factors for another trait. This he called the *law of independent assortment.*

After 8 years of carefully crossing peas and gathering facts, Mendel published his data, presenting his conclusions, or so he intended, to the world. But no one responded, for the significance of what he was saying would become apparent only three decades later. Mendel became submerged in church duties and gave up further studies of heredity in garden peas.

Darwin could have utilized Mendel's principles to explain in part the nature of hereditary variation in populations and to show that variations would not disappear through blending. Although Darwin had conducted almost identical crosses with pea plants, he failed to interpret his results meaningfully. It is perhaps ironic that Mendel, who was familiar with Darwin's writings on natural selection and his search for the source of variation, did not emphasize the relevance of his own findings to the theory of natural selection. Mendel could have pointed out that variation is not generally new but is primarily a reshuffling of hereditary factors already there. This remains one of the incongruities in recent intellectual history. Darwin became a hero in his day, and remained so, while Mendel, a hero only in the next century, died with only local recognition of his teaching and priestly duties. But Mendel told his friend Niessl, "My time will come."

REDISCOVERY

During the thirty-five years after the reading of Mendel's paper and leading up to the turn of the century, many investigators were pursuing the baffling problems of heredity. They began to develop a better understanding of the cell, sexual reproduction, and cell division. This led them closer to Mendel's paper. Finally, around the turn of the century, three men, Hugo de Vries in Holland, Karl Erich Correns, in Germany, and Gustav Tschermak von Seysenegg in Austria independently reached conclusions and were ready to publish their findings. Individually each man had uncovered Mendel's paper and realized that his own generalizations were not new, that Mendel had presented the same principles 35 years earlier. Each man acknowledged that Mendel deserved the acclaim though he had died 16 years before.

Mendel's paper was republished, and now the scientific world appreciated its significance. The difference was that by the turn of the century the structure and function of living things was better understood. The cell was recognized as the basic unit of structure and function in living things, and the means by which cells reproduced and inherited traits was identified as the key to an understanding of reproduction and heredity in organisms made up of cells. Let us now see how this understanding developed.

ORIGINS OF THE
MODERN CELL THEORY

A landmark in the post-Renaissance history of biology was William Harvey's discovery (1628) of the circulation of blood. For many centuries it had been believed that blood flowed only toward the heart in currents resembling the tides of the ocean. Harvey demonstrated that blood travels in only one direction, along a circular path, from heart to arteries to veins and back to the heart. His only problem was in explaining how the blood got from the arteries to the veins, a problem solved 3 years after his death when in 1660 the Italian biologist Marcello Malpighi (1638–1694) discovered, with a primitive microscope, that tiny vessels connect the arteries with the veins. They are named *capillaries,* from the Latin word for hair. People were forced to admit the existence of a world not visible to the unaided eye.

The man who deserves the most credit for bringing the microscope to the attention of the world of science is Anton van Leeuwenhoek, a draper and caretaker of the town hall in Delft, Holland, and a lens grinder by hobby. Using single lenses ground from tiny flawless pieces of glass, van Leeuwenhoek was able to magnify objects to 200 times their normal size. Often, the lenses were no bigger than the head of a pin, but they served him well. He occupied every spare moment observing anything he could collect and place under his optical eye. He observed "wee little beasties" in rainwater, bacterial suspensions, blood, and a host of other living things which he described in a stream of letters to the Royal Society of London over a period of 50 years, until he died at the age of ninety-one.

Another man of van Leeuwenhoek's era who had a great impact on the future growth of science was Robert Hooke (1635-1703), a master mechanic and curator of experiments for the Royal Society during the last half of the seventeenth century. In 1665, Hooke published a book of drawings he had made of objects viewed under his microscopes. One of the drawings was of a thin slice of cork. He found it to be made up of tiny polyhedral boxes arranged like honeycomb. Small rooms were commonly called *cells* in those days, and this was the term Hooke applied to the spaces in the cork. Hooke's microscope could magnify only thirty times, and he was limited to a description of cell walls and a statement that cork cells were dead while living cells contained "juices."

Even without a microscope, a French physician, Marie François Xavier Bichat (1771-1802), pointed out that various organs are made up of diverse types of living material which he called *tissues*. Later it was stated that the organs of animals with backbones contain only five kinds of tissues, epithelial, connective, muscle, nerve, and blood. (Today we know of many more tissue types.) Microscopes are necessary, however, to observe the cellular structures of which the tissues are composed.

In 1838, 173 years after Hooke's description of cork cells, a botanist, Matthias Schleiden, happened to sit down at a party next to a zoologist, Theodor Schwann. During the evening Schleiden described how he had observed that all plants are made of cells, and Schwann countered with the statement that all the animal tissues he had seen were also made of cells. From this conversation emanated one of the greatest generalizations of biology, the *cell theory*.

Without giving credit to his predecessors or contemporaries, Schleiden proposed three hypotheses: (1) Plants and animals are composed entirely of cells, which are the basic units of structure, function, and organization; (2) cells lead relatively independent lives within organisms; and (3) cells arise through a process similar to the way in which crystals are formed. Schwann also believed plant and animal cells to be quite similar and published statements like Schleiden's. Together these men are considered to be the originators of the concept of the *cell as the basic structural and functional unit within living things*.

The cork cells described by Hooke were empty, but living tissue was seen to contain cells filled with a clear gelatinous fluid, named *protoplasm* in 1839 by the Czech physiologist Johannes Purkinje (1787-1869). In 1861 Max Schultze stated that the jellylike substance in cells was the physical basis of all life and differed only slightly from species to species. This concept, supported by Thomas Huxley in 1868, was another of the great generalizations of nineteenth-century biology. Cells and protoplasm were accepted as the universal substance from which living things are made.

The cell theory quickly flourished and grew with the addition of many bits of information, even though parts of the theory had to be amended. The idea that cells are independent within a multicellular organism was challenged when studies revealed a great deal of interaction and dependence between cells in both animals and plants. In 1845, Karl von Siebold had described the "wee little beasties" of van Leeuwenhoek as being single-celled organisms. They became known as *protozoa*, and it could be seen that such cells do indeed live independent lives. On the other hand, the millions of cells forming a tree or a cow clearly do not lead independent lives.

William Harvey (1578–1657)
(The Bettmann Archive.)

Anton van Leeuwenhoek
(1632–1723)
(The Bettmann Archive.)

THE SOURCE OF CELLS

FIGURE 2.6 Ever since Aristotle (and probably before) it has commonly been believed that certain forms of life are spontaneously generated. This adaptation of a seventeenth-century woodcut shows snakes, frogs, crustaceans, insects, and worms being ''born'' out of a rotten log.

As time passed, most biologists began to discount Schleiden's idea that cells originate in a manner similar to crystals. By the mid-1800s it was firmly established that cells could come only from cells or, as the German physiologist Virchow put it: ''Omnis cellula e cellula'' or ''all cells from cells.'' Cells were accepted as the units of life, and cells could come only from previously existing cells by the parent cell's dividing into two halves. This idea was in direct opposition to the concept of spontaneous generation current at that time (Figure 2.6).

Francesco Redi had demonstrated back in the 1600s that maggots would not appear in meat unless flies had laid eggs on it, but many people continued to believe that various life forms arose spontaneously from nonliving sources, such as eels from the muck of rivers, bees from the entrails of dead bulls, worms from mud, and mice and rats from trash and garbage. Long before the middle of the nineteenth century biologists had accepted the proof of Redi and believed that at least the larger organisms arose only from previously living organisms through cell division, but doubts about the origin of microorganisms such as bacteria persisted. In the case of Redi's experiments such doubts were encouraged by the observation that microbes still grew in the meat that had been protected against insects by gauze.

Louis Pasteur (1822–1895) and his contemporaries knew that microorganisms are present in wine, milk, meat broth, and other nutrient materials even when they are covered with materials which exclude flies. Pasteur demonstrated that applying enough *heat* would kill the microbes and that if the heated material were *sealed from the air,* they would not appear again. Pasteur had shown that microbes were carried to the meat by air currents would not form spontaneously from a nonliving source if a barrier to unsterilized air was supplied.

Pasteur's critics did not give up, however, and concentrated their attention on the process of fermentation. They understood that fermentation is caused by microbes and persisted in their claim that the microbes could form from the nonliving nutrients. They claimed that when Pasteur sealed the flasks, he suffocated the life forming spontaneously within the nutrients. Pasteur answered them with an ingenious and simple experiment. He fashioned two flasks with S-shaped necks which would allow air to enter but would trap dust particles and their bacterial passengers in the curve of the necks. After placing broth in the flasks and boiling it, he found that no bacterial growth resulted even though air could reach the broth. When the necks were snapped and ordinary air moved in, bacteria and molds usually began growing (see Figure 2.7).

Louis Pasteur (1822–1895) (*The Bettmann Archive.*)

The rise and fall of the concept of spontaneous generation also had religious implications. The idea of spontaneous generation had been accepted for many years despite the fact that it contradicted the idea that living things had been created only at the dawn of life, as described in Genesis. Although many religious bodies had accepted the idea of a multitude of creations through spontaneous generation, when science demonstrated that this was highly improbable, they rebelled. And when science presented the view that life originated on our planet through a long series of chemical and physical reactions in the remote geological past, there was even more intense resistance.

Even with the improved microscopes of the late 1800s biologists were severely restricted in what they could see inside the cells they studied. Since cellular contents are almost transparent, biologists could barely perceive the faint particles and sacs they contain. The comparatively dense *nucleus,* or central part, was hazily seen and described by Robert Brown (1773–1858) in 1833, and Schleiden was able to make out a spherical structure inside the nucleus which he named the *nucleolus* (small nucleus). Observation of further details of cells were made only after some significant developments in optics and in chemistry.

In Germany, in the latter part of the nineteenth century, a great synthetic-dye industry developed. Artificial dyes of many bright colors were invented, and when biologists began applying dyes to cellular material in a trial-and-error attempt to obtain greater detail, previously invisible structures were revealed to microscopists even though no one knew how the stains worked.

Outstandingly successful in the use of synthetic dyes to stain tissue was Walter Flemming (1843–1905), a German. While studying animal cells he found that certain structures in the cell nucleus strongly absorbed a particular dye he was testing. Since these tiny particles stood out brightly against the rest of the cell's colorless background, Flemming named them *chromatin* (from the Greek word for color).

Most of Flemming's studies were of tissues which had been killed and stained, and many of the cells he examined had been killed while in the act of dividing. Thus by the 1870s Flemming was able to describe the stages through which the cells proceed in dividing. He saw that in cell division the chromatin becomes parceled out equally between the two cells formed from the original cell. He also verified his observations on living tissue.

Flemming reported that the chromatin forms into threads as cell division begins and that the threads are lined up in a row and then pulled to opposite sides of the cell in an exquisitely precise fashion. He named the process by which cells divide *mitosis* (from the Greek word for thread) and published his definitive description of it in 1882. He described how a tiny particle called an *aster* (a Greek word meaning star) divides into two smaller particles, which in turn form tiny rays as they move to opposite sides of the nucleus. From these opposite positions the asters seem to extend their rays to the threads, which are lined up in the center of the cell. Meanwhile the chromatin threads show up as longitudinally duplicate structures. Next the rays from the opposing asters appear to pull the duplicate half of each thread apart from its mate and then draw it to the asters on each side. Thus a duplicate complete set of chromatin threads arrives at each aster. The cell divides down the middle, and each of the two resultant cells receives a duplicate set of threads. Soon afterward these chromatin threads were given the name of

HOW DO CELLS REPRODUCE?

FIGURE 2.7 Pasteur disproved the theory of spontaneous generation with a simple, ingenious experiment. He filled a flask with a solution that fermented easily but curved the neck, which he left open. He boiled and then cooled the solution, and even though air was in contact with the solution, the solution remained uncontaminated. Once the neck was broken off, however, growths formed in the solution within 48 hours. Pasteur's conclusion was that growths in liquids originate from corpuscles in the air.

chromosomes (from the Greek for colored bodies), and they assumed an increasingly important position in the understanding of heredity.

The enormous importance of chromosomes rapidly became evident. During the 1870s a number of careful observers studied the process of fertilization on the microscopic level, painstakingly searching newly fertilized eggs to see what became of the sperm after it entered the egg. It was known that sperm and eggs bear the hereditary factors from either parent, and the disposition of these factors in fertilization was correctly seen as a question of critical significance. By 1879 it was clear that the sperm, upon entering the egg, gives rise to a nucleus (the *male pronucleus*), which soon fuses with the egg nucleus (the *female pronucleus*). The most important discovery came about the same time as Flemming's account of mitosis and was made by the Belgian biologist Edward van Beneden (1846–1910). Choosing a particularly opportune material, the eggs of a parasitic worm *Ascaris* which commonly infested horses, van Beneden was able to observe the fate of the chromosomes in fertilization. Both the male and female pronuclei contain chromatin, which condenses into chromosomes, two from each pronucleus. The pronuclei intermingle and form the total chromosome complement of the fertilized egg. As the egg begins to develop mitosis occurs, and each cell of the embryo inherits replicas of the same four chromosomes. Van Beneden's great discovery was that the *hereditary factors are transmitted from the parents in the chromosomes* and that they are located in the cell nuclei and reproduced every time cells divide by mitosis. By 1886, just 2 years after the publication of van Beneden's classic studies, three of the great biologists of the time, Weismann, whose germ theory we have already considered, Hertwig, one of those who first investigated the intracellular nature of fertilization, and Strasburger, a leading botanist who studied fertilization in plants, had all placed the pieces of the puzzle together and formulated the *chromosome theory of heredity*. This development easily ranks in importance with the advances made by Mendel and Darwin and forms the foundation for much of the developmental biology of our own time. The chromosome theory states that the hereditary factors of an organism (animal or plant) are carried in the chromosomes of the germ cell nuclei. The union of the parental chromosome complements occurs at fertilization, and every cell of the organism then receives a complete set of these hereditary factors, or *genes,* in its own nuclear chromosome complement by means of mitosis.

Continuing his studies, van Beneden showed in 1887 that the number of chromosomes is constant throughout all the various cells of an organism and that each species seems to have a certain characteristic number. Later, van Beneden and others found that the chromosomes of sperm and eggs are distributed by a process differing from mitosis and occurring just previous to fertilization. In this process (called *meiosis*) the daughter cells (eggs or sperm) receive only one-half the number of chromosomes of the parental cell. Thus the normal number of chromosomes is restored upon fusion of a sperm cell and egg during fertilization.

When Mendel's work was rediscovered at the beginning of this century, the American biologist Walter S. Sutton (1876–1916) pointed out that the manner in which the traits of Mendel's peas are inherited follows exactly the same pattern as the parceling out of the chromosomes during meiosis. He proposed that the hereditary particles described by Mendel are really the chromosomes in the nuclei of the germ cells. Thus chromosomes exist in pairs (one member of each pair from each parent) and remain segregated from each other during meiosis.

By the dawning of the twentieth century the patterns of order enunciated by Darwin, Mendel, Weismann, van Beneden, Strasburger, Hertwig, and the many others whose patient and intelligent investigations paved the way for those we have mentioned here had established the orientation of biological investigation for years to come. *Genetics* (as the study of heredity became known) and cell biology were now in a vastly improved position to bring real understanding to our view of the living world.

1 Contrast the Grand Scale of Being with the system of categories devised by Linnaeus.
2 Describe some of the evidence that allowed Darwin to generalize that organisms compete and struggle to exist.
3 Contrast the ways Lamarck and Darwin would explain the evolution of the long neck of the giraffe.
4 How did Weismann prove that traits are not inherited from body cells? What did he propose as the source of sperm and egg cells?
5 Why does the disappearance of one form of a trait in one generation and its reappearance in a following generation prove that alternate forms of a trait do not blend and must be due to particles instead of fluids?
6 Why did the ratios of pea plants observed by Mendel prove that the hereditary particles must exist in pairs?
7 Choose one of the scientists described in this chapter and explain how his work incorporated the scientific method.

Asimov, I.: *A Short History of Biology,* The Natural History Press, New York, 1964. A concise and readable history of biology from ancient Greeks to today.

Eiseley, L.: *Darwin's Century: Evolution and the Men Who Discovered It,* Doubleday Anchor Books, New York, 1958. A spellbinding story of the men and ideas that shaped the concept of evolution.

Irvine, W.: *Apes, Angels, and Victorians,* McGraw-Hill Book Company, New York, 1955. A fascinating account of Darwin, Huxley, and their contemporaries as they debated the concept of evolution; with emphasis on the lives of Darwin and Huxley.

* Available in paperback.

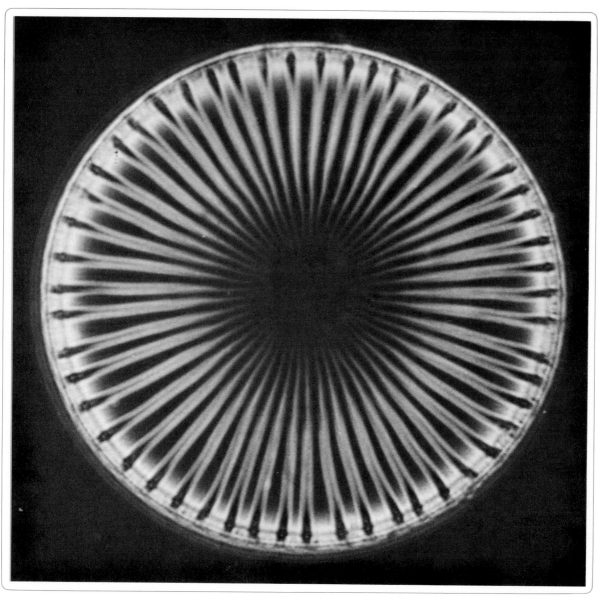

Cyclotella, a diatom (900 ×). (Eric V. Grave, Photo Researchers, Inc.)

Chapter 3

Cells:
The Basic Units of Order
in the Living World

Nature makes so gradual a transition from the inanimate to the animate kingdom that the boundary lines which separate them are indistinct and doubtful.

Aristotle

It has long been apparent that most inanimate things in the world can be placed in categories of greater and lesser complexity. Atoms and molecules are arranged in combinations, the complexity and diversity of which are particularly striking.

In the living world the complicated parts of cells are constructed of molecules, some of which are themselves enormously complex. Only the largest molecules can be perceived directly by using immensely powerful electron microscopes. Cells, in their turn, form organisms, the independent units of life in nature. Organisms interact with each other and with their physical environment, forming patterns known as *ecosystems*.

Within the levels of organization of the living world, from molecule to cell to organism to ecosystem, the smallest unit which has all the characteristics we associate with life is the cell. In this chapter we shall focus most of our attention on the cell as the basic unit of order in the living world. In following chapters molecules, organisms, and ecosystems and their patterns of organization will be discussed. To begin this discussion we address ourselves to a fundamental question: What does it mean to be alive?

WHAT IS LIFE?   To say "life" to someone will probably make him form mental images of dogs, cats, bees, grass, trees, people, and other objects from his memories of past experiences that he knows are *living*.   Asked to explain why he thinks of these organisms when asked to think of life, he will probably say that these objects move, grow, reproduce, eat (or are eaten), respond, and do other *lively* things.   It was with the study of such obviously living things that the science of biology started, though eventually biologists began investigating bacteria and other small objects that are not so obviously alive.   A need arose for precise criteria for judging whether something is *alive*.

Life is commonly defined on an *operational* or *functional* basis; that is, life is defined by *what living things do*.   After observing enough living things, we can form some generalizations which seem to describe the activities of all living things.   These characteristic activities of living things can be grouped under three headings, *acquisition and metabolism of nutrients, homeostasis,* and *growth and reproduction.*

All living things seem to be in a constant search for food: a green plant spreading its energy-trapping leaves beneath the rays of the sun or a shark prowling under the ocean's surface.   All living things must supply themselves with food from which to build their own structures and extract the chemical energy to operate them. Acquisition and metabolism of nutrients are the means by which an organism supplies itself with food and then builds up and tears down structure with the expenditure of energy.   They involve three separate processes: (1) *nutrition,* an organism's supplying itself with raw materials from its environment; (2) *metabolic breakdown,* an organism's extracting energy from nutrient molecules by breaking them up into smaller molecules; and (3) *synthesis,* the bonding together of small molecules into larger molecules and cellular structure by utilizing some of the energy released in the metabolic breakdown of food.   All these metabolic activities require a high degree of regulation, which falls under the heading of homeostasis.

Homeostasis means any kind of response an organism can make that will tend to *balance* the effects of changes in the internal or external environment.   In hot weather, for example, one sweats, resulting in cooling of the skin and prevention of overheating.   In the same environment a nonliving object, such as a rock, simply becomes as hot as the environment.   The motions you make as you drive a car, the movements you make as you sit in your chair, the rate of your heart beat, and the size of the pupils of your eyes—all are examples of responses you make to stimuli from your internal and external environments.   Other examples include muscular contraction in response to nerve impulses or hormone level and increase or decrease in levels of production of various molecules in various tissues of the body.

If living things are to prevail, they must also be able to *grow and reproduce* their own kind or their kind will become extinct.   This is true not only of organisms but of the cells of the organisms as well.   Growth and reproduction of organisms is closely identified with living things and is the most obvious of the various activities of life; no one can dispute that something is alive if it is able to increase in size and then reproduce.

To review, let us consider a hypothetical transparent blob lying on the ground. If we are asked whether it is alive, our first inclination will probably be to poke it with a stick or our foot. Through this behavior we are testing the blob for homeostasis. If we still are unsure, we can take its temperature. If it is hotter or cooler than the environment, we might conclude that the blob is releasing and using chemical energy in order to maintain its preferred temperature. If closer observation reveals that the blob is dissolving the grass underneath it, our suspicions may be even better founded. There will be no doubt about its state if it suddenly divides and produces two separate blobs.

This example may seem like hypothetical nonsense. Most living things are large and have behavioral responses that are easily detectable. But turn over a wet, rotten log and examine a slime mold clinging to its lower surface. Or spend a few minutes looking at bacteria and the countless other tiny forms that become visible only under a microscope. You will find yourself often asking: Is this thing alive or not? Physicians are now wondering more and more how they can legally decide when a person is dead. Traditionally, a person is dead when his heart stops beating, but his cells still live, some for many hours! Certain organs can be kept alive in refrigerated bone banks, eye banks, and other kinds of banks for days. The difference between the legal and biological points of view about the nature of life is obvious. We shall not even attempt to discuss the philosophical and religious attitudes to life; our subject is the biological interpretation of life.

To summarize, a living thing has the following general characteristics:

1   It is able to react to changes threatening to alter its state or condition in such a way as to counterbalance undesirable alterations.
2   It is able to obtain nutrients from its environment and transform them chemically, harnessing the chemical energy released in the process and using it to perform the syntheses and other chemical work it requires.
3   It is able to increase its size at the expense of the environment (grow) and to produce copies of itself (reproduce).

The impact of the cell theory was dramatic (it still jars some people to learn they are made of cells). Looking at your own hand, your neighbor, your dog, or a tree, you may find it odd to think that all living objects are constructed of millions of tiny units called cells. Life is the sum of the functions of living cells. The production of food by plants, the galloping of a horse, or the movement of a man's eyes—these are examples of what organisms can do because of what their cells can do. In studying the living world we must ultimately arrive at the level of the cell.

HOW ARE CELLS ORGANIZED?

Most cells cannot simply be placed on a table and dissected in order to study the function of their inner parts. Special techniques must be used. The development of

METHODS OF STUDYING CELLS

such techniques and the tools associated with them have been the primary agents pacing the rate of progress in biology. For example, one of the important factors in the early development of biology was the invention of the microscope.

We saw in the last chapter how use of the microscope, along with the technique of staining tissues, permitted observation of parts of cells invisible to the unaided eye. Microscopes using transmitted light have since been improved to the theoretical limit of their potential. Since this limit is imposed by the physical nature of optical magnification, it is not possible to exceed it by improvements in the technique of lens manufacture or microscope construction. The light microscope in its most sophisticated form can magnify with good resolution up to about 2,000 times and no further. The correct way to describe the power of a magnifying device is to state how close together two points can be and still be distinguished as separate points. This is called the *resolution* of the microscope. In the light microscope the maximum resolution is about 0.1 micron, that is, about 1/100,000 centimeter (there are about $2\frac{1}{2}$ centimeters in an inch). Two points that far apart can be distinguished with a good light microscope, under optimal conditions. To obtain higher magnification a form of energy other than light is needed, and special microscopes use a beam of electrons.

The *electron microscope* relies on a beam of electrons rather than a beam of light. The electrons are projected through a series of circular magnets instead of glass lenses. The electron microscope in its present form can provide magnifications of up to several hundred thousand diameters, and the highest resolution of this remarkable instrument is down around 5 angstroms, or 1/20,000,000 centimeter. Thus, with the electron microscope, observations can be made on a far smaller scale than is possible with the light microscope. Even individual large molecules and molecular aggregates can be perceived.

Another important tool of the modern cell biologist is the *centrifuge,* which is basically a high-speed wheel with sockets around the outside in which samples can be placed. If fluid suspensions are placed in tubes fitted into these sockets and the wheel is rotated fast enough, suspended particles sink to the bottom of the tubes as sediment. Centrifuges have played a significant role in permitting the isolation of many different cellular components and even molecules and molecular aggregates.

In order to study cells one must have a source of cells and a means of maintaining them. The problems met in achieving these goals vary according to whether the cells are bacteria, single-celled organisms, or multicellular organisms. A common procedure in the study of liver cells, for instance, begins with mincing the liver into tiny pieces and then rupturing the cells in a homogenizer so that the cellular contents are released. This suspension of cell parts, called *homogenate,* is then centrifuged, and since the various parts of the cells have different densities, the parts of the cells settle to the bottoms of the test tubes at different speeds and can be collected according to their relative densities (mass per unit volume) and the speed of centrifugation. Thus by proper choice of the centrifugation conditions it is possible to collect just those cell parts which are wanted.

By far the most penetrating means of analyzing the workings of the cell are biochemical. Understanding of the actual structure and function of the complex organization of the cell means understanding what molecules these structures are made of, how they perform their work, and what controls their activity. Biochemical studies have shed light on almost all aspects of cell function. However, it is not easy to move from the biochemical or molecular level of analysis to the scale of the microscopically visible cell parts. Sometimes it is possible to predict the biochemical function of a cell part from its structure and the circumstances of its presence as observed with the electron microscope. It is becoming increasingly evident that structure and function are related: One cannot be studied without the other.

To make progress in scientific inquiry into the processes of the cell we must consider each cell as a little machine whose parts are responsible for its actions. Without this mechanistic view the study would become vitalistic, that is, it would depend on the assumption of an unknowable ''life force'' animating the cell. Such assumptions have led nowhere in biological science and are now generally discredited. If an automobile mechanic believed that your car's engine was run by ''vital forces'' as well as by physical and chemical ones, your confidence in his understanding of its structure and function would be severely limited. A living cell is fantastically more complicated than a man-made engine, but its structure and function can be understood if it is regarded as a machine whose parts are made of molecules obeying the laws of physics and chemistry.

The cellular machine is made of parts that not only look quite different from each other but have different functions as well (see Figure 3.1). There is a division of labor among the components of cells, and each kind of part carries on a different function. Such activities as digestion, respiration, photosynthesis, reproduction, and excretion are carried on by specialized parts of the cell. The intracellular units that perform these functions are called *organelles*. Table 3.1 contains a summary of the structure and function of the major organelles of the cell which will be discussed in the following pages.

CELL ORGANELLES

In addition to organelles, cells contain complex fluids in which are dissolved proteins, fats, and a host of other kinds of molecules. Most of the weight of the cell is actually that of the water in the *cell sap,* as the cellular fluid is sometimes termed.

When cells are ruptured and spun in a centrifuge at low speeds, the heaviest objects (and therefore the first to sink to the bottom of the test tube) are large organelles called *nuclei.* The *nucleus* is the control center of a cell since it contains the *chromosomes,* the threadlike structures in which the genes are located. The chromosomes lie in the fluid nucleoplasm. The nucleus also contains spherical darkly staining structures called *nucleoli,* usually two in number. A nucleolus is produced by chromosomes and plays a role in protein synthesis that is not well

THE NUCLEUS:
REGION OF CONTROL

FIGURE 3.1 Schematic drawing
of a generalized cell, showing
that it is like a machine, different
parts having different functions,
such as digestion, respiration,
photosynthesis, reproduction,
and excretion.

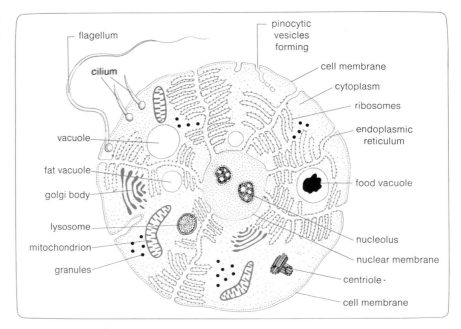

understood. The function of the chromosomes is at present a subject of intense interest to many cell biologists, since the instructions according to which the rest of the cellular machinery is run emanate from the chromosomes. We shall return again and again in many of the following chapters to genes and chromosomes and their role in the government of the cell.

CYTOPLASM: REGION OF
SYNTHESIS AND METABOLISM

Outside the nuclear membrane lies the rest of the cell, the *cytoplasm,* a region containing diverse organelles, particles, and fluids. The organelles are enclosed by membranes, to which some of the particles are attached. Membranes divide the cytoplasm into compartments and also serve as the outermost boundary of the cell, separating its unique structure from its nonliving environment. Clearly, in order to understand living things we must know more about membranes.

MEMBRANES

The boundary of a cell appears under a light microscope like the edge of a soap bubble, and even under the highest magnification of the light microscope very little detail of a typical cell membrane can be seen. The original evidence for the idea that the cell is surrounded by a membrane was circumstantial. Cells had been stabbed with needles, and the outflow was often seen to stop immediately; cells were indented with probes, and the dent disappeared upon removal of the pressure; cells

LOCATION	STRUCTURE	FUNCTION
Nucleus	Chromosome	Carrying genes, which determine traits of organism
	Nucleolus	Aiding protein synthesis
	Nuclear membrane	Controlling what goes in and out of nucleus
Cytoplasm	Endoplasmic reticulum	Channeling internal transport; attachment for ribosomes
	Ribosome	Site of protein synthesis
	Golgi complex	Site of specific secretion activity
	Vacuole	Transporting, storing, and processing materials
	Lysosome	Site of digestion
	Mitochondrion	Site of respiration
	Chloroplast	Site of photosynthesis
	Myofibril	Contraction
	Centriole	Participating in cell division
Surface	Cell membrane	Determining what goes in and out of cytoplasm
	Cell wall	Providing support, protection, and shape for most plant cells
	Cilia and flagella	Locomotion; causing water currents; gathering food
	Pseudopodia	Locomotion; engulfing food

TABLE 3.1 Structure and function of some organelles

were injected with phenol red, and the dye diffused around inside the cells but did not come out. It has long been clear that the cell is bounded by a membrane, although the details of its structure were invisible until the advent of the electron microscope.

Some of the early investigators of cell membranes imagined them to be like window screens which small particles could pass through. Further experience, however, showed that membranes are not like simple screens and that size is not the only criterion for passage.

Many years ago it was noticed that fat-soluble substances move rapidly in and out of cells. Such behavior provides a strong argument that cell membranes contain fatty layers themselves. It was also found, however, that water appears to adhere to the outside of cells, which indicates that membranes also contain proteins. In 1935 two British biologists, J. F. Danielli and H. Davson, proposed that cell membranes consist of four layers, each layer being one molecule in thickness. Their model resembled a sandwich with two slices of bread and two layers of butter. The slices of bread represent the layers of protein molecules on each side of the membrane, and the two layers of butter represent two layers of fat molecules. In cross section, from one side to the other, a membrane would be made of molecules in the sequence protein—fat —fat—protein (see Figure 3.2). Such a membrane would be extremely thin, about 80 angstroms (1 angstrom = 1/100,000,000 centimeter). In recent years many kinds of experimental facts have been adduced in support of this model. Studies with the electron microscope have been particularly convincing, showing (after certain staining procedures) a three-layered dark-light-dark membrane structure in cross section. The central light portion represents the fat molecules of the middle layer of the

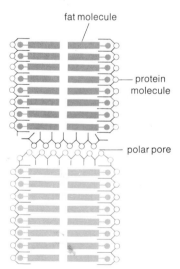

FIGURE 3.2 Diagram of structure of cell membrane. From left to right the sequence is protein-fat-fat-protein. Pores are lined with protein.

sandwich and the outer dark lines the ends of these molecules in combination with the protein boundaries of the sandwich structure. This structure is termed the *unit membrane.*

J. D. Robertson, of Harvard Medical School, suggested that the protein-fat-protein, or unit-membrane model, is valid not only for the outer cell membranes but is also the design of all the membranes in the cell. The universality of the unit membrane remains in doubt, however. The membranes making up the various organelles of cells may in some cases be different from each other. Organelles have different functions, many of which are carried on by the membranes of the organelles. Recent electron micrographs show specialized regions of membranes, which may be in part responsible for the unique activities of the various organelles.

INTERNAL MEMBRANE SYSTEMS

Imagine for a moment that we have spun down and removed all the larger organelles in the cells in our hypothetical test tube. With use of high-speed centrifuges a myriad of tiny structures from the fluid remaining after the earlier centrifugations can be recovered. Biochemists have studied a class of such granules which contain 40 percent protein and 60 percent ribonucleic acid, two substances we shall have more to say about later. Because of their composition these granules were named *ribosomes.* Ribosomes are the sites of protein synthesis in the cell and as such constitute some of the most essential components of the cellular machinery. We shall discuss their function in detail in a later chapter.

Work with the electron microscope has revealed that the ribosomes are not only scattered about in the cytoplasm but that many of them are attached to membranes arranged as minute sacs and tubules in the fluids of the cytoplasm. The internal membrane system of the cell is named the *endoplasmic reticulum.* The endoplasmic reticulum sometimes consists of channels extending throughout the cytoplasm. In the electron microscope individual elements of the endoplasmic reticulum look like sacs. Some forms of endoplasmic reticulum are *smooth* and lack ribosomes, while other forms are *rough* because they have ribosomes along the surface of their membranes.

The substances cells secrete are synthesized in various regions of the cytoplasm and seem to be transported and circulated within the cell by way of the endoplasmic reticulum. In some cells, structures called *Golgi complexes* (Figure 3.1) appear to be associated with secretory activity. Golgi complexes look like concentric layers of smooth endoplasmic reticulum surrounded by small vesicles. Cases are known in which the vesicles, filled with newly synthesized secretory products, break away and move to the edge of the cell, where they burst and unload their secretions to the outside of the cell. The Golgi complexes may release secretions that have become highly concentrated into granules. This activity has been studied in some detail in the pancreas, where certain cells have the function of contributing digestive enzymes to the pancreatic juices as they move through the duct leading to the small intestine.

There, the enzymes break the foods down into smaller molecules which can pass through the lining of the intestine and into the bloodstream of the capillaries located in its wall. These digestive enzymes were initially collected from their dispersed intracellular sites of synthesis and accumulated in the vesicles of the Golgi apparatus.

Vacuoles are fluid-filled bags separated from the rest of the cytoplasm by their enclosing membranes. Most animal cells either have very small vacuoles or lack them entirely. Vacuoles found in single-celled organisms and very simple multicellular organisms may be the equivalent of a stomach (the food vacuoles) or of kidneys (the contractile vacuoles). These organelles will also be discussed later.

In plant cells, vacuoles may occupy 90 percent of the cell's volume and contain salts, sugars, water, and pigments. For example, the red color of flower petals is due to pigments contained in the vacuoles. When water pressure builds up in the vacuoles, the plants stand rigidly erect; wilting occurs when the water pressure drops unless the plant contains supportive tissue.

The cytoplasm of all cells except bacteria and blue-green algae contains *mitochondria*, and many plant cells contain green chloroplasts and colorless starch grains. We discuss these cytoplasmic organelles later, after we have considered membranes and the problems of entry and exit in cells.

THE CELL MEMBRANE
REGULATION OF WHAT
GOES IN AND OUT OF CELLS

A cell membrane forms a boundary between the living contents of a cell and its nonliving environment, a border that selects what goes in and what goes out of a cell. Without this *selective permeability* in the cell membrane the contents of the cell would become identical with the environment of the cell. The passage of materials through the cell membrane is called *transport,* and to understand this process we must look into the nature of the cell membrane and the problems it presents to penetration by particles.

Picture a barrier consisting of an extremely thin layer of fat covered on each side by equally thin layers of protein. Here and there "pores" a few times larger than individual water molecules are found (such pores are estimated at 5 to 10 angstroms in diameter), and their total area is less than one one-thousandth of the total surface of the cell. To add more complexities to the picture, the layer of fat allows passage only of molecules that can dissolve in the fat. Protein molecules bear either positive or negative charges over much of their surface, and most particles bearing a charge would never get past the protein molecules without some help, except for a limited number of very small negatively charged particles such as the chloride from common salt (sodium chloride). Even if a particle comes into contact with a pore, it must be small enough to get through the pore, and since the pore is surrounded by charged proteins, the particle must be of the correct charge to get through. Particles must be transported through the membrane if the cell is to live, however. There are basically two ways in which this transport takes place, called *passive transport* and *active transport*.

If particles lack an electric charge and are either fat-soluble or small enough to get through the pores, they can enter or leave the cell simply as a result of their own molecular motion. The cell need not expend any energy in order to effect the passage of particles by this means; the role of the cell is passive. The passage of substances through the cell membrane without the expenditure of energy by the cell is passive transport.

Examples of passive transport are afforded by water and dissolved gases, the molecules of which are small and lack charges. Such molecules are able to pass directly through the pores. Ether, a fat-soluble, electrically neutral molecule, is an example of a substance that can pass directly through the membrane. Such substances can enter or leave cells quickly, with dramatic results. This raises another problem, however; which way will the substance tend to go?

Diffusion is a term used to describe the movement of particles from regions of higher to regions of lower concentration. This movement is due to molecular motion, and the direction of diffusion is determined primarily by the relative amount of interference that the molecules meet with as they are moving. If a table contained billiard balls endowed with constant motion and perfect elasticity, we could imagine how with time they would tend to move away from an initial cluster and distribute themselves in regions originally empty of billiard balls. Eventually the table would be covered with billiard balls evenly distributed and experiencing approximately equal rates of collision with each other.

When two fluids containing different concentrations of dissolved materials are placed so that there is no barrier preventing migration of molecules from one fluid to another, diffusion will occur until the concentration of molecules is equal throughout the combined fluids. Most of the diffusion will have taken place toward the fluid with the smaller number of molecules and therefore with the most room.

Suppose, however, that there is a barrier between the two fluids, a barrier which is not a simple screen but a membrane made of proteins and fats and containing tiny pores. Would water from the fluids pass back and forth through the pores in equal amounts, or would it pass through the pores in one direction more than in another? If so, which way will the water go? The answer to this question, we shall see, depends on which fluid has the greatest concentration of dissolved materials. This process is called osmosis.

Osmosis is the diffusion of water molecules through a selectively permeable membrane toward a region with fewer molecules of water. This is a vitally important process in cells, since all cells live in a watery environment containing dissolved materials in varying concentrations. The question whether water will diffuse *in* or *out* of the cells depends on the relative concentrations of the solutions inside and outside the cell membrane.

Since dilute solutions have more water per unit volume than concentrated solutions, water will tend to diffuse through membranes toward the more highly concentrated solution. For example, a codfish in the ocean swims in an environment containing a higher concentration of dissolved salts per cubic inch than within the fish. There is, therefore, less water per unit volume in the ocean than in the fish, and water will tend to diffuse out of the fish and into the ocean. Freshwater fishes have the opposite problem since their tissues contain a higher concentration of dissolved salts than the surrounding fresh water, and, as a result, they take in water. Therefore, oceanic fishes must constantly drink water while freshwater fishes never drink water except for what comes in with their food. The coat of mucus covering fishes serves as a barrier to osmosis.

The process of photosynthesis in plant cells provides them not only with nutrients but with an osmotic problem as well. As photosynthesis progresses, the amount of carbohydrates in the cell increases proportionately (carbohydrates are compounds made of carbon, hydrogen, and oxygen often used as nutrients by cells). One could say that the syrup gets thicker and thicker. As a result, water moves in by osmosis in greater and greater quantities, and the cell tends to swell. Plant cells deal with their osmotic problems through two special features, starch and cell walls. Sugars produced by photosynthesis are converted into insoluble starch granules, and the concentration of dissolved sugars stays relatively uniform (this of course is only one of the ways in which the synthesis of starch is useful to the plant). A second feature is the secretion of cellulose *cell walls* around plant cells, structures which provide support to the bulging cells much as nets around balloons do. Cellulose cell walls are found in nongreen plant cells as well as in green cells. In woody plants, the cell walls may become very thick and form what we call wood, bark, cork, etc. In addition to the support gained from the cellulose cell-wall material itself, a plant may be supported by osmotic pressure exerted by the water vacuoles against the cell walls. This type of support in plants is called *turgor* and explains why nonwoody plants wilt when the water pressure in them is low.

ACTIVE TRANSPORT

It has been known for years that some charged particles and molecules move into or out of cells *toward regions with higher concentrations,* a movement opposite to that of diffusion. In this case the cell is not passive but is actively using energy and doing work to transport the materials it needs through the cell membrane. This process is called *active transport,* and its mechanisms are largely still a mystery. The process is currently under intensive study in the cells of bladders, salivary glands, sweat glands, stomachs, roots, and many other tissues where there is a dramatic movement of particles from regions of lower concentration to regions of higher concentration or where particles appear to move through membranes at a pace faster than would be possible by passive transport alone.

Very small charged particles called *ions,* as well as larger molecules, somehow get into cells. This requires that the cells do work and consume energy. Two models have been proposed for this process, ion pumps and carrier molecules.

FIGURE 3.3 Ion pumps are involved in a nerve impulse. Because of the operation of ion pumps, sodium ions are concentrated outside the membrane, causing it to become polarized positively. Stimulation temporarily stops ion pumps and depolarizes the area. Within 0.001 second the ion pumps are restored.

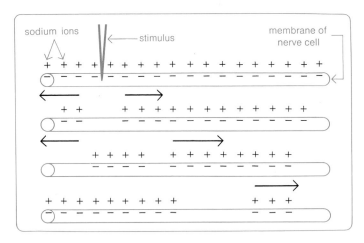

FIGURE 3.4 Two forms of feeding by cells.

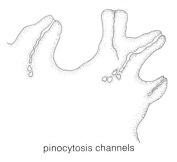

pinocytosis channels

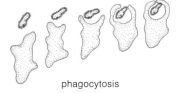

phagocytosis

Ion pumps (Figure 3.3) have been shown to operate across the membranes of many cell types; they force sodium ions out of cells while potassium ions are pumped in. (The sodium ion is the positively charged form of the sodium atom, most commonly present as the sodium of sodium chloride, Na^+Cl^-. The sodium ion is written Na^+.) Since sodium is the most common positively charged ion in the cellular environment (seawater or blood, for example) the activity of ion pumps affects the overall balance in salt content between the inside and the outside of the cells and hence the tendency for water to flow in or out of the cells by osmosis. Ion pumps thus regulate cellular water content as well as ion content. Ion pumps are known to be active processes because if the cellular supply of energy is interfered with, as by some metabolic poison, the ion pumps stop working.

The second form of active transport, in which *carrier molecules* are used, is more familiar. So many substances, charged and uncharged, have been found to require carrier molecules that many biologists believe that ion-pump systems are just one more aspect of carrier-molecule systems.

Carrier molecules function by first attaching to the molecules or ions to be transported when the latter first come into contact with the inner or outer surface of the cell membrane. The carrier, combined with the molecule being transported, then diffuses through the layers of protein and fat and releases the particle on the other side. Skeptics once referred to this model of active transport as the "steamboat hypothesis," but its probable validity has now been admitted since a number of carrier molecules have actually been isolated in the last few years.

FEEDING IN CELLS   Cells take in or get rid of individual particles through active or passive transport across their membranes. In addition, many cells take in food in solid or liquid form by direct engulfment, by folding the food into the cell membrane. If the food is solid, the process is called *phagocytosis* (from words meaning eating and cell); if the food is in fluid form, the process is called *pinocytosis* (from words meaning drinking and cell) (see Figure 3.4).

Phagocytosis can be observed in many single-celled organisms and in certain cells of animals. Some animal cells move among the tissues and eat substances foreign to the animal's body. By eating these foreign materials the phagocytic cells help defend against infection (see Figure 3.5). In certain cases, cells carry on phagocytosis of fellow body cells, causing removal of portions of the body. For example, phagocytosis is responsible for the disappearance of amphibian tails during metamorphosis, the destruction of worn-out red blood cells in the spleen, and the removal of bone cells during the reshaping of bone. Phagocytosis is not only a means by which individual cells take in foods, but it is also a process of immense importance in the defense and repair mechanisms of multicellular animals.

Phagocytosis takes place in two steps. First, the external particles come into contact with the cell membrane, which either folds in or flows around them so that they wind

FIGURE 3.5 (a) Normal mammalian cells (note the clearly defined nuclei).

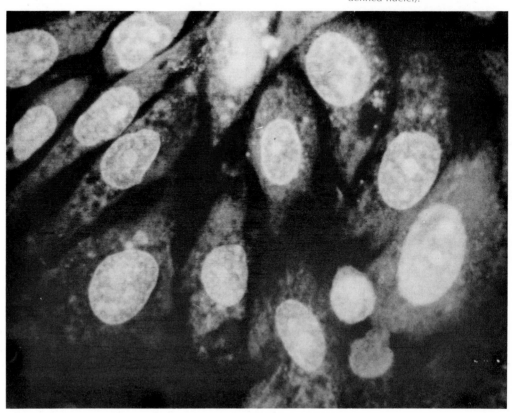

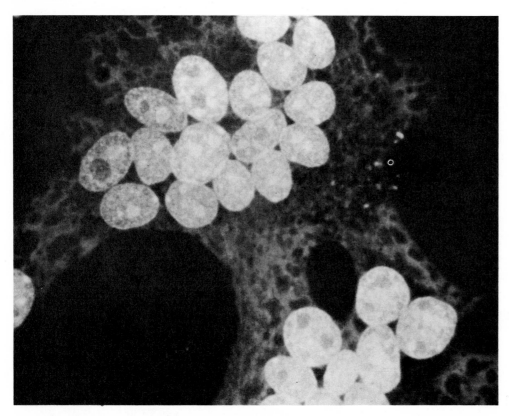

FIGURE 3.5 (*b*) Living cells under attack by the measles virus (dark shapes), causing the cell nuclei to clump together and fuse their cytoplasm into a single mass.

up inside a vacuole in the cytoplasm. During the initial contact with the particle, the cell membrane may "recognize" it through various properties, and it may either be engulfed or ignored. This is another example of how the cell membrane selects what is to go in or come out of the cell.

In addition to engulfing solids, cells can also take in fluids through pinocytosis. When viewed under a microscope, cells taking in fluids show vigorous activity along their edges. Closer examination reveals that the cell surface is forming numerous channels leading into the cytoplasm. The fluid engulfed at the cell surface is taken in as vacuoles. The contents of the vacuoles themselves must be actively or passively transported through the membrane of the vacuole before it is part of the cytoplasmic fluid.

Pinocytosis is a means by which large protein molecules can get into a cell directly. This idea has been proved valid by tracing the course of fluorescent proteins as they enter the cell through pinocytosis. Certain proteins, in fact, seem to stimulate cells to begin pinocytosis. Some biologists believe that protein molecules are "recognized" before pinocytosis begins. Like phagocytosis, pinocytosis requires surface contact with dissolved materials in the cell's environment before the cell membrane

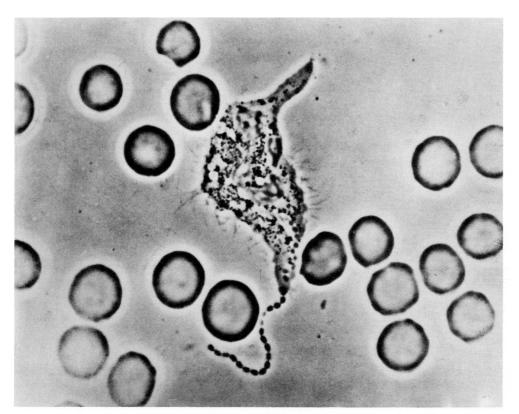

turns in. Both processes imply a selection on the part of the cell surface of what is to be admitted into the cell.

FIGURE 3.5 (c) A living human blood cell (*center*) shown ingesting a chain of streptococci, as example of phagocytosis. (*Chas. Pfizer & Co., Inc.*)

If the cytoplasmic material in animal-tissue homogenate is centrifuged at a little higher speed than that at which the nuclei settled out, a sediment called the *mitochondrial fraction* will form at the bottom of the tube. Biochemical studies have revealed the presence of two kinds of organelles in this sediment, *lysosomes,* with digestive functions, and *mitochondria,* which carry on respiration.

Lysosomes are slightly smaller than mitochondria and are barely visible in the light microscope as tiny granules. Chemical studies show that lysosomes are bags of digestive enzymes enclosed by membranes which rupture under certain conditions. This may happen if the cell dies or is subjected to high-frequency sound or other types of experimental damage. Lysosomes are believed to form from pieces of the endoplasmic reticulum which have broken away, enclosing cellular enzymes. A lysosome may then fuse with a food vacuole and digest the nutrients it contains. The nutrients are then absorbed through the vacuole membrane, and the vacuole con-

LYSOSOMES: THE CELL'S DIGESTIVE SYSTEM

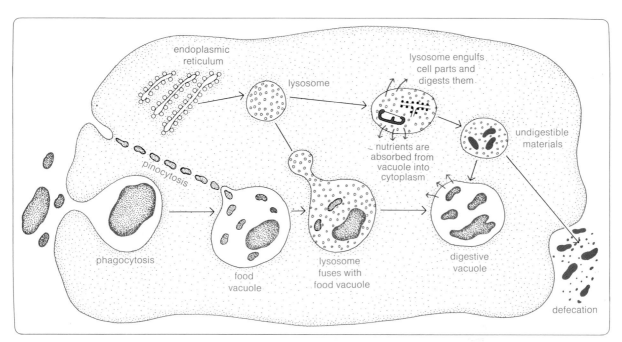

FIGURE 3.6 Digestion inside the cell. (*Adapted from De Duve.*)

taining undigestible materials moves to the cell's surface, where it is eliminated in cellular "defecation" (see Figure 3.6).

Thus, a cell may have the equivalent of the processes by which higher organisms manage their nutrition, ingestion, digestion, and defecation. Lysosomal activities have been clearly described in white blood cells. It has been known for years that white blood cells enter the bloodstream packed with granular packages of digestive enzymes, and it is now clear that these granules are lysosomes. When a white blood cell takes in particles such as bacteria through phagocytosis, the lysosomes can be seen discharging their contents into the food vacuoles. The bacteria dissolve, and, in a melodramatic climax, the white blood cell dies. Lysosomes are known in many kinds of animal cells, and their function is implicated in a variety of situations. For example, it is believed that lysosomal digestion follows phagocytosis involved in the resorption of bone during the constant remodeling of the skeleton, during absorption of the tadpole tail in amphibian metamorphosis, and in the removal of worn out cells from the body.

ENERGY IN CELLS
MITOCHONDRIA: THE CELL'S RESPIRATORY SYSTEM

As a result of uptake of nutrients through passive and active transport and of intracellular digestive activity, the cell is provided with nutrient molecules packed with stored chemical energy. The function of *mitochondria*, tiny organelles first observed with the light microscope about 70 years ago, is to release this stored chemical energy through *respiration*. Electron-microscope studies reveal mitochondria to be sacs with double-membrane walls (see Figure 3.7). The inner membrane is highly convoluted and has much more surface area than the outer one. In Chapter 5 we shall see that a critical part of the respiration carried on in most cell types is mediated by enzymes contained on the inner mitochondrial membrane. Years ago it was observed that metabolically active cells have more mitochondria than inactive cells, suggesting that mitochondria play a role in *respiration,* the release of energy from nutrient molecules, a hypothesis that has since been shown to be valid. Mitochondria not only carry out respiratory activity in cells but continue to carry out these activities even when removed from cells and placed in artificial media in test tubes.

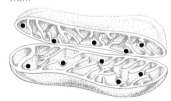

FIGURE 3.7 A three-dimensional diagram of a mitochondrion, showing the double-membraned wall.

CHLOROPLASTS: THE
TRAPPERS OF ENERGY

We have learned that mitochondria contain enzymes which generate energy from nutrient molecules, but this presupposes that a supply of nutrient molecules is available. Tracing foods back to their original sources, we find that plants are the producers of the original nutrients, which are then passed on and used by a sequence of consumers. Chloroplasts (Figure 3.8) are the organelles of green plants which trap the energy of the sun's rays and use it to produce energy-containing chemical nutrients. This is the process called photosynthesis, and it is to be the subject of a detailed discussion later in this book. Chloroplasts, like the other organelles we have studied, have a characteristic structure when viewed in the electron microscope. They too contain enzymes and complex membrane systems, and in addition they contain the green pigment chlorophyll. It is chlorophyll, the chemical which

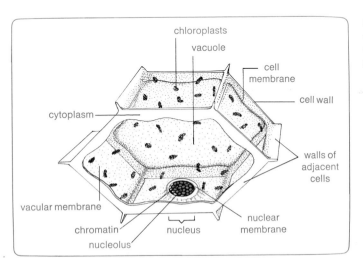

FIGURE 3.8 A generalized plant cell; note the cell walls and chloroplasts, structures that animal cells do not have.

makes plants look green, that actually absorbs some of the sun's energy and sets it to work in the reactions of photosynthesis.

CELL MOTION

Either food must be brought to the cell or the cell must go to the food. In addition, some cells must be able to move internally or as a whole if they are to be able to react properly and escape hazardous conditions. And, since the behavior of organisms is due to the behavior of cells, it follows that the feeding, environmental response, and all other movements of organisms are actually due to the movement of cells or parts of cells.

CYTOPLASMIC STREAMING

A characteristic of all cells, except for those of bacteria and blue-green algae, is the streaming of cytoplasm. This flow of the cell contents serves as a cellular version of a circulatory system, furnishing all parts of the cell with nutrients, enzymes, and hormones and transporting wastes and secretions to the surface. Although it is very easy to observe cytoplasmic streaming under a microscope, it is far more difficult to explain and the real mechanism of streaming remains unclear.

AMEBOID MOVEMENT

Cytoplasmic streaming usually does not cause cells to change in shape, but ameboid movement is a type of cell motion in which cell shape and position are altered. The ameba, after whom this type of motion is named, actively changes shape when the cytoplasm streams forth into extensions of the cytoplasms called *pseudopodia* (false feet). Pseudopodia not only serve in locomotion but may also feed by extending

FIGURE 3.9 Ameboid motion as explained by the advancing-tube theory.

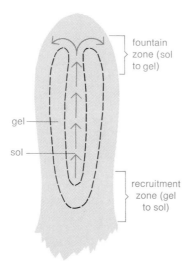

toward food.   The extending pseudopodia form a food cup which surrounds the food and takes it into the cytoplasm as a food vacuole.

Ameboid movement is observed in many free-living cells and in some cells in multicellular animals.   For example, blood cells can be kept alive for a short time if they are placed on a slide, covered with a cover glass, and kept warm.   Under a microscope the white blood cells will be seen changing shapes, sending out pseudopodia, and wandering about just as they do in your blood vessels and tissues.

Ameboid movement is not well understood, but there are several theories attempting to explain it.   One widely held idea is that cytoplasm in a relatively fluid state moves forward through a tunnel formed by other fractions of the cytoplasm which have formed a *gel*.   When the fluid cytoplasm reaches the front end of the tube, it flows to the side as a "fountain," and changes to a gel itself.   Thus, you may imagine an advancing tube in which the wall at the back end becomes fluid and moves through the tube to the front end, where it becomes part of the gel tube.   The force involved in the advancement of the tube is possibly due to contractile proteins in the gel (see Figure 3.9).

Ameboid motion requires *contact* between pseudopodia and a solid surface and involves a *change in shape* of the cell.   Another type of cell motion, called *ciliary motion,* involves movement of fibrous extensions of the cell membrane and not the cell itself.   The extensions are called *cilia* when they are short and numerous and *flagella* when they are long and few in number.   Cilia contract and push against a liquid environment like flexible oars, while flagella, due to their greater lengths, function more like a whip.   Their waving action causes the cell, or its liquid environment, or both to move.   A cell does not change in shape as a result of this type of motion, and no contact with a solid surface is required.

MOVEMENT WITH
CILIA AND FLAGELLA

In 1676 van Leeuwenhoek described a "wee little beastie" in the following terms: "The belly is flat and provided with diverse incredibly thin feet, or little legs, which were moved very nimbly."   The nimble little legs were cilia.   Microscopic studies through the years since then have shown cilia and flagella to be very common in protozoa, plants, and animals, but among the higher animals, the only cells which move independently with flagella are sperm cells.   It is very common in higher animals, however, for internal passageways of the body to be covered with ciliated cells.   In man, ciliated sheets of tissue line respiratory passages, for example.   The cilia on these sheets all move simultaneously in the same direction and produce a current in the mucus lying on the cells.   As a result of this current, particles are removed from the respiratory tract.

In the late 1890s the tails of sperm cells were observed fraying into minute filaments. Much later, the electron microscope revealed that the flagellum of a sperm contains eleven of these filaments, and when cilia were similarly examined, they revealed the same plan as the flagella.   The structure of either a cilium or a flagellum consists of two central short filaments surrounded by a ring of nine filaments, a "9 + 2" arrangement. The eleven filaments are enclosed in a membrane continuous with the cell membrane. It is believed that the membrane carries an impulse to the two inner filaments, which act as telegraph lines in carrying the impulses up the length of the cilium to cause total, instantaneous contraction. This is followed by a recovery stroke which is much slower. Evidence indicates the possibility that the filaments in cilia and flagella contract because they contain myosin, the same contractile protein which causes muscle fibrils to contract.

CILIA WITHOUT MOVEMENT

Cilia in some cell types have become so modified that they can conduct impulses but cannot move. Usually these specialized cilia lack the two central filaments. The vertebrate eye contains marvelous examples of modified nonmoving cilia. *Rods* and *cones* of the retina of the vertebrate eye have evolved from ciliated cells which have changed so that the tips of the cilia contain bulblike stacks of membranes with the light-sensitive molecule *rhodopsin* arrayed on them. Light bleaches the rhodopsin and releases energy, which causes a nerve impulse to travel down the cilium to the sensory nerves and on to the brain. As a result of this process you are able to see this page. Many kinds of cilia modified in specialized ways are found, for example, in the ears of insects, eyes of scallops, and brains of fishes.

CENTRIOLES AND THE
MOVEMENT OF CHROMOSOMES

Near the nuclei of single-celled organisms and all animal cells the electron microscope reveals a pair of small bundles called *centrioles*. Each centriole consists of nine short parallel filaments arranged as a circle in cross section, a structure quite similar to a portion of a cilium without the two central fibrils. The paired centrioles lie at right angles to each other, but during cell division they separate and move to opposite sides of the cell, where they become part of the machinery of cell reproduction. Following division of the cell into two daughter cells each centriole reproduces itself, so that each cell has a pair of centrioles. Centrioles are discussed in Chapter 7, where cell division is considered in more detail.

MUSCULAR MOVEMENT: AN
EXAMPLE OF ORGANELLE
SPECIALIZATION AND
COOPERATION

Contraction of cells or parts of cells reaches its peak of development in muscle cells. Since muscle contractions take place in only one direction, muscle cells are typically long and thin. Muscle cells are long cylinders filled with fine threads called *myofibrils* extending the full length of the cell. The following description does not refer to all types of muscle but to the major muscles responsible for skeletal movement, called *striated muscles*. Between the myofibrils are mitochondria and other organelles of the cytoplasm. The myofibrils themselves are made of *filaments* of two types, *thick* and *thin*. A muscle cell is a bundle of myofibrils which are themselves bundles of filaments. An individual muscle cell is about 50 microns in diameter, that is, about 0.005 centimeter, a thread just barely visible to the naked eye. The myofibrils are 1 or 2 microns thick, and their components, the filaments, are barely large enough to hold three contractile molecules side by side. The myofibrils are surrounded by mitochondria, endoplasmic reticulum, and many infoldings of the cell membrane. An immediate source of energy is supplied by the mitochondria, while the folded cell membranes carry incoming nerve impulses and cause the entire muscle cell to contract quickly as a unit.

Development of a theory explaining muscle contraction began in the 1930s when a protein complex later called *actomyosin* was extracted from muscle. In 1939 Albert Szent-Györgi showed that a preparation of this protein spread into a film and rolled into a fiber could develop tension and do work in a fashion similar to a living muscle, providing a source of chemical energy is added. Further studies showed, however, that actomyosin, as such, does not actually exist in muscle. Instead of one protein, *two* proteins were identified in living muscle, *actin* and *myosin*. In the earlier investigations, actin and myosin had been studied outside the muscle cell and had combined into the artificial protein actomyosin.

H. E. Huxley has shown that myosin makes up the thick filaments and actin the thin filaments of the myofibrils seen with the electron microscope. Huxley has proposed the *sliding-filament theory* of muscle contraction, a model in which thin actin filaments lie parallel and equally distant from thick myosin filaments and slide past each other like ratchets (see Figure 3.10). To picture this, imagine thin rods projecting toward each other from opposite walls of a room. In the center of the room are thicker rods arranged so that each thin rod is surrounded by three thick rods lying

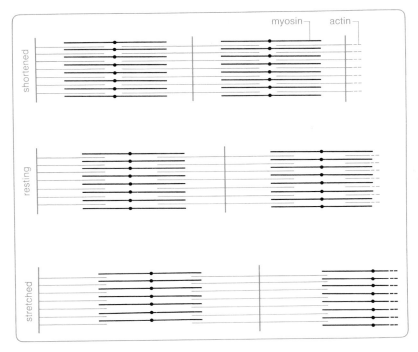

FIGURE 3.10 The sliding-filament theory of muscular movement. Contraction of muscle occurs as a result of thick and thin filaments in the myofibrils sliding past each other in a telescoping action. The thick central filaments are myosin, and the thin filaments projecting from each side are actin. Projections from the myosin touch the actin and may move along the length of the actin like a ratchet, drawing the two sets of actin filaments toward each other and shortening the length of the unit.

parallel to the thin rods and attached to them with small projections called *bridges*. Now picture energy being released at the points where the bridges touch the thin filaments and imagine the bridges pulling the thin filaments toward the center of the room. As a result, the walls of the room move closer together, and the room shrinks. By a similar process thick myosin filaments pull on thin actin filaments and bring them closer to the center of the contractile units making up the myofibrils. The units shorten, the myofibrils shorten, the muscles shorten, and by such a process your eyes are able to move across this page and your fingers are able to move a pencil.

The necessity for certain forms of chemical energy in all forms of cell motion, in addition to the increasing evidence that contractile proteins are present in most cells, seems to indicate that a basic mechanism is involved in all forms of cell motion. It may turn out that ciliary and flagellar motion, ameboid flow, muscle contraction, and the movement of chromosomes during cell division are *all* caused by sliding filaments of proteins.

APPENDIX LEVELS OF ORGANIZATION

In Chapter 1 we described how the living world is organized into various levels of complexity, and we saw how each level may be studied by different disciplines. Cells specialize into *tissues,* and tissues join to form *organs* which cooperate as an *organ system* within the next higher level of organization, the *organism* (see Figure 3.11).

Of all the levels of organization, that of the organism bears the brunt of the pressures of the environment. The cell is the smallest unit of life, but the organism is the unit of life that reproduces its kind, feeds, grows, and interacts with other organisms in an evolutionary contest of efficiency. It is the competition between organisms that provides the driving force of natural selection. The organism is the package of inherited traits that must be tested against the environment if the species is to survive.

LEVELS OF ORGANIZATION
IN ANIMALS

Every vertebrate animal (an animal having a spinal column) has a *skeletal system* supporting its body while a *muscular system* provides movement to the skeleton and internal organs. This locomotion makes possible the taking in of food by the *digestive system*. Food is digested and absorbed into the *circulatory system* and transported to the cells of the body. The blood contains oxygen absorbed from the *respiratory system*. Energy-rich nutrients are transported to all parts of the body, and following respiration and metabolism the wastes are carried away by the bloodstream and removed by the *excretory system*. All these complex activities are coordinated by the *nervous* and *endocrine systems,* fast reactions by nerves and slower, more prolonged responses by hormones. The entire organism is covered by an *integumentary system,* which provides the outer barrier between the environment and the organism, controls water transport, and prevents the invasion of germs. All these systems cooperate in the perpetuation of the individual organism, but an additional one perpetuates the species, the *reproductive system*.

FIGURE 3.11

ORGANISM

MAN	PLANT
Skeletal system	Roots
Muscular system	Stems
Digestive system	Leaves
Circulatory system	Reproductive organs
Respiratory system	
Excretory system	
Nervous and endocrine (sensory) system	
Integumentary system	
Reproductive system	

Total organ systems = *organisms*
Each system made of organs, e.g.,
  Digestive system
    Teeth
    Tongue
    Esophagus
    Stomach wall
    Intestinal wall
    Liver
    Pancreas
    Gall bladder
Each organ made of tissues

Epithelial lining	Epidermis
Parenchymal cell masses	Cortex
Muscle tissue, smooth, striated, cardiac	Xylem
Nervous tissue	Phloem } vascular (system) tissues
Connective tissue	Sieve plates
Fibrous connective tissue	
Fat or adipose tissue	*Cells* (in xylem)
Polysaccharides	Tracheids
Cartilage cell	Vessels
Bone cell	Pith
Blood cell	

Each organ system is made of organs, and there are many of these in complex animals such as man. For example, man's digestive system contains such organs as teeth, tongue, esophagus, stomach wall, intestinal wall, liver, pancreas, and gall bladder. And each organ is made up of tissues. Let us consider some of the tissue types of which organs are composed.

Epithelial linings are composed of cells which are usually closely packed together into one or more layers. The layers of cells cover, line, and protect inner and outer body surfaces against injury, dehydration, and invasion by germs. Epithelial linings may function in the organs and systems of absorption (digestion and breathing) and excretion (lungs, skin, and kidneys) and may perform secretory functions as well (for example, oil glands in the skin). The shape of a cell free from external pressures is a sphere, but cells of epithelial linings are in various kinds of contact, and the nature of these contacts and pressures produces cells which are flat like a fried egg, cube-shaped, or columnar. Some are ciliated, like the cells lining the upper respiratory tract and the egg ducts. Cells producing mucus in the various membranes of the body are shaped like goblets.

Parenchymal cell masses with specialized metabolic and secretory functions compose the major working portions of essential organs such as liver and many internal glands. Such glands are the pancreas, pituitary, thyroid, and adrenals. These specialized cells typically contain highly developed intracellular secretory organelles, such as endoplasmic reticulum, Golgi apparatus, and many ribosomes. The cells are packed together in complex ways to form solid, three-dimensional structures, often perforated by blood vessels and other channels and cavities.

Muscle tissue is responsible for most of the motion which takes place in an organism. Motion in an organism is due to shortening of muscles when the muscle cells in them contract. Muscle tissue of higher animals such as man is of three types, *smooth, striated,* and *cardiac* (see Figure 3.12).

Movement of internal organs is due to *smooth muscle cells,* long tapering spindle-shaped cells with a single centrally located nucleus. They are the only cells capable of great stretching, and they undergo slow contraction.

Muscles attached to bones are made of *striated muscle cells,* so called because of the presence of cross-striping, or striations (see Figure 3.13). The smooth muscle of internal organs generally cannot be voluntarily moved, but striated muscle can be moved at will. Striated muscle is skeletal muscle and makes up 40 percent of the weight of the body in man. The cells of striated muscle are long cylinders containing many nuclei and are referred to as *fibers.* Groups of fibers are enclosed in connective-tissue envelopes which are continuous with the tissue of tendons connected to bones. Telescoping together of the countless numbers of myofibrils in the millions of striated muscle cells causes shortening of the muscle and ultimately the movement of the attached bones.

Cardiac muscle tissue is found only in the heart and has characteristics of both smooth and striated muscle. There are many nuclei in each cell, and the muscle has striations but not as many as striated muscle cells. As in smooth muscle, action is involuntary. Cardiac muscle is unique in that its cells form a branching network in which the cells have joined together at various points so that cell contents may flow from cell to cell. (Could the heart be called one cell?) This arrangement is fantastically effective, for the heart is extremely resistant to fatigue.

Nervous tissue is built up from highly specialized *nerve cells,* or *neurons,* the structural units of the nervous system. Neurons in vertebrates are organized into a continuous network of cells forming the brain and spinal cord and the many extensions of the spinal cord branching from this central trunk. Neurons are composed of a *cell body* containing the center of control, the nucleus, while the rest of the cell projects

FIGURE 3.12 The chief types of vertebrate muscle tissue.

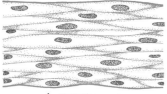

A. smooth muscle

B. striated muscle

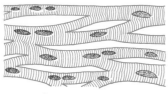

C. cardiac muscle

FIGURE 3.13 Cardiac muscle
showing striated muscle cells.
(*Carolina Biological Supply Co.*)

out as processes called *axons* and *dendrites* (see Figure 3.14). Neurons are specialized in that they can transmit impulses along their cell membranes. An axon is an
extension which conducts impulses away from the cell body, while a dendrite conducts impulses toward the cell body. An impulse can be transmitted from one
neuron to another by the impulse traveling out to the ends of an axon, where a chemical is produced which stimulates the contiguous dendrites of the next neuron after
diffusing across the intervening space. This connection is called a *synapse*.
Sensory neurons conduct impulses toward the brain and spinal cord, while *motor*
neurons bring impulses out to muscles, which are thus caused to contract. Other
neurons interact only with each other. These *associative* neurons make up most of
the tissue of the brain and spinal cord. Much remains to be learned about the nature
of the neurons and the means by which they bring about integration of the parts
of an organism, generate its behavior, and maintain contact with the external
environment.

Connective-tissue cells support the body and interconnect its parts. The four types
of tissues previously described have cells which are in close contact, but some types
of connective-tissue cells are separated by spaces filled with material unique to the
particular type of connective tissue. There are many types of connective tissue,
including *cartilage, bone, fat,* and the wandering connective-tissue cells which are
the first to invade the site of an injury and begin the process of tissue reconstruction
(see Figure 3.15).

FIGURE 3.14 Motor neuron. Two large masses are cell bodies, each with a nucleus. The axons are the thick extensions from the cell bodies, and the dendrites are the thin network of fibers. (*Carolina Biological Supply Co.*)

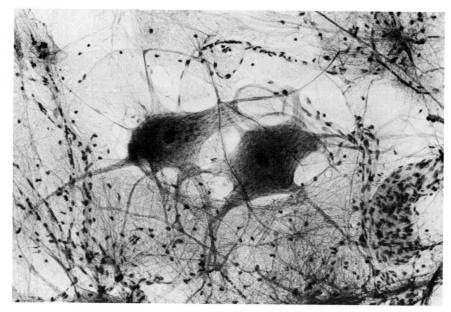

Fibrous connective tissue produces strands of intercellular material which form the sheaths holding many organs and tissues in place. Certain connective-tissue cells synthesize bundles of fibers which are tightly packed together and oriented in one direction, such as tendons and ligaments. Tendons connect muscles to bones, and ligaments bind bones to other bones with varying degrees of freedom of movement.

Some connective tissue cells become *fat* or *adipose* tissue through the secretion of fat. The fat usually is secreted as one huge oil droplet occupying most of the space of the cell and giving it the appearance of a ring, with the nucleus as the precious stone. Fat cells exist singly or may be packed together into a mass called adipose tissue.

Other connective-tissue cell types synthesize and secrete special substances which serve as lubricants in joints such as the knee and perform other special functions. These substances, called *polysaccharides,* are large molecules composed of many small sugar molecules bonded together. The optically clear jellylike fluid which fills the eyeball contains a high concentration of such polysaccharides, and other polysaccharides are a major constituent of cartilage.

Cartilage cells secrete a rubbery form of polysaccharide as well as tough protein fibers, and these substances are arranged in the spaces between the cartilage cells. In adult man, some cartilage exists in many joints, at the end of ribs, in rings around the trachea, in the ears, and in the nose. Cartilage is also formed in embryos and in wound repair as a precursor to bone.

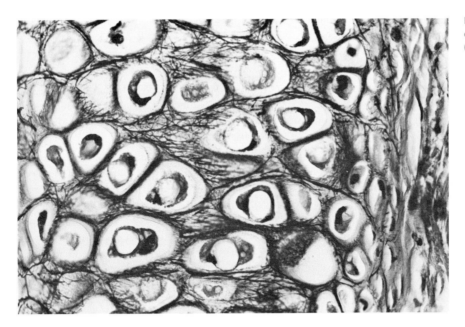

FIGURE 3.15 Connective tissue:
cartilage (*left*) and bone (*below*).
(*Carolina Biological Supply Co.*)

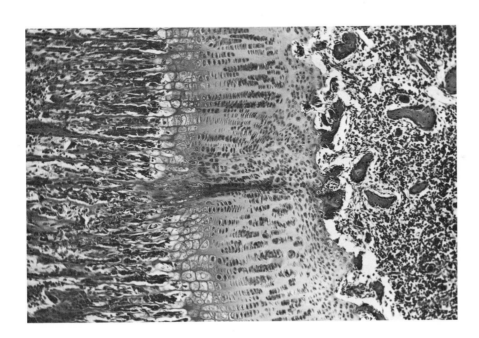

Bone cells secrete organic matter as well as the inorganic salts calcium carbonate and calcium phosphate. The salts are secreted in the organic material and give great strength to the bones. In old age when the salts become more numerous than the organic material, the bones become brittle and break more easily.

Long bones, as in the arms and legs, have a shaft with large round ends. Inside the shaft is *yellow marrow* containing a great deal of fat; *hard compact bone* forms the walls of the tube. The ends are made primarily of *red marrow,* which produces red blood cells and some types of white blood cells.

Blood tissue is made of various types of cells separated from each other by a watery solution of salts and proteins called *plasma.* When plasma diffuses out of the blood vessels and circulates among the tissues, it is called *lymph.* There are three main types of blood cells, red blood cells, white blood cells, and blood platelets. *Red blood cells* in mammals lack nuclei, being basically nothing but membrane-bound bags full of hemoglobin functioning in the transport of oxygen to the different body tissues. *White blood cells* change shape as they move about in the blood and other tissues and fight disease by phygocytizing materials foreign to the body and by producing antibodies which neutralize foreign proteins. Some kinds of white blood cells are produced in the red bone marrow, and some kinds originate in the lymph vessels, which drain lymph from the tissues. *Blood platelets,* fragments of cells produced in the red bone marrow function in blood-clotting processes.

LEVELS OF ORGANIZATION
IN PLANTS

The organs of higher plants are roots, stems, leaves, and reproductive parts. *Roots* anchor plants in soil and absorb water and minerals from it. These nutrients are conducted to the *stem,* which not only supports the plant but conducts solutions of various materials up and down the plant body and provides the necessary raw materials for the production of food by the *leaves.* *Reproductive organs* of seed plants are either cones or flowers. Much more will be said about these structures and their role in the successful invasion of land by plants in Chapter 18.

Plant stems are organs composed of the following tissues: *epidermis, cortex, xylem, phloem,* and *pith.* Roots contain all these tissues except pith but are unique in having tissues specialized for absorption processes. *Epidermis* is a layer one cell thick which covers the plant and acts as a barrier against loss of water and other vital materials while preventing the entry of harmful substances.

Underneath the epidermis, in nonwoody green plants, is a tissue called *cortex,* which is made of several layers of unspecialized cells. Cortex cells may be green and carry on photosynthesis, or they may be colorless and store food.

Dissolved materials are transported in higher plants through *vascular tissues* called *xylem* and *phloem.* Phloem tissue is made of several types of cells. The unique structures in phloem are the sieve tubes, which form vertical columns extending through the plant. When mature, sieve-tube cells lose their nuclei but retain their cytoplasm. Perforations appear in the cell walls where adjoining ends of sieve-tube cells meet. These specialized end walls, called *sieve plates,* are believed to aid sieve tubes in their primary function, the transport of nutrients between the various parts of the plant. Since this transport is fairly rapid, it cannot depend solely on diffusion alone. An "escalator" mechanism is believed to occur as a result of streaming of cell contents in a circular fashion.

The other vascular tissue of higher plants is *xylem,* a Greek word for wood. Xylem is characterized by types of cells and structures, particularly notable being *tracheids* and *vessels.* Tracheids are thick-walled, long, spindle-shaped cells whose contents disappear when mature. Vessels are noncellular structures originally formed from cells which have lost not only their cell contents but also the cell walls on the upper and lower sides where they join other vessel cells. Tracheids and vessels form continuous vertical columns of water from root to leaf.

The thick-walled cells of xylem tissue allow it to serve a dual function in not only supporting the plant but supplying it with water and minerals received from the roots. When enough xylem is present to be visible to the naked eye, it is called *wood* (see Figure 3.16).

The last of the tissues of the stem and root to be considered is *pith,* a mass of cells at the center of the stem functioning in food storage. Usually little pith is found in woody plants though there are exceptions. In more primitive plants, such as cattails,

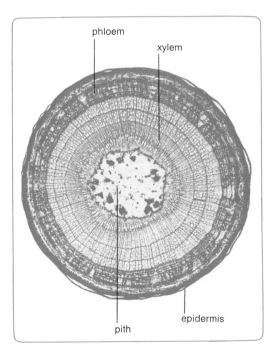

phloem

xylem

pith

epidermis

FIGURE 3.16 Cross section of tree trunk, showing epidermis, phloem, xylem, and pith. The xylem, the main body of a tree, is the part we call wood.

pith is more prominent and is easily visible as the pulpy material in the interior of the stem.

As in animals, we can discern several functional systems in plants which involve the activities of more than one type of tissue and which involve several of the organs of the plant. (1) We find that the roots, stems, and leaves all contain xylem and phloem tissues, which cooperate in transporting water and certain dissolved substances through the plant. We call this the *vascular system* of the plant. (2) We find epidermis tissue covering roots, stems, and leaves and forming an *integumentary system*. (3) We find in some plants cones or flowers which are either male or female and cones or flowers of the opposite sex in other regions of the plant or in other plants. Sometimes both male and female organs occur together in the same flower. These reproductive organs can be considered to form a *reproductive organ system*. (4) Vascular and other tissues existing in the various organs which support the plant may be considered to constitute a *skeletal system*. To compare this organization with the organ systems of a vertebrate animal we may say that the plant systems represent, in order, the circulatory system, integumentary system, reproductive system, and the skeletal system, but we cannot find organ systems in plants which are analogous to the muscular, nervous, endocrine, sensory, digestive, or excretory systems of animals.

REVIEW QUESTIONS

1 What is life?
2 List the names of the structures in a typical animal cell and briefly describe their functions.
3 How is a plant cell different from an animal cell?
4 What is the role of membranes in cells?
5 How are substances transported into and out of cells?
6 How do cells move?

SUGGESTIONS FOR
FURTHER READING
* Available in paperback.

Jensen, W. A., and R. B. Park: *Cell Ultrastructure*, Wadsworth Publishing Company, Inc., Belmont, Calif., 1967. Electron-microscope photographs that are not only technically accurate and instructive but aesthetically pleasing, with clear and concise explanations.

Kennedy, D. (ed.): *The Living Cell: Readings from Scientific American*, W. H. Freeman and Company, San Francisco, 1965. Twenty-four articles from *Scientific American* selected and introduced by the editor.

Loewy, A. G., and P. Siekevitz: *Cell Structure and Function,* Holt, Rinehart and Winston, Inc., New York, 1963. A concise, authoritative, but often difficult discussion of the structure and function of cells.

Morrison, J. H.: *Functional Organelles,* Reinhold Publishing Corporation, New York, 1966. A concise survey of the structures of the cell and their function.

Swanson, C. P.: *The Cell,* 3d ed., Prentice-Hall, Inc., Englewood Cliffs, N.J. 1969. Brief survey of structure and function of cells and the means by which they are studied.

Part 2

Metabolism: A Characteristic of Living Things

The living world consists of matter and energy from the nonliving world. Photosynthesis is the process by which matter and energy are trapped and changed into nutrients, which can then be used by organisms as a source of structural raw materials or as a source of energy. The means by which the energy is harvested from nutrients is called respiration. You and all other organisms form links in food chains of interacting systems of organisms called ecosystems.

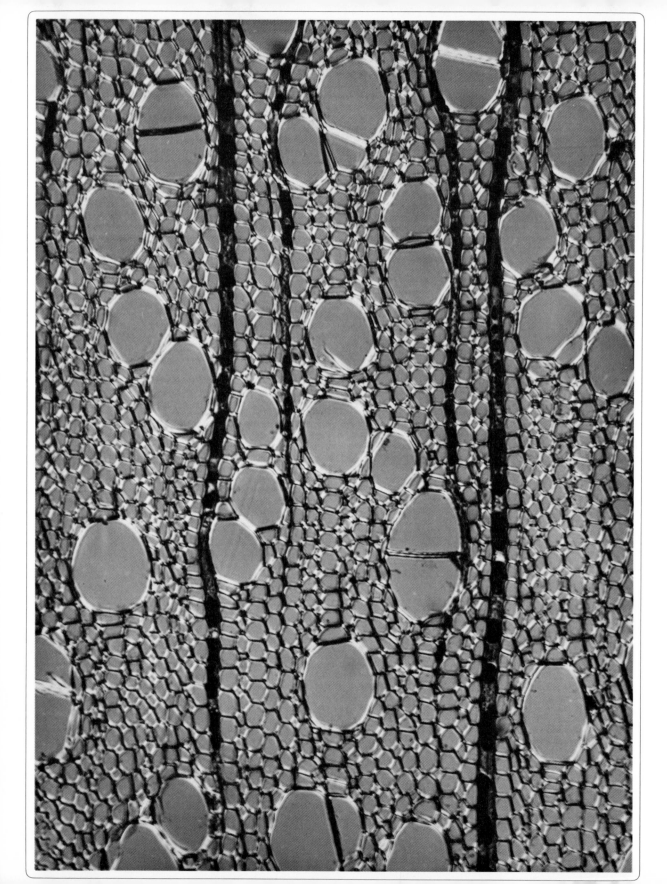

Chapter 4
What Are Living Things Made Of?

It's a very odd thing—
As odd as can be—
That whatever Miss T. eats
Turns into Miss T.

De la Mare

Every organism is a portion of the world arranged in a unique way. The food you eat is a small part of the external environment that you take in and make part of your body. Most of this food was previously part of a living thing, a morsel made of cells or the products of cells. Food contains the matter and energy from which you build your structure and harvest the energy to run it. The means by which this is done is called *respiration*, a part of the process of *metabolism*. We could define matter as "that which has weight and fills space" and energy as "that which has the ability to do work," but we would be no closer to an understanding of the structure of living things. We had better embark on a short excursion into the world of the atom, the unit of matter and energy. Only two characteristics of the atom will be considered in this text, *elementary structure* and the mechanism of *bonding*.

Maple wood, cross section ⟵ (210 ×). (*Eric V. Grave, Photo Researchers, Inc.*)

WHAT IS THE WORLD
MADE OF?

WHAT ARE ATOMS?

Basically, an atom consists of an extremely dense nucleus with electrons vibrating around it. The nucleus contains positively charged *protons* and neutral *neutrons* and therefore has a positive charge. The *electrons* are negatively charged, and if there is the same number of electrons as protons, the atom is electrically neutral. Electrons are usually vibrating around the nucleus in spatial areas called *shells,* which are arranged outside each other like the layers of an onion. The number of shells an atom has is determined by the number of electrons. The reason for this is that the innermost shell can hold only two electrons, but other shells may hold more, up to a maximum of eight (see Figure 4.1).

For example, an electrically neutral sodium atom has a total of eleven electrons, arranged with two electrons in the first shell, eight in the second, and one in the outermost shell (Figure 4.1). A sodium atom is electrically neutral, but its outer shell is not complete. It is a general rule that all atoms tend to complete their outer shells if conditions permit. An atom like sodium has two ways of obtaining a complete outer shell: It can either gain seven electrons, or it can lose one. Under the usual conditions, when the sodium is in solution, it loses one and the sodium atom becomes stable (Figure 4.2). But now it is no longer electrically neutral, because it has eleven positive charges and only ten negative charges, thus making an overall positive charge of one. The properties of such an atom are very different from those of a neutral atom, and it is given a special name, *ion.* *An ion is an atom which has gained or lost electrons.* Sodium atoms form positive ions because the ions have fewer electrons than protons. The opposite condition exists in chlorine because it has seventeen protons and seventeen electrons when electrically neutral. Electrons in chlorine are arranged with two in the first shell, eight in the second, and seven in the outermost shell. In this case it would be easier to gain a complete outer shell by gaining one electron (from an atom of another element) than by losing seven. For example, when they come together, sodium and chlorine can become stable through a reciprocal trade. That is, sodium can give up its electron to chlorine and become positively charged while chlorine becomes negatively charged (Figure 4.3).

Sodium and chlorine ions tend to move near each other because of their opposite

FIGURE 4.1 Electrons vibrate around the nucleus in spatial areas called *shells.* The innermost shell can hold only two electrons. Other shells hold more but the outermost shell never has more than eight.

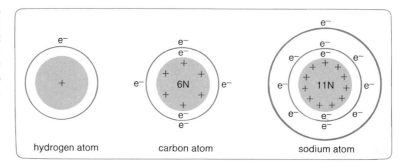

hydrogen atom   carbon atom   sodium atom

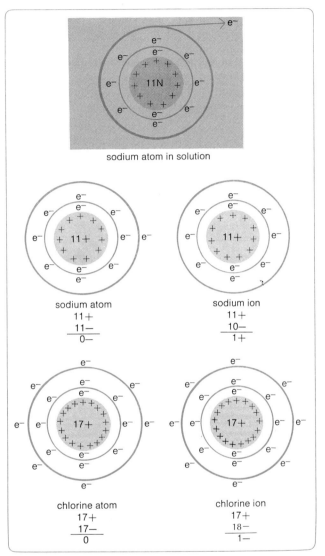

sodium atom in solution

sodium atom
11+
11—
─────
0—

sodium ion
11+
10—
─────
1+

chlorine atom
17+
17—
─────
0

chlorine ion
17+
18—
─────
1—

FIGURE 4.2 In solution a sodium atom loses one electron and becomes stable. But because it has eleven positive charges and only ten negative charges, it is no longer neutral: It is now a sodium ion.

charges. While held in this field of mutual attraction the ions form an *ionic bond*. Ionic bonds produce *ionic compounds,* in which the ions remain at a certain distance because of an attraction between unlike charges and a repulsion between like charges (the two positively charged ionic nuclei). When they are dissolved in water, ionic compounds are called *electrolytes* because their solution can conduct an electric current. When water is lost from the solution through evaporation, the ionic

FIGURE 4.3 Sodium atom and chlorine atom forming an ionic bond: Sodium loses an electron to chlorine and each becomes electrically neutral but charged. The loss of an electron makes the sodium ion positive; the chloride ion is negative as a result of having accepted the electron. Because of their opposite charges they attract each other in an ionic bond.

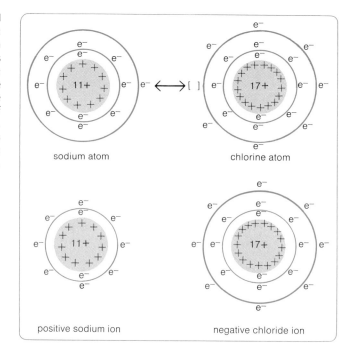

WHAT ARE MOLECULES?

FIGURE 4.4 Crystals are formed from ionic compounds when water evaporates from solution.

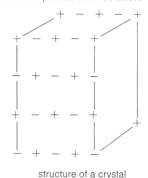

structure of a crystal

compounds become *crystals,* with unique geometric patterns caused by the mutual attractions and repulsions (see Figure 4.4).

In another type of bonding on the atomic level there is no loss or gain of electrons by either atom. Picture two atoms, neither with complete outer shells but neither giving up an electron for the other's gain. Such atoms *share electrons* in their outer shells so that the same electrons are included in the outer shell of both atoms. A bond formed by a mutual sharing of electrons is called a *covalent bond,* and the result is a *molecular compound.* A huge number of the compounds of which living things are made contain carbon atoms. To know why carbon is able to share electrons, an understanding of the structure of carbon is necessary.

Carbon has six protons in the nucleus and six orbital electrons arranged with two in the first shell and four in the outermost. It can either lose or gain electrons, and under rare circumstances it can function as either a positive or negative ion. More important to our story of life, carbon tends to share electrons and form covalent bonds with many atoms, *including other carbon atoms.* A carbon atom has four electrons to share and may form as many as four covalent bonds if it contributes only a single electron to each pair of shared electrons. Covalent bonds can also consist of a mutual sharing of either four electrons (two from the carbon) or six electrons (three from the carbon) (see Figure 4.5).

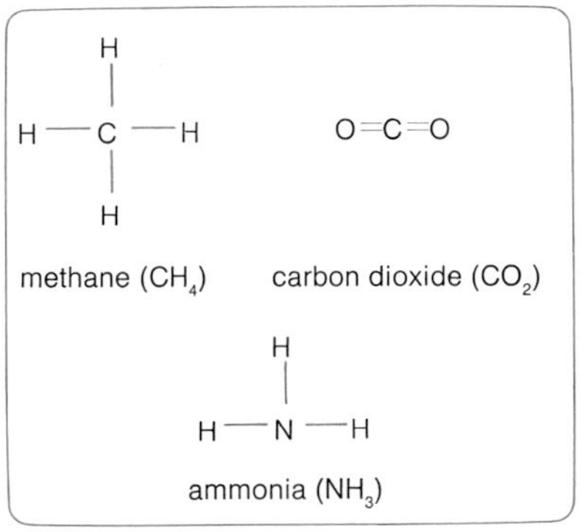

FIGURE 4.5 The dash represents a covalent bond and stands for a pair of shared electrons. The double dash represents two pairs of shared electrons.

ACIDS, BASES, AND SALTS

In the adjoining diagram

$$\underset{\text{sodium chloride}}{NaCl} \xrightarrow{H_2O} \underset{\text{sodium ion}}{Na^+} + \underset{\text{chloride ion}}{Cl^-}$$

$$\underset{\text{hydrochloric acid}}{HCl} \xrightarrow{H_2O} \underset{\text{hydrogen ion}}{H^+} + \underset{\text{chloride ion}}{Cl^-}$$

$$\underset{\text{sodium hydroxide}}{NaOH} \xrightarrow{H_2O} \underset{\text{sodium ion}}{Na^+} + \underset{\text{hydroxyl ion}}{OH^-}$$

each compound forms equal amounts of positive and negative ions when it breaks up, and the solution remains electrically neutral. The presence of all these free ions allows the passage of an electric current and is the reason why living things can conduct electricity.

Notice that hydrogen ions are formed when hydrochloric acid breaks up in water, whereas hydroxyl ions, OH^-, are formed from the sodium hydroxide. This difference in the way compounds form ions when dissolved in water places them in the categories of *acids, bases,* or *salts.* An *acid* is a compound which produces hydrogen ions when dissolved in water. A *base* (also called an alkali) is a compound that yields hydroxyl ions. A *salt* is formed when an acid reacts with a base. For example, table salt, or sodium chloride, is formed when sodium hydroxide reacts with hydrochloric acid:

$$\underset{\text{acid}}{HCl} + \underset{\text{base}}{NaOH} \longrightarrow \underset{\text{salt}}{NaCl} + H_2O$$

WHAT ARE YOU
MADE OF?

Now that you are equipped with a better understanding of the nature of matter, we return to the question of what you eat and what you are. Since the processes by which the substances you eat are utilized by your body are complex, we begin our discussion with the minerals because they change very little as they become part of you.

WATER AND MINERALS

Cells contain ionic and molecular compounds, the ionic compounds usually being called *minerals*. Unlike molecular compounds, minerals are not synthesized by living things but occur naturally in the rocks and soils of the earth's crust. From these nonliving sources the minerals dissolve in the rains and rivers of the earth and eventually become part of the watery solutions of body fluids and cells.

Almost all chemical reactions of living organisms take place in their watery fluids. To react, the compounds must be dispersed among the water molecules; they must be dissolved and in solution. Aggregates of molecules and crystals may dissolve in water by breaking up into individual molecules, as when crystals of table sugar become sugary syrup. Many molecular compounds and all ionic compounds dissolve in water by breaking up into charged atoms or groups of charged atoms called ions. How table salt or the hydrochloric acid of your stomach or the sodium hydroxide of lye will form ions was shown in the diagram on page 75.

The minerals of our diet are combinations of acids, bases, salts, and water. Obviously these watery solutions contain ions. We must complicate the picture, however, by saying that the number of ions in the solution varies according to the nature of the substance and its concentration. Each acid, base, and salt varies in its ability to form ions when placed in water. For example, strong acids yield many hydrogen ions, and weak acids yield relatively few. In a similar way, there are strong bases, weak bases, strong salts, and weak salts. Words like strong and weak are too vague for an accurate description of the quantity of ions present in a solution. The total quantity of ions in a solution can be determined by the degree to which an electric current is conducted through it, but that measurement does not reveal the concentration of hydrogen and hydroxyl ions in the solution. This is vital information because these are the active units of acids and bases. Instead, the *pH scale* is used, a system that indicates the concentration of hydrogen ions in a solution.

When a mineral dissolves in water, its ions react with the water, causing hydrogen and hydroxyl ions to be released from it. Some salts give rise to ions which trap more of the hydroxyl ions released from the water than of the hydrogen ions, and other salts give rise to ions which have the reverse effect. The result is that many minerals, when dissolved, do not produce neutral solutions. Instead some solutions may contain more free hydrogen ions than hydroxyl ions or more free hydroxyl ions than hydrogen ions. Thus, depending upon the nature of the minerals dissolved in it, a solution can be an extremely strong acid or an extremely strong base or somewhere between these two extremes. To convey a precise description of where a particular solution fits into this range between the two extremes the pH scale is used.

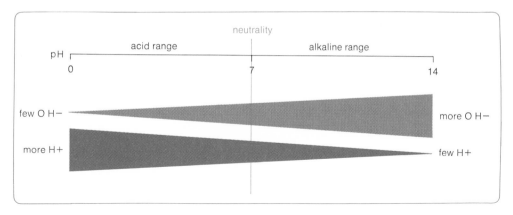

FIGURE 4.6 The pH scale.
(*Adapted from Paul B. Weisz, Elements of Biology, 3rd ed. Copyright McGraw-Hill Book Company, 1969. Used by permission.*)

The pH scale begins at 0 and goes to 14 (see Figure 4.6). On this scale a pH of 7 indicates neutrality, numbers between 0 and 7 indicate an acid, and numbers between 7 and 14 indicate a base. At a pH of 0 a solution contains only hydrogen ions, but as the pH increases, the number of hydroxyl ions increases until, at a pH of 7, there are as many hydrogen ions as hydroxyl ions. Above a pH of 7, there are increasingly more hydroxyl ions than hydrogen ions until, at a pH of 14, there are only hydroxyl ions. Therefore, solutions with pH numbers above 7 are basic.

The living material of cells contains many kinds of acids, bases, and salts and usually has a pH very close to 7, or neutrality. Often, however, certain special regions and parts of organisms contain strongly acidic or basic solutions. For instance, your stomach secretes strongly acidic juices, while your pancreas and intestine secrete strongly basic solutions. The fluids of plants are usually slightly acidic, and such specialized parts as lemons, limes, and nettles may be strongly acidic.

Organisms can tolerate only very small variations in the pH of their body fluids. Human blood, for example, can vary only slightly from a pH of 7.3 without bringing on acidosis or alkalosis, both of which may cause death.

We have seen that the fluids of the earth and its living things are made of water and minerals, acids, bases, and salts. These minerals may become part of us by being absorbed from our drinking water and from the fluids of ruptured cells that we eat. Minerals do not change in this move from the external to the internal environment; in other words the body uses certain common minerals of the earth for its own fluids.

ORGANIC COMPOUNDS

Living material is mostly water, and we have just learned that it contains many kinds of dissolved minerals. It is, however, the remaining material that has intrigued man for several hundred years, the substances not found in the nonliving world. These mysterious substances occur not only dissolved in the cell's water along with the minerals but also are found to make up the cell's structure. Tests performed on these substances revealed properties largely unknown in the nonliving world. Heat, for example, does not damage most minerals, but it may cause the substances of living cells to burst into flame or to decompose into other forms.

As early as 1807, chemists noticed the unique way in which materials from living cells reacted to certain chemical tests and named them *organic* compounds, meaning that these compounds were produced by living organisms. The minerals from the nonliving world were called *inorganic*.

PROTEIN MOLECULES

By 1820, three types of organic compounds had been recognized, *carbohydrates, fats,* and *proteins*. All three types were actively studied, and by 1850 it was believed that, of the three, proteins were the most complicated and must be the most important. The name protein was applied because it meant "of first importance." As time passed, protein was found not only in the membranes of cell structures but also dissolved in the watery solutions in the cells. Biologists consistently found that where there was protein there was life, and some scientists began to believe that proteins were the molecules specifically responsible for life. To them, proteins were the sites of vital force, and they felt compelled to learn about the structure and function of proteins.

FIGURE 4.7 The amino acid glycine. All amino acids are made of an amino group plus a carboxylic acid group.

H — N — C — C — O — H

amino group   carboxylic acid group

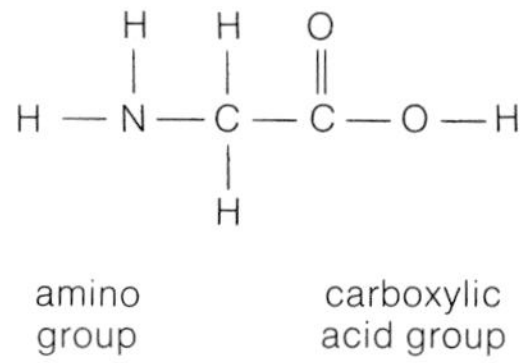

In 1820, a French chemist named Braconnot heated gelatin, a protein, and after the water had been driven off, found crystals of a sweet-tasting substance in the residue. He named the substance *glycine,* from the Greek word for sweet. Further study showed that glycine had a simple construction, a carbon atom at its center and an amine group, $-NH_2$, and a carboxylic acid group, $-COOH$, projecting from opposite ends (see Figure 4.7). Through the following years more *amino acids* were discovered until the list grew to twenty, the number now accepted as the building blocks from which all proteins of all organisms are constructed. All amino acids found in proteins have an amino group at one end and a carboxyl group at the other. How are these twenty amino acids assembled into proteins?

If we picture two glycine molecules (see Figure 4.8) lying side by side, we notice an OH^- projecting from one glycine close to where a H^+ projects from the other glycine. Under appropriate conditions the H^+ and the OH^- will be removed and bond together to form water, leaving an unshared electron on the carbon of one glycine and on the nitrogen of the other. As a result, the carbon and nitrogen atoms move closer and share electrons in a covalent bond; the two amino acids bond together. Additional amino acids can bond together in the same way. This bonding together with the loss of water is called *dehydration synthesis,* and we shall find that carbohydrates and fats are also synthesized in this way.

Amino acids may bond together through dehydration synthesis until a chain of them has been formed called a *peptide*. When a peptide chain is long, it is called a *polypeptide,* and, arbitrarily, when a polypeptide is made up of over forty or fifty amino acid units, it is called a *protein*. Proteins are often made up of several

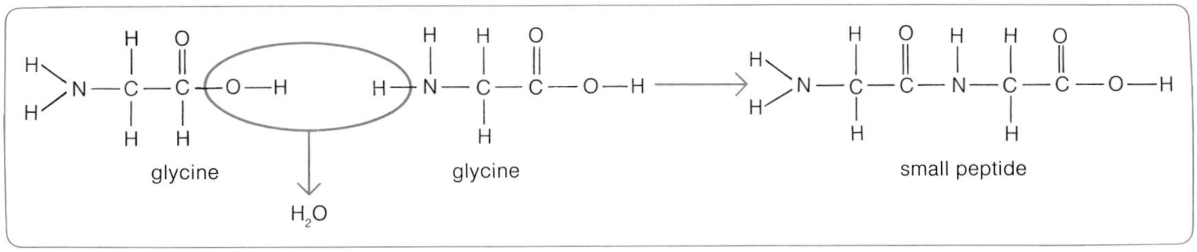

FIGURE 4.8 Bonding together of amino acids with the loss of water.

polypeptide chains. For example, hemoglobin, one of the proteins in red blood cells, is made of four polypeptide chains, each about 150 amino acids long.

Proteins are made of one or more chains of amino acids folded and twisted into various shapes. The sequence of amino acids in these chains may vary immensely from chain to chain. To grasp the fantastic variety of ways in which the chains can be fashioned, picture polypeptides in which all twenty amino acids are present but lined up in different sequences. You may compare these polypeptides to twenty soldiers in single file lined up in different sequences. This may come as a shock, but the number of ways in which the twenty soldiers or amino acids can be lined up is factorial 20, that is, 20!, or about 2×10^{18}. This is an enormous number, but the actual number of possible kinds of proteins is far greater. Our example was limited by fictitious ground rules requiring each of the twenty amino acids to appear only once. Actually, some amino acids may not appear in some proteins but may appear in other proteins more than once. Many proteins are quite large and contain hundreds and even thousands of amino acids. Because proteins vary so much in size and composition it is probable that there are more kinds of proteins possible than there are stars in the universe.

Chains of amino acids form polypeptides. How are proteins formed from these? The amino acids of a polypeptide have different groups of atoms projecting from their sides. These side chains contain carbon, hydrogen, and sometimes oxygen, nitrogen, or sulfur. Bonding forces between these atoms on the outside of the chains cause polypeptides to coil into structures resembling ribbons twisted around invisible cylinders, folded into balls, or organized in several other configurations. Further bonding between atoms on the sides of the amino acids causes the twisted ribbons to fold and pack into protein molecules with unique surface shapes and properties. To summarize, the properties of a finished protein are due to the sequence of its amino acids and, given the sequence, their tendency to twist, fold, and pack together. To picture this process, twist a towel until it is almost rigid, then fold and pack it into various shapes. Note the variety of surface shapes you can achieve. Of course, in a protein, the twisting, folding, and packing are due to the forces of attraction and repulsion between the atoms on the sides of the amino acids (see Figure 4.9).

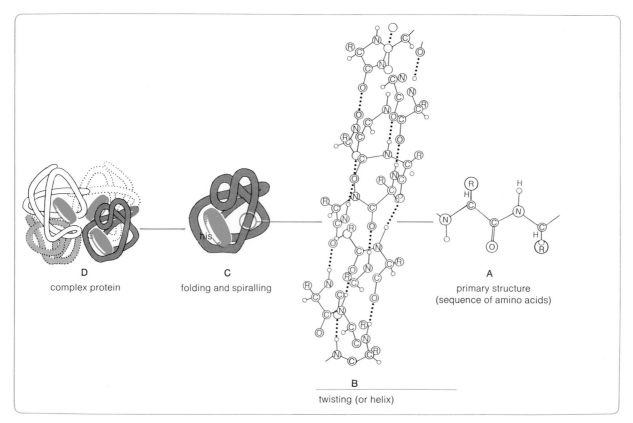

D
complex protein

C
folding and spiralling

A
primary structure
(sequence of amino acids)

B
twisting (or helix)

FIGURE 4.9 The nature of a protein is due to the sequence of amino acids *forming* its structure. Interactions between atoms projecting to the side from the amino acids cause the string of amino acids to twist, fold, and spiral to form a protein molecule with unique properties. This protein can bond with other proteins to form a complex protein structure, as with hemoglobin in the figure.

The twisting and folding of amino acid chains in proteins cause special surface shapes and properties, and, just as keys fit only certain locks, substances may fit onto the surface of proteins only if their shapes and chemical properties are compatible. If they do fit, the substances may touch and interact before being released from the protein's surface. A protein which brings selected substances to its surface where they can come into contact and interact is called an *enzyme*. An enzyme is a protein molecule whose surface properties induce the interaction of substances which collide and bind to it. Since proteins acting as enzymes are not consumed in these reactions, they can serve as chemical matchmakers over and over.

Enzymes were given their general name in 1878, the year in which they were discovered in yeasts. It has been known for many years that yeasts cause bread to rise and fruit juice to ferment. In 1897 some investigators were surprised to find that when yeast cells were mashed up, juices alone worked just as well as the intact cells in inducing fermentation. During the next few years, several enzymes were isolated from yeast juice, but no one knew what kind of chemical the enzymes were. In 1926, James B. Sumner, an American biochemist, isolated an enzyme named urease from the seed of the jack bean and proved that it was a protein. Since that time, many more enzymes have been isolated and *all have been found to be proteins.* Most of the chemical reactions of life are regulated by enzymes. Proteins, therefore, are the molecules in *direct* charge of controlling the reactions within the cell (see Figure 4.10).

For a chemical reaction to take place, the reacting particles must come into contact so that they can either form or break bonds. Given enough time, particles may come together and react through random chance, but living systems cannot depend on chance. The rate at which nonliving substances react can be speeded up by adding heat to increase the molecular motion of the reactants and therefore the rate at which they collide. With organic substances, however, the addition of heat beyond a certain point will drastically alter the nature of the organization of the molecules. If this occurs in proteins, they become *denatured,* that is, the nature of their folding and spiraling will change, and if the protein served as an enzyme before the heat was added, the nature of its role in chemical reactions will be changed. Instead of using heat to speed up the rate of reactions involving organic compounds, cells use enzymes, the protein molecules which bring specific substances into controlled contact on their surfaces and facilitate the breaking and formation of chemical bonds while these substances are bound to them.

Each enzyme has an environment in which it functions best. The most important factors in an enzyme's environment are *temperature* and the degree of *acidity* or *alkalinity.* In man the best temperature for enzymes is near 98.6°F, but the best pH (acidity or alkalinity) varies with the region in the body. For example, the enzymes in the stomach function best in a strongly acidic environment, while the enzymes in the intestine require a fairly strong alkalinity. Variation beyond the ranges of tolerance for temperature, acidity, and alkalinity cause the enzyme to become inoperative.

Since there is a fantastic variety of different proteins, it is clear that a vast number of enzymes might exist. The activities of most of these enzymes, however, are limited

FIGURE 4.10 The reactants might eventually collide by chance, but if an enzyme presents its unique surface, the reactants are attracted to the surface, where they bond, first to the enzyme, then to each other. The enzyme is not consumed in this controlled contact and can be used over and over. As indicated by the arrows, an enzyme may cause the building up or the tearing down of substances.

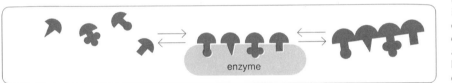
enzyme

to specific reactions.   This exclusiveness of action is used as the basis for the naming
of enzymes.   The name of the substance being acted upon comes first and is
followed by the ending *ase,* which means "acting upon."   Thus, proteinases means
"enzymes acting upon proteins."   An excellent example of how proteinases operate
is the process of digestion.

Digestion can be summarized by two words, *enzymatic hydrolysis,* or the breaking
down of a molecule with the addition of water in the presence of the proper
enzymes.   Earlier we described how amino acids bond together to form proteins
with a loss of water in dehydration synthesis.   In digestion proteins break up into
amino acids with an *addition* of water in enzymatic hydrolysis, at the very same sites
as those from which the water was subtracted when the protein was synthesized, the
peptide bonds.   Addition of water causes these bonds to break, and the protein thus
falls apart into amino acids.

GENES, PROTEINS,
AND REGULATION

We have seen that the chemical reactions of life are not just chance collisions of molecules but are due to the specific assistance and guidance of a vast number of
enzymes.   Many enzymes are found to be part of the internal membrane structures
of the cell.   Thus enzyme molecules in the membranes are separated from the rest of
the cell fluids, and enzymes of the cell fluids can be excluded from the internal contents of cell organelles.

Since enzymes are synthesized in cells, a cell clearly must be capable of highly
specific processes of synthesizing proteins.   Certain proteins are identified with
certain groups of organisms.   Your family, for instance, probably share certain proteins that other groups of people cannot synthesize.   *Proteins are synthesized
according to genetic instructions,* which represent an inherited pattern of order.
This genetic recipe for the proteins of an organism is carried by genes in the
chromosomes, as we see in Chapter 9.   Let us now consider another class of carbon
compounds, the carbohydrate.

CARBOHYDRATE MOLECULES

The carbohydrates are molecular compounds made up of carbon, hydrogen, and
oxygen.   In most cases the hydrogen and oxygen are present in a 2:1 ratio, as in
water, H_2O.   Recognition of this fact over 100 years ago was responsible for the
name "carbon hydrates," later shortened to its present form.

Familiar examples of carbohydrates are sugars, starches, and cellulose.   Cellulose is
the most abundant organic material in the world since it forms most of the bulk of
plants (and even the paper you are looking at this moment).   Some carbohydrate
molecules are as big as large proteins, while others are among the smallest of organic
molecules, but no matter how complex they may be, all carbohydrate molecules are
made up of structural units called *simple sugars.*   Just as the building blocks of proteins are amino acids, simple sugars are the parts from which carbohydrates are
made.

Simple sugars differ from each other in the arrangement of the —H and —OH groups
around the carbon atoms in the carbon-to-carbon chain.   For example, glucose, the

six-carbon sugar so vital to most organisms, has the arrangement around the second to the fifth carbon atoms shown in Figure 4.11.   At one end of the glucose molecule, at the carbon numbered one, the structure is —$\overset{\overset{\displaystyle C}{\|}}{C}$—H while at the other end, the sixth carbon, the structure is —CH_2OH.   Without changing the structure at carbons one and six, it is possible to have sixteen different structural arrangements around carbons two to five.   Each of these arrangements provides the molecule with strikingly different characteristic properties, and each of these sugars has a different name.   All these sugars, including glucose, have the same general formula, $C_6H_{12}O_6$, but each sugar has its atoms arranged in a different way and has different properties as a result.   Only a few sugars function in the metabolism of plants and animals because the organisms do not have protein enzymes capable of processing the other sugars.   Only certain sugars can fit onto the enzymes present in living cells.

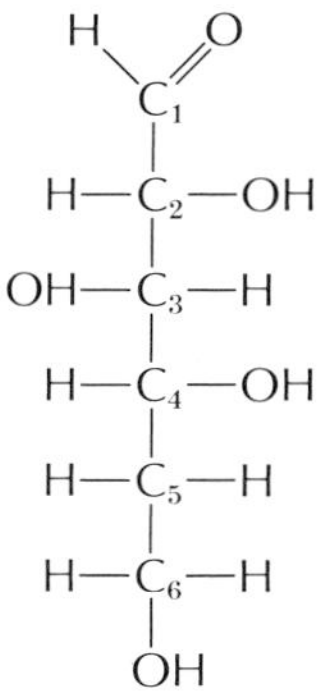

In addition to simple sugars, carbohydrates may also be double or complex sugars. *Double sugars* are formed from two simple sugars through the loss of a water molecule.   This is, again, dehydration synthesis, and is analogous to the process already discussed for proteins.   For example, table sugar is sucrose, a double sugar synthesized from glucose and fructose, two simple sugars.   *Polysaccharides* are formed when many simple sugars bond together.   The starch and cellulose of plants and the glycogen of animals (animal starch) are polysaccharides synthesized from hundreds of glucose units.

In the digestive tracts of animals carbohydrates must be broken down into simple sugars since large molecules cannot pass through the membranes of the intestinal wall.   We have enzymes capable of digesting double sugars and starch, but we cannot digest cellulose, and therefore cannot utilize the most prevalent carbohydrates on earth as a source of food.   Other organisms, for example, some snails and some bacteria, have the enzymes we lack and are able to digest and use cellulose for food.   We cannot eat and digest this book, but they can.

We shall learn in Chapter 6 how plants synthesize carbohydrates and in Chapter 5 how plants and animals utilize simple sugars as their principal source of energy. Now let us turn our attention to the third class of nutrient carbon compounds, the lipids.

FIGURE 4.11 A glucose molecule. Sixteen different kinds of simple sugars can be formed by means of changes in the arrangement of the –H and –OH around the second to fifth carbons.

FAT AND OTHER LIPIDS

Living things are more than mere bags of watery solutions.   If living things were soluble in water, the first rainfall would reduce life to bouillon.   Obviously, living things must contain many molecules which will not dissolve in water.

Externally, such protein structures as fingernails, hair, and the outer layer of skin are clearly insoluble in water.   Internally, such solid structures as bones are capable of going into and out of solution according to the level of certain hormones and vitamins present.   In contrast, the membranes of cells are always insoluble in water. Why should cell membranes be so insoluble?   The answer lies in their structure: They contain a layer of fatty material insoluble in water, a substance belonging to a third major group of molecular compounds called lipids.

Lipids (the word means similar to fat) are similar to carbohydrates in that they are composed primarily of carbon, hydrogen, and oxygen. They differ from carbohydrates not only in that they contain a much smaller amount of oxygen but also in that they may contain other elements, such as phosphorus, nitrogen, and sulfur.

Lipids include such fats as butter, corn oil, and lard; membrane lipids of all cells; the insulating materials of brain- and nerve-cell sheaths; the protective waxes and oils of skin, ears, and leaves; and the fat stored under the skin, around the heart and kidneys, and other regions of the body. All these lipid compounds share the property of being insoluble in water, and most lipids contain fatty acids.

Fatty acids are made up of chains of $-CH_2-$ units with one end terminating with $-COOH$, the same carboxyl unit in amino acids, which can ionize to release H^+ ions and function as an acid. In mammals, most fatty acids range in chain length from twelve to twenty-four carbons and are even-numbered straight-chain compounds. Fatty acids shorter than twelve carbons do exist in nature their solubility in water increasing as the chain gets shorter. Two examples of short-chain fatty acids are formic acid (one carbon) and acetic acid (two carbons). They are vitally important in metabolism since they not only have a role in the formation of amino acids and simple sugars but also serve as building blocks from which all the complex lipids and many hormones are made.

Fats are the best known of the lipids since edible fats form a part of our diet. Each fat molecule is made up of one *glycerol* molecule (an alcohol often called glycerine) with three *fatty acid* molecules attached to it. Glycerol has three hydroxyls on one side, and these $-OH$ units can react with the $-COOH$ end groups of the fatty acids, thus forming bonds between the glycerol and the fatty acids, with the loss of one molecule of water for each fatty acid bound. Thus the synthesis of fats, like that of proteins and polysaccharides, also involves dehydration synthesis.

During digestion, lipases (enzymes acting upon lipids) cause water molecules to intrude on the bonds joining the glycerols and fatty acids, thus causing these bonds to break. This is another example of the *enzymatic hydrolysis* described earlier. Not all fats are digested all the way down to glycerols and fatty acids, however, and fat molecules may enter directly into the bloodstream. After a hearty meal, the blood may become turbid with tiny fat droplets, which soon become deposited as fat vacuoles in certain specialized cells in the fat depots of the body. There the fat lies until mobilized as a reserve source of energy.

Fat functions as a source of energy. It is in fact the most concentrated form of energy that living systems have evolved. Carbohydrates serve as the most common source of energy in respiration, but when they have been consumed, the fats become the fuel for the body. Only when the fat reserves are depleted are the valuable proteins of the body converted to amino acids, which then take their turn as the fuel of respiration. Thus, an inadequate diet would cause a loss, in order, of carbohydrates, then fats, and finally proteins. The bodily changes in human beings who suffered starvation dramatically illustrate the results of using one's own protein structure as a fuel. Lipids, then, have two major functional roles in living systems: They serve either as structural components or as sources of energy.

A fourth class of large carbon compounds found in living systems is not important as nutrients, as structural parts of the body, or as sources of energy; however, in a basic sense the nucleic acids are the most important class of large molecules in the cell, for they constitute the self-replicating genes each cell has inherited, and they direct the synthesis of proteins. Since an organism's structure, function, and behavior are the result of chemical reactions, and since all chemical reactions in a cell are regulated by protein enzymes, it follows that nucleic acids are the molecules that permit life, the regulated use of matter and energy, to persist. Chapter 9 discusses nucleic acids.

NUCLEIC ACIDS

In Chapter 3, metabolism was described as the sum of the processes by which an organism utilizes food as a source of matter and energy from which it can build its structure and extract energy to operate that structure. We have just discussed the means by which larger molecules can be synthesized from smaller ones and how the large molecules can be broken up into smaller ones again. All this building up and tearing down of molecules requires chemical energy, which we have not yet defined. The next two chapters deal with the processes by which living things acquire food and how they harvest chemical energy from it to perform their life's work.

METABOLISM

1 Contrast ionic bonds with covalent bonds and ionic compounds with molecular compounds.
2 What determines the nature of a protein?
3 How does an enzyme regulate chemical reactions?
4 Contrast synthesis of proteins with the digestion of proteins.
5 Why must the synthesis of proteins be regulated by inherited genetic recipes?
6 What is the role of carbohydrates in living processes?
7 What is the role of lipids in living processes?
8 Defend the statement that nucleic acids are the molecules that permit life.

REVIEW QUESTIONS

All the following paperbacks go into much more detail than this text.

Baker, J. J. W., and G. E. Allen: *Matter, Energy, and Life,* Addison-Wesley Publishing Company, Inc., Reading, Mass., 1965.

Bennett, T. P., and E. Frieden: *Modern Topics in Biochemistry,* The Macmillan Company, New York, 1966.

SUGGESTIONS FOR
FURTHER READING

Goldsby, R. A.: *Cells and Energy,* The Macmillan Company, New York, 1967.

McElroy, W. D.: *Cell Physiology and Biochemistry,* 2d ed., Prentice-Hall, Inc., Engelwood Cliffs, N.J., 1964.

Stephenson, W. K.: *Concepts in Biochemistry: A Programmed Text,* John Wiley & Sons, Inc., New York, 1967.

White, E. H.: *Chemical Background for the Biological Sciences,* Prentice-Hall, Inc., Englewood Cliffs, N.J., 1964.

Pond. (Courtesy of M. Chapman.)

Chapter 5
Matter and Energy, Cycle and Flow: I

This and the following chapter discuss how chemical energy is trapped and stored by plants in the bonds of their carbon compounds and how these compounds provide food for the plant which synthesizes them and for any consumer of the plant.

A brief glance at one small part of the living world, an ordinary pond, provides a visual image we can recall during the discussion which follows. The living world exists as a thin film of organisms distributed as a mosaic over the surface of the earth where the sky meets the land and the sea. The dominant colors of the living mosaic are the blues of the oceans and the greens of the plants. Observation of any small part of the earth's vital green film reveals the organization and interactions characteristic of life. Arbitrarily we have chosen to consider a pond as an example of an ecosystem since almost everyone has seen a pond and the limits of a pond are sharply defined.

The arrival of spring awakens a pond, and its surface may become grassy green because of the reproduction of fantastic numbers of minute, green organisms called *algae,* some of which are single-celled. This spring bloom is caused by the shifting of waters in the pond following the changes in temperature and water density brought about by the warming sun of spring. The circulating waters bring minerals and organic compounds from the bacteria-containing sediment at the bottom of the pond to the surface. Here, algae utilize the light from the sun to change these raw materials into various carbon-containing compounds. The algae can then grow and reproduce.

Dining on the green cells are multitudes of minute single-celled organisms called *protozoa.* Both algae and protozoa serve as food for other kinds of animals so small they are barely able to ingest the cells or so large that they harvest the cells en masse

FIGURE 5.1(a) Commensalism. The remora fish attach themselves by the suction "device" on their heads to a shark. This is one-sided symbiosis; the remora benefit, not the shark. (*Courtesy of The American Museum of Natural History.*)

FIGURE 5.1(*b*)   Close-up view
of remora fish. They attach themselves to sharks and share in their
meals.

by straining them out of the pond water. The algae-eating animals, in their turn, are
eaten by larger animals. Thus, matter and energy are only temporarily possessed by
an organism before another organism eats it and takes them over. This transfer of
nutrients from organism to organism in a sequence of eaters is called a *food chain*.
A food chain begins with a producer, the green-plant cell, and continues with a succession of consumers. Clearly, the biblical statement that "all flesh is grass" is valid.

The interactions and relationships existing between organisms are often quite close
and direct, so that organisms depend on one another for their livelihood. Close relationships such as this may exist between members of different species and are called
symbiosis. There are three types of symbiosis, mutualism, commensalism, and
parasitism.

Mutualism is a type of symbiosis in which two or more species live together to their
mutual benefit. The traditional example of mutualistic symbiosis is the lichen, a
plant actually consisting of two very different organisms, a fungus and an alga. The
colorless filaments of the fungus support and elevate single-celled green algal cells,
which trap water and sunlight and produce food for both. Both alga and fungus
benefit from this relationship.

In *commensalism* there is a one-sided relationship between organisms of two
species. One organism is benefited while the other is neither benefited nor
harmed. An example is remora fish, which attach themselves to the bellies of sharks
and feed on leftovers of the shark's meals but do not help or hinder the sharks (see
Figure 5.1).

Parasitism is the form of symbiosis in which two organisms exist together in such a
way that one lives at the expense of the other. Parasites derive their nourishment di-

FEEDING RELATIONSHIPS
IN AN ECOSYSTEM
SYMBIOSIS

rectly from the tissues of the host. If a given species has been parasitic on the other species for a long time, the parasitic species usually has become adapted so that it does not kill the host but is able to draw nutrients from it over a long time. Parasites may live either on the outside or the inside of a host and may be full- or part-time consumers of the host's tissues. There are many kinds of parasites. Some examples are mistletoe on oak trees, athlete's foot fungus on man, tapeworms, liver flukes, hookworms, and pork roundworms. Parasites are often host-specific; that is, they live in or on only one species of host organism.

PREDATOR AND PREY

Predation, the eating of one organism by another, is the means by which matter and energy are transferred in an ecosystem. Many people react emotionally when they see one organism devouring another, probably associating predation with the idea of the strong attacking the weak. We often identify with the underdog, but man is the most important predator on the face of the earth, and he is scarcely the underdog!

Predator and prey relationships are vitally important in an ecosystem as exemplifying the interactions between species, the eaters and the eaten, as well as the routes by which matter and energy flow. The sizes of populations of different species in an ecosystem are also controlled, at least to a large extent, by the food supply. Clearly, the nature of an ecosystem is defined by the nature of the flow of matter and energy from organism to organism, from prey to predator.

FEEDING, OR TROPHIC, LEVELS

The organisms of an ecosystem have certain relationships to each other and to the environment and can be placed in categories according to their part in the structure and function of the ecosystem. These relationships are usually called *feeding levels* or *trophic levels,* since the interactions in an ecosystem are concerned with the trapping, storing, and use of nutrients by a succession of organisms in various food chains.

The basic feeding, or trophic, level is that of the *producer organisms,* either algae or higher plants, which have chlorophyll molecules and therefore the ability to trap energy from the sun and store it in the covalent bonds of carbon compounds. Certain bacteria which lack the ability to carry out photosynthesis are also producers, though many are parasites or rely on organic compounds made by other creatures. Producer organisms make their own food and do not depend directly upon other organisms as sources of nutrients. Organisms which are dependent on producer organisms for their existence are called *consumer organisms.* Consumers eat producers and other (usually smaller) consumers. Thus matter and energy trapped by green plants are passed on from one trophic level to the next.

Since the chemical energy locked into food flows from producers to consumers, it is a one-way flow. If matter also passed along a food chain in a one-way flow, before long all the carbon compounds in the world would be held in the bodies of the largest consumers. When they died, the carbon atoms so vital to life would be destroyed with them and life on earth would cease. Instead of such a one-way flow, however, matter is continuously cycled back as a result of the action of such *decomposers* and scavengers as fungi, many bacteria, and other creatures of greater complexity. Decomposers digest the bodies of dead organisms and return their atoms and molecules to the physical environment of the ecosystem.

The trophic levels of producers, consumers, and decomposers are, in a way, the "tissues and organs" of the ecosystem, in the sense that a division of labor exists among the parts of an ecosystem just as it does among the parts of an organism.

Predator-prey relationships are complicated by the fact that predators usually eat more than one kind of prey. For example, a bear eats a salmon that had eaten minnows that had eaten algae, and this can be diagrammed as a food chain:

FOOD WEBS

Algae → minnows → salmon → bear

Bears, however, include more than salmon in their diet, and salmon eat more than just minnows. The arrows drawn to indicate the feeding relationships between members of an ecosystem thus resemble a *web* more than a chain. At the base of the web are the producer organisms. Branching up from the base is a succession of various consumers leading up to the final consumers, which are eaten only by decomposers. The consumers of the producers (plants) are called *herbivores,* while the name *carnivore* is applied to those animals which eat either herbivores or carnivores. Animals that consume both plant and animal foods are called *omnivores.* A horse is a herbivore, dogs are carnivores, and bears are omnivores.

The transfer of matter and energy from producer to herbivore and on to carnivore is not very efficient. Some of the food eaten is not digested and absorbed but merely passes through the animal and is extruded in its feces. When food is digested and absorbed, much of the energy released in respiration is lost as body heat. In addition, much of the energy in food is used up by an animal in performing its vital activities. When a cow is eaten, therefore, it yields only a fraction of the matter and energy it has consumed during its lifetime.

FOOD PYRAMIDS

As a general rule, it can be said that producers are able to trap only about 1 percent of the energy that reaches them from the sun. From that point on the efficiency of transfer of food from organism to organism is about 10 percent. For example, 1,000 pounds of grass would support 100 pounds of cattle, which would support about 10 pounds of wolf, which would support only 1 pound of an organism preying on wolves.

Let us look at a diagram in which the total weight of organisms in each trophic, or feeding, level from producers to herbivores to carnivores is represented by rectangles whose sizes are proportional to the weight of living material in each level. If these rectangles are placed above each other in the sequence of a food chain, they form a

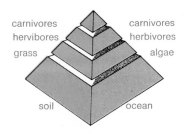

carnivores   carnivores
hervibores   herbivores
grass   algae

soil   ocean

FIGURE 5.2 The general pattern of food pyramids. Soil and ocean support plant life, herbivorous animals subsist on the plants, and carnivorous animals subsist on the herbivores. (*Adapted from Paul B. Weisz, Elements of Biology, 3rd ed. Copyright McGraw-Hill Book Company, 1969. Used by permission.*)

food pyramid (see Figure 5.2). This is a graphic portrayal of the use of matter and energy in an ecosystem.

If each consumer retains only 10 percent of the matter and energy of the organisms it consumes, clearly the amount of matter and energy available to second- and third-level carnivores becomes so minute that it is impractical for creatures to exist in this way. A food chain, therefore, usually has only three or four links, rarely five. It is no accident, then, that human beings living in the most overpopulated regions of the world are forced to be mainly herbivores, with a diet consisting primarily of rice and other grains. If all Chinese, for example, became carnivorous, their numbers would have to decrease to 10 percent of their present size. Some amelioration of such a drastic effect might be obtained by heavy reliance on domesticated animals, which, when properly raised, have a somewhat higher energy conversion rate than 10 percent. It is a luxury for most of the world's people to have meat in their diet, and, as man's population continues to grow, there will have to be a proportional shift of the diet of more and more human beings from that of an omnivore to that of a herbivore. Improvements in raising livestock might delay or temporarily reverse this process, but sooner or later, unless human population growth is curbed, this will be the result.

WHAT IS THE SOURCE OF ENERGY FOR WORK?

Organisms must carry out many kinds of work in order to live, including chemical work, the forming and breaking of bonds; mechanical work, such as muscular contraction and other forms of movement of organisms is actually done by their cells, and on a lower level or organization the work of cells is done by their organelles and molecular structures. In Chapter 3, we discussed the parts of cells and how they functioned. Now we briefly consider how cells harness the energy in the nutrients they obtain and store it in a form useful for carrying out cellular work.

A cell is like a car motor in that it takes in organic fuels, releases energy, does work, and releases carbon dioxide and water as wastes. But beyond these generalities, there are few similarities between cells and car motors. A motor uses heat energy to expand the gases that drive its pistons. A cell, however, is not a heat engine, and it does not rely upon heat as its source of energy. Cells do not utilize heat energy directly but rely on the chemical energy stored in the bonds of nutrient molecules. The useful energy of a cell is stored in chemical bonds until the actual work is to be performed. Energy converted into heat by cells is lost forever from the living system and cannot be used by the cell.

Wiggle your finger before your eyes. You may imagine that the energy driving this cellular work is released from sugars as they are burned in a sort of cellular campfire. Two things are wrong with this idea: (1) Such a rapid release of energy would destroy the cell, and (2) the immediate source of energy for the work of cells is not sugar. The source of the energy used directly in the life processes of all cells from bacteria to flowering plants to man is *adenosine triphosphate* (ATP) (see Figure 5.3).

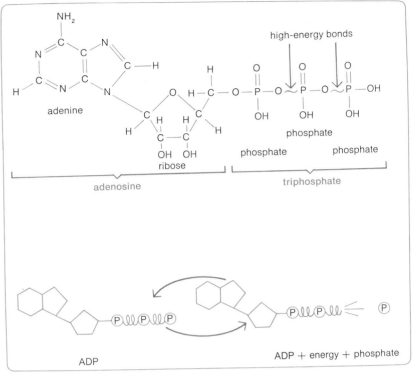

FIGURE 5.3 Adenosine triphosphate (ATP): the chemical formula and a model (*adapted from W. L. Smallwood and E. R. Green, Biology, Silver Burdett*). The last two phosphates contain high-energy bonds indicated by wavy lines. When broken, these high-energy bonds contribute 12,000 calories of energy for cellular work. High-energy bonds are represented in the lower figure by coiled springs, and the low-energy bond holding on the first phosphate is represented by a string.

Stored energy reaches a cell in a variety of nutrient organic compounds, but the molecule which actually delivers the energy to cell parts is ATP. The structure of ATP is simple, a combination of one molecule of *adenine,* one molecule of *sugar,* and three molecules of *phosphate.* When the bonds connecting the phosphate groups to each other are broken, chemical energy is released. An analogy is two wooden blocks pressing a coiled spring between them. If just a little bit more energy is added, to move one block to the side or otherwise detach the spring, the spring will release its stored energy and expand instantly to its relaxed state. As in many familiar machines, the spring can be *coupled* to another moving part thereby doing useful work when it expands. The same is true of the chemical energy in the phosphate-phosphate bonds of ATP. Their rupture, which releases energy, is generally *coupled* to another biochemical reaction which requires an input of energy, a sort of chemical shove, in order to make it go in the desired direction. Thus ATP breakdown is used in cellular metabolism to drive energy-requiring reactions in the cell. As we might expect, these reactions are controlled and directed by the enzymes of the cell. Such enzymes may bind the ATP and the compounds whose further reaction is desired. Thus enzymes serve as the agents which organize the coupling of ATP breakdown with cellular metabolism.

Since life requires a constant supply of energy in the form of ATP, a problem becomes readily apparent: How is the supply of ATP generated? Clearly, the cell must have some means of obtaining chemical energy and using it to synthesize ATP. The sources of energy for the generation of ATP are the nutrient molecules, carbohydrates, fats, and proteins. The means by which energy is extracted from the nutrient molecules and stored in the phosphate-phosphate bonds of ATP is *respiration*. ATP is also generated directly by green plants in photosynthesis.

RESPIRATION   Nutrients are gathered by organisms in many ways, and the type of nutrition defines an organism's place in the food web of an ecosystem. We have learned that carnivores and herbivores take in large chunks of either animal or plant tissue while omnivores may take in both and decomposers act upon the dead remains of organisms, returning their component elements to the cycles of the ecosystem. We have not yet explained, however, what consumers of protoplasm do with the food they ingest. In the cells the nutrients derived from the food are used as raw material for the construction of new cell structures and to provide chemical energy for the generation of new molecules of ATP.

Respiration can be defined as the biologically controlled release of energy from nutrient molecules and the eventual storage of this energy in the phosphate-phosphate bonds of ATP and a few similar molecules. While being transported from nutrient molecule to ATP, the energy is never actually released but is conveyed within the bonds of a series of molecules.

In general terms, the respiration of an animal, say yourself, can be described as:

Carbon compounds from food + oxygen →

carbon dioxide + water + stored chemical energy

This is looking only at the beginning and end of the process, at what goes in and what comes out in respiration. The actual mechanism is complex and indirect. We shall find, for example, that oxygen gas never combines directly with a nutrient molecule, when it is involved at all, but enters only into the later stages of respiration. We shall also find that many more compounds are involved in energy liberation than the equation above would imply. Their abundance means that respiration occurs in extremely small steps in an exquisitely balanced control system. The release of energy is gradual, each bond is broken individually, and the released energy is trapped by carrier molecules which transfer the stored energy to other molecules for eventual storage in ATP.

Since the commonest starting point for respiration metabolism is the carbohydrate glucose, we shall restrict our discussion to its possible respiratory fates. Depending upon the type of respiration, glucose may eventually give rise to ethyl alcohol, lactic acid, or carbon dioxide plus water. The route that glucose respiration follows in any particular case is determined by two criteria: (1) the set of enzymes belonging to the cell type being studied and (2) the presence or absence of oxygen. Conditions in a cell without oxygen are called *anaerobic* (meaning "life without air") and those in a cell with oxygen are called *aerobic* (life with air). Respiration of glucose can take place under either set of conditions.

Both anaerobic and aerobic respiration of glucose occur in the cells of higher plants and animals. The anaerobic phase occurs in the cytoplasm, but the aerobic phase is restricted to specialized cytoplasmic organelles, the mitochondria. Variants of aerobic respiratory processes, as well as aerobic respiration, also occur in cell nuclei.

GLYCOLYSIS

Respiration commonly begins with the splitting of a six-carbon glucose molecule into two three-carbon *pyruvic acid* molecules (see Figure 5.4). This is called *glycolysis,* meaning "splitting of glucose." Glycolysis is actually a complicated sequence of reactions, the overall result of which is that two ATP molecules are constructed with the energy harvested during the alteration of a single glucose molecule into the two smaller pyruvic acid molecules.

FERMENTATION

The fate of a pyruvic acid molecule depends on the enzyme system of the cell it is in and whether oxygen is present. When no oxygen is present, some microorganisms and many plants convert their pyruvic acid to two-carbon *ethyl alcohol* with the release of a molecule of carbon dioxide. Though ethyl alcohol production is a major way of using pyruvic acid in aerobic respiration by plants and microorganisms, other less common ways of using pyruvic acid also exist. In animals, if no oxygen is present, the pyruvic acid has some hydrogens bonded to it and becomes *lactic acid.* Formation of lactic acid, ethyl alcohol, or several other less common products from pyruvic acid is called *fermentation.* Lactic acid fermentation is usually studied in muscle, and alcoholic fermentation has been studied extensively in yeast cells.

The most ancient records show that almost every civilization has made alcoholic beverages by fermenting sugar-bearing fruits and grains. Although the men of earlier periods of history enjoyed the effects, they could explain the process only as the work of gods. They thought there were spirits in the brew and, even today, beverages and medicinal mixtures containing ethyl alcohol are often referred to as "spirits." You and all other animals lack the enzymes necessary for alcoholic fermentation and cannot manufacture alcohol in your cells. This is fortunate; otherwise a slight muscular exertion would put you into a state of intoxication. You do, however, have the enzymes for lactic acid fermentation. All muscles can contract in the absence of oxygen for a few minutes, utilizing energy extracted from glucose through glycolysis and lactic acid fermentation; but soon the muscles will suffer from fatigue brought on by the accumulation of lactic acid. Such accumulations of lactic acid in animals and alcohol in plants are removed by processes requiring oxygen.

FIGURE 5.4 Glycolysis.

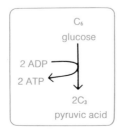

In review, the respiration of glucose begins with glycolysis, or splitting of glucose into two pyruvic acid molecules. If no oxygen is present, the pyruvic acid molecules may be transformed further giving rise to (1) lactic acid in animal cells, (2) alcohol in bacterial cells and plants, and (3) more rarely other products. *Glucose splitting causes two* ATP *molecules to be generated with the energy transferred from the glucose molecule.* Actually, this is a harvest of only a few percent of the total chemical energy stored in the chemical bank of one glucose molecule. Both ethyl alcohol and lactic acid still contain much of this stored energy. Further energy can be released only when oxygen is present. Under these conditions, the carbon compounds are broken all the way down to simple, energy-poor carbon dioxide and water molecules.

Earlier we said that fermentation occurs only when there is no oxygen. Now we ask: What happens to the pyruvic acid if oxygen is present?

AEROBIC RESPIRATION

Aerobic respiration not only requires gaseous oxygen but also enzymes and receptor molecules to direct this complicated process. In general, the process is carried out by two sequences of enzymes which have the property of removing (or *accepting*) *electrons.* To form a visual image of these two sequences, we may picture one sequence arranged in a *cycle* and the other in a linear *chain* (see Figure 5.5), called the *electron-transport* chain.

FIGURE 5.5 The electron-transport chain is carried on by enzymes and receptor molecules that are part of the membrane structure. (*a*) Cross section and (*b*) top view of a membrane. The dark spheres indicate molecules making up one assembly of an electron-transport chain. Most of the inner membrane of each mitochondrion is thought to be specialized in this way.

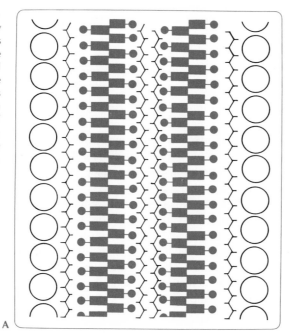

A

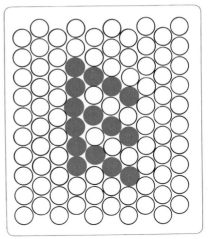

FIGURE 5.5 B

The sequences of the electron-accepting enzyme molecules responsible for aerobic respiration are located in the cell membranes of bacteria, which lack internal membranes. In almost all other cells, however, the molecules of the aerobic respiratory system are contained in membranous structures in the cytoplasm, the organelles called *mitochondria* (see Figure 3.7). Basically, a mitochondrion is a bag within a bag, a smooth outer membrane surrounding a highly folded inner membrane. Most of the enzymes which carry out aerobic respiration are contained in the fluid of the inner membranes of the mitochondrion. Thus these inner membranes are not merely containers but function as part of the active respiratory machinery. It is fascinating and significant that the electron-accepting molecules embedded in the membranes are arranged physically according to the *sequence* of the individual steps in the electron-transport chain. The sequence of reactions in the electron-transport chain is possible, in fact, because the inner membranes of mitochondria operate as molecular machines containing assemblies of enzymes arranged in the correct spatial relationships. Energy is transferred from molecule to molecule in these assemblies in very small steps and is trapped and kept for eventual use, as the stored energy in newly synthesized ATP molecules.

Aerobic respiration begins the same way as anaerobic respiration, with glycolysis and the splitting of glucose into two pyruvic acid molecules and the formation of two ATP molecules. This, as we said earlier, occurs in the cytoplasm as well as in the nuclear sap. The pyruvic acid is now transported from the cytoplasm into the mitochondria. Inside these organelles it is led into a series of reactions during which it throws off a carbon dioxide and becomes a two-carbon compound (acetate) attached to a substance called coenzyme A. This complex, called *acetyl coenzyme A*, is a basic fuel material for the reactions of aerobic metabolism, as well as for numerous other biochemical reactions. Acetyl coenzyme A can be formed not only from glucose but from amino acids and fatty acids. Thus, all three classes of

FIGURE 5.6 Krebs cycle.

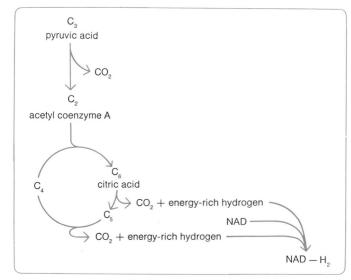

nutrients may serve as fuel in aerobic respiration. When a person has an inadequate supply of carbohydrates, his body depletes its supply of carbohydrates and then utilizes fats and proteins as sources of energy. He begins to lose weight.

The enzymes in the inner fluid of mitochondria carry out the metabolism of acetyl coenzyme A. They begin by combining a four-carbon compound with the two-carbon acetyl group to form a six-carbon citric acid molecule (see Figure 5.6). This reaction sequence is often called the *citric acid cycle* or the *Krebs cycle,* after its discoverer, the German-English biochemist Sir Hans Krebs. Citric acid is broken down further, the enzymes of the cycle next tearing away two carbon dioxide molecules. What becomes of the bond energy that held the original carbon molecules together in the larger starting compounds? Some of this energy is lost as heat as the carbon dioxide molecules are released. *Most of it, however, is transferred to electrons of hydrogen atoms, released as the carbon compounds deriving from citric acid are progressively broken down.* These hydrogens and their energy-rich electrons are picked up by receptor molecules, nicotinamide adenine dinucleotide (NAD), containing niacin, one of the B vitamins.

The NAD plus the hydrogens form a complex called $NADH_2$, which moves to the inner membrane of the mitochondrion, where it transfers the hydrogen and its energy-rich electron to another vitamin B–containing compound, flavine adenine dinucleotide (FAD). The vitamin in FAD is riboflavin, and FAD forms the first link in the *electron-transport chain* (see Figure 5.7).

The *electron-acceptor* molecules making up the electron-transport chain are FAD, and the enzymes cytochrome *b*, cytochrome *c*, cytochrome *a*, and cytochrome a_3.

The *cytochromes,* like any other enzymes, are proteins, but they also contain iron. The iron functions as the active unit of the cytochrome molecule in electron transfer. During the transfer of the hydrogen from NAD to FAD it loses energy; that is, the hydrogen electron moves to a position closer to the nucleus of the atom. Such a position requires less energy to maintain the electron in orbit. Thus in dropping from a higher to a lower energy state the hydrogens transferred from NADH$_2$ to FAD release some energy. *This energy is transferred to an ADP molecule and is used to drive the reaction in which a phosphate is added to the ADP to form an ATP molecule.* The FAD plus the hydrogen forms FADH$_2$. Ionization of the hydrogen now occurs, and only the electron is passed on (to cytochrome *b*) while the hydrogen ion is set free in the fluid of the mitochondrion.

The cytochromes contain iron atoms in the ionic form (Fe^{3+}); they have lost three electrons to form fer*ric* ions with a surplus of three positive charges. (As you recall, an ion is an atom that has gained or lost one or more electron.) When a fer*ric* ion accepts an electron, it becomes a fer*rous* ion with a charge of positive 2 (Fe^{++}). This is only a momentary change, however, since the ferrous ion now gives the electron off to the next cytochrome in the series, and its ferric ion becomes a ferrous ion:

$$Fe^{++} \rightarrow Fe^{3+} + electron$$

When the electron is handed on from cytochrome *b* to cytochrome *c* and from cytochrome *c* to cytochrome *a*, the electron drops into lower energy levels. Each time the excess energy is transferred, so that ATP molecules are formed from ADP and phosphates.

The last electron acceptor in the electron-transport chain is cytochrome a_3. It passes the electrons, now at a low energy state, two at a time to the final electron acceptor, *oxygen.* The oxygen accepts the electrons and attracts two hydrogen ions to form H$_2$O, a molecule of water.

By removing the electrons, the oxygen clears the way for more energy-rich electrons to pass down the electron-transport chain so that they in turn can be drained of their energy. Without oxygen, the final electron acceptor, the respiratory machine comes quickly to a halt. Several phenomena familiar to most of us can now be explained.

1 You are able to undergo great exertion, such as running up a flight of stairs, because you are able to extract energy from glucose in the absence of oxygen by anaerobic respiration of glucose to lactic acid. Afterward you pay this "oxygen debt" by aerobically metabolizing the lactic acid while you rest and breathe. If you had to rely upon aerobic respiration as the only source of energy, you would be forced to move at a constant and slow pace limited by the immediate supply of oxygen to your cells.

2 The synthesis of ATP in aerobic respiration depends upon the transfer of energy-rich electrons along the electron-transport chain. Clearly, a deficiency of either of the B vitamins, niacin or riboflavin, or the mineral iron would result in a vital weakness in the respiratory chain. With a subnormal energy-generating mechanism, sickness or death can result.

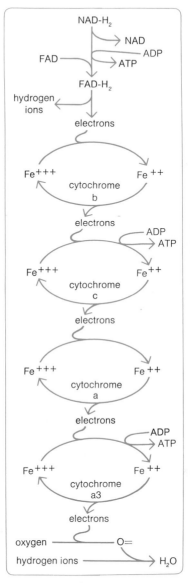

FIGURE 5.7 Electron transport chain.

FIGURE 5.8 Summary of anaerobic and aerobic respiration. Glycolysis yields 2 ATP molecules, and in the absence of oxygen pyruvic acid undergoes fermentation and produces lactic acid in animals and ethyl alcohol and carbon dioxide in plants and microbes. If oxygen and the proper enzyme assemblies are present, the pyruvic acid will produce carbon dioxide and water and an additional 36 ATPs from the electron-transport chain.

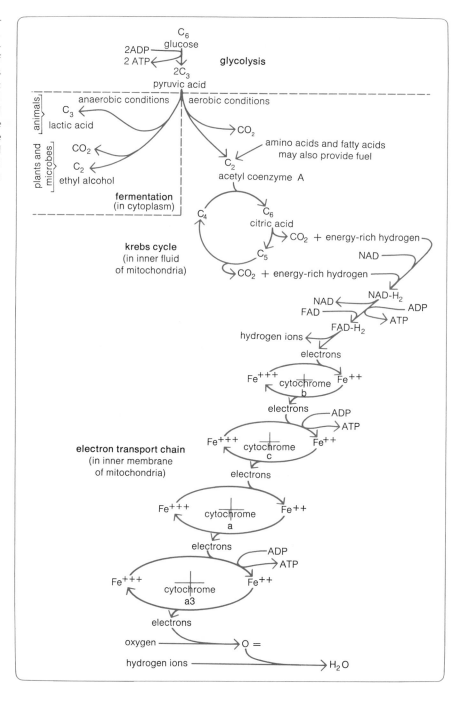

3   Consider the result of oxygen deprivation.   We have seen that oxygen is necessary as an acceptor of both the negative electrons and the positive hydrogen ions at the end of the electron-transport chain.   If there is no oxygen, the electrons will not be removed from the chain, the flow of electrons will stop, and the formation of ATP will be almost halted.   Aerobic ATP production is far more efficient than anaerobic ATP production from glucose.   *Thus in simple anaerobic splitting of glucose only two ATP molecules are formed per molecule of glucose split, while in aerobic respiration thirty-six additional molecules of ATP are synthesized per starting molecule of glucose* (see Figure 5.8).   Interference with breathing or the oxygen-carrying capacity of blood will interfere with this flow of electrons and the supply of energy to the body.   Our cells cannot survive with anaerobic respiration alone as a source of ATP.   We all know that cyanide is a deadly poison.   Cyanide acts by binding to the cytochromes and preventing them from acting as electron acceptors.   It causes sudden death because it blocks the supply of energy instantaneously in all cells of the body.

As a means of extracting energy from glucose, aerobic respiration yields about 45 percent of the energy theoretically stored in the glucose molecule.   The other 55 percent of the energy in the glucose molecule is lost, partly as heat.   You may doubt the efficiency of the process until you realize that the best designed energy-transforming machines of man have efficiencies of only about 40 percent.

We return for a moment to the general equation for respiration:

Glucose + oxygen $\rightarrow$ carbon dioxide + water + energy

We have learned that oxygen does not combine directly with glucose but enters in only at the very end of the electron-transport chain, while glucose is consumed immediately in glycolysis at the beginning.   Carbon dioxide is formed during both alcoholic fermentation and the Krebs cycle, while water is formed at the end of the electron-transport chain.   The general equation indicates only the overall result of respiration, namely the substances consumed and produced during the transfer and storage of energy in respiration.

As a result of respiration, our supply of ATP, the immediate source of energy for all biochemical work, is maintained.   Sometimes much of the chemical energy stored in cells requiring large reserves, such as muscle cells, is in a form other than ATP, for example, creatine phosphate.   These compounds can be instantly utilized to make ATP on demand, and it is almost always ATP which, in all cells, from bacterial to human, is actually the working energy source coupled to the biochemical machinery of the cell.

Obviously respiration is possible only with a constant supply of nutrients.   The problem of how to get nutrients for respiration is solved by animals through their ability to eat plants and other animals, but the entire flow of food has its beginning in plant cells, the sites of photosynthesis.   In the next chapter we discuss the mechanisms by which plants make food and the processes by which the matter in this food eventually finds its way back to the producers of the food chain.

1 Why do predator-prey relationships describe the flow of matter and energy in an ecosystem?

2 Why can trophic levels of an ecosystem be portrayed as a pyramid?

3 How does ATP act as the currency of energy exchange in all organisms?

4 What is respiration?

5 Describe briefly the activities of glycolysis, Krebs cycle, and electron-transport chain.

SUGGESTIONS FOR
FURTHER READING
* Available in paperback.

Buchsbaum, R., and M. Buchsbaum: *Basic Ecology,* Boxwood Press, Pittsburgh, Pa., 1957.   A clear statement of ecological principles.

Odum, E. P.: *Ecology,* Holt, Rinehart and Winston, Inc., New York, 1963.   A clear and authoritative description of principles of ecology.

The following are all well written and illustrated:

Bennett, T. P., and E. Frieden: *Modern Topics in Biochemistry,* The Macmillan Company, New York, 1966.

Goldsby, R. A.: *Cells and Energy,* The Macmillan Company, New York, 1967.

McElroy, W. D.: *Cell Physiology and Biochemistry,* 2d ed., Prentice-Hall, Inc., Englewood Cliffs, N.J., 1964.

Morrison, J. H.: *Functional Organelles,* Reinhold Publishing Corporation, New York, 1966.

Sunlight on fern. (*Mary M. Thacher, Photo Researchers, Inc.*)

Chapter 6
Matter and Energy, Cycle and Flow: II

Shall I not have intelligence with the earth? Am I not partly leaves and vegetable mould myself?

Thoreau

We are now familiar with some of the means by which organisms extract matter and energy from their foods, and we have seen how the food of one organism is the tissue of another, except for plants. Plants, of course, generally do not consume the tissues of other organisms but make their own food out of simple, easily available chemicals. They become, in turn, the food for other organisms. In this chapter we see how plants make the food that forms the first link in all food chains and how *photosynthesis* and *respiration* serve as the channels through which matter is cycled from the nonliving to the living and back to the nonliving world.

PHOTOSYNTHESIS: HOW
PLANTS MAKE FOOD

Both the food we eat and the air we breathe are ultimately the products of plants. The history of this insight into the natural world begins with Aristotle, several centuries before Christ. Aristotle believed that plants grew by eating soil. This idea persisted until 1630, when a Belgian botanist named van Helmont performed an experiment to test the Aristotelian view. He weighed a pot of soil, planted a willow tree in it, and after 5 years of watering and watching it grow carefully removed the tree and found that it had gained 164 pounds while the soil had lost only 2 ounces. Obviously, the gain in weight had not been due to an uptake of soil. Van Helmont believed that the gain in weight had been caused by absorbing water.

In 1772, Joseph Priestley, an English physician, became concerned about air pollution. Growing crowds of people and animals in London had provided ample cause for a popular notion that animals "injured" the air. Priestley wondered what further damage would be done to the air by the increasing population of London and the rest of Europe. He began to do simple experiments and found that a sprig of mint would "restore" air and that when it was placed in a sealed container with a mouse neither mint nor mouse would die. He saw a grand global scheme in which plants and animals balanced each other: "Animals harmed the air and plants restored the air." Priestley was awarded a medal, and others attempted to repeat his fascinating demonstration but without success. Even Priestley could not repeat his earlier work. Some people now guess that his first experiment was carried on in the kitchen and then he moved to the basement. He did not realize that light was necessary for the growth of plants!

Seven years later, in 1778, Jan Ingenhousz, a young medical student, spent his summer vacation conducting 500 experiments to see why Priestley's results could not be repeated. In 3 months he had found that (1) *sunlight* is necessary for the vital balance to be maintained between plants and animals, (2) only leaves and other *green* parts could restore the air, and (3) plants in the dark "injure" air just as much as animals do. Ingenhousz had demonstrated that both light and the green pigment of plants are necessary for what was later termed *photosynthesis*. He also demonstrated that plants as well as animals carry on respiration and injure the air when the vital sunlight is missing. The injury to the atmosphere under dark conditions is simply the use of oxygen by plants. The amount of oxygen consumed by plants in the dark is not great, and the removal of plants from sickrooms—the practice in Ingenhousz's time—is unnecessary.

During the following twenty-five years the great French chemist Lavoisier made the revolutionary discovery of oxygen and the nature of oxidation and carbon dioxide. A few years later he was guillotined in the French Revolution. In 1784 Cavendish synthesized water from hydrogen and oxygen, and in 1800 Nicholson and Carlisle decomposed water to hydrogen and oxygen by electrolysis. The discovery of oxygen was a necessary link in the long chain leading to our current understanding of photosynthesis.

In 1804, de Saussure carried on simultaneous studies of plants and the air they live in. He weighed a plant and the surrounding air before and after exposure of the plant to light and found that *carbon dioxide had been removed from the air.* He also found that the increase in dry weight of the plant was greater than the weight of carbon dioxide removed from the air. He concluded that plant growth must be the result of water and carbon dioxide being combined in the presence of sunlight. This is the process we now call *photosynthesis* (from the words for light and putting together). Thus, over 160 years ago, photosynthesis was described by the equation

$CO_2 + H_2O$ + light energy from the sun $\rightarrow$ organic material + O_2

De Saussure suggested that the sunlight splits the carbon dioxide into carbon and oxygen. If correct, this would mean that carbon dioxide serves as the source of carbon for the carbon compounds produced in photosynthesis as well as the source of the oxygen released into the atmosphere as a by-product. It is clear that the carbon dioxide used by plants in the light must serve as the source of food carbon, but it is not necessary that the oxygen released in photosynthesis arise from the carbon dioxide as well; it could come also from water, H_2O.

In 1941 some University of California scientists helped solve this problem by exposing the green alga *Chlorella* to water containing isotopic oxygen (O^{18}). This form of oxygen is 2 atomic mass units heavier than normal oxygen and can be detected by a sensitive instrument called the *mass spectrometer.* The results showed that O^{18} appears only in the oxygen released when the *Chlorella* carries out photosynthesis and not in the carbohydrates produced at the same time. When these men repeated the experiment with the carbon dioxide now containing the O^{18}, none of the oxygen released was O^{18}. This clinched the matter: The oxygen released into the air in the process of photosynthesis comes originally from water molecules. To be more specific, we can say that about 80 to 90 percent of the oxygen we breathe was originally part of the ocean, since most photosynthesis takes place in algae in the top 300 to 400 feet of the ocean.

Only within the last twenty years has the mystery of photosynthesis been unraveled to the point that its mechanisms can be partially understood. We now know that de Saussure's formula was correct in describing what went in and what came out but was not correct for actual chemical reactions. The full story lay hidden in the green pigments of cellular organelles called *chloroplasts*.

Among the cells of algae and higher plants several kinds of organelles are associated with photosynthesis or its products. For example, colorless *leucoplasts* store starch, and brightly colored *chromoplasts* store fat-soluble *carotenoid* pigments that are yellow, orange, or brown. The organelles we are interested in at the moment are the green *chloroplasts*, the sites of photosynthesis.

Chloroplasts can be isolated for studies of their function by putting leaves in a sugar solution and grinding the mixture in sand. The grinding breaks the cell walls and cell membranes so that the cell contents are free in suspension. By centrifuging this suspension at various speeds particles of different weights can be collected at the bottom of the tube.

CHLOROPLASTS

FIGURE 6.1 Levels of organization.
Tree
  Leaf
    Tissue
      Cell
        Chloroplast
          Grana and stroma

FIGURE 6.2 Schematic drawing
of a cell showing (a) position of
chloroplasts and (b) a section
through a whole chloroplast. The
many-layered sandwiches are
grana, and the fluid between them
is the stroma. Chlorophyll and
other pigments are contained in the
grana, the sites of the light reaction
of photosynthesis. (c) Drawing of
a higher magnification of a granum
in a chloroplast. Each granum is
made of many disks stacked on top
of each other. (d) Drawing of a
still higher magnification, showing
thin layers of chlorophyll in a
granum. Note that in these
drawings the layers of membranes
of the chloroplast are continuous
through the grana. (*Drawings b
and c adapted from A. J. Hodge,
California Institute of Technology,
and J. Biophys. Biochem. Cytol.,
vol. 1, p. 605; and d from W. M.
Smallwood and E. R. Green,
Biology, Silver Burdett, 1968.*)

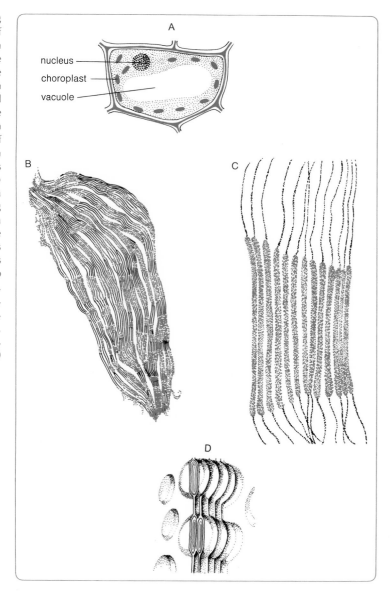

The structure of a chloroplast can be seen by viewing extremely thin slices of leaves
under an electron microscope and is seen to be basically a sack with a wall that is a
double membrane enclosing many highly ordered stacks of disks immersed in a
watery solution of proteins and other compounds (see Figure 6.2). Each stack of
disks is called a *granum* (plural is grana), and the solution separating them is called
stroma. The grana are connected by membranes passing through the stroma.

Located in the membranes of the grana and stroma are enzymes, lipids, yellowish-orange pigments called *carotenoids,* and the vital green pigments called *chlorophyll.* There are four kinds of chlorophyll, *a, b, c,* and *d,* but only *a* and *b* are found in the green cells of land plants and green algae. The other forms occur only in the red and brown algae discussed in Chapter 17. Most of what we know about photosynthesis was discovered in investigations of cells containing chlorophylls *a* and *b,* and we shall restrict this brief discussion to those studies.

The structures of chlorophylls *a* and *b* are quite similar (see Figure 6.3). Both forms of chlorophyll have a head composed of four carbon-nitrogen rings grouped around an atom of magnesium, plus a long tail of twenty carbon atoms. The only difference is that chlorophyll *b* has a —CHO group in one corner of a ring in the head where chlorophyll *a* has a —CH₃ group. These molecules are able to trap light energy and allow the chloroplast to carry on photosynthesis.

In 1937 the English biologist Robin Hill found that photosynthesis is really a complex series of reactions. He demonstrated that chloroplasts removed from plant cells can produce oxygen in the presence of light. Photosynthesis in green plants is therefore a process restricted to their chloroplasts and requires an exposure to light. A few years later, it was shown that assimilation of carbon dioxide and manufacture of carbohydrates by green plants take place not only in the light but *in the dark* as well. But since this can occur only if there has already been exposure to *light,* it was concluded that photosynthesis consists of at least two phases: a *light reaction,* occurring only in the presence of light, and a *dark reaction,* taking place in either the presence or absence of light but depending upon chemical energy derived from the light reaction. Light energy is trapped during the light reaction and is transformed into chemical energy. This chemical energy can then be used in the dark reaction to synthesize carbon compounds from water and carbon dioxide.

The first step in photosynthesis is the absorption of light—but not all colors of light; if that were true, plants would be black. Instead, plants are green, an indication that chlorophyll absorbs the remaining major colors of the spectrum, red and blue. This hypothesis is supported by the evidence; research has shown that, of all the colors, red and blue light are the most effective in providing the energy for photosynthesis.

It is believed that chlorophyll *a* becomes activated in the presence of light as a result of the absorption of light energy by electrons in the covalent bonds between the carbon atoms in the head of the molecules (see Figure 6.4). If these excited electrons do not escape from the chlorophyll molecule, they expend their excess energy as a *fluorescence.* Some of the chlorophyll molecules exposed to light lose their energy in this manner, but others may transfer excited electrons in the chloroplast membranes to an electron acceptor substance. From this substance the energy-rich electron is transferred along an electron-transport chain similar to that described in the discussion of aerobic respiration in Chapter 5. Much of the energy carried by

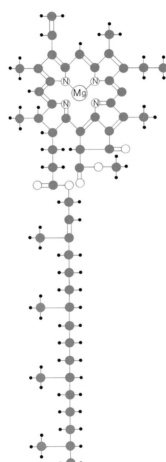

FIGURE 6.3 Structure of chlorophyll a molecule includes a head, containing four nitrogenous rings surrounding a magnesium atom, and a tail with many carbon atoms in a chain.

these electrons along the electron-transport chain is transferred to ADP, and phosphate molecules and ATP are formed.

At the end of the electron-transport chain the electrons, now at a much lower energy level, are passed on to a different kind of chlorophyll *a*, a form that absorbs long wavelengths of light instead of short wavelengths. This second kind of chlorophyll *a* absorbs light energy and excites the electrons it receives from the electron-transport chain up to a high energy level again. These energy-rich electrons are passed on to an electron-acceptor substance, which then passes them on to NADP, the same electron acceptor discussed in Chapter 5 but with a phosphate added. The result of this transfer of an electron is the formation of NADP with an electric charge. This negatively charged $NADP^-$ can now attract a positively charged hydrogen ion, H^+, from water, and NADPH will be formed.

The mechanism by which a hydrogen ion (a proton, H^+) is transferred from water to $NADP^-$ in the membranes of chloroplasts is not well understood. The source

FIGURE 6.4 Summary of non-cyclic photophosphorylation in the light reaction of photosynthesis. Water and light are consumed, and oxygen gas, ATP, and NADPH are formed.

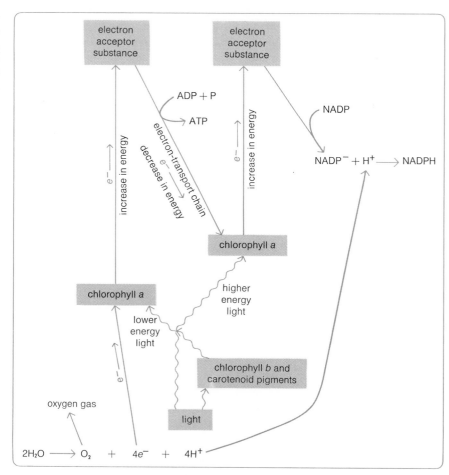

of the hydrogen ion is believed to be ionized water. An extremely small portion of water is normally in an ionized state (2 $H_2O \rightarrow O_2 + H^+ + OH^-$) and these ions can be induced by light to produce oxygen gas plus hydrogen ions and electrons (2 $H_2O \rightarrow O_2 + 4H^+ + 4e^-$). The oxygen gas passes off as a by-product (and becomes available for aerobic respiration) while the electrons are passed on to the first form of chlorophyll *a* to replace those electrons lost to the electron-transport chain and eventually join the hydrogen ions in the formation of NADPH (see Figure 6.4).

Since 1954 it has been known that there are actually two pathways that excited electrons from chlorophyll *a* can follow: (1) the pathway just described, in which the electron is transferred from chlorophyll *a* to electron acceptors and does not return to its chlorophyll source but is replaced by electrons from water molecules. This pathway involves two forms of chlorophyll *a* and is distinguished by the release of oxygen gas. (2) In the other pathway, which involves only one form of chlorophyll *a*, the excited electron *returns* to the chlorophyll *a* molecule after traversing an electron-transport chain. The first type of pathway is known as *noncyclic photophosphorylation* and produces ATP, NADPH, and oxygen gas. The second pathway is called *cyclic photophosphorylation* and produces only ATP (Figure 6.5).

The end result of the *noncyclic* light reaction is the formation of two energy-rich substances, ATP and NADPH, as well as the release of oxygen gas as a by-product. The oxygen gas may be consumed in aerobic respiration while the ATP and NADPH provide the energy for the synthesis of carbon compounds from carbon dioxide and water in the dark reaction. The *cyclic* light reaction is also able to provide energy in the form of ATP for this process.

The other pigments in the chloroplasts, chlorophyll *b* and the carotenoids, seem to play only a supporting role in photosynthesis. They cannot produce excited electrons themselves, but they can gather light energy and add it to that being trapped by chlorophyll *a*. The mechanism accomplishing this transfer of trapped energy is not known.

As described earlier, complex cellular chemical systems may require their guiding enzymes to be arranged in appropriate sequences as part of membranes or other structures. Thus the transport of excited electrons down the chain of electron acceptors requires a definite pattern of electron-transporting molecules arranged in the correct sequence. This represents a division of labor on the level of molecules.

A division of labor can also be seen at the chloroplast level. The light reaction takes place in the grana, but the dark reaction occurs in the stroma of the chloroplasts. We now direct our attention to the stroma and the dark reaction.

THE DARK REACTION OF PHOTOSYNTHESIS

The name *dark reaction* does not mean that the reaction cannot occur in the presence of light but that *simultaneous light is not necessary*. During the dark phase of photosynthesis, the carbon of carbon dioxide is used in the formation of nutrient carbon compounds. In a manner reminiscent of respiration, the dark reaction consists of a *cycle* in which one carbon dioxide molecule is handled at a time and the

FIGURE 6.5 Summary of cyclic photophosphorylation in the light reaction of photosynthesis. Light is consumed and ATP is produced.

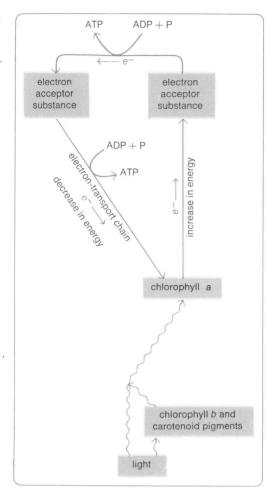

chemicals consumed in the reactions are re-formed during the course of each reaction cycle. Since the steps constituting the dark reaction are exceedingly complex, only an outline of the cycle will be presented.

The nature of the compounds and their order of appearance in the sequence of reactions between the introduction of carbon dioxide and the production of the final carbohydrates has been determined largely through the efforts of Melvin Calvin and his colleagues. In recognition of his work Calvin was awarded the Nobel Prize in 1962. One fruitful approach in analyzing the dark phase of photosynthesis consisted of supplying plants with carbon dioxide bearing radioactive carbon while exposing the plants to light for varying periods of time. In light the plant would produce ATP and NADPH through the light reactions of photosynthesis. With these energy-rich compounds the dark reactions would begin. The sequence in which various compounds are formed in the dark reaction is indicated by the sequence in which radioactive carbon compounds appeared in plants killed after different lengths of exposure to light.

Calvin and his colleagues found that glucose is synthesized after 30 seconds. They also found that 5 seconds of exposure of the green alga *Chlorella* to light and radioactive carbon dioxide resulted in most of the radioactive carbon being trapped in the —COOH group in a certain three-carbon compound, *phosphoglyceric acid* (PGA). As shown in Figure 6.6, two PGA molecules are formed by the addition of carbon dioxide to a five-carbon compound, ribulose disphosphate, in the stroma of the chloroplast. These in turn are altered with the use of chemical energy from ATP and NADPH to form two molecules of phosphoglyceraldehyde (PGAL). This alteration is basically the replacement of an oxygen ion in PGA (COO$^-$) with a hydrogen from NADPH to form PGAL (COH). PGAL, an end product of photosynthesis, may be used immediately for various metabolic pathways according to the needs of the plant and conditions. It may serve as a nutrient in glycolysis, that is, as a source of chemical energy in the respiration of the plant; but if there is not immediate need for energy, the PGAL can be converted into glucose, more complex sugars, or starch, the main form of stored food substance in higher plants. Some of the PGAL must, of course, be synthesized into ribulose diphosphate so that further carbon dioxide can be fixed and enter into the dark reaction and the cycle can continue. This synthesis requires ATP.

FIGURE 6.6 Summary of carbon dioxide fixation in the dark reaction of photosynthesis. Energy-rich ATP and NADPH molecules from the light reaction yield energy for the replacement of an oxygen ion, 0^-, in PGA with a hydrogen from PGAL. ATP is also required for regeneration of ribulose diphosphate, the substance to which carbon dioxide is fixed. One product is glucose, but other carbohydrates, fatty acids, and amino acids may also be synthesized.

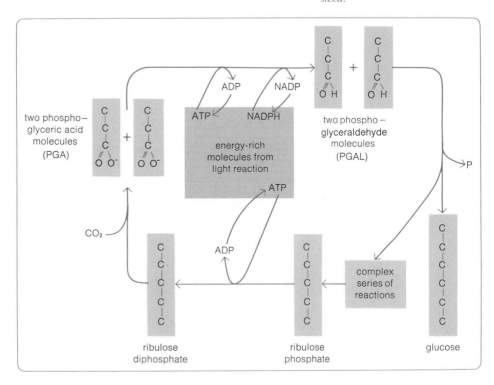

To summarize, the dark reaction of photosynthesis consists of the use of energy-rich ATP and NADPH from the light reaction to provide the energy to produce large carbon compounds, carbohydrates, fats, and proteins, from small carbon compounds with an input of carbon and oxygen from carbon dioxide and hydrogen from NADPH. Carbon is pulled into the living world as a result of energy from the sun and hydrogen from water. Living things are built of parts made from water, carbon dioxide, and other minerals, and these parts are powered by the energy of a star.

Though in many plants phosphoglyceraldehyde formed in the dark reaction is the source for other carbohydrates, some plants use slightly different pathways, but the result is always the same: use of energy stored in ATP and NADPH to accomplish *fixation of carbon dioxide* in an organic molecule which can then serve as the starting point for the other biosynthetic products the plant requires. These include amino acids, needed for the synthesis of proteins, and fatty acids, used to form lipids. Thus, the immediate products of photosynthesis are carbohydrates, but they may be altered into the other classes of carbon compounds, fats and proteins, discussed in Chapters 4 and 5.

THE CYCLING OF MATTER AND THE FLOW OF ENERGY

Food chains, unless they begin with photosynthesizing bacteria or blue-green algae, must begin with the green chloroplast. Inside these microscopic green bodies energy from the sun is trapped and used to do the chemical work of forming the bonds that shape nutrient carbon compounds from carbon dioxide and water. These carbon compounds are used by the plant not only as nutrients but as the matter from which it builds its own structures.

Animals which eat plant cells and their carbon compounds break them down into the basic building blocks from which their own carbohydrates, fats, proteins, and nucleic acids are formed. These animals, in turn, may be eaten by other animals, and, again, the carbon compounds can be converted into other forms.

The matter contained in the carbon compounds and in the minerals must be cycled back to the producers, the green plant cells. The energy, however, is not recycled. After being transferred to ATP during respiration and consumed in the performance of work, energy is eventually lost as heat and in the chemical bonds of waste products. Energy, therefore, does not cycle, it moves along the food chain in a one-way flow. Since energy flow is only in one direction, we can see that there is a constant flow of energy from the sun to chloroplasts and on into the bonds of the carbon compounds formed there. It is the sun that drives the processes of life on earth.

Energy does not cycle, but matter does. We shall now briefly discuss the means by which matter cycles in an ecosystem.

CYCLING OF MATERIALS IN AN ECOSYSTEM

All living things are products of the earth and are part of it. Organisms are made of thirty to forty elements found in the atmosphere and surface of the earth. Of these chemical elements, the most important are carbon, hydrogen, oxygen, phosphorus, potassium, nitrogen, sulfur, calcium, iron, magnesium, boron, zinc, chlorine, molybdenum, cobalt, iodine, and fluorine.   These materials are taken in by plants and animals from air, soil, water, and foods; they pass in a cyclical sequence from nonliving to living and back to the nonliving original source.   The elements which are so vital to life are present either as *gases* of the atmosphere, such as carbon dioxide, nitrogen, oxygen, and water vapor, or as *minerals* dissolved in the water of the earth (see Figure 6.7).

Minerals begin their cycles as salts in the rocks of the earth's crust, and after being dissolved out of the rocks by rainwater, they are carried to the soil and on to the streams, lakes, and seas in varying concentrations of salty solutions.   All along the water pathway, minerals are assimilated by living things and utilized for various functions before being returned to the waters of the earth or passed on to the tissues of another organism by being eaten.   How long various minerals stay in the bodies of organisms varies with the nature of the mineral and the organism.   Some minerals have a very rapid turnover, while others are laid down as a more long-lasting component of an organism's structure.   Vital minerals such as phosphorus are in short supply in most ecosystems, and organisms which concentrate phosphorus are vital to the system's productivity.   The old adage about a chain being only as strong as its weakest link is strikingly demonstrated in the food chains of an ecosystem.

The gases which we and most living things require are present in air and represent one phase of the cycles of carbon, oxygen, nitrogen, and water.   *Carbon* compounds serve as sources of energy as well as structure in the organisms forming an ecosystem.   When carbon compounds are used as sources of energy, carbon leaves the organisms as a direct product of respiration, carbon dioxide gas.   When used in living structures, the carbon may remain locked in organic compounds until further consumers or decomposers have ingested and metabolized it.   In the end, however, it is released as carbon dioxide.   In this form it is available to algae and higher plants for use in photosynthesis.

Photosynthesis may produce *oxygen* as a by-product, and this gas is required for aerobic respiration by most organisms.   In respiration oxygen is eventually combined with carbon to form energy-rich carbohydrates.   The utilization of carbohydrate nutrients, as we have seen, ends with release of carbon dioxide.   Thus, the carbon cycle and oxygen cycle are linked together in the processes of photosynthesis and respiration (see Figure 6.7).

Nitrogen is also required by all living things, since it is contained in the amino acids composing proteins.   It would seem that there would be no shortage of nitrogen since four-fifths of the atmosphere consists of this vital gas, but it is of no direct use to plants or animals in its atmospheric form.   It must first be *fixed* by bacteria or blue-green algae in ammonia, NH_3, or nitrates (compounds containing the group $—NO_3$) (see Figure 6.8).   In this form it can be absorbed from the soil water or from the waters of lakes, rivers, and oceans by algae and green plants and utilized in the syn-

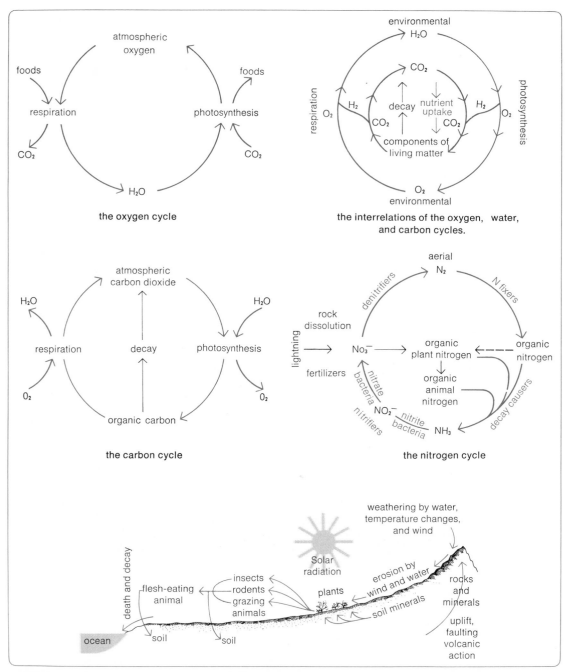

the oxygen cycle

the interrelations of the oxygen, water, and carbon cycles.

the carbon cycle

the nitrogen cycle

FIGURE 6.7 The mineral cycle. Rocks become disintegrated into soil. The soil becomes eroded and is transported by water toward the lowlands. The soluble materials become dissolved in the soil water and are eventually carried into rivers and lakes and to the sea. (*Top four drawings adapted from Paul B. Weisz, Elements of Biology, 3rd ed. Copyright by McGraw-Hill Book Company, 1969. Used by permission. Bottom adapted from T. I. Storer and R. L. Usinger, General Zoology, 4th ed. Copyright 1965. McGraw-Hill Book Company. Used by permission.*)

FIGURE 6.8 Nodules of nitrogen-fixing bacteria on roots of white clover (15×). (*Courtesy Hugh Spencer from The National Audubon Society.*)

thesis of amino acids into proteins and for various other biosyntheses. In this way nitrogen enters the food chain. Amino acids and proteins are eventually broken down in living organisms, and the nitrogen is excreted as ammonia, urea, uric acid, or other nitrogenous compounds. Dead organisms are broken down by bacteria and fungi, and ammonia and other nitrogenous compounds are released. Thus, the carbon cycle, oxygen cycle, and nitrogen cycle are eventually linked together in the process of photosynthesis, respiration, and metabolism, and the three cycles point up the relationship which exists between the plants, the animals, and the inorganic environment (see Figure 6.7).

Water obviously has a vital role in the carbon, oxygen, and nitrogen cycles as well as the cycling of minerals (see Figure 6.9). Living systems all include water solutions, and the gases and minerals we have mentioned must be dissolved in water before they can enter into living processes. For example ammonia, nitrates, carbon dioxide, and oxygen, as well as minerals and salts, are dissolved in water and utilized by both plants and animals. In addition, living things are obliged to take in water directly in order to maintain salinity and osmotic pressure and to avoid desiccation.

MATTER AND ENERGY,
CYCLE AND FLOW:
A REVIEW

It is on the level of the *cell* that light energy is trapped and used to build carbon compounds, in particular carbohydrates, from water and carbon dioxide, and it is in the cell that energy is released from these nutrient molecules through respiration. It is, however, on the level of the *organism* that nutrients are stored or, if animal, that they are captured, eaten, digested, and assimilated. In addition, it is on the level of the *ecosystem* that energy flows from light through living matter. Matter, in the form of carbon compounds and minerals, cycles over and over again through the ecosystem.

FIGURE 6.9 The water cycle. The interchange of water between the atmosphere, land, and sea is a major factor in producing the soil so necessary to most land plants and the seasonal changes which affect all organisms. Water is evaporated from the ocean and carried over the land, where it falls as rain or snow. Water is also evaporated from the soil and from the bodies of plants and animals to be later precipitated over the land or sea. (*Adapted from T. I. Storer and R. L. Usinger, General Zoology, 4th ed. Copyright 1965. McGraw-Hill Book Company. Used by permission.*)

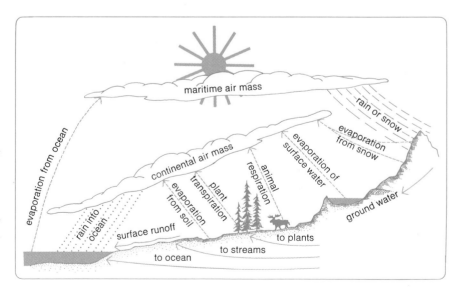

We can now form a clearer picture of the role of organisms such as ourselves within this dynamic process: We are clearly not alone; we are the functional parts of an enormously complex ecosystem.

1   Trace an electron from its origin in water through chlorophyll a to its use in the formation of NADPH and ATP.
2   Trace a carbon dioxide molecule through the dark reaction until it is a part of PGAL.
3   Defend the statment that all higher animals are modified chloroplasts.
4   Explain briefly why photosynthesis and respiration are the processes which link together the carbon, oxygen, and nitrogen cycles.
5   Why must a valid concept of metabolism encompass cell, organism, and ecosystem?

* Available in paperback.

Buchsbaum, R., and M. Buchsbaum: *Basic Ecology,* Boxwood Press, Pittsburgh, Pa., 1957.   A clear statement of ecological principles.

Odum, E. P.: *Ecology,* Holt, Rinehart and Winston, Inc., New York, 1963.   A clear and authoritative description of principles of ecology.

Smith, R. L.: *Ecology and Field Biology,* Harper & Row, Publishers, Incorporated, New York, 1966.   A well-written and beautifully illustrated text.

The following offer more information on photosynthesis:

Goldsby, R. A.: *Cells and Energy,* The Macmillan Company, New York, 1967.

McElroy, W. D.: *Cell Physiology and Biochemistry,* 2d ed., Prentice-Hall, Englewood Cliffs, N.J., 1964.

Morrison, J. H.: *Functional Organelles,* Reinhold Publishing Corporation, New York, 1966.

Part 3

Growth and Reproduction:
A Characteristic of Living Things

Populations of organisms escape extinction by reproducing themselves. The young organisms that replace the old are very similar to their ancestors because their traits result from genes inherited from them. Genes determine the nature of proteins, which then regulate the formation of traits during growth and development. As a result, living things give rise to living things in highly regulated patterns of order.

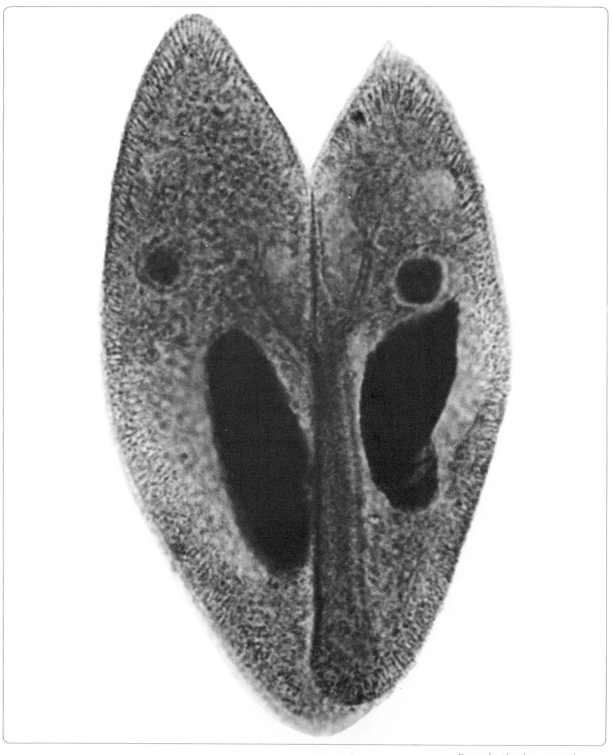

Reproduction in paramecia.
(*Carolina Biological Supply Co.*)

Chapter 7
Continuity of Life: How Are Cells and Organisms Reproduced?

Abraham begat Isaac; and Isaac begat Jacob; and Jacob begat Judas and his brethren;
And Judas begat Phares and Zara of Thamar; and Phares begat Esrom; and Esrom begat Aram;
And Aram begat Aminadab; and Aminadab begat Naasson; and Naasson begat Salmon; . . .

Matt. 1: 2–4.

All life comes only from previous life, or—to put it in a slightly different way—all cells arise from cells. Living forms are not spontaneously generated; they come only from other living things through the orderly process of reproduction.

In Chapter 2 we discussed how the experiments of Mendel and others proved that heredity is due to the transmission of particulate units rather than a blending of fluids. Since the turn of the century it has been known that the pairs of hereditary particles which Mendel's experiments suggested are actually pairs of *chromosomes*. The great nineteenth-century cell biologists whose work we summarized in Chapter 2, men such as Strasburger, Weismann, and Hertwig, showed that hereditary traits are determined by genes carried on these chromosomes.

In Chapter 2 we also considered the process of evolution by natural selection as Charles Darwin perceived it. Darwin was ignorant of the biological mechanisms of heredity and consequently unable to give an acceptable explanation of how heritable variation of the organisms within a population can occur.

In this chapter we shall deal in more detail with some of these matters, in particular the means by which chromosomes and their genes are assorted and distributed to descendant cells and the different ways in which organisms reproduce. We shall find that the *heritable variation* so vital to the processes of evolution stems in part from the mechanisms by which chromosomes, cells, and organisms reproduce.

REPRODUCTION OF
CHROMOSOMES

Since we are to take up the chemical nature of genes and chromosomes in Chapter 9, here we simply note in passing that chromosomes contain three kinds of molecules, *proteins, ribonucleic acid* (RNA), and *deoxyribonucleic acid* (DNA). Each chromosome may be pictured as a randomly coiled cable (see Figure 7.1) in which the inner core, the DNA of the genes, is surrounded and supported by an outer covering (the chromosomal protein). We shall delay until Chapter 9 a more realistic explanation of genes and chromosomes and concern ourselves in this chapter only with the behavior of chromosomes during the reproduction of cells.

When a cell reproduces, it always produces *two* offspring cells, or *daughter cells.* The apparatus that forms in a cell undergoing division is structurally arranged so that normally the cell can split into only two parts.

If the two daughter cells formed from a parent cell are to have the same hereditary information (genes) as the parent cell, the chromosomes of the parent cell must duplicate themselves before the division begins. The chromosomes become duplicated and then pull away from each other to form two strands (called *chromatids*) bearing identical genes. These two chromatids are held together somewhere along their lengths at a point called the *centromere.*

The reproduction of the chromosomes takes place while the cell is not dividing, during the part of the cell's life called *interphase.* Cells spend most of their time in interphase, the act of cell division being a comparatively rapid affair.

REPRODUCTION OF CELLS

In general terms, reproduction of a cell may be thought of as a sequence in which the cell doubles in mass and then is halved by cell division. In multicellular organisms growth is mainly the result of an increase in number of cells, although sometimes growth occurs as a result of increase in cell size as well. The number of cells is increased by cell division, and the cellular material needed for the new cells is formed by synthesis of additional cytoplasmic machinery. The sequence of cellular activities leading to repeated cell divisions is called the *cell cycle* (see Figure 7.2).

The cell cycle is basically a sequence in which the genetic material is doubled and then separated into two halves. The cytoplasm then cleaves into two parts, each containing half of the previously doubled genetic material. The time required for a cell cycle varies from 20 minutes in bacteria to at least 12 hours in the actively dividing cells of many plants and animals. The duration of the cell cycle in more slowly dividing cell types may of course be much greater; some cells divide only once every few months or even years.

Each species of organism has a characteristic number of chromosomes called a *chromosome number* (see Figure 7.3). This number is said to be a *diploid,* and a set of chromosomes of half this number is said to be a *haploid.* For example, adult animals bear diploid cells, but their sperm or egg cells are haploid. The sperm, eggs, or spores (gametophytes) of plants and animals contain only half this number of chromosomes, the haploid number (see Figure 7.4). To produce cells which contain

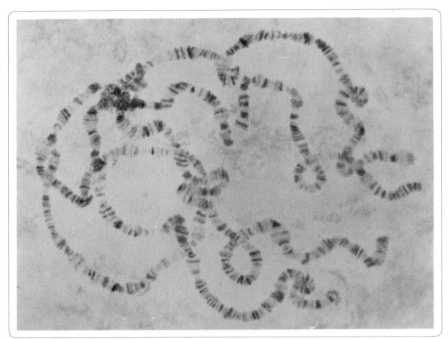

FIGURE 7.1 Giant chromosomes of *Drosophila* (fruit fly) from salivary gland. (*Carolina Biological Supply Co.*)

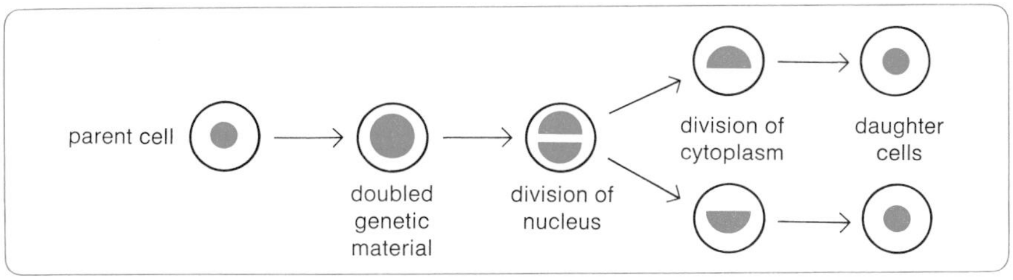

FIGURE 7.2 In the cell cycle the genetic material is doubled and then separated into two halves. The cytoplasm then splits, and each daughter cell grows until it is the size of the original parental cell.

FIGURE 7.3 Chromosome numbers.

SPECIES	DIPLOID NUMBER
Neurospora fungus	14
Corn (*Zea mays*)	20
Onion (*Allium cepa*)	16
Garlic (*A. sativum*)	16
Guppy (*Lebistes reticulatus*)	48
Tree frog (*Hyla arborea*)	24
Mouse (*Mus musculus*)	40
Rat (*Rattus norvegicus*)	42
Cat (*Felis familiaris*)	38
Dog (*Canis familiaris*)	58
Chimpanzee (*Pan troglodytes*)	48
Man (*Homo sapiens*)	46

GROWTH AND REPRODUCTION: A
CHARACTERISTIC OF LIVING
THINGS

FIGURE 7.4 Human chromosomes showing the metaphase of
cultured blood leucocyte of a
person with leukemia. The arrow
points to the so-called Philadelphia
(Ph¹) chromosome. At bottom is
the caryotype of metaphase.
(*Courtesy of the American Cancer
Society.*)

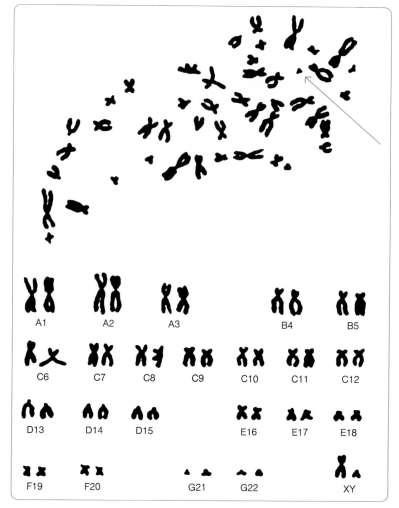

either the same number or half the number of chromosomes of the parent cell, two
kinds of cell division must be possible.

Mitosis is cell division in which the daughter cells each inherit a set of chromosomes
identical to those of the parent cell. The formation of animal sperm and eggs and
plant spores, however, involves a *reduction* in the number of chromosomes per
nucleus to the haploid number, and this special result is attained through *meiosis*.

MITOSIS   One might hypothesize that a cell could reproduce itself by simply making copies of
its structures and then accumulating the new parts at one edge, where they could
gather to form a new, duplicate cell next to the original. Cells, however, reproduce
in a very different way. In mitosis, cells duplicate the *blueprints* for their components in that each daughter cell receives an identical set of genes.

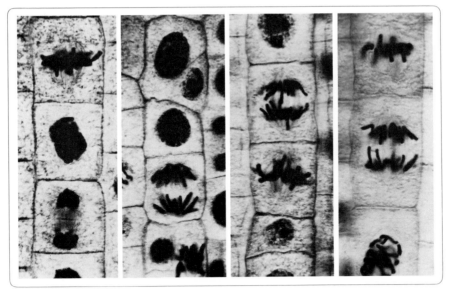

FIGURE 7.5 Mitosis in the onion, showing prophase, meta-phase, anaphase, and telophase. (*Carolina Biological Supply Co.*)

Mitosis is a continuous sequence of events but, just as in a movie or a play, the action must be divided up into phases or acts to be understood. Mitosis is arbitrarily divided into four phases, with each phase describing a particular set of events. In order of occurrence these phases are *prophase, metaphase, anaphase,* and *telophase* (see Figure 7.5 and Plate 3). The last phase, telophase, is followed by *interphase,* the stage of the cell cycle when the cell is not dividing. Interphase is, however, the period of a dividing cell's life when the DNA of the chromosomes is duplicated, in preparation for the next mitosis. By the time mitosis begins, each chromosome is therefore a *double* structure composed of two perfect duplicates side by side.

Prophase is the first stage of cell division. Entrance of a cell into prophase marks the onset of the mitotic process. During the interphase, chromosomes cannot be distin-guished as individual structures under the light microscope but are seen only as a maze of darkly staining fibrous material. During interphase the chromosomes are extremely long and slender, but *during prophase, the chromosomes become shorter and thicker as a result of coiling.* We can compare the chromosomes to long nylon threads. During interphase, the threads lie all over each other in a network called *chromatin.* It would be just as difficult to see individual threads of nylon in this network from a distance of several hundred yards as it would be to see the unstained chromosomes through a microscope. If you and a friend stood at opposite ends of a long nylon thread and coiled it tighter and tighter, however, eventually you would both be face to face holding a short compact mass of nylon. In a similar way, chromosomes are believed to condense into short thick rodlike structures only a small fraction of their original length.

As the chromosomes, with their double strands, coil and become shorter and thicker, their centromeres become even more obvious (see Figure 7.6). The centromeres

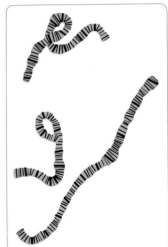

FIGURE 7.6 During prophase, chromosomes twist and become short and thick. As a result, the DNA forms dense crossbands in chromosomes of cells undergoing cell division. This drawing clearly shows the characteristic cross-bands which are now thought to be portions of a continuous strand of DNA. (*Adapted from a pho-tograph in D. F. Poulson and C. W. Metz, J. Morphol., vol. 63, 1938.*)

FIGURE 7.7 Stages of mitosis, showing spindle fibers and their action.

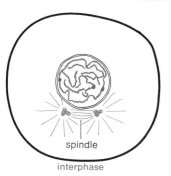

spindle

interphase

early prophase

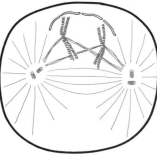

middle prophase

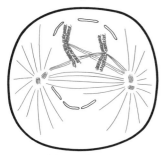

late prophase

become the points of attachment for the fibers which form during metaphase, the stage that follows. These fibers pull the chromosomes to opposite sides of the cell during anaphase. The nuclear membrane might present a barrier to this migration, but as prophase progresses, the nuclear membrane, as well as the nucleolus, disappears.

In animal cells and some plant cells, the first visible sign that prophase is beginning is the reproduction of centrioles. Centrioles consist of two cylinders lying at right angles to each other, each resembling a short piece of pipe the sides of which are made from nine rods. Each rod is made of one, two, or three tubes. Centrioles always have this design, and they are able to perpetuate themselves and their structure in that a new centriole can grow out of an old one. The new centriole is always synthesized at right angles from the parent centriole.

The reproduction of centrioles during prophase in animal cells results in two pairs of centrioles. Fibers form around each pair of centrioles and radiate out in a fashion resembling light emanating from a star. Because of this appearance, a pair of centrioles with its fibers is called an *aster,* meaning "star." The two asters move rapidly away from each other and migrate to opposite sides of the cell, where they form the poles to which the chromosomes will be pulled.

Although centrioles exist in the cells of lower plants, they are not present in seed plants, which therefore do not have asters. The regions from which the fibers project toward the chromosomes are simply called *poles* in the cells of higher plants.

Metaphase is the stage of cell division during which a large transparent structure, the *spindle,* forms (see Figure 7.7). The spindle is shaped like two cones with their bases together. At the two opposite points are the asters (if it is an animal cell) or poles (if it is a seed-plant cell). The spindle has enough rigidity to permit it to be poked and pushed about inside the cell. The assemblage of substances into the spindle apparatus must be selective, since mitochondria, chloroplasts, and other cytoplasmic objects are excluded. The spindle is made of fibers running from pole to pole and from chromosome to pole. Somehow, through a process that is not understood, these spindle fibers pull the chromosomes to a plane equally distant from each centriole, the *metaphase plane.* Then, spindle fibers extending from the poles to the centromeres of the double chromosomes begin to shorten, perhaps in a manner similar to the sliding filaments in muscle. The centromeres then split, and the two duplicate strands of each chromosome are pulled to opposite sides of the cell. This stage, in which the two sets of chromosomes migrate away from each other, is called *anaphase* (see Figures 7.5 and 7.7).

As far as is known, the chromatids, the duplicate chromosome strands, are *pulled* to the opposite poles or asters of the spindle. The word pulled seems appropriate since the two ends of each chromosome may be seen trailing along behind the centromeres during their advance to the poles, as in Figure 7.7.

Telophase begins when the chromosomes reach the poles. The events of telophase are basically the events of prophase in reverse. The chromosomes uncoil and become long, thin, and difficult to see. Nuclear membranes form again around each of the two clusters of chromosomes, and two or more nucleoli form in each nucleus. The spindle apparatus disappears, and the cytoplasm now begins to divide. In animal cells the cytoplasm divides by *furrowing,* a process in which the cytoplasm pinches in as if there were a drawstring being pulled tighter and tighter around it. The mechanism of furrowing is not understood. In plant cells the rigid cellulose cell wall does not permit cleaving of the cytoplasm through furrowing. Instead, tiny fibers and vacuoles appear in the cytoplasm where the metaphase plane had been and accumulate as a *cell plate.* The cell plate extends until it divides the cytoplasm into two compartments.

Mitosis is a highly regulated process whereby one parent cell gives rise to two daughter cells which contain exact duplicates of the chromosomes present in the parent. Mitosis is required in the *replacement* of old and damaged cells and in *growth* through the addition of cells. In one-celled organisms mitosis may be the means by which the *reproduction* of the organism is accomplished. The most significant aspect of cell reproduction by mitosis is that the number of chromosomes characteristic of the organism is perpetuated so that (except for certain special cases) all the cells of a many-celled organism have the same number of chromosomes as the original cell from which all the other cells descended (the fertilized egg). The nature of mitosis therefore suggests, though it does not prove, that all the genes for all the traits of the organism are present in every cell. Other evidence, to be reviewed in later chapters, shows that this is almost certainly a correct view.

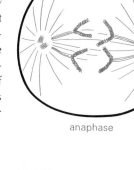

late metaphase

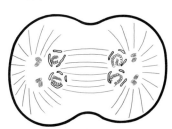

anaphase

Earlier we said that certain cells of an organism, for example, the eggs and sperm, may have a haploid number of chromosomes which is one-half of the diploid number. We now ask: How does a diploid number become a haploid number, and how is the diploid number restored from the haploid? The answer to these questions is that haploid cells are produced by meiosis and the diploid number of chromosomes is restored by fertilization.

Meiosis produces daughter cells with only half the chromosome number of the parent cell. The reason is the existence of an extra process in meiosis, the *pairing of homologous chromosomes.*

The pairing of meiotic chromosomes is not a haphazard pairing of any two chromosomes. Chromosomes pair up in the prophase of meiosis so that each chromosome in a pair contains genes for the same traits. Chromosomes exist in such pairs because they originally came from two sources, the father and mother of the organism now carrying on meiosis. For example, each of your cells contains forty-six chromosomes, and twenty-three of these are descended from those which came originally from your father's sperm cell and twenty-three from those which came originally from your mother's egg cell. With fertilization, these two haploid cells were fused into a single cell, the fertilized egg, containing the diploid number of forty-six. Thus you contain *twenty-three pairs of homologous chromosomes.* Each

MEIOSIS

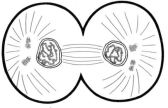

early telophase

late telophase

pair contains genes for the same traits. In each pair of homologous chromosomes one chromosome is paternal (it stems originally from the male parent) and the other maternal (it stems originally from the female parent).

In mitosis, homologous chromosomes do not pair up but simply form a single line of individual chromosomes. These are pulled apart during anaphase, and the duplicate strands, or chromatids, are pulled to opposite poles. Each daughter cell produced by mitosis therefore contains the same number of chromosomes as the parent cell. In meiosis, however, the homologous chromosomes pair up and during anaphase are pulled to opposite poles as complete double-stranded chromosomes. Within each pair, one complete double-stranded chromosome goes to one side and its homologous partner to the other. The result is a *reduction* in chromosome number to one-half that of the parental cell (see Figure 7.8).

Meiosis, unlike mitosis, consists of *two* successive divisions. The first, as described in the last paragraph, is a *reduction division* that produces two haploid cells from one diploid cell. This division is followed by another called an *equational division,* which is, in a practical sense, very similar to mitosis, for the chromosomes now line up in a single row at metaphase and have their centromeres pulled apart during anaphase. Each of the two haploid cells gives rise to two haploid daughter cells; the result is that four haploid daughter cells are formed from one diploid parent cell in meiosis.

Sperm and eggs of animals and spores of plants are produced through meiosis. Each of these haploid cells contains a sampling of one-half of the parent's chromosomes but not just a random sampling of any haploid number of chromosomes. In meiosis, the daughter cells get one chromosome, either maternal or paternal, from each homologous pair.

Meiosis, then, is the secret that Darwin was searching for; it is the reason why there is variation among the members of a population. The haploid cells produced by meiosis contain a sampling of one-half of the chromosomes of a parent, and when two haploid cells fuse in fertilization, the resultant diploid cell contains chromosomes from two parents. With each meiosis and a subsequent fertilization there is a shuffling of genes in the population. We shall return to this concept later.

REPRODUCTION OF ORGANISMS

Generally, the pattern of reproduction of organisms has two phases: (1) The parent organism forms a *reproductive unit* which in multicellular organisms above a low level of complexity is separated from the rest of the parent organism. (2) The reproductive unit undergoes *growth and development* into an organism that may be identical or similar to the parent. Some organisms accomplish reproduction without going through the process of fertilization, a type of reproduction termed *vegetative.*

Vegetative reproduction is the result of mitosis in organisms more complex than bacteria. In single-celled organisms, such as protozoa and some algae, the reproductive unit is the entire organism, and mitosis produces two independent organisms. Bac-

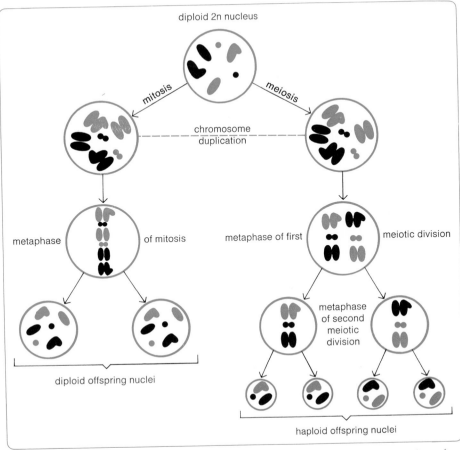

diploid 2n nucleus

mitosis meiosis

chromosome
duplication

metaphase   of mitosis   metaphase of first   meiotic division

metaphase
of second
meiotic
division

diploid offspring nuclei

haploid offspring nuclei

FIGURE 7.8 A comparison of
mitosis and meiosis, on the
assumption that $2n = 6$. Note that
the key difference between the two
processes is the way the chromosomes line up in metaphase.
(*Adapted from Paul B. Weisz, Elements of Biology, 3rd ed. Copyright McGraw-Hill Book Company,
1969. Used by permission.*)

teria are single-celled organisms which have only one strand of DNA instead of
chromosomes. They do not undergo mitosis but reproduce by simply dividing into
two sections with a duplicate DNA strand in each section. Multicellular organisms
reproduce vegetatively when portions of the parent body break away and grow into
offspring through a regeneration of the missing parts. Some animals, such as
flatworms, separate into two or more parts, each of which can regenerate the missing
tissues and organs. If the broken end of a fallen tree branch becomes covered by
water or soil, roots may develop, and a new tree can be formed. Strawberry plants
send out horizontal stems which are able to form buds, leaves and roots and give rise
to new, individual offspring. Injury to animals such as starfish can result in a breaking up of the parent into two or more parts, each of which can regenerate what is
missing. These are examples of vegetative reproduction. This form of reproduction
results in offspring which contain chromosomal complements identical to those of
the parent organism. It is clear, however, that there are evolutionary advantages to
reproduction by means of a life cycle which includes meiotic production of haploid

sexual cells such as eggs and sperm. It may be that this advantage stems from the increase in variability within the species which results from meiosis, since more organisms able to deal with special environmental problems in more ways can be expected to occur in organisms whose life cycle includes such a "variation generator." In any case, we find that almost all higher organisms use haploid reproductive cells and that these cells are formed in special reproductive tissues. According to the way in which these special reproductive cells grow and develop into offspring, they are classified as either *spores* or *gametes*.

Spores are reproductive cells capable of developing, under proper conditions, *directly into an offspring*. That is, a spore does not fuse with another cell before becoming an organism; it begins dividing mitotically and develops directly into an offspring. Each offspring resulting from reproduction with spores has *only one parent*.

FIGURE 7.9 Schematic summary of the three principal patterns of organismic reproduction.

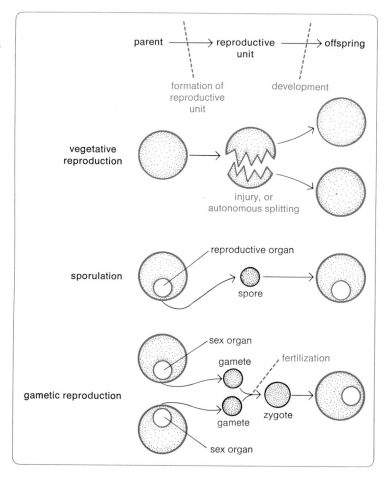

Spores are frequently highly resistant to environmental hazards and may be distributed over a wide area. Their disadvantage, for higher organisms, is that they carry genes from only one parent. Reproduction with spores is often followed by reproduction with gametes in higher organisms.

Gametes differ from spores in that they usually *must fuse with another gamete* before they can develop into a new organism. Each offspring resulting from reproduction with gametes therefore has *two parents* instead of *one*. Organisms resulting from reproduction with gametes have a genetic makeup different from the two parents producing the gametes, as we pointed out in discussing meiosis.

Reproduction with gametes is a sexual process since it requires two parents, each a differently specialized sexual type. The offspring produced by gametic, or sexual, reproduction may vary greatly from their parents and from each other. The genetic variability found within populations and contributing so much to the process of evolution by natural selection is the result of the meiotic shuffling of chromosomes. In order to translate that process into the actual production of new, variant organisms, sexual reproduction, involving fertilization, is needed. Sexual reproduction is therefore a feature with great survival significance. Without it, most populations would contain organisms so similar in their traits that changes in the environment could easily threaten the survival of the entire group. Populations must contain organisms that differ from each other so that some may be successful when the environment shifts. It is no surprise to learn that sexual reproduction has been observed to occur in almost all organisms at some time during their life cycles (see Figure 7.9).

All plants and animals and most single-celled organisms carry on both mitosis and meiosis and at different times give rise to both haploid and diploid cells, which have various roles in reproduction. The course of events leading to the reproduction of an organism constitutes the *life cycle* of the organism. Since there are many kinds of life cycles, a description of them all in a text of this length would be impossible. We shall therefore describe only the life cycles of animals and of ferns and seed plants. Some additional details will be added in Chapters 17 to 20.

LIFE CYCLES

Most animals have relatively simple life cycles, being diploid many-celled organisms throughout their lives. The only haploid cells occurring in the typical animal life cycle are the single-celled haploid gametes, the sperm and eggs resulting from meiosis during the period of reproduction. When the nuclei of the sperm and egg fuse in fertilization, the result is a diploid *zygote*. This cell and its descendants divide mitotically to produce the many-celled organism which eventually becomes an adult. By this time certain specialized cells of the gonads, organs that produce sperm or eggs, have already begun the process of meiosis, and these cells will again produce haploid gametes.

LIFE CYCLE OF ANIMALS

In male mammals, sperm cells are produced by meiosis in the cells lining the tubules in the testes. The cells which will give rise to sperm cells were formed through mitosis, but eventually they undergo meiosis instead. Each haploid cell produced in the testes may become a functional sperm.

In female mammals, eggs are produced by meiosis in fluid-filled sacs, called Graafian follicles, in the ovaries. The daughter cells resulting from the first division of meiosis are unequal in size. The egg cell gets almost all the cytoplasm, while the other cell, called a *polar body* is tiny. The second meiotic division results in the formation of two more polar bodies, each haploid, plus the one haploid egg nucleus, which will soon enter into fertilization (see Figure 7.10). The end result of meiosis in female mammals is the formation of only one functional egg with two nonfunctional polar bodies attached to its surface.

One cell gives rise to four sperm cells in males and only one egg in females. The advantage of this inequality is clear. The unequal divisions of the egg-forming cells result in large eggs containing a great deal of cytoplasm which will provide, along with the yolk to be absorbed later, the molecular machinery with which the embryo will be formed. In contrast, the sperm cells contain very little cytoplasm and consist primarily of a nucleus with a tail and mitochondria attached. We shall discuss fertilization itself below.

FIGURE 7.10 Meiosis in males and females. In males, all four haploid cells formed become functional sperms. In females, one cell formed by the first meiotic division is small, degenerates, and becomes the first polar body. Similarly, one cell formed by the second meiotic division becomes the second polar body. Thus only one cell matures as a functional egg. (*Adapted from Paul B. Weisz, Elements of Biology, 3rd ed. Copyright McGraw-Hill Book Company, 1969. Used by permission.*)

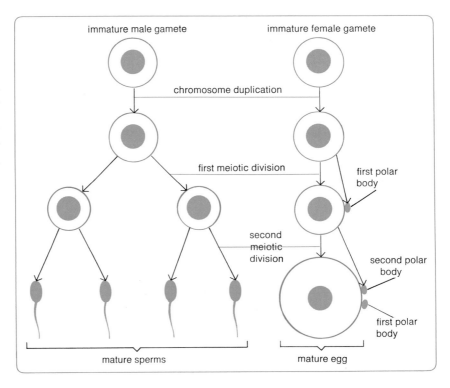

immature male gamete   immature female gamete

chromosome duplication

first meiotic division

first polar body

second meiotic division

second polar body

first polar body

mature sperms   mature egg

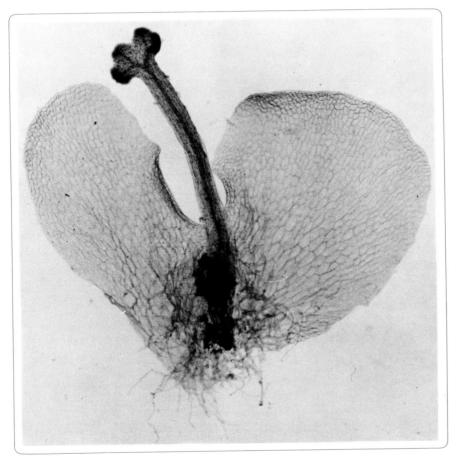

LIFE CYCLE OF PLANTS

Meiosis in animals gives rise to either sperm cells or eggs. This is not the case in plants. Meiosis in ferns gives rise to spores, which germinate if they land on wet soil (see Figure 7.11). From the spores there arises a haploid many-celled green plant which is self-supporting. These haploid plants contain special cells which give rise to haploid sperm cells or eggs *through mitosis*. The sperm cells swim to the eggs, and the diploid condition is restored with fertilization. This diploid zygote divides many times through mitosis and forms a diploid plant, which then may produce spores through meiosis and the cycle continues (see Figure 7.12).

The cone-bearing and flowering plants have the same cycle, but the haploid stage is less noticeable; it consists of a tiny nongreen plant containing only a few cells parasitic within the cells of the diploid tissue (see Figure 7.13). The fern, pine, and petunia so familiar to us all are diploid. It is usually much more difficult to recognize the haploid phases of these plants and to accept them as being just as much individual plants as the diploid phase. Nevertheless, the tiny green sheet of cells

FIGURE 7.12 Summary of the
life cycle of ferns. (*Adapted from
Paul B. Weisz, Elements of Biology,
3rd ed. Copyright McGraw-Hill
Book Company, 1969. Used by
permission.*)

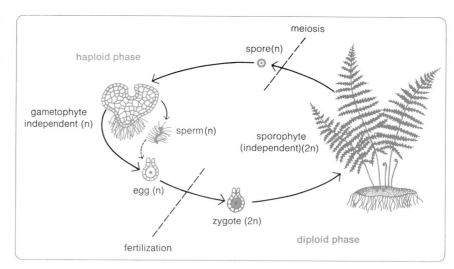

FIGURE 7.13 The basic pattern
of reproduction in seed plants.
Diploid generation is shown in
color, haploid in black. (*Adapted
from Paul B. Weisz, Elements of
Biology, 3rd ed. Copyright
McGraw-Hill Book Company,
1969. Used by permission.*)

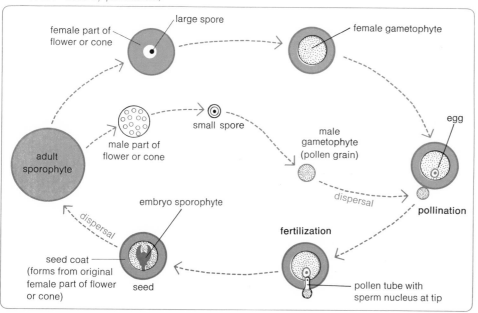

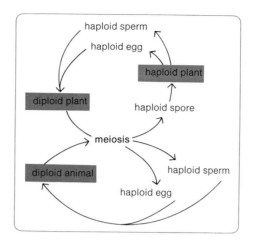

FIGURE 7.14 The place of
meiosis in the life cycles of plants
and animals. Meiosis occurs only
in diploid organisms.

growing near the large fern and the tiny colorless pollen tubes and clumps of cells growing in the cones and flowers represent visible examples of the haploid phase of the life cycle.

In review, meiosis in plants produces spores, and meiosis in animals produces gametes. In many cases gametes are very sensitive to the hazards of the environment, since the act of fertilization requires that the sperm and egg be unprotected and capable of fusing. Alternatively, the sperm must have a way of penetrating whatever protection the egg has around it. We shall find in later chapters that animals have evolved special structures and behavioral patterns which tend to decrease the exposure of gametes to environmental hazards. With many animals sperm is transferred to the female with special mating structures, and fertilization is internal, though the sperm must swim about to reach the egg and only one or a few sperm do reach it. With ferns, the sperm must swim through water to permit fertilization, but fertilization, when it occurs, is also internal. With the seed plants, fertilization is also internal, and the only stage of the life cycle exposed to the outside rigors of the environment are the microscopic haploid gamete-forming structures (pollen) and the seeds. The seed plants have reduced the haploid phase of their life cycle to the tiny pollen grains *outside* and the gamete-forming tissues which grow *inside* the parent diploid plant (see Figure 7.13). We shall see in Chapter 18 that the development of the highly resistant pollen grains plus the internalization of gamete-forming tissues are the major reasons for the success of seed plants.

Your life can be said to have begun with fertilization, the fusion of an egg cell from your mother with a sperm cell from your father.

An egg is a highly specialized cell with many unique properties. Once fertilized, it will give rise to all the different specialized cells that form a many-celled organism. The egg possesses certain specialized features that are vitally important during fertil-

FERTILIZATION: HOW
DID OUR LIVES BEGIN?

THE EGG

ization and development. The most important structures of an egg are the *yolk,* which supplies the matter and energy for the early, nonfeeding embryo; the *spatial arrangement of cytoplasmic material,* which determines not only the planes of future cell divisions but also the early patterns of differentiation in the embryo; and the nucleus, which bears the maternal set of genes which the embryo will inherit. Before fertilization can be accomplished the sperm must penetrate into the interior of the eggs.

THE SPERM

A sperm cell is also highly specialized and differs from an egg in that it is *able to move,* has *little cytoplasmic material,* is small, and is capable of digesting its way through substances in the periphery of the egg and effecting an entrance (see Figure 7.14). Sperm cells have two fundamental functions: They *activate eggs* into beginning development, and they contribute their *haploid nucleus* to the new organism.

FIGURE 7.15 Variations in sperm morphology: (*a*) crayfish, (*b*) sea urchin, (*c*) toadfish, (*d*) toad, (*e*) opossum, and (*f*) guinea pig. (*From Interacting Systems in Development by James D. Ebert. Copyright © 1965 by Holt, Rinehart and Winston, Inc. Reprinted by permission of Holt, Rinehart and Winston, Inc.*)

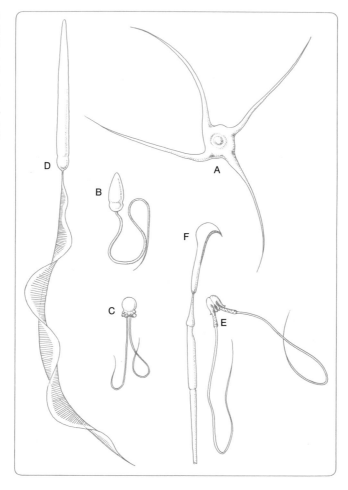

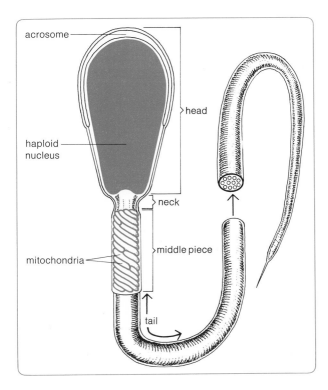

Sperm cells of animals vary greatly in size and shape (see Figure 7.15).   Generally, sperm cells have three main divisions: head, middle piece, and tail. The *head* is specialized to activate the egg and contribute the haploid nucleus; the *middle piece* carries mitochondria and is responsible for metabolism, and the *tail* provides locomotion.   The tail is a typical flagellum with the characteristic "9 + 2" arrangement of flagellum fibrils (see Chapter 3).   A diagram of bull sperm, which is very similar to human sperm, is shown in Figure 7.16.   Genetically, the important part of the sperm is obviously the nucleus, which makes up most of the head.   In the sperm head the chromosomal material is packed tightly, so that it appears to be a homogeneous mass.   The forward end of the sperm head is covered by a membranous sac containing a region called the *acrosome,* which functions in the penetration of the sperm into the egg.

The mature human egg is probably capable of being fertilized for only about 24 to 48 hours after its release from the ovary.   Human sperm can live several days under re-frigeration but are thought to live only about 24 hours in the female reproductive tract.   Exceptional animals such as female bats mate in the fall and store living sperm until spring, when fertilization occurs.   One reason for the fantastic success of insects is that because they can also store sperm for long periods of time, continued contact with males is not necessary for the laying of tremendous numbers of fertilized eggs.

FERTILIZATION

FIGURE 7.17 Human sperm.

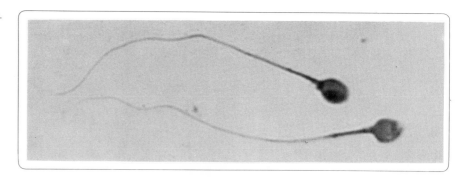

For fertilization, there are characteristically a great many more sperm than eggs. The size of the ejaculation of semen varies from 0.05 milliliter in bats to 2 milliliters in goats to 500 milliliters in pigs. The number of sperm cells per milliliter of semen in this group is 6 billion, 4 billion, and 100 million, respectively. A few forms of mammals are able to mate many times during a single day. For example, a male goat, or ram, is capable of twenty ejaculations a day.

The average size of an ejaculation from a human male is about 3 milliliters and contains about 300 million sperm cells. If the sperm cell count falls below 20 million sperm per milliliter, the man is considered to be sterile. The fantastic number of sperm that seems to be required for fertilization is necessary for several reasons. Parts of the female tract are either harmfully acidic or may produce substances that are toxic to sperm. Furthermore, many sperm have some abnormality which interferes with locomotion or performance at the site of the egg. The main problem is simply the necessity of ensuring a high concentration of sperm.

The time required for sperm to reach the upper end of the oviduct, where fertilization occurs, varies from 15 minutes in mice to 3 hours in rabbits and human beings. Apparently, forces other than locomotion are responsible for this rapid movement. Perhaps ciliated cells of the mucous membrane that lines the oviduct sweep the sperm along, or the muscular walls of the oviduct may perform rhythmical contractions that squeeze the sperm toward the ovary.

Recent studies on fertilization using the electron microscope have shown that the sperm does not bore into the egg, as many previous researchers assumed. Instead, when the sperm head collides with an outer egg envelope, the membraneous sac covering the front of the sperm head breaks down, exposing the acrosome. This structure apparently releases digestive enzymes, since the material between the egg envelope and egg cell membrane begins to dissolve. (An enzyme called hyaluronidase has been extracted from human sperm and may perform this function in human fertilization.) Tubules grow down from the rear of the membraneous sac, touch the egg cell membrane, and stimulate it to rise as a *fertilization cone*. This sequence of events may require only a few seconds. During this brief time, the egg becomes *activated* through a series of biochemical changes, and a *fertilization*

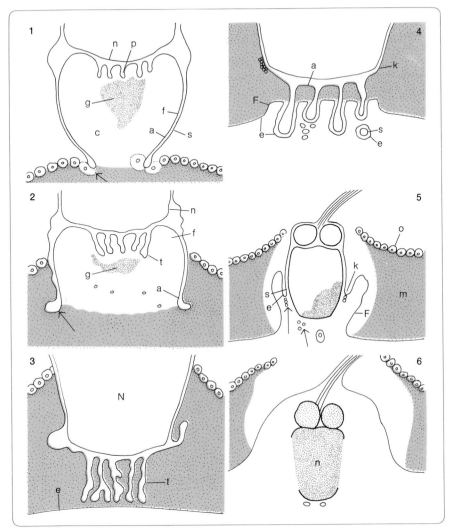

FIGURE 7.18 Fertilization in *Hydroides,* a segmented worm, demonstrating interaction between sperm and egg. The sperm tip opens soon after contact with the egg envelope, the membranes of the acrosome and sperm become continuous (*a* and *s*), and the acrosomal granule (*g*) releases digestive enzymes which digest tubules (*t*) through the egg envelope (*m*, the region with color) so that the sperm nucleus (*N*) membrane comes into contact with the egg cytoplasm (step 5). In step 6, a zygote has been formed by the mingling of sperm parts with egg cytoplasm. (*After A. L. Colwin and L. H. Colwin, in Journal of Biophysical and Biochemical Cytology, vol. 10, p. 233, June, 1961, and Rockefeller Institute Press.*)

membrane forms, which blocks entrance of additional sperm. (In some animal species more than one sperm can enter the egg, but only one fuses with the egg nucleus. See Figure 7.18.)

After the membranes of the sperm and egg have fused and the head, middle piece, and tail have entered the egg, the sperm and egg nuclei move toward each other. The nuclear membranes break down, and the chromosomes which originated from the male and female parents align themselves as a metaphase stage in a *mitotic spindle.* A new individual has been formed with its unique combination of genes and traits!

Modern man is faced with a moral dilemma regarding the theological interpretations of fertilization and the development that follows. The issue revolves around the legal aspects of abortion and concerns the problem of when a human zygote becomes human. Some theologians even debate the question of when the zygote becomes *alive!* Certainly, both sperm and egg were alive when their protoplasm fused to form a zygote, and the activities associated with life persisted throughout the following growth of the embryo. It is a strictly philosophical question when the embryo can be said to be human. The sperm and egg from which it developed were alive, and the living embryo possesses human genes throughout its existence. However, only after fertilization is the diploid chromosome complement required for a human organism established.

REVIEW QUESTIONS

1 Describe briefly the reproduction of cells from the reproduction of chromosomes in interphase to the last events of telophase.
2 Discuss the basic differences between mitosis and meiosis.
3 Contrast the three ways in which organisms may reproduce.
4 Discuss the role that reproduction with gametes has in the survival of populations.
5 Contrast the life cycles of animals and plants.
6 Contrast the life cycles of ferns and seed plants.
7 Describe briefly the process of fertilization.

SUGGESTIONS FOR
FURTHER READING
* Available in paperback.

Cook, S. A.: *Reproduction, Heredity, and Sexuality,* Wadsworth Publishing Company, Inc., Belmont, Calif., 1964. Combines the principles of genetics with the means of reproduction in the various plant groups.

Kennedy, D. (ed.): *The Living Cell: Readings from Scientific American,* W. H. Freeman and Company, San Francisco, 1965. Articles by Mazia and others describe how cells divide.

Scotch thistle. (*Courtesy of Paul Caponigro.*)

Chapter 8

Genetics: How Are Traits Transmitted?

Man's yesterday may ne'er be like his morrow;
Naught may endure but Mutability.

Shelley

You are a continuation of the lives of your parents or, to be more specific, the lives of a sperm cell from your father and an egg from your mother. Your parents gave rise to you, a creature neither fish nor fowl but a human being, resembling other human beings and your parents in particular. You are the same sort of creature as your parents, a human being constructed from nonhuman materials from your environment. Why should men beget men? What is the actual material you receive from your parents that causes you to be a creature similar to them?

We learned in Chapter 2 that we do not inherit traits by way of the bloodstream. We do not have our mother's or father's blood flowing through our blood vessels. Mendel demonstrated over 100 years ago that the hereditary material transmitted from one generation to the next is not a fluid blending with every generation but a solid substance existing as pairs of particles.

Today we know that Mendel's seven pairs of particles were actually seven pairs of chromosomes and that he studied only a single pair of genes on each of the seven pairs of chromosomes. The material we inherit from our parents that makes us resemble them rather than a new species of tree or insect is the set of twenty-three pairs of chromosomes and their thousands of genes.

MEIOSIS, GAMETES, AND
THE TRANSMISSION OF
CHROMOSOMES

An organism and its traits develop either vegetatively or from the fusion of gametes, the sperm and egg. Each gamete carries half of the chromosomes of the parent that produced it. The process by which a gamete receives only one-half of the chromosomes of the parent cell is meiosis, discussed in the last chapter.

Let us consider a husband and wife and picture a cell in each of them undergoing meiosis into a sperm or egg. We shall follow only one pair of chromosomes and ignore the other twenty-two pairs (we recall that the human has twenty-three pairs of chromosomes, see Figure 8.1). Since we are beginning our discussion with these two persons as the first, or parental, generation, we shall consider all chromosomes in his sperm cells as paternal and all chromosomes in her eggs as maternal.

Chromosomes in a living cell are, of course, colorless. If the chromosomes of the parental generation could be given some dye that would not harm them, we could follow them through the following generations. Let us *imagine* that we can put a lot of yellow dye in one pair of homologous chromosomes of the man and just a little of the yellow dye in the corresponding pair of homologous chromosomes of the wife. Paternal chromosomes would now be dark yellow and maternal chromosomes light yellow. With respect to this *pair* of chromosomes, the husband could be called *dark yellow–dark yellow* and the wife *light yellow–light yellow*. All his sperm cells contain a dark yellow chromosome, and all the wife's eggs contain a light yellow chromosome. All their children will contain cells bearing one dark yellow chromosome and one light yellow chromosome, as well as the forty-four other chromosomes which we have not labeled with our dyes (see Figure 8.2).

FIGURE 8.1 Chromosomes of a normal human female. Compare these with the giant chromosomes of the fruit fly (*Drosophila*) in Figure 7.1. (*Carolina Biological Supply Co.*)

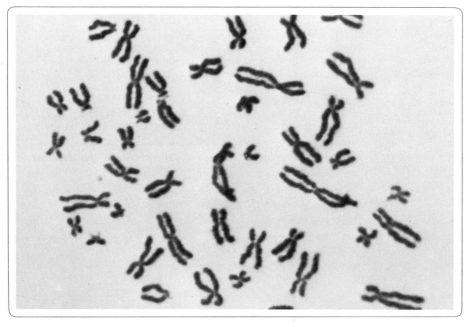

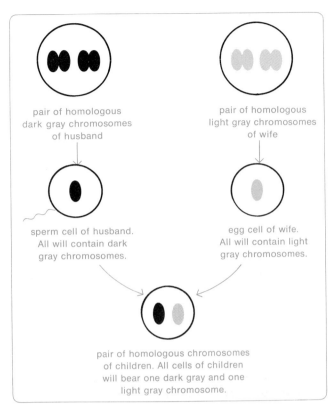

FIGURE 8.2 Pattern of inheritance of chromosomes in man.

pair of homologous
dark gray chromosomes
of husband

pair of homologous
light gray chromosomes
of wife

sperm cell of husband.
All will contain dark
gray chromosomes.

egg cell of wife.
All will contain light
gray chromosomes.

pair of homologous chromosomes
of children. All cells of children
will bear one dark gray and one
light gray chromosome.

When these children begin to produce gametes themselves, they produce gametes bearing a dark yellow chromosome and gametes bearing a light yellow chromosome. Half of the eggs from this generation will bear dark yellow chromosomes and half light yellow chromosomes, and this will also be true of the sperm cells (see Figure 8.3). Fertilization between these gametes could be of several kinds. A sperm cell bearing a dark yellow chromosome could fertilize either an egg bearing a dark yellow chromosome or a light yellow chromosome, and it would be equally possible for a sperm cell bearing a light yellow chromosome to fertilize either of these two types of egg. The possible kinds of fertilizations are shown in Figure 8.4.

The grandchildren in this family would be of three kinds: dark yellow–dark yellow, dark yellow–light yellow, and light yellow–light yellow. Since there would be two ways of producing dark yellow–light yellow, there would be twice as many of them as in each of the other two kinds. If each of the dark yellow chromosomes contains a dominant gene, let us say an imaginary "dark–yellowness trait," three-fourths of the grandchildren will be dark yellow and one-fourth light yellow.

Crosses with a flowering plant called the four-o'clock demonstrate this point very nicely. We start with crosses between one parent from a group of plants that can

FIGURE 8.3 The types of
gametes the children can form.

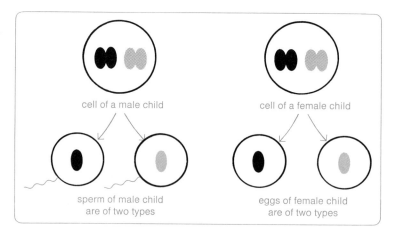

produce only red flowers and another parent from a group of plants producing only
white flowers. Neither of the genes responsible for flower color is dominant. In
crosses between a red and white strain the offspring inherit a gene for red color from
one parent and a gene for white color from the other parent. The flowers of the offspring are all pink. Each pink-flowering plant produces gametes of two kinds, those
with genes for red flower color and those with genes for white flower color. Fertilization between these gametes will produce a third generation of plants of the following types: plants bearing two genes for red flower color, which will be red-
flowered; plants whose *genotype* is red-white, that is, which contain a gene for red
color and a gene for white color, and which will have pink flowers, and plants whose
genotype is white-white, which bear white flowers. These types of plants will occur
in the ratio 1:2:1. This ratio, as is now evident from our discussion of stained
chromosomes, is the direct result of the fact that genes are carried on chromosomes
and of the meiotic and fertilization processes by which parental chromosomes are
distributed to offspring. This understanding dates from the first few years of the
twentieth century, when Sutton pointed out that traits are inherited in the same patterns as those by which chromosomes are distributed. In 1909, the Danish biologist
Wilhelm Johannsen suggested the word *gene* as a replacement for the earlier word
determiner.

Conclusive evidence that genes are parts of chromosomes was provided by Thomas
Hunt Morgan and his students. He selected the fruit fly *Drosophila melanogaster* as
an animal suited for genetic experiments. Fruit fly larvae have salivary glands with
large cells containing giant chromosomes which are easily removed from the larvae,
stained, and observed under a microscope. Fortunately, the fruit fly has only four
pairs of chromosomes, and the investigators were able to become very familiar with
the structural details of the giant chromosomes. They observed that in individual
larvae in which certain regions of the chromosomes were missing, certain traits
would also be missing if the larvae were allowed to become adults. Through these

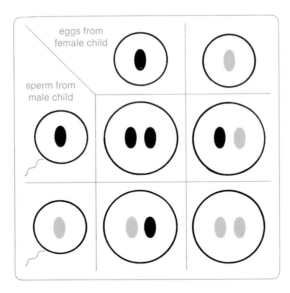

FIGURE 8.4 Possible fertilizations with gametes from the children. Note that the grandchildren
are of three types.

and a great many other similar studies in which structural peculiarities in the
chromosomes were shown to be correlated with changes in the inheritance of certain
traits, *genes were proved to be parts of chromosomes.*

A *gene* may be thought of as a region of a chromosome that can be identified as
having a role in the development of a trait. Genes are arranged in linear sequence
along the chromosomes. The genes at identical regions on a pair of homologous
chromosomes relate to the same trait, but they do not always cause the same form of
the trait. For example, the gene on one chromosome may be for redness in four-
o'clock flowers while the gene on the other chromosome in the homologous pair
may be for whiteness. These alternate forms of genes at specific regions of
homologous chromosomes are called *alleles.* The gene for redness is an allele of the
gene for whiteness.

SOME TERMS AND CONCEPTS

Mendel and others investigating heredity recognized that one allele may interfere with the expression of the other. The one that is expressed is termed the *dominant* gene, and the one whose property is not manifested in the presence of the dominant allele is termed *recessive.* Complete masking of one allele by another, as
observed in peas by Mendel, is very uncommon, however. Usually it is a question
of the *degree* to which each allele is expressed.

Homozygous and *heterozygous* are the terms used to describe whether given pairs of
genes, or alleles, are identical. If both genes present are for redness, the organism is
said to be *homozygous.* If the pair of genes includes one gene for redness and one
for whiteness, the organism is *heterozygous.* The common name for homozygous

organisms is *pure-breeding* since they can produce gametes bearing genes for only one form of the trait. Individuals heterozygous for one or more traits are often called *hybrids.*

Johannsen not only originated the term gene but also differentiated between cause-and-effect relationships in heredity. He designated as the *genotype* the set of genes responsible, along with the effects of the *environment,* for the development of the visible traits of an offspring. These observable, measurable traits he designated the *phenotype.* For example, red and white flowers, blue and brown eyes, height, blood type, intelligence, and other such traits are all phenotypes. By studying the ways in which phenotypes are inherited, it is possible to figure out what genes in the organism are responsible for given phenotypic traits. These genes constitute the genotype of the organism for the properties in question. Thus from studies of phenotypes, genotypes can be determined, and, knowing these, the phenotypes can be predicted.

MODERN INTERPRETATION OF MENDEL'S WORK

With the knowledge that chromosomes are packages of genes we can now see the reason for Mendel's results. Mendel pictured a pair of "determiners" for each of the seven traits he studied. These determiners did not blend with each other but remained segregated and thus behaved as individual particles. Mendel's particulate determiners correspond to our genes. He found that a pair of genes does not blend with other pairs of genes. It is now obvious why such results are obtained. A pair of genes for a trait cannot blend, because they are on separate homologous chromosomes, which do not blend. Furthermore, pairs of genes for two traits will not blend if they are on separate pairs of chromosomes.

MONOHYBRID CROSSES

A monohybrid cross involves genes for a single trait. Mendel began with a cross between homozygous round and homozygous wrinkled peas and produced heterozygous round hybrids, which he allowed to self-fertilize to form a third generation. The fact that the recessive wrinkledness trait reappeared in the third generation in a ratio of 3:1 led him to suggest that members of a gene pair do not blend.

Students are usually less interested in ratios of pea plants than they are in such questions as: What are the chances my children will have pattern baldness? Is there any chance that my son will be a hemophiliac?

A human trait which seems to be determined by a single pair of genes and which demonstrates dominance and recessiveness is the trait called *tongue rolling.* You can easily determine as you read this sentence whether you can roll the sides of your tongue together into a trough or tube. The ability to roll your tongue is inherited as a dominant trait, and the inability is recessive. We shall refer to the trait as *roller* versus *nonroller* and symbolize the genes by *R* for roller and *r* for nonroller.

If one parent is a homozygous roller and the other parent is a homozygous nonroller, the genotypes of the parents in the cross are *RR* × *rr.* This actually means that one parent has a pair of chromosomes which both bear *R* genes and the other parent has a pair of chromosomes both of which carry *r* genes. For the trait of tongue rolling one parent can produce gametes bearing only genes for roller while the other can contribute only genes for nonroller. Fertilizations of these two classes of gametes would produce hybrids, heterozygous children with the genotype *Rr,* and the roller phenotype (see Figure 8.5). When each of these hybrid *Rr* children in turn produces children, their gametes will be of two classes, *R*-bearing and *r*-bearing. Fertilizations between these two classes of gametes produce the genotypes in Figure 8.6: The various combinations possible are *R* with *R, R* with *r,* and *r* with *r.* The genotypes *RR* and *Rr* produce the roller phenotype, and the genotype *rr* produces a nonroller phenotype. This exemplifies the fact that the genes we are discussing are actually on chromosomes and that if we placed our roller and nonroller genes on the "dark yellow" and "light yellow" chromosomes discussed at the beginning of this chapter, we would find the ratios of chromosomes and genes to be the same. Genes are parts of chromosomes, and for the cases we have so far discussed the behavior of genes in their transmission from one generation to the next can be predicted simply by following the transmission of the chromosomes and their genetic cargo from one generation to the next, by way of the gametes.

As we have seen, *pairs* of genes for different traits remain segregated from each other in inheritance. Thus Mendel found that each of the seven pairs of genes for the

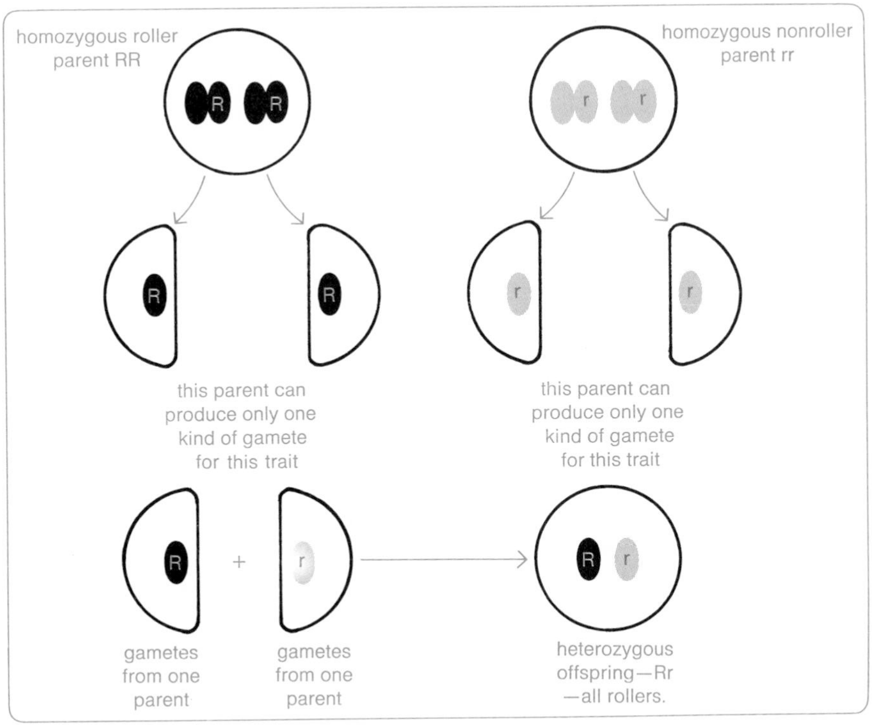

DIHYBRID CROSSES

FIGURE 8.5 How chromosomes bearing genes for the ability to roll the tongue are inherited. If parents are homozygous for opposite forms of the trait, all the children will be heterozygous; that is, they will all be hybrid for this trait.

FIGURE 8.6 Transmission of tongue-rolling to children of parents who are both hybrid for this trait. Each parent is called a monohybrid and their mating is called a monohybrid cross. Note that because of dominance their children will be three-fourths roller and one-fourth nonroller. As each child is born, the chance that it will be a roller is 3 out of 4.

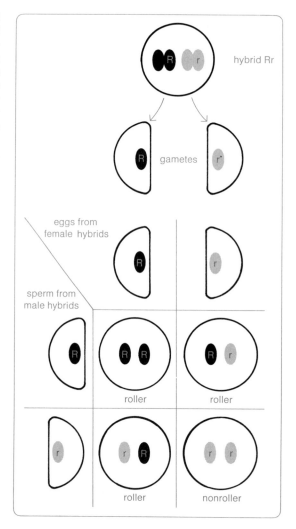

seven traits remained separate from each other and were independently assorted during the formation of gametes. For example, the pair of genes for seed shape (round versus wrinkled) and the pair of genes for seed color (yellow versus green) were segregated from each other. This concept is known as Mendel's law of independent assortment. The independent assortment of genes can be demonstrated, however, *only when the pairs of genes in question are on different pairs of chromosomes*. The independent assortment of genes actually relies upon *independent assortment of the chromosomes* containing the genes. To show how this principle works let us again return to an imaginary experiment in which we apply colored dye to particular chromosomes.

Earlier in this chapter, we figuratively colored one pair of the chromosomes of the father dark yellow and the same pair of the mother light yellow. Now, let us color a second pair of chromosomes dark gray and light gray in the father and mother respectively; this experiment is diagrammed in Figure 8.7. We start with a male parent homozygous for dark yellow and dark gray chromosomes and a female parent homozygous for light yellow and light gray. The father produces sperm cells bearing one dark yellow and one dark gray chromosome. The mother produces eggs bearing a light yellow and a light gray chromosome for these same two chromosomes. Fertilization between these sperm cells and eggs, as Figure 8.7 shows, produces fertilized eggs bearing one dark yellow and one light yellow chromosome in one homologous pair and one dark gray and one light gray chromosome in the other homologous pair.

When these children mature, they could produce gametes with four different combinations of colored chromosomes. These possibilities are diagrammed in Figure 8.8, which shows the genotypes and phenotypes which would result from random fertilizations among these gametes. Four kinds of gametes are possible: dark yellow and dark gray, light yellow and light gray, dark yellow and light gray, and light yellow

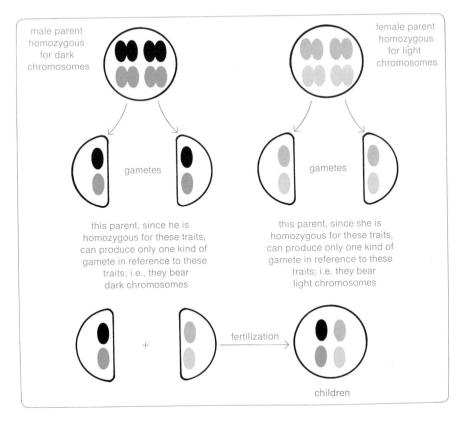

FIGURE 8.7 Pattern of transmission of two pairs of homologous chromosomes from homozygous parents to their children. The children are all heterozygous for these traits.

FIGURE 8.8   The various ways
chromosomes can line up vertically. This causes the variety of
gametes a parent may produce
other than that due to mutation.

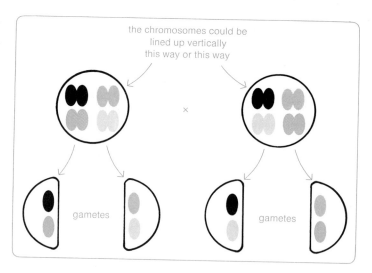

the chromosomes could be
lined up vertically
this way or this way

gametes   gametes

and dark gray.   This would be true only if the dark yellow and light yellow pair of
homologous chromosomes were able to assort themselves independently of the dark
gray and light gray pair of homologous chromosomes.   (You might want to go
through the exercise described using pennies and nickels instead of dark yellow and
light yellow chromosomes and dimes and quarters instead of dark gray and light gray
chromosomes.)

A more true-to-life example may be used to demonstrate how the inheritance of
genes will follow this pattern.   In the 1930s it was discovered that about 70 percent
of the college students in the United States could taste a harmless chemical compound called phenylthiocarbamide (PTC).   Further study showed that the taster-nontaster trait is due to a single pair of alleles and that the allele for taster is dominant
over the allele for nontaster.   Let us pretend that the allele for taster is on the dark
gray chromosome and the allele for nontaster is on the light gray chromosome.

If a person homozygous for tongue rolling and PTC tasting is married to a person
homozygous for nonroller and nontaster, all their children will be dihybrids; that is,
they will be heterozygous for two traits, the ability to taste PTC and the ability to roll
their tongues (see Figure 8.9).   Since the ability to do either of these things is dominant, all their children will express only the dominant phenotypes.   Each child can
produce four kinds of gametes (we described them by color of chromosome earlier);
if we call the gene by the name of the trait it determines, these are taster-roller, non-
taster-nonroller, taster-nonroller, and nontaster-roller (see Figure 8.10).   The possible fertilizations between these four kinds of sperm cells from the males and the four
kinds of eggs from the females are shown in Figure 8.11.   (Since matings of this kind
are regarded as incestuous and are the subject of social taboos in human society, our
knowledge of such crosses comes from experiments with other organisms.)   If you
count the numbers of each kind of phenotype produced by the genotypes in the
sixteen squares in Figure 8.11, you will find that nine-sixteenths will be tasters and

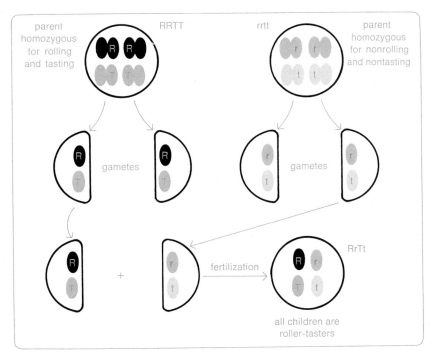

FIGURE 8.9 If rolling-nonrolling of tongue is associated with dark yellow and light yellow chromosomes and tasting-nontasting of PTC with the dark gray and light gray chromosomes, the pattern of inheritance of genes is seen to be the same as the chromosomes of which they are a part.

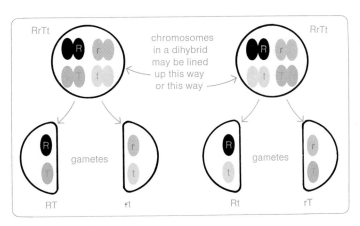

FIGURE 8.10 Each child produced in Figure 8.9 can produce four kinds of gametes for these traits because there are two ways in which the chromosomes can be lined up vertically.

rollers, three-sixteenths will be tasters and nonrollers, three-sixteenths will be nontasters and rollers, and one-sixteenth will be nontasters and nonrollers.

Actually, these probabilities could have been calculated without filling in the time-consuming squares with the sixteen possible fertilizations. Since tasting of PTC and curling of the tongue are determined by genes on two separate pairs of chromosomes, we may think of the two traits as two separate events. If we consider

FIGURE 8.11 Parents heterozygous for tongue rolling and PTC tasting will produce children with traits in the frequency of nine-sixteenths roller-taster, three-sixteenths roller-nontaster, three-sixteenths nonroller-taster, and one-sixteenth nonroller-nontaster.

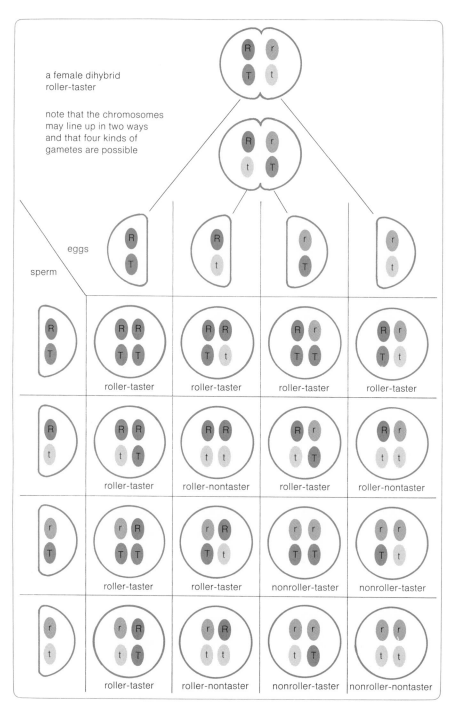

a cross between persons heterozygous for taster-nontaster, we can see that three-fourths of their children will be tasters and one-fourth nontasters. Likewise, if we consider these same two persons as being heterozygous for roller-nonroller, we can see that three-fourths of their children will be rollers and one-fourth nonrollers. We can calculate what the chances will be for children combining both kinds of traits. For example, how many of the children will be both tasters and curlers? Mathematically, the chance for separate events occuring simultaneously is the product of the chances for the separate events. Therefore, we simply multiply the chances for tasters in the children ($\frac{3}{4}$) times the chances for rollers ($\frac{3}{4}$), and we get $\frac{9}{16}$, the result we obtain by filling in the squares in Figure 8.11. Table 8.1 demonstrates how all the chances can be quickly calculated.

TABLE 8.1

CHANCES FOR ONE TRAIT × CHANCES FOR ONE TRAIT = CHANCES FOR COMBINED TRAITS

Rollers $\frac{3}{4}$	Tasters $\frac{3}{4}$	Rollers and tasters $\frac{9}{16}$
Rollers $\frac{3}{4}$	Nontasters $\frac{1}{4}$	Rollers and nontasters $\frac{3}{16}$
Nonrollers $\frac{1}{4}$	Tasters $\frac{3}{4}$	Nonrollers and tasters $\frac{3}{16}$
Nonrollers $\frac{1}{4}$	Nontasters $\frac{1}{4}$	Nonrollers and nontasters $\frac{1}{16}$

LINKED GENES

Mendel was very fortunate in the traits he chose for his experiments because each is determined by genes contained in separate pairs of chromosomes. Today we know that many genes are found on any one chromosome. For example, the fruit fly has only four pairs of chromosomes, but about 15,000 genes have been recognized on these four pairs, and many more obviously exist. In other words, many thousands of genes must be present on each chromosome.

Genes located on the same chromosome are called *linked genes*. None of the traits studied by Mendel were linked. We can, however, set up a purely hypothetical example based on human beings. We can infer that hair color and eye color are caused by linked genes, since blond hair and blue eyes seem to be as natural a combination as dark hair and dark eyes. Most people with dark hair have dark eyes, and most blonds have blue eyes. Yet, we know many people who are blond-haired and brown-eyed and others who are dark-haired and blue-eyed. How can this happen if the genes for blond hair and blue eyes are on one chromosome together and the genes for dark hair and dark eyes are together on the homologous chromosome? To be dark-haired and blue-eyed would mean that at least one of the chromosomes of the homologous pair has a gene for the dominant dark hair trait, while both chromosomes contain a gene for the recessive blue eye trait. That is, a gene for blue eyes must be present on the same chromosome as a gene for dark hair. How could this happen? Hair color and eye color are not individually due to single pairs of genes but are, instead, caused by many pairs of genes—a concept discussed later in this chapter. But, because these traits lend themselves to the present discussion, we shall pretend that each of the two traits is caused by a single pair of genes.

During the stage of meiosis when homologous chromosomes pair, the chromosomes of each homologous pair touch, and bridges often form between them. Sometimes the chromosomes loop over each other. As the pairs separate later in meiosis the chromosomes may break in such a way that the new chromosomes formed consist partly of segments of the chromosomes with which they were originally paired. For example, a simple exchange may take place so that if one chromosome had genes *ABCDEFGHIJ* and the homologous chromosome had *abcdefghij*, they might now have *ABCDEfghij* and *abcdeFGHIJ*. Exchange of chromosomal segments at meiosis is called *crossover*. The gametes formed in crossovers contain chromosomes with different packages of genes than those of the ancestral line, as shown in Figure 8.12.

Suppose, for example, a dark-haired, brown-eyed group of Italian men and blond-haired, blue-eyed group of Swedish girls began a settlement on an oceanic island. During the production of the first generation of children, all the sperm cells (from the Italians) would contain genes for dark eyes and hair while all the eggs (from the Swedes) would contain genes for blond hair and genes for blue eyes. All the heterozygous children would demonstrate the dominant dark hair and dark eyes; we recall that we are pretending that each trait is caused by a single pair of genes and that these genes are linked on the same chromosome.

When the children produced gametes, they would be of two kinds. The gametes would be either of dark hair–dark eye genotype or a blond hair–blue eye genotype. Fertilizations among these people would produce grandchildren of either Italian genotype (dark-haired, dark-eyed phenotype), Italian-Swede genotype (dark-haired, dark-eyed phenotype), or Swede-Swede genotype (blond-hair, blue-eyed phenotype). Down through the following centuries all the gametes formed by each generation would bear a chromosome that was either Italian or Swedish in origin and would have the original package of linked genes except when crossover takes place.

If crossover occurs between homologous chromosomes so that one chromosome now has a gene for dark hair and a gene for blue eyes while the homologous chromosome has a gene for blond hair and brown eyes, a new combination of traits could appear in the population (see Figure 8.13). The new combinations are called *recombination types*, and the original combinations are called *parental types*.

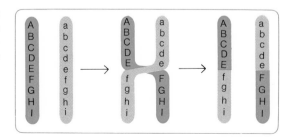

Though crossover is a rare event, its importance is evident: *Crossover produces new combinations of genes.*

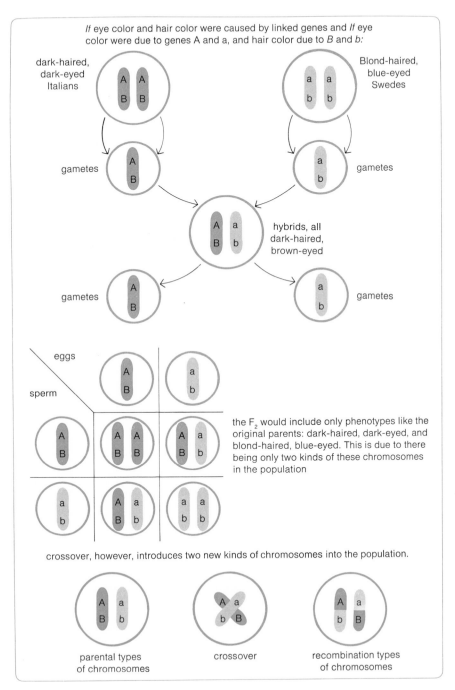

If eye color and hair color were caused by linked genes and If eye color were due to genes A and a, and hair color due to B and b:

dark-haired, dark-eyed Italians

Blond-haired, blue-eyed Swedes

gametes

gametes

hybrids, all dark-haired, brown-eyed

gametes

gametes

eggs

sperm

the F$_2$ would include only phenotypes like the original parents: dark-haired, dark-eyed, and blond-haired, blue-eyed. This is due to there being only two kinds of these chromosomes in the population

crossover, however, introduces two new kinds of chromosomes into the population.

parental types of chromosomes

crossover

recombination types of chromosomes

FIGURE 8.13 Crossover between homologous chromosomes introduces new kinds of chromosomes into a population.

CHROMOSOME MAPPING

The distance between genes on a chromosome can be determined by the rate of crossover between them; this in turn is indicated by the frequency at which recombination types appear in the offspring. If one chromosome has both gene *A* and gene *B* while the other member of the homologous pair has genes *a* and *b*, the chance that crossover may take place between the *A* or *a* region and the *B* or *b* region is directly proportional to the distance between the two regions. The farther apart the two regions are, the greater the chance of a crossover between them. Since the frequency with which crossover takes place between two gene regions on a chromosome indicates their distance apart, it can be used to map the position of genes with reference to each other on the chromosome.

To see how chromosome mapping would work let us consider three traits and assume that all three are determined by genes carried on the same chromosome. Suppose eye color and hair color were each controlled by a single pair of linked genes (actually several pairs of genes acting together determine these phenotypes). Our third trait will be tongue-rolling. We shall refer to the genes for eye color as alleles *A* and *a*, for hair color as alleles *B* and *b*, and for tongue rolling as *R* and *r*, as before.

If recombination types such as dark-haired persons with blue eyes and blond-haired persons with brown eyes make up 10 percent of a particular generation, we can assume that crossover has taken place between the gene *A* and the gene *B* regions of this chromosome in 10 percent of the previous generation of the meiotic cells. Let us say that the percentage of crossover between gene *B* and gene *R* is 5 percent. If we use percentages as map units, we can say that the distance from *A* to *B* is 10 and from *B* to *R* is 5 map units. With this much information we cannot tell whether gene *R* is between genes *A* and *B* or on the other side of gene *B* from *A*. If we also knew that the percentage of recombination between genes *A* and *R* is 15 percent, we could locate gene *R* at a point 5 map units on the other side of gene *B*, away from gene *A* (see Figure 8.14).

THE DETERMINATION OF SEX

For countless years man has wondered how the sex of offspring is determined. Some people believed that boys result if the father is very masculine and girls if the mother is very feminine. Some believed that potions like blood from a rooster or tissue fluid squeezed from the testes of a bull would determine the sex of the child as male when the mother drank them. After the discovery of the ovary and how each ovary releases an egg every other month, it was sometimes believed that the left ovary produced eggs resulting in girls and the right ovary eggs resulting in boys.

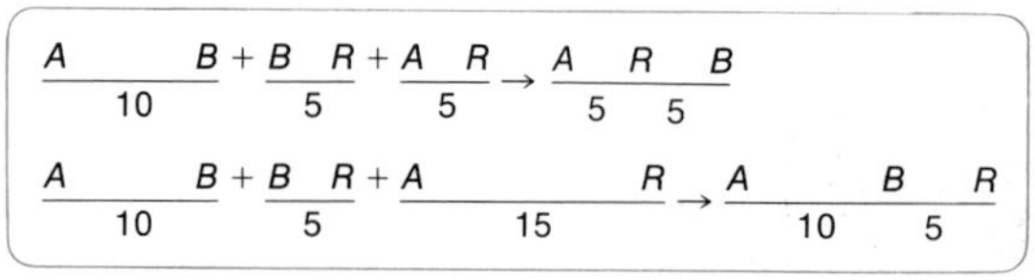

FIGURE 8.14 Knowing whether it is 5 or 15 map units from *A* to *R* helps us to locate point *R* relative to points *A* and *B*. Two possibilities are shown here.

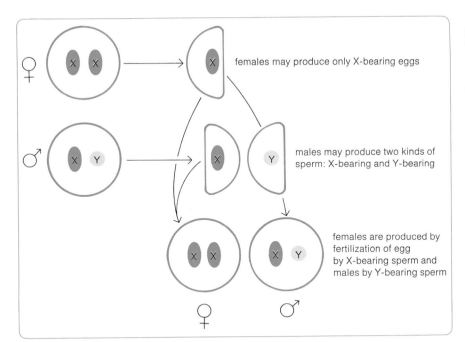

females may produce only X-bearing eggs

males may produce two kinds of
sperp: X-bearing and Y-bearing

females are produced by
fertilization of egg
by X-bearing sperm and
males by Y-bearing sperm

FIGURE 8.15 Sex is determined
by whether an X-bearing or
Y-bearing sperm fertilizes the
X-bearing egg. Females bear two
X chromosomes and males an X
and a Y.

Another belief was that diet determines sex and that a pregnant woman who eats meat will give birth to a boy while one who eats sweets will give birth to a girl.

The true nature of sex determination was not known until after the role of chromosomes in heredity became clear early in the twentieth century. At first it was thought that the 1:1 ratio of sex in offspring was caused by one parent's being homozygous and the other heterozygous for a particular pair of genes. This would produce one-half *AA* and one-half *Aa* generation after generation. (Diagram it to see for yourself.) Further work showed that a single pair of genes is not involved; in fact, it was even questioned whether sex determination is genetic. The solution came when information from two fields, cytology and genetics, was put together. Workers in cytology, the study of cells, noticed that chromosomes exist in pairs and that *the two members of each pair look alike except for a pair of chromosomes from a male.* This discovery was made in fruit flies, but the same is true for many other organisms. In male cells one pair consisted of a long and a short chromosome. Since the meaning was unknown, algebraic symbols for unknowns were applied: The long chromosome was called X and the short one Y. It was postulated that sex is determined by these diverse chromosomes rather than by a single pair of allelic genes. Further studies showed that *females have two* X *chromosomes and males one* X *and one* Y *chromosome.* By this scheme, the female can produce only X-bearing eggs, and the sex of the offspring is determined by the sperm, which can be either X-bearing or Y-bearing (see Figure 8-15).

Thus, the male *determines* the sex of the offspring but he has *no control* over it. It is a 50:50 chance whether an X-bearing or Y-bearing sperm fertilizes the X-bearing egg.

SEX-LINKED GENES

Morgan began his famous experiments with fruit flies to see whether the principles of Mendel applied to animals as well as plants. He found that most of the crosses of various types of fruit flies produced offspring in ratios following the pattern of inheritance described by Mendel in peas. Some traits, however, gave bewildering results because their appearance seemed to be related to sex, and the ratio of the appearance of the traits differed with how the cross had been set up. For example, if a white-eyed female was crossed with a red-eyed male, the offspring included only red-eyed females and white-eyed males. On the other hand, if a red-eyed female was crossed with a white-eyed male, the offspring were all red-eyed. It was found that the genes for this trait in fruit flies were carried on the X chromosome. (The Y chromosome may be considered as a genetic blank in this discussion since in fruit flies the gene for eye color is missing in the Y chromosome.)

The genes carried on the X chromosome are called *sex-linked* since the pattern of their inheritance varies with sex. That is, the pattern of inheritance of sex-linked genes varies according as the genotype is XX or XY. Sex-linked means X-linked! About sixty traits are known to be caused in the human beings by genes on the X chromosome and only one, hairy ear lobes, on the Y chromosome.

The female has a pair of X chromosomes and therefore pairs of genes for sex-linked traits, but males have just one X chromosome and therefore only single genes for sex-linked traits. Thus, a sex-linked gene in a male is expressed even if it is recessive for there is no other allele to dominate over it (see Figure 8.16). Since sex-linked traits in males involve only one gene, the frequency of sex-linked recessive traits is much higher in males than in females. For example, the well-known sex-linked trait color blindness is found in 8 percent of American men and only 0.5 percent of American women.

FIGURE 8.16 Recessive sex-linked traits appear much more frequently in males than in females because their alleles cannot be present in males. Males are haploid for sex-linked traits.

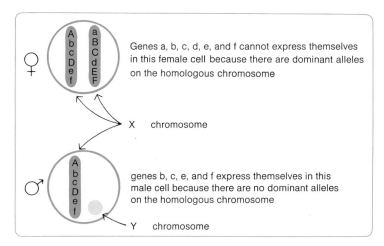

Genes a, b, c, d, e, and f cannot express themselves in this female cell because there are dominant alleles on the homologous chromosome

X   chromosome

genes b, c, e, and f express themselves in this male cell because there are no dominant alleles on the homologous chromosome

Y   chromosome

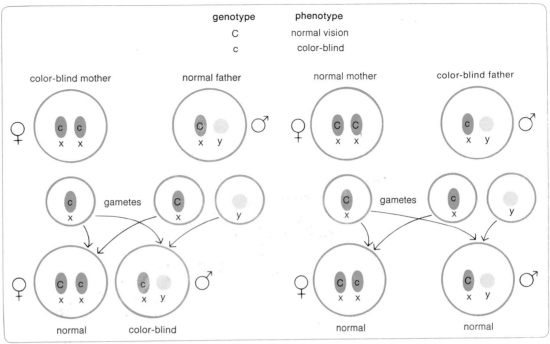

FIGURE 8.17 Sex-linked inheritance of color vision. Frequency of appearance of sex-linked traits depends on whether it is the mother or the father who bears the trait.

Sex-linked genes are inherited by a male from his mother since he must receive his Y chromosome from his father (Figure 8.17). The mother of a color-blind man must be either color-blind or a carrier (heterozygous). A color-blind daughter must have a color-blind father and a mother who is either color-blind or a carrier. In sex-linked (X-linked) inheritance, a heterozygous mother may transmit the gene to half her sons and half her daughters, but the affected father transmits the gene to all his daughters and none of his sons.

SEX-INFLUENCED GENES

Some traits show a different ratio or frequency in the sexes but for a reason that is not related to the X and Y chromosomes. Instead, the genes are on other pairs of chromosomes, and the expression of the gene is *influenced* by sex hormones. For example, the male hormone testosterone causes the gene for baldness to be dominant in males and recessive in females. If two heterozygous parents mate, the chances for bald or normal children are as shown in Figure 8.18. Some forms of baldness, of course, are not genetic, but result from disease or some other environmental cause.

MULTIPLE ALLELES

Alleles are the alternate forms of genes located at a particular spot on a homologous pair of chromosomes. Since the chromosomes exist in pairs, there can be only two alleles for any trait in any *one organism*. But, *in a whole population*, there can be

FIGURE 8.18 Sex-influenced inheritance. Sex hormone testosterone determines whether gene for baldness (B_2) is dominant or recessive. These genes are not carried on the X and Y chromosomes.

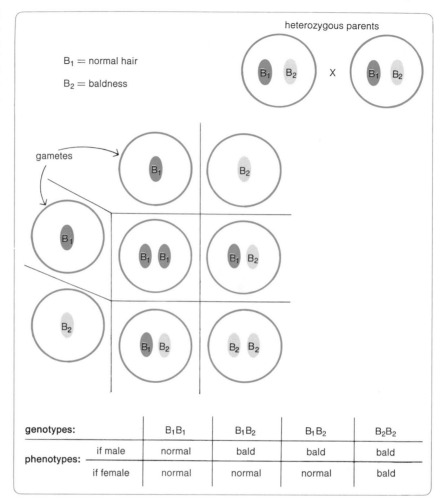

genotypes:		B_1B_1	B_1B_2	B_1B_2	B_2B_2
phenotypes:	if male	normal	bald	bald	bald
	if female	normal	normal	normal	bald

more than two alleles for any given trait. A well-known example is the human blood type. Types A, B, AB, and O depend on whether proteins A or B are present in the red blood cells. The presence of these proteins depends on the presence of alleles A, B, or O. Neither of the alleles A or B is dominant over the other, but both are dominant over O. The relationships are as shown in Table 8.2. A chromosome that bears a gene for blood type may have any one of three alleles, A, B, or O. Since a person has a *pair* of chromosomes, someone with blood type O or AB has only one genotype (OO or AB), but a person with blood types A or B may be homozygous or heterozygous (AA, AO, BB, or BO). The genotypes of the persons of blood types A or B can be determined from the blood types of their parents or offspring. With organisms other than man, it is much easier to settle such questions. A *testcross* is set up

TABLE 8.2

PHENOTYPE	GENOTYPE	TYPE OF THIS PROTEIN IN RED BLOOD CELLS
A	AA or AO	A
B	BB or BO	B
AB	AB	A and B
O	OO	None

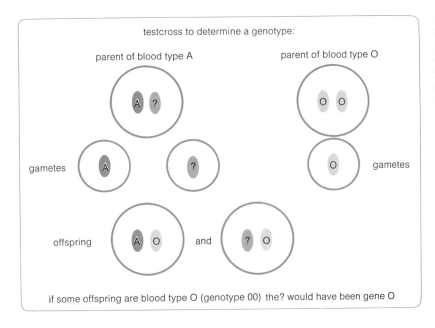

in which the organism in question is crossed with a homozygous recessive so that its recessive gene will allow the two genes in the "unknown" to be expressed. If it were possible with human beings, a parent of blood type A or B would be crossed with persons of blood type O to determine whether he were homozygous or heterozygous. If any offspring resulted with blood type O, it could be assumed that the parent was AO or BO (see Figure 8.19); if not, the parent must have been AA or BB.

INCOMPLETE DOMINANCE

It has become increasingly clear that the dominance of one allele over the other that Mendel described is a rarity. Few genes have such clear-cut dominance and recessiveness. The heterozygote commonly has a phenotype intermediate between the parents. It often looks *as if* blending had taken place, but the fact that blending has not occurred is demonstrated when the heterozygotes are crossed. The alleles segregate from each other and produce gametes bearing the two forms of alleles. An example of incomplete dominance would be a cross between a curly-haired person and a straight-haired person. The resulting children would have wavy hair. Mating between these wavy-haired persons would produce children with a one-fourth chance of curly hair, a two-fourths chance of wavy hair, and a one-fourth chance of straight hair. (Diagram this to see why.) If dominance had been present, the ratio would have been 3:1. Apparently, in incomplete dominance, both alleles express themselves, and the resulting phenotype is a combination of the two genetic messages.

MULTIPLE GENES   Mendel saw a picture of inheritance in which each trait is determined by a pair of particular genes separate from each other and demonstrating dominance. We have seen this concept modified by the realization that genes are on chromosomes and are linked with all the other genes on that chromosome. We have also learned that dominance is a rarity and not the rule. Now we shall see that cases where one trait is due to a single pair of genes are also rare.

Traits determined by a single pair of genes, with or without dominance, would occur in only two or three variations of the trait. For example, peas would be only tall or short, round or wrinkled, etc.; four-o'clock flowers could only be red, white, or pink; human beings could be only tall or short, dumb or smart. Obviously, most traits do not fall into limited categories but form a continuous variation from one extreme to the other. Variation is due to a range of environmental factors such as nutrition, but it is also clear that a range of variation in a trait can be due to *several pairs of genes acting in an additive fashion.*

Determination of traits by the action of more than one pair of genes is called *multiple gene inheritance.* One of its first investigators was Davenport, who studied skin color in Negroes and whites in Bermuda and Jamaica. He concluded that skin color is determined by two pairs of genes on different pairs of chromosomes without any dominance being involved. One allele of each pair causes production of brown melanin granules in the skin, and the other allele does not cause pigment formation. If we use capital letters to stand for alleles that cause pigmentation and small letters to stand for alleles that do not, we see that skin color could range from black (*AABB*) to white (*aabb*). A person with black skin color would produce gametes bearing *AB*, and a person with white skin would produce gametes with *ab*. The offspring of such a cross would all be mulattos with medium brown skin and the genotype *AaBb*. Offspring of mulattos of this genotype can vary from white to black, as shown in Figure 8.20.

Thus, if two heterozygous mulattos mate, the possibility for a child being black or white are 1 out of 16, the chances for dark brown or tan are 4 out of 16, and the chances for mulatto like the parents are 6 out of 16. These chances describe statistical probabilities, and a tremendously large family would be necessary to demonstrate an actual range of distribution of 1:4:6:4:1. To compound the complexity it has been recently suggested that five pairs of genes instead of two are involved in skin-color determination in crosses between blacks and whites. Without attempting

to diagram such a cross, we can imagine the enormous numbers of different phenotypes possible with so many genes determining the skin color.

The pattern of inheritance of skin color shows that a cross between white and any of
the other four types cannot produce any offspring darker than the nonwhite parent.
And, since skin color involves incomplete dominance, it is impossible for a white to
be a carrier of genes for darker pigmentation.

FIGURE 8.20 Inheritance of skin
color in blacks and whites is determined by at least two pairs of
genes. These genes are not linked
and do not possess dominance.

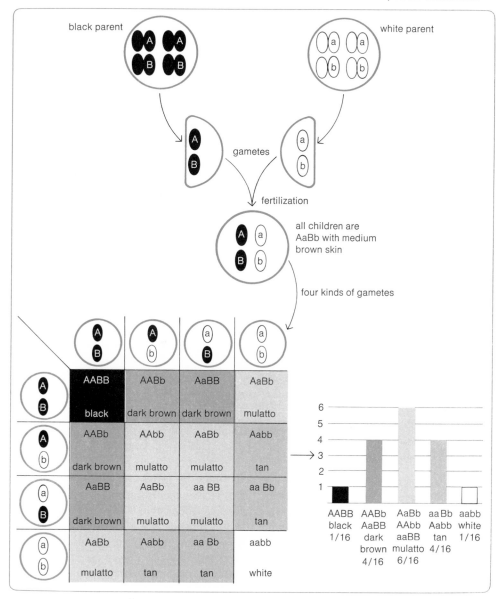

Other examples of traits involving multiple genes with incomplete dominance in man are height, weight, and intelligence. To get some idea of their inheritance just substitute the appropriate phenotypes into the above diagram. You will then have a better understanding of the source of the "normal curve of distribution" of these traits in the general population.

GENE INTERACTION

In the early days of genetics it was believed that traits are determined by separate pairs of genes acting independently of other pairs of genes. This belief permitted many basic principles of genetics to be discovered, and it still allows beginning students in biology to develop a clear picture of gene and chromosome behavior. But, in reality, *a trait may be determined by many different genes* acting in concert. By 1915, Morgan had found that the normal red eye color of fruit flies was produced by the joint action of at least thirteen different pairs of genes. It became evident that traits result from the combined actions of many physiological processes within the organism. Genes express themselves by directing the synthesis of enzymes, which then interact in particular ways to permit the functioning of the organism. There may, in fact, be many genes whose sole function is to affect the activity of other genes.

NATURE OR NURTURE?

Darwin, one of the greatest naturalists of the nineteenth century, believed that the environment caused inheritable changes. This idea was championed by fellow naturalists until the second decade of this century. Naturalists traditionally dealt with organisms in the field and felt that traits were interpretable in terms of the environmental pressures to which the organisms were exposed. With the rediscovery of Mendel's paper and the growth of the new field of genetics, the geneticists developed an equally narrow view that all traits were caused by the action of genes functioning independently of the environment. This obsolete disagreement has been dubbed the *nature-nurture controversy*, in which nature meant genes and nurture meant environment.

Psychologists applied these concepts to the study of man and his traits, and two camps developed, the *hereditarians* and the *environmentalists*. Remnants of their argument still persist today. Some psychologists argue that the nature of the human mind is affected more by genes and others believe the environment to be more important. The relative effect of nature or nurture is a question of *degree*, for it should certainly not be debatable whether traits are determined by genes *or* by environment. The brilliant geneticist Johannsen, who developed the concepts of genotype and phenotype, demonstrated in various ways that particular phenotypes are caused by *interaction* between genes and environment. This relationship is described by the following diagram:

With man it is obvious that an environment offering good nutrition will cause the sizes of the people it feeds to be as big as their inherited sets of genes will allow. There are many other examples of the environment influencing how genes are expressed. For example, the Chinese primrose develops red flowers if grown at 55 to 65°F but white flowers at 95°F; a strain of *Drosophila* develops branched legs if grown at low temperatures and normal legs at normal temperatures; a strain of corn retains white kernels if the husks are kept in place but turns red if they are peeled back. These are just a few crude examples of how environment can influence gene expression. In the cases which interest us most, such as the development of intelligence, the interaction of environment and heredity appears to be an extremely subtle and complex matter.

Some traits, of course, are not affected by the environment: blood type, eye color, and the ability to taste PTC are not affected by the environment in which the person lives. Most traits, however, are determined by interaction between genes and environment during embryological development and later in the individual's life. During the 1920s geneticists and naturalists (and many psychologists) formed the integrated view that traits are not caused by *either* genes or environment but by an interaction between them. The environment cannot cause an organism to develop in a fashion that contradicts genetic systems of control, and the genes cannot express themselves if the necessary nutrients and other environmental factors are not present. Thus the genotype and the environment control and limit each other in the development of the phenotype of the individual, whether the traits in question are anatomical, physiological, or behavioral.

Some human diseases, however, have relatively little to do with environmental effects. For example, a type of mental retardation called *phenylketonuria* (PKU) is found in persons with a homozygous recessive genotype designated *pp*. Without the dominant gene *P* an enzyme is not produced that is necessary for the conversion of the amino acid phenylalanine into the amino acid tyrosine. Instead, phenyl-pyruvic acid is produced, which apparently produces mental retardation by damaging organs and tissues such as the brain. Early recognition and treatment with enzymes or diet may prevent this damage. If so, the environment will have been altered by man to modify his heredity.

Examples of how genes can determine behavioral traits in man are furnished by Huntington's chorea and Down's syndrome (formerly called mongoloid idiocy), two conditions which display opposite types of personality. The first is inherited but does not express itself until middle age or later, when the muscles and nerves are affected shaking and jerking result, and the victim develops a very unpleasant personality. Down's syndrome is also inherited but is apparent at birth. Victims have a very low intelligence but a very pleasant personality and are cheerful and friendly. Thus, two genetically caused diseases demonstrate patterns of behavior which are related to specific genotypes. Unfortunately, no environmental remedies are known which will alter the course of these two diseases.

MUTATIONS

One of the sources of variation within a population was described in Chapter 7, namely, sexual recombination, the reshuffling of genes through sexual reproduction. Another form of genetic reshuffling occurs in crossovers. A further source of variation in the genetic material is *mutation,* an inheritable change in the genetic material. Mutations may occur in the *gene* or may involve the entire *chromosome.*

Gene mutations, which may be caused by mistakes in the way genes duplicate themselves, are considered in the following chapter at more length. The alterations resulting from such mistakes will be copied through the future generations of gene replication.

Chromosome mutations may occur through mistakes in *meiosis.* During meiosis the chromosomes normally pair up in the middle of the cell and are eventually pulled to opposite sides of the cell. Sometimes, however, both chromosomes of a pair go to the *same* side, causing one daughter cell to have both homologous chromosomes and the other to lack them. This is called *chromosomal nondisjunction.* Several human illnesses are due to chromosome abnormality of this type. Klinefelter's disease characterizes males with very small testes, sparse body hair, feminine breast development, and *an extra* X *chromosome* (XXY *genotype*). Either the egg or the sperm brought an extra chromosome to the fertilization. Turner's syndrome is a condition in women marked by short stature, webbed neck, low-set ears, broad shieldlike chest, underdeveloped breasts, small uterus, and undeveloped ovaries. A chromosome count reveals *just one* X *chromosome* (XO *genotype*). Either the egg or sperm lacked the other sex chromosome at fertilization.

Down's syndrome (mongoloid idiocy), mentioned above, is due to *an extra chromosome,* number 21. This is caused by nondisjunction of chromosome number 21 during the formation of egg or sperm. One daughter cell gets two number 21 chromosomes while the other gets none. The daughter cell lacking chromosome number 21 would die. Thus far, no people have been found with fewer than 44 *autosomes* (the chromosomes other than X and Y). A person may live with only one sex chromosome (Turner's syndrome), but apparently all forty-four autosomes are necessary for life.

We have previously discussed *chromosome breakage* in connection with crossover. In crossovers chromosome segments may be simply exchanged so that no genes are missing from either chromosome, though the *sequence* and combinations of alleles on each chromosome become different. Unequal exchange of chromosomal material resulting in extra genes on one chromosome and missing genes on the other may

TABLE 8.3*

DOMINANT	RECESSIVE
Hair:	
Dark	Blond
Nonred	Red
Curly	Straight
Abundant on body	Little on body
Early baldness (dominant in male)	Normal
White forelock	Self-colored
Skin:	
Piebald (skin and hair spotted with white)	Self-colored
Pigmented skin, hair, eyes	Albinism
Black skin (5 pairs of genes, dominance incomplete)	White skin
Ichthyosis (scaly skin)	Normal
Epidermis bullosa (sensitiveness to slight abrasions)	Normal
Normal	Absence of sweat glands
Mouth and teeth:	
Absence of enamel	Normal
Broad lips	Thin lips
Eyes:	
Long eyelashes	Short eyelashes
Large eyes	Small eyes
Brown iris	Blue or gray iris
Hazel or green iris	Blue or gray iris
Mongolian fold	No fold
Congenital cataract	Normal
Nearsightedness	Normal vision
Farsightedness	Normal vision
Astigmatism	Normal vision
Aniridia (absence of iris)	Normal
Congenital displacement of lens	Normal
Ears:	
Free ear lobes	Attached earlobes
Nose:	
Broad nostrils	Narrow nostrils
High, narrow bridge	Low, broad bridge
Roman	Straight
Hands and feet:	
Polydactyly (more than 5 fingers or toes)	Normal
Syndactyly (webbing between some fingers or toes)	Normal
Brachydactyly (short fingers or toes)	Normal
Circulatory system:	
Hypertension (high blood pressure)	Normal
Normal	Hemophilia (sex-linked)
Respiratory system:	
Resistance to tuberculosis	Susceptibility to tuberculosis
Endocrine system:	
Normal	Diabetes mellitus
Nervous system and senses:	
Tasters of PTC	Nontasters
Normal	Congenital deafness
Normal	Schizophrenia (several pairs of genes involved)

* Adapted from C. A. Villee, *Biology*, 4th ed., W. B. Saunders Company, Philadelphia, 1962.

also occur, however. *Additions* or *deletions* can cause dramatic hereditary effects in the offspring.

The appearance of gene and chromosome mutations seems to be due to chance, but various agents have been found to increase that chance. Temperature, ionizing radiation, mustard gas, coal tars, and numerous other agents have an effect on *mutation rates*. Also, the rate at which a gene will mutate seems to vary with the particular gene and the species of the organism. In man and many other living things, most genes spontaneously mutate about once in 100,000 to 1 million gametes per generation. This may result from mistakes in copying of the gene or from chromosome breakage. If there are 10,000 genes in a hypothetical organism, then there would be about 1 gamete in 100 bearing a mutation. Since there are usually millions of individuals in each species, you can imagine the tremendous number of new mutations in the population with each new generation. Mutations supply the new genetic material, and sexual reproduction brings them together in various combinations. The effect of the expression of these diverse combinations of genes is the *variation of traits in populations*. Variation in genotype is one of the fundamental creative forces in evolution by natural selection.

HUMAN HEREDITY   The study of human heredity is more difficult than the genetic study of many other organisms for several reasons, among them being the fact that (1) testcrosses cannot be used, (2) human beings have only a few offspring each generation, and (3) a period of 20 or more years must elapse between generations, so that data are usually available only from one or two or a few generations.

There has been great progress in human heredity over the past decades, however, and problems in this field are being studied intensively with new methods of statistical analysis. The genetics of some traits of man which have been studied are indicated in Table 8.3.

REVIEW QUESTIONS
1   Why do human beings give rise to human beings?
2   Describe why gametes may be said to be controlled samplings of chromosomes from parental cells.
3   Define chromosome, gene, allele, dominant, recessive, gene penetration, homozygous, heterozygous, hybrid, genotype, and phenotype.
4   Define linked genes, crossing-over, chromosome mapping, X and Y chromosomes, multiple alleles, multiple genes, gene interaction, gene mutations, nondisjunction, and chromosome breakage.
5   Why are some traits inherited in a different pattern in males and females?
6   What is the difference between multiple allele inheritance and multiple gene inheritance?
7   Why are dominant forms of traits not always the most abundant in a population?

Beadle, G., and M. Beadle: *The Language of Life,* Doubleday & Company, Inc., Garden City, N.J., 1966.   A Nobel Prize winner and his wife discuss the history of genetics and its principles in a manner easily understood by nonscientists.

Lerner, I. M.: *Heredity, Evolution, and Society,* W. H. Freeman and Company, San Francisco, 1968.   A somewhat technical description of the biological bases of many social issues.

Levine, R. P.: *Genetics,* Holt, Rinehart and Winston, Inc., New York, 1962.   A concise, technical, but clear description of genetics.

Srb, A. M., R. D. Owen, and R. S. Edgar: *General Genetics,* W. H. Freeman and Company, San Francisco, 1965.   A widely used textbook.

Stern, C.: *Principles of Human Genetics,* W. F. Freeman and Company, San Francisco, 1960.   Technical but clear presentation of heredity and environment, eugenics, race, and radiation effects.

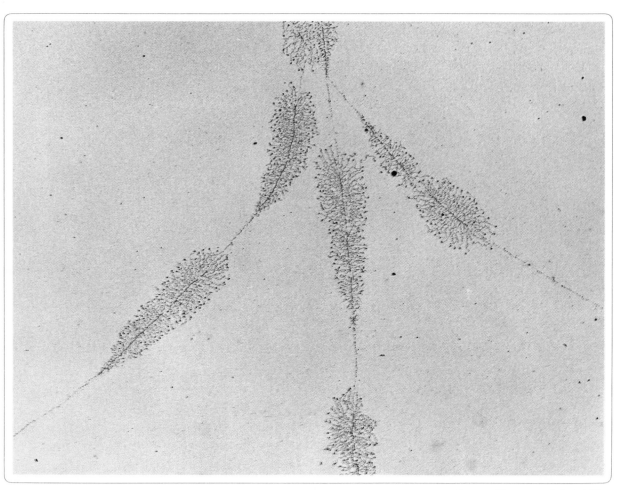

Genes. (Courtesy of O. L. Miller, Jr., and Barbara R. Beatty, Biology Division, Oak Ridge National Laboratory.)

Chapter 9

Genetics: How Are Genes Expressed as Traits?

. . . for I am fearfully and wonderfully made. . . . Psalms 139:14

In 1869, just 3 years after Mendel published his paper describing patterns of inheritance in peas, DNA was discovered by Friedrich Miescher, a young Swiss biochemist. Miescher applied hydrochloric acid and pepsin, an enzyme that breaks down proteins, to pus from hospital patients. Pus is a dense suspension of white blood cells of certain types. These cells have prominent nuclei, and the treatment Miescher used left the nucleus of each cell intact, although slightly shriveled, while dissolving away the cytoplasm. From this preparation of isolated nuclei Miescher extracted a substance which was resistant to alkali and contained phosphorus, as well as carbon, hydrogen, oxygen, and nitrogen. Both the alkali resistance and the composition differentiated the new substance from proteins, which have no phosphorus and are hydrolyzed by alkali. Miescher isolated this phosphorus-containing nuclear component by precipitating it with alcohol, and he named it *nuclein* to indicate its source in the nuclei of cells. Within a short time he had also found nuclein in the sperm of the Rhine salmon, which in those days used to swim up as far as Basle, where Miescher worked, to breed. The substance Miescher had found is the nucleic acid we call today deoxyribonucleic acid (DNA).

In the 1890s several cytologists suggested that DNA is located in the chromosomes of the cell nuclei on the basis of staining experiments with fixed tissue sections. The chemistry of DNA began to be unraveled a few years later by the German chemist Albrecht Kossel, who began the work of analyzing the components of which deoxyribonucleic acid is made. In 1914, Robert Feulgen, another German chemist, developed a means by which DNA could be stained a brilliant crimson in the test tube. When 10 years later he applied this highly specific procedure to cells, he found that only the chromosomes bear the deep crimson red denoting DNA. This proved the speculations of earlier biologists and conclusively placed DNA in the chromosomes.

THE NATURE
OF THE GENE

Chromosomes thus had been shown to contain DNA as well as proteins. Since genes, the determiners of inheritable traits, were known to be carried in the chromosomes, a basic question now arose: Are genes made of DNA or protein?

ARE GENES PROTEIN?

George Beadle and Edward Tatum proposed in 1941 that genes operate by causing the synthesis of enzyme proteins. They suggested that each gene causes one enzyme to be produced which has a specific role in the metabolism of the organism, an idea that became known as the *one-gene–one-enzyme theory*.

Many biologists believed each protein enzyme to be formed directly on its specific gene through enzymatic action of the gene itself. In other words, they believed that the gene is a protein molecule functioning as an enzyme in forming more proteins like itself and that these new enzymes leave the nucleus to enter the cytoplasm and regulate the metabolic processes and formation of traits of the cell and organism. This seemed reasonable, since the twenty or more amino acids could allow for the synthesis of enough different proteins to account for genetic diversity. Nonetheless, the idea that "protein genes" produce protein enzymes was eventually excluded by an impressive accumulation of evidence from diverse sources that it is DNA, not protein, which constitutes the genetic material.

CONSTANCY OF DNA

During the late 1940s Mirsky in the United States and the Vendrelys in Europe showed that the amount of DNA varies from organism to organism, in proportion to the amount of chromosomal material, but that it is *constant* in the body cells of each organism. Thus the amount of DNA in the liver-cell nuclei of a calf is the same as in its gland-cell nuclei or a kidney-cell nuclei. Furthermore, in any particular organism, the amount of DNA in the diploid body cells is twice that found in the haploid gametes. The distribution of DNA thus was found to match the distribution of genes in the organism: *Each cell contains a diploid set of genes in the nucleus, except for the germ cells, which contain half this amount.* The discovery that bovine sperm cells in fact contain half as much DNA as liver cells in the same animal provided impressive evidence that the genes must be made of DNA. Other powerful evidence stemmed from experiments with bacteria.

Some strange and mysterious events had been reported by the English bacteriologist Griffith in 1928. He had been trying to develop a better vaccine to control pneumonia and was working with two strains of bacteria. The cells of one strain were enclosed in a polysaccharide capsule and appeared smooth-coated under the microscope. The cells of the other strain were genetically unable to form these coats and looked rough-coated under the microscope. The rough type, or R strain, does not cause pneumonia, but the capsulated type, the smooth or S strain results in fatal illness in mice. Bacteria with polysaccharide coats are virulent disease producers because the capsule prevents the body's white blood cells from engulfing and destroying them. Griffith found that he could inactivate the virulent S-strain bacteria by boiling them. Injection of heat-killed S-strain bacteria would cause no more effect than injection of the harmless R-strain cells. One day, however, he injected mice with a mixture of live R-strain and dead S-strain bacteria, and some mice died of pneumonia. Examination of the dead mice showed a heavy infestation of *living S-strain bacteria*. Griffith rechecked the remainder of the S-strain bacteria that he assumed had been killed by boiling, and they were definitely dead. He found that he could inject them, by themselves, into mice and no sickness would result. Yet when injected along with harmless R-strain bacteria, the injection led to the death of the mice from pneumonia. Somehow, the hereditary qualities of the dead S-strain bacteria (ability to form capsules) had been transferred to the living R-strain bacteria, so that they were now producing capsules. In other words, the R-strain bacteria had been transformed to S strain!

What was this "transforming substance" that could diffuse from one cell to another and change its heredity? The next step was taken by Alloway, who performed a critical experiment with the bacterial transformation system. He showed that treatment of R-type bacteria in a test tube with extracts of killed S-type bacteria would in fact change some of the R-type bacteria to S-type. The way was now open for an examination of the chemical nature of the active substances in the extracts. Whatever it was, it had to be the material of which the bacterial genes are made, because the transformed bacteria retained their newly acquired trait and passed it on to their descendants. Investigation of the chemistry of the transforming substance would go far to settle the controversy whether genes are DNA or protein.

By 1944, techniques had become available for identifying the transforming substance. Avery, McCarty, and MacLeod showed that pure S-type DNA *alone* could transform R-strain bacteria into S-strain capsule-producing bacteria. This finding provided strong evidence that DNA is the genetic material.

FIGURE 9.1 Diagram of a bacteriophage, a virus parasite on bacteria.

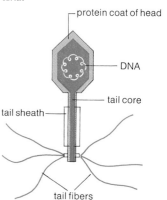

Rod-shaped bacteria called *Escherichia coli* are abundant in the human intestine. Normally harmless, they live peacefully in your colon but are sometimes attacked by viruses called *bacteriophage*. Phages might be described as being similar to a hypodermic syringe made of protein and filled with DNA (see Figure 9.1). Electron micrographs reveal that the phage viruses attack *E. coli* by attaching themselves to the bacterial cell wall and squirting their contents into the bacterial cell. The "syringe" portion remains outside the bacterial cell while its contents enter the cell. Within a short time immense numbers of new viruses appear, until the cell literally bursts with an explosion of newly formed virus particles.

In 1952, Hershey and Chase designed an experiment in which the DNA and the protein of the bacteriophage were labeled with radioisotopes. They made use of the fact that DNA contains phosphorus while proteins do not and proteins contain sulfur

THE DNA GENES OF A VIRUS

while DNA does not. By growing phage viruses in bacterial cells containing radio-active sulfur and phosphorus they could label the protein and DNA of the viruses.

The labeled viruses were then introduced to a culture of nonradioactive bacteria, in order to determine whether it is the protein or the DNA which the virus injects into the bacterial cells and which is responsible for the production of the new viruses. Their experiment showed that the protein of the phage viruses is not injected into the bacterial cells. Only DNA is injected, and it, by itself, is sufficient to cause the formation of the new viruses in the bacterial cells. The Hershey-Chase experiment proved that for these bacteriophages as well the genetic material is DNA.

Though these experiments had identified the hereditary material as DNA, they had not explained how the DNA functions. Only DNA had been injected into the bacterial cells from the phage viruses in the Hershey-Chase experiments, but whole viruses, complete with protein coats and DNA cores, form in the bacterial cytoplasm. In other words the DNA must contain a genetic recipe with directions for making more DNA as well as more viral proteins. Thus the question becomes one of explaining how this genetic recipe is actually put into operation.

To understand the solution to this puzzle, we must first understand the structure of nucleic acids.

WHAT ARE NUCLEIC ACIDS? By the end of the nineteenth century it was known that nucleic acids are composed in part of ringlike substances containing nitrogen. These compounds are of the type that chemists call bases since they bear a weak positive charge in solution, and we shall refer to them as *nitrogenous bases*.

The nitrogenous bases of nucleic acids are of two kinds, single-ring and double-ring. The double-ring bases are called *purines* and are themselves of two kinds, *adenine* and *guanine* (Figure 9.2). The single-ring bases are called *pyrimidines* and are of three kinds, *cytosine, thymine,* and *uracil.*

Besides these five kinds of nitrogenous bases, nucleic acids contain phosphate groups and sugars. The phosphate groups are all alike, but the sugars are of two kinds, *ribose sugar* and *deoxyribose sugar*. The primary difference between the two is that deoxyribose sugar lacks an oxygen atom occurring in ribose sugar—hence the name.

Nucleic acids always contain one of the two kinds of sugar, but never both. The nucleic acids containing ribose sugar are called *ribonucleic acid* (RNA), and those containing deoxyribose sugar are known as *deoxyribonucleic acid* (DNA). DNA contains the purines adenine (A) and guanine (G) and the pyrimidines thymine (T) and cytosine (C). Instead of thymine RNA contains the closely related pyrimidine uracil (U).

FIGURE 9.2 The nitrogenous
bases of nucleic acids. Along with
sugars and phosphates they make
up the nucleotide units of nucleic
acids.

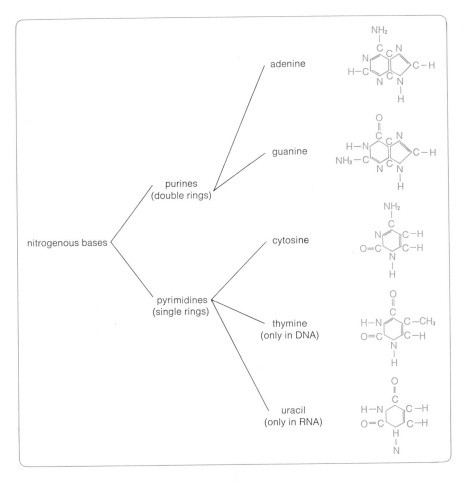

During the 1920s and 1930s Levene, a Russian-American chemist, demonstrated
that the three components of nucleic acids, sugar, phosphate, and nitrogenous base,
form three-part units called *nucleotides.* He showed that *nucleic acid molecules
consist of linear chains of nucleotides in which there is a sequence of
sugar—phosphate—sugar—phosphate— · · ·, with the nitrogenous bases projecting to the side from the sugars.* Even before this, in the late 1920s, it was discovered
that DNA as it is naturally present in cells is a molecule of enormous dimensions.
This discovery depended on improved methods for extracting DNA. Earlier
procedures such as Miescher's had extracted only small DNA fragments.

DNA is the material of the genes, and genes determine the structure of proteins such
as enzymes. It is now known that the *sequence of nitrogenous bases determines the
sequence of the amino acids of these proteins* (Figure 9.3).

FIGURE 9.3 Early concept of
DNA and RNA as single-stranded
molecules made of strings of
nucleotides, each with a phosphate, sugar, and nitrogenous base.
In this figure the straight line symbolizes the sequence of phosphates
and sugars and the circles the
single-ring and double-ring bases
projecting from the sugars.
Compare this concept of DNA with
that shown in Figure 9.6.

SOME CLUES TO DNA STRUCTURE

It had been assumed for many years that the four nitrogenous bases of DNA (A, C, T, and G) were present in equal amounts in all molecules of DNA. In the early 1950s, however, Chargaff and other workers carried out studies with many different DNAs which clearly showed this assumption to be invalid. Although phosphates and sugars are always present in equal amounts in all DNA, the amount of each kind of base in DNA molecules varies from organism to organism. Table 9.1 shows that the

TABLE 9.1 Percentage of nitrogenous bases in DNA

	ADENINE	THYMINE	GUANINE	CYTOSINE
Bacterium (tuberculosis)	15.1	14.6	34.9	35.4
Bone marrow (rat)	28.6	28.4	21.4	20.4
Sperm (bull)	28.7	27.2	22.2	20.7
Testes (herring)	27.9	28.2	19.5	21.5
Thymus (bull)	28.2	27.8	21.5	21.2
Wheat germ	27.3	27.1	22.7	22.8
Yeast	31.3	32.9	18.7	17.1

amount of adenine varies between species and that this is also true of the other three bases. On the other hand, compare the amounts of adenine and thymine and the amounts of guanine and cytosine *within* each species. *The amount of adenine is always the same as that of thymine, and the amount of guanine is always the same as that of cytosine.* What does this pattern mean?

The chemical components of DNA were known, but how these components are combined in the DNA molecule remained a mystery. One approach to this problem was supplied by biophysicists, who applied the technique of x-ray diffraction to the analysis of the structure of the DNA molecule. To use this method, however, the DNA had to be in crystalline form; and DNA is normally either a gluelike fluid or an amorphous, stringy solid. The regular repetitive structure of a crystal can be used to divert a beam of electrons from their paths and by projecting them onto a photographic plate an image is formed from which the structure of the crystal can be deduced.

Wilkins developed a technique for lowering a needle into a solution of DNA and slowly withdrawing the point so that a crystalline fiber of DNA was formed. He and his colleague Franklin began making x-ray pictures of these DNA fibers in order to examine the structure of this fascinating molecule.

THE WATSON-CRICK
MODEL OF DNA

At Cambridge University Crick, an English physicist, and Watson, a young American biologist, began to put together the pieces of evidence gathered by Chargaff, Wilkins, and others in an attempt to arrive at the structure of DNA. Examination of the pictures made by Wilkins and Franklin convinced them that DNA is a *coiled molecule* (*helix*) and that it has a constant diameter along its entire length.   (Only a year or two previously Pauling had pointed out that protein molecules consist of a coiled chain of amino acids.)   The symmetry of the DNA helix means that the linear sugar-phosphate backbone of the molecule is on the outside with the various nitrogenous bases projecting inward toward the central core of the molecule.   Even with this

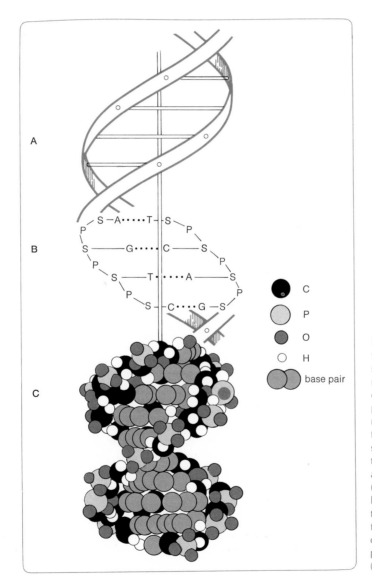

FIGURE 9.4 The helix of DNA, with three different ways of representing the molecular arrangement. (*a*) General picture of the double helix, with the phosphate-sugar combinations making up the outside spirals and the base pairs the crossbars. (*b*) A somewhat more detailed representation: phosphate (P), sugar (S), adenine (A), thymine (T), guanine (G), cytosine (C), and hydrogen bonding(. . .). (*c*) Detailed structure, showing how the space is filled with atoms: carbon (C), oxygen (O), hydrogen (H), phosphorus (P), and the base pairs. (*Redrawn from Swanson*, 1964.)

information there remained the question of the number of helical strands in each DNA molecule.

Aware that *pairing* is a basic aspect of genetic behavior in cells and organisms, Watson guessed that pairing might be reflected in the molecular structure of DNA. With this in mind he and Crick began to build a metal and wire model of their version of the DNA molecule. They found that their theory and the laws of chemistry were compatible and that the components of DNA could be fit together adequately in the form of a *double helix,* that is, a helical DNA molecule composed of *two individual nucleotide strands* (see Figures 9.4 and 9.5). The model was published in 1953. Understanding of the double helical structure of DNA was a significant milestone in twentieth-century biology because it provided a means of interpreting genetic replication of DNA in molecular terms.

Watson and Crick suggested that the DNA double helix is bonded together like a ladder twisted into a spiral staircase. To picture this form, imagine a rubber ladder wrapped in a spiral around a long cylinder. If the cylinder is removed, the coiled ladder that remains provides a good representation of the DNA molecule, with the steps representing the bonds holding the two polynucleotide strands together.

The photographs made by Wilkins and Franklin revealed that DNA is a symmetrical molecule; that is, its diameter is constant. For this to be possible, the steps of the ladder must always be made of a bond connecting one double-ring (purine) to one single-ring (pyrimidine) nitrogenous base. Steps made of two pyrimidines or two purines would cause asymmetry in the molecule. The steps of the DNA ladder could therefore consist only of adenine paired with thymine and of cytosine paired with guanine. Four kinds of bonded base pairs are possible in the DNA ladder: A—T, T—A, C—G, and G—C.

The Watson-Crick model of DNA explained the circumstantial evidence that Chargaff had uncovered. The 1:1 ratio of purine to pyrimidine bases in DNA resulted from the way the bases are always paired in a purine-to-pyrimidine fashion. For example, if the sequence of bases on one side of the ladder is CATCATCATCAT-CAT, the sequence on the strand forming the other side of the ladder is the complementary one (Figure 9.6).

The two bases of each base pair of the DNA ladder are held together by weak chemical bonds. When DNA duplicates itself, as it must before the replication of genetic information, the bonds between the pairs of bases in each step are broken. Picture this as a separation of the double-stranded molecule into two single strands, each looking like one side of a ladder. Each half-ladder, or single strand, then provides a unique pattern, or *template,* for the synthesis of a new DNA strand from the nucleic acid precursors in the cellular fluid. For example, a cytosine-containing nucleotide attracts a guanine-containing nucleotide, and an adenine nucleotide attracts a thymine nucleotide, and so on. The new nucleotides line up in the *sequence determined by the template provided in the preexistent DNA strand.* Thus two double-

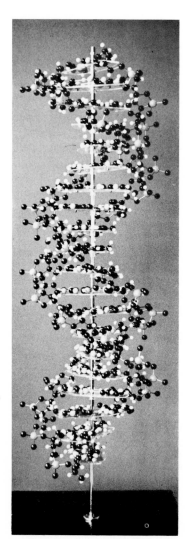

FIGURE 9.5 Model of molecular structure of DNA. (*Chas. Pfizer & Co., Inc.*)

stranded molecules can be formed from one double-stranded molecule, and each will be an exact replica, in nucleotide sequence, of the original. (Figure 9.7.)

There is still some disagreement about exactly how DNA is arranged in the chromosome. Most cell biologists, however, agree that DNA molecules extend throughout chromosomes and are not discrete clumps located at intervals along it. You may form a mental picture of a chromosome as an extremely long double-helical DNA structure covered with a mass of protein molecules. Since each chromosome seems to have just one set of genetic instructions, it would appear that only one kind of DNA molecule is arranged along each particular chromosome. In some chromosomes, however, there are duplicate strands lying side by side.

GENE ACTION

A gene is a section of DNA that has a single specific function. An individual gene carries information for the formation of a particular protein. The genetic recipe for the protein is the sequence of nitrogenous bases along one of the strands in the gene. How are such recipes *decoded* in living systems?

A code is a mechanism that allows one sequence of letters in a message to be translated into another sequence of letters. In this case we require a *genetic code*,

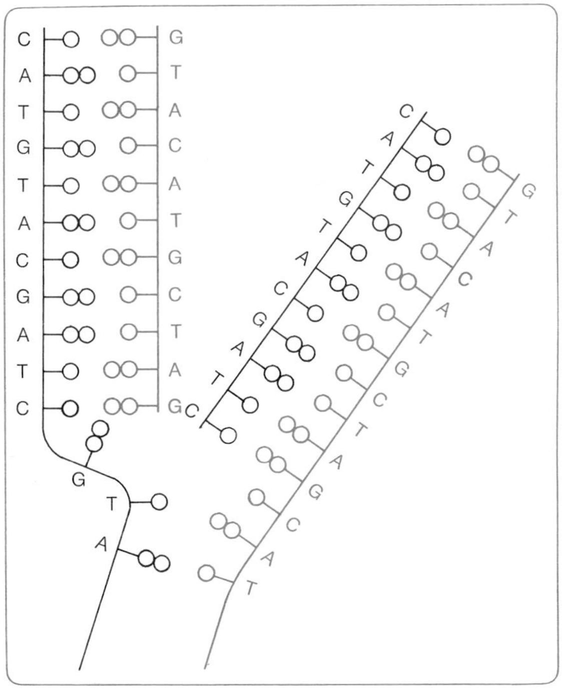

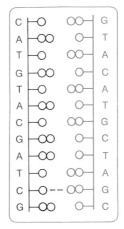

FIGURE 9.6 (*right*) The sequences of bases on two sides of the DNA ladder complement each other. Contrast this with the concept of DNA shown in Figure 9.3. Unlike RNA, DNA is made of two strands of nucleotides. The nitrogenous bases are held together by weak chemical bonds. The resulting DNA resembles a ladder with pairs of nitrogen bases as the steps.

FIGURE 9.7 (*left*) Duplication of DNA occurs as the double strand unzips into single strands, which immediately become double strands through bonding with complementary bases. The lines on the sides of the ladders indicate sugars and phosphates.

one that will allow a DNA genetic message phrased in a language whose words are purines and pyrimidines to be translated into a protein language whose words are amino acids.

Protein synthesis takes place in the ribosomal structures we discussed in Chapter 3. How does the genetic message, the recipe for proteins, get from the chromosomes in the nucleus out to the ribosomes, most or all of which are in the cytoplasm? The answer lies in one of the roles played by the second kind of nucleic acid, RNA.

FIGURE 9.8 Transcription of coded genetic message in DNA by a type of RNA called messenger RNA (*mRNA*). Note that only a region of DNA, the gene, opens and single-strand RNA is formed on one strand and then freed.

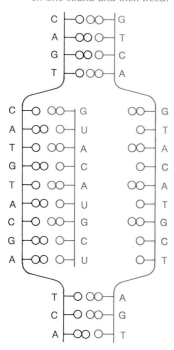

It has been found that DNA is double-stranded and ladderlike. Except in some viruses which use RNA as their genetic material instead of DNA, RNA is present as a single-stranded molecule. We have seen that DNA duplicates by strand separation followed by *template-directed synthesis* of new strands from single nucleotides in the cellular fluids (see Figure 9.8). How are RNA molecules duplicated if they are single-stranded? The answer is that *RNA is always formed on a DNA template* (again with the exception of RNA viruses). The sequence of nucleotides in RNA is determined by the sequence of bases in DNA. There is a gene for each kind of RNA. Said in the opposite way, the nature of each kind of RNA is determined by the gene on which it was formed.

Gene action consists, in molecular terms, of RNA synthesis. One strand of the DNA of the active genes serves as a template for the synthesis of an RNA molecule bearing the nucleotide sequence specified by the base-pairing relationships possible between the nucleotides in the DNA template and the pool of free nucleotides available in the cellular fluid. For example, if a DNA nucleotide sequence is TAGCT, an RNA sequence will be formed which is AUCGA (note that U, uracil, is present in RNA where thymine would have been present in DNA). The nucleotides forming the RNA are different from those in DNA; as we noted above, RNA nucleotides contain a *ribose* instead of a deoxyribose sugar. In this way, through the use of a DNA template to specify RNA nucleotide sequence, the DNA genetic message is translated into a different language, an RNA language.

Some RNAs are used to direct the synthesis of proteins. These are called *messenger RNA* (*mRNA*). The *mRNA* peels off the DNA gene as it is synthesized and moves out to the ribosomes. Here, the coded genetic message borne in the *mRNA* will provide the directions for the assembly of amino acids into proteins.

Many ribosomes may attach to one *mRNA* strand and form a *polyribosome;* but, since the events taking place on each ribosome are identical, we shall concentrate our attention on one of the ribosomes and the *mRNA* attached to it. We shall see how a protein can be assembled.

BUILDING A PROTEIN

An enormous variety of amino acid sequences is possible and hence an enormous variety of possible proteins. On the other hand, there are only four kinds of nucleo-

FIGURE 9.9 Electron micrograph (25,000×) showing the ultrastructure of genes at work. These genes, which were isolated from a salamander oocyte, carry the code for ribosomal ribonucleic acid (rRNA). This RNA is a major component of small particles called ribosomes, which are essential elements of the protein-synthesizing machinery of all living cells. The shortest fibrils of RNA are not complete yet; they have read only part of a gene. The longest fibrils of RNA are complete; they have transcribed an entire gene. A strand of ribosomal RNA has been assembled according to the sequence of bases in the DNA gene. The techniques for visualizing the ribosomal RNA genes were developed by O. L. Miller, Jr. and Barbara R. Beatty. (*Courtesy of O. L. Miller, Jr., and Barbara R. Beatty, Biology Division, Oak Ridge National Laboratory.*)

tides in an RNA molecule. How can four kinds of nucleotides be arranged in a code that assembles twenty kinds of amino acids into a particular sequence out of an almost infinite variety of possible sequences?

Amino acids are delivered to the polyribosomal assembly plant and are incorporated into proteins. They are delivered by a type of RNA which, because of its function, is called *transfer RNA* (*tRNA*). Ribosomes also contain RNA (ribosomal RNA, or *r*RNA). So far we have considered three kinds of RNA, *m*RNA, *t*RNA and *r*RNA. Ribosomal RNA seems to play no role in selecting the amino acids for assembly into proteins, though its presence is necessary for protein synthesis to occur at all. It may be needed in order to *bind* *m*RNA and *t*RNA to the site where protein synthesis will take place (see Figure 9.9 and the photograph at the beginning of the chapter).

Transfer RNAs function by binding to amino acids in the cellular fluid and bringing them to the ribosomal sites of protein synthesis. They are essential elements of the code-reading machinery of the cell. Each RNA molecule bears a special nucleotide sequence which is complementary to a sequence in the *m*RNA. Since there are twenty different kinds of amino acids that can be summoned to the genetic recipe on the *m*RNA, we may ask whether there are twenty different kinds of *t*RNA molecules, each kind bearing a different amino acid. Actually there are over sixty different kinds, since several *t*RNA types exist for each amino acid.

It was proposed by Crick that the *t*RNA molecules bond temporarily to the *m*RNA by complementary base pairing, just as we have already seen in DNA duplication and *m*RNA formation. A *t*RNA binds to an *m*RNA molecule at the ribosome with specific bonds between C and G, A and U (see Figure 9.10). Thus *t*RNAs bind to an *m*RNA molecule when the *m*RNA presents to the outside medium a set of bases or genetic code word which is complementary to a specific set of bases carried in the *t*RNA molecule. Since each *t*RNA molecule bears an amino acid at the end opposite to the one bearing the binding bases, the arrival of a *t*RNA means the delivery of an amino acid. As more and more amino acids arrive, a protein is assembled.

How many bases are there in a genetic code word, and how many bases are needed to represent an amino acid? Is the bond that matches *t*RNA with *m*RNA the matching of a single pair of bases—an A on the *t*RNA and a U on the *m*RNA, for example? A moment's thought shows that this could not work, because there are twenty kinds of amino acids and only four kinds of bases; a one-nucleotide code could specify only four kinds of amino acids. Genetic code words consisting of two bases would allow $4^2 = 16$ combinations of bases, but sixteen species of *t*RNA could still not account for twenty kinds of amino acids. Crick proposed that genetic words consist of *triplets* of bases, a system which would allow for 4^3 combinations of the four bases or sixty-four genetic words. This is more than enough to specify the twenty kinds of amino acid found in proteins.

Genetic code words are three-nucleotide words, and a sentence consisting of these three-letter words is a gene (see Table 9.2). A genetic sentence might look like this

UUU CCA GCA GAG AUG GGG CAA UUU UAA

A sentence like this makes little sense to us, but it would be "read" by nine *t*RNA molecules bringing in nine specific amino acids. Each *t*RNA would have a special set of three bases which would complement each of the three-base code words on the *m*RNA. For example, using the same complementary base pairs we used before,

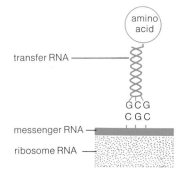

FIGURE 9.10 Relationship between transfer RNA, messenger RNA, and ribosomal RNA. Note that the transfer RNA bears an amino acid as its "cargo."

amino acid

transfer RNA

GCG
CGC

messenger RNA

ribosome RNA

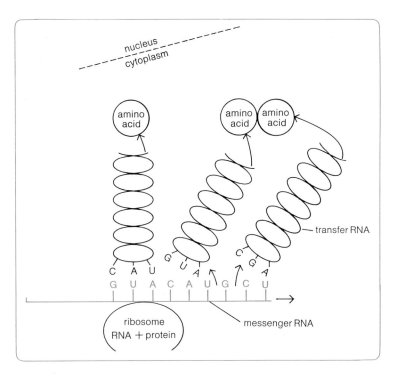

FIGURE 9.11 Diagram of
protein synthesis. Amino acids are
assembled into proteins according
to a sequence determined by
sequence of nitrogenous bases in
DNA. The sequence of
three-letter "words" in one strand
of DNA determines sequence of
three-letter words in messenger
RNA. This "sentence" then determines the sequence in which
amino acids are delivered by
transfer RNA. The amino acids are
released and bond together to form
a protein. Using Table 9.2, can
you identify the three amino acids
delivered to the messenger RNA?

a *t*RNA binding to the *m*RNA code word UCA would bind by means of the sequence
AGU. The result is that a sequence of transfer RNAs, each bearing a particular
amino acid, is specified by the *m*RNA nucleotide sequence. Once delivered in the
right sequence by their *t*RNAs, the amino acids can be hooked together with chemical bonds, thereby producing a new protein molecule. These events, which
account for protein synthesis, are diagrammed in Figure 9.11.

To picture how this molecular assembly plant actually operates requires some imagination. Each three-letter word in the genetic message is read by an appropriate
*t*RNA as the *m*RNA moves over the surface of the ribosome. Thousands of *t*RNA
molecules, each bearing a particular amino acid, are diffusing about in the fluid
around the ribosome. When a particular three-letter word appears at the site where
binding can take place, the appropriate *t*RNA binds specifically on that spot. As the
*m*RNA moves across the ribosome, the *t*RNA falls away and leaves its amino acid
cargo behind. Each amino acid is bonded with the amino acid delivered by the
previous *t*RNA as the *t*RNAs free them and diffuse away. More amino acids are delivered, each in its turn, and a string of amino acids thus forms. This string of amino
acids will twist, fold, or coil, depending on the amino acids and their location in the
sequence, to form a mature protein molecule. In this way proteins are assembled
according to the genetic directions inherited in the DNA.

The relationship between the three-letter code words of *m*RNA and the amino acids these words specify is known as the *genetic code*. If this code could be broken, the sequence of genetic words in an *m*RNA specifying any particular sequence of amino acids could be deduced. And if the sequence of code words in an *m*RNA were known, the *sequence* of purines and pyrimidines in the DNA segment coding for the protein could be deduced. In other words, once the amino acid sequence of a given protein is known, the structure of the gene coding for that protein could be stated. Since protein molecules control and regulate our lives, a knowledge of the nature of the genes that form them is important.

BREAKING THE GENETIC CODE

To break the genetic code, coded messages were presented to the ribosomal protein synthesis machinery and the participation of specific amino acids was determined. In this research it has been useful to work with isolated ribosome systems extracted from cells. Such subcellular systems are called *cell-free systems*.

Cell-free systems for studies of protein synthesis can be prepared from *E. coli,* the well-studied intestinal bacteria mentioned above, by grinding them to rupture the cell walls. The DNA, RNA, enzymes, and ribosomes are not damaged and continue to function in protein synthesis if provided with ATP as a source of energy and amino acids as the building blocks of protein.

In 1961, two young biochemists, Nirenberg and Matthaei, synthesized an artificial *m*RNA with only one kind of base, uracil. This genetic message was a repetition of three-letter words in a long, redundant sentence: UUU UUU UUU UUU UUU · · · . They placed the synthetic *m*RNA with its coded message in test tubes containing the cell-free protein synthesis system including ATP and all twenty amino acids. Their intent was to determine which of the twenty amino acids would be specified by the artificially made code word UUU. By collecting and analyzing the newly synthesized proteins from the mixture they learned that only one kind of amino acid, phenylalanine, had been incorporated into these proteins. Thus the *m*RNA code word UUU is translated as the amino acid phenylalanine by the protein-synthesis apparatus of the cell. From this information it follows that a sequence of AAA in DNA forms the genetic code word UUU in *m*RNA. It follows that at the ribosome phenylalanine must be delivered by a *t*RNA containing the *m*RNA-binding sequence AAA.

Other investigators joined Nirenberg and Matthaei in deciphering the genetic code and soon found that a better technique was to make artificial *m*RNA molecules with just one three-letter word and put them, one at a time, into cell-free systems containing ATP and all twenty amino acids. It was then possible to determine which amino acid was summoned by each of the 64 possible (4^3) combinations of bases into three-letter code words.

By 1965 the studies of Nirenberg and his colleagues permitted the construction of a "dictionary" of the genetic code as shown in Table 9.2. Knowing the genetic code, we can look at the amino acid sequence of a protein such as hemoglobin and deter-

TABLE 9.2* The genetic code, consisting of 64 triplet combinations and their corresponding amino acids, is shown in its most likely version. The importance of the first two letters in each triplet is apparent. Some of the allocations are still not completely certain, particularly for organisms other than the colon bacillus (*E. coli*). The terms amber and ochre referred originally to certain mutant strains of bacteria and designate two triplets, UAA and UAG, that may act as signals for terminating polypeptide chains.

FIRST BASE IN TRIPLET	SECOND BASE IN TRIPLET				THIRD BASE IN TRIPLET
	U	C	A	G	
U	UUU / UUC — Phenyl-alanine; UUA / UUG — Leucine	UCU / UCC / UCA / UCG — Serine	UAU / UAC — Tyrosine; UAA — Ochre; UAG — Amber	UGU / UGC — Cysteine; UGA — ?; UGG — Trypto-phan	U / C / A / G
C	CUU / CUC / CUA / CUG — Leucine	CCU / CCC / CCA / CCG — Proline	CAU / CAC — Histidine; CAA / CAG — Glutamine	CGU / CGC / CGA / CGG — Arginine	U / C / A / G
A	AUU / AUC / AUA — Isoleucine; AUG — Methionine	ACU / ACC / ACA / ACG — Threonine	AAU / AAC — Asparagine; AAA / AAG — Lysine	AGU / AGC — Serine; A A / AGG — Arginine	U / C / A / G
G	GUU / GUC / GUA / GUG — Valine	GCU / GCC / GCA / GCG — Alanine	GAU / GAC — Aspartic acid; GAA / GAG — Glutamic acid	GGU / GSC / GGA / GGG — Glycine	U / C / A / G

* Adapted by permission from F. H. C. Crick, "The Genetic Code: III," *Scientific American*, October, 1966.

mine the probable nucleotide sequence of the *m*RNA that directed its assembly. From the knowledge of the sequence of bases on this *m*RNA the sequence of bases on the DNA on which it was formed (the hemoglobin gene) can in turn be deduced. (See Figure 9.12.)

WHAT IS A GENE MUTATION?

If all the DNA from one human cell could be put together from all forty-six chromosomes, it would form a strand about 36 inches long. There, in the genetic code, would be the genetic recipe for a human being! Put another way, Crick has estimated that if the biochemical instructions for building a man could be placed into 500-page recipe books, almost 1,000 volumes would be necessary. Suppose this set of recipe books is to be inherited by two heirs and the entire set has to be copied. Imagine a typist sitting down to the job. Do you think she would make a few errors? Perhaps several per page?

The DNA in a human cell contains over 10^9 nucleotides, each of which must attract the complementary nucleotide during the duplication of DNA if each daughter cell is to receive an identical set of genetic messages. It is not difficult to imagine how a nucleotide may "fall off" while the DNA is being replicated. The missing nucleotide may either not be replaced, or a different nucleotide may replace the missing one. When this new, or mutated, DNA duplicates itself, the mistake will be perpetuated, and all the descendants will inherit the new sequence and the different amino acid sequence it might specify.

The effects of a mutation in a single gene are clearly shown by studies of sickle-cell anemia. Normal red blood cells are shown in Figure 9.13. The red blood cells of persons suffering from sickle-cell anemia are shown in Figure 9.14. Comparisons of hemoglobin molecules from the two types indicates that there is only one difference: The sickle-cell hemoglobin has the amino acid valine where normal hemoglobin has glutamic acid at one site in their long molecular structure.

By looking at Table 9.2 you can see that glutamic acid is specified by either the nucleotide triplet GAA or GAG. The nucleotide triplet for this would therefore have been either CTT or CTC. At some time in the past, one of these must have mutated

FIGURE 9.12

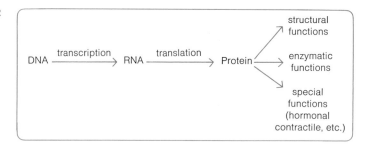

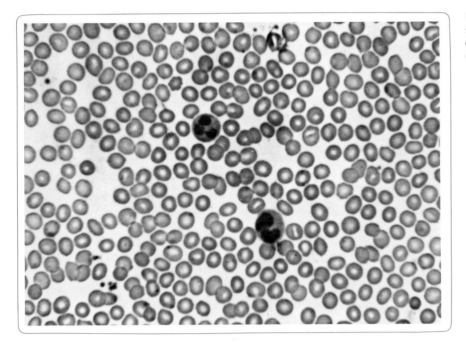

FIGURE 9.13 Human blood smear, showing normal red blood cells and two white blood cells. (*Carolina Biological Supply Co.*)

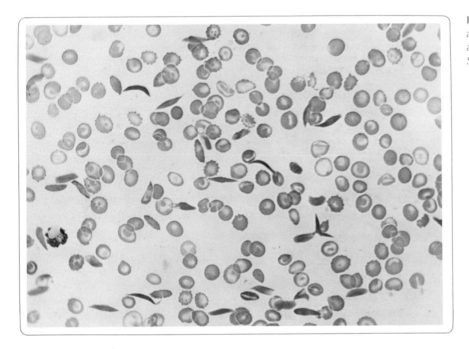

FIGURE 9.14 Red blood cells of a person suffering from sickle-cell anemia. (*Carolina Biological Supply Co.*)

to CAA, CAG, CAT, or CAC.   These three-letter words cause *m*RNA to form with
either GUU, GUC, GUA, or GUG, and any of the four specify valine instead of glutamic acid.

The results of this mutation in a single three-letter word are shown in Figure 9.15.
The abnormal hemoglobin causes the red blood cells to change from the normal
doughnut shape to a crumpled sickle shape.   The sickle-shaped cell is not only inef-
ficient in carrying oxygen but also breaks up easily.   The resulting anemia usually
leads to death from one or more of the causes indicated in the drawing.   They are all
the result of a single change in a single triplet code word!

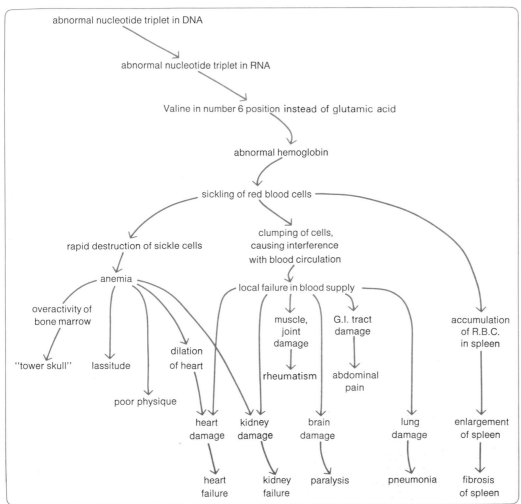

Many mutations might be expected to upset the biochemical balance or an organism to some degree because a mutation can result in the introduction of a new protein molecule into the organism, and such changes, if they affect anything, are likely to affect it badly. The effects of most mutations are, however, very slight, and their presence is usually not even noticed. It has been calculated that several thousand mutations occur in the cells of every person during his lifetime, and most of these are not noticed. Some, however, may be the cause of abnormal cell division, which results in tumors. On the other hand, mutations occur spontaneously at a constant rate in all cells. Some people have calculated the rate of mutation to be about 1 in 10 million in most organisms. This rate, however, can be increased by such agents as ionizing radiation and chemicals such as coal tar, mustard gas, tobacco smoke, etc.

As we noted in Chapter 8, mutations cannot be all bad since they serve as a source of variation upon which natural selection acts. Without some form of heritable change in the genetic material, evolution would never have occurred. It may be difficult to admit, but all the traits you are so proud of arose as mutations.

The material we have considered in this chapter is in some respects the heart of modern molecular biology. Though they have brought us great new insights into the nature of living systems, the discoveries which led to molecular understanding of the genetic material have also introduced a perplexing new problem. If all the DNA inherited by way of the sperm cell and the egg cell is present in equal amounts in all the cells of the body, how is it that all these genes do not express themselves in all the cells at once? Why do some genes express themselves in the embryo, some in babyhood, some in childhood, adolescence, adulthood, middle age, and old age? Why do some genes express themselves throughout the life of the organism but only in certain cells of certain organs?

We know that a gene must be "turned on" so that the genetic message can be trans-mitted to *m*RNA. The mechanism by which each region of the DNA strand is turned on while other regions are not remains generally unknown, however. We shall discuss this problem, one of the most important and challenging in modern biology, in the next chapter as we describe the still mysterious processes of growth and development.

1   Describe the Watson-Crick model of DNA.
2   Describe briefly the means by which amino acids are assembled into proteins in a regulated fashion.
3   Describe briefly how a change in one nucleotide in one three-letter word can change the nature of a protein.

4   What is the sequence of amino acids assembled with the inherited genetic message of CCA AGT TCA CAT TAC GAT?

5   Describe the expression of a gene as a protein.

SUGGESTIONS FOR
FURTHER READING
* Available in paperback.

Beadle, G., and M. Beadle: *The Language of Life, Doubleday & Company, Inc., Garden City, N.Y., 1966.   A Nobel Prize winner and his wife discuss the history of genetics and its principles in a manner easily understood by nonscientists.

Bennett, T. P., and E. Frieden: *Modern Topics in Biochemistry, The Macmillan Company, New York, 1966.   Well written and illustrated; includes a discussion of gene expression.

Lerner, I. M.: *Heredity, Evolution, and Society, W. H. Freeman and Company, San Francisco, 1968.   Includes a good section on gene expression.

Watson, J. D.: *Molecular Biology of the Gene, W. A. Benjamin, Inc., New York, 1965.   A technical but authoritative account of biochemistry and expression of genes by one of the men who developed the theory of its mechanisms.

Watson, J. D.: *The Double Helix, Atheneum Publishers, New York, 1968.   A popular and controversial description of the personal experiences and thoughts of one man in the small group of individuals who developed the theory as to what genes are and how they function.

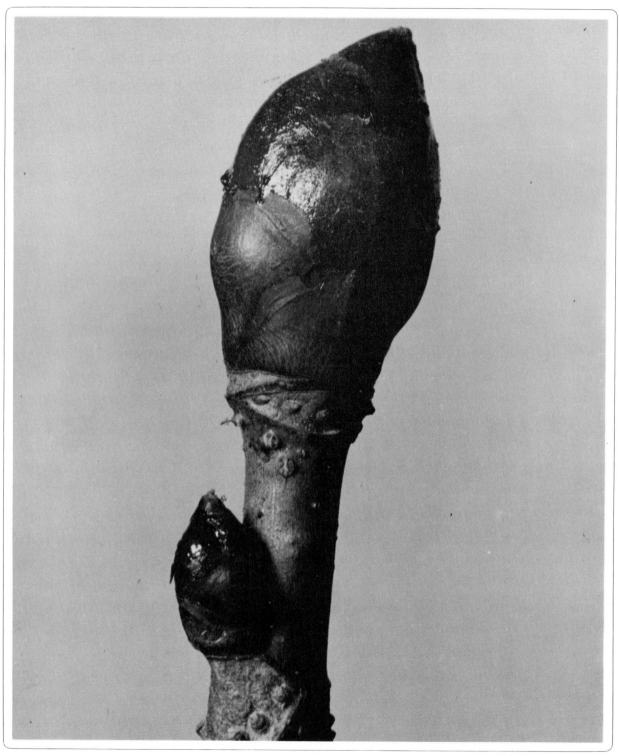

Horse chestnut. (*Courtesy of William J. Jahoda from The National Audubon Society.*)

Chapter 10

Growth and Development: How Does an Embryo Become an Organism?

This being of mine,
whatever it really is,
consists of a little flesh,
a little breath,
and the part which governs.

Marcus Aurelius

The genetic information for development is carried in two sets of chromosomes, one from the father and one from the mother, and in combination they spell out the basic traits of the offspring. The fertilized egg with which this offspring begins may be as small as the head of a pin, though many creatures have larger eggs. The egg is a single cell, whatever its size. As this cell develops, it turns into an integrated complex of billions of cells, an adult capable of reproducing its kind.

Though the fertilized eggs of different species give rise to diverse multicellular organisms, they begin with a more or less similar form. Each organism follows its inherited genetic recipe and develops structures closely resembling those of the other members of its species. The mechanisms by which this occurs are only now beginning to be understood. Change in a living thing through time is called *growth and development,* and knowledge of its underlying causes are among the dominant mysteries and main challenges in modern biological research.

In this chapter we shall see that the phenomena underlying growth and development occur on the molecular level and that the course of development is directed by interactions between the genes in cell nuclei and their chemical environments. We shall find that genes are turned on (activated) at one point in time and turned off at others, thus bringing about changes in the cells of the organism. A living organism never stops changing, but during embryonic growth the rate of change is fastest and most dramatic.

The process of growth and development begins at fertilization, when the sperm cell is fused with the egg cell, and continues with repeated mitotic cell divisions as the embryo increases in size and develops into its mature form. Before considering the specific mechanisms of growth and development, we shall look briefly at the overall development of a flowering plant, the garden bean, and a vertebrate animal, the frog.

GROWTH AND DEVELOPMENT OF A FLOWERING PLANT

At the base of the flower, just above the insertion of the petals, the fertilized egg of the bean plant divides mitotically and develops into an embryo. Meanwhile some of the surrounding tissue becomes saturated with stored food. After the embryo reaches a certain size, it ceases to grow, probably as a result of changes in the balance of hormones which control growth. It then enters into a state of suppressed metabolism. The surrounding maternal tissues form a hard coating around the embryo and the endosperm, and this structure, including embryo, endosperm, and protective coating, is what we call a *seed* (see Figure 10.1).

FIGURE 10.1 Bean and corn seeds. Epicotyl gives rise to the leaves and stem; the hypocotyl produces the root. Endosperm is stored food which may persist for a while or be absorbed into a cotyledon or seed leaf. All are enclosed by the hard protective seed coat.

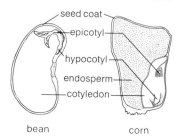

bean   corn

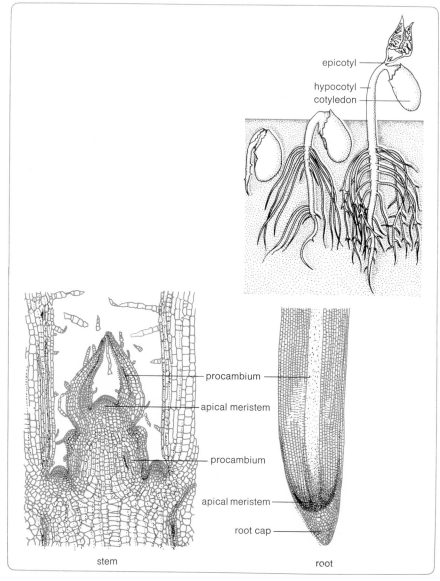

FIGURE 10.2 New cells are produced by mitosis at the tips of the roots and the shoots in the meristem and procambium. The young cells elongate, and the plant grows.

Germination of a seed begins when it soaks up water. The embryo resumes its mitotic cell divisions, and the new daughter cells grow by synthesizing new protoplasm and absorbing more water. Soon the embryo bursts out of the seed coat and can be recognized as a plant with a shoot and root.

A plant embryo can be thought of as a cylinder that is constantly growing in length by the elongation of its cells and as a result of the mitosis taking place at both ends. The plant embryo contains a leaflike accumulation of reserve food (called a *cotyledon* or seed leaf) which provides both matter and energy for growth, just as the yolk does for vertebrate embryos. At the lower end of the cylinder is the root, which turns downward to anchor the young plant and absorbs water and minerals. The simple embryonic root gives rise to an extensive root system, while the other end of the cylinder is growing and extending itself above the soil and eventually forming a shoot that produces leaves.

Growth in length of the root and shoot is the result mainly of cell elongation. At the growing end of a root is a *root cap* of cells, many of which are dead or dying. These cells wear off as the root cap pushes through the soil. Directly behind the cap is a region where both elongation and active cell division take place (see Figure 10.2). The end of the root is extended by these processes.

Leaves are formed at regularly spaced intervals at sites where a high rate of cell division has been established. A leaf grows as a flattened sheet, and when it falls away, a leaf scar is formed; directly above the scar is a region of embryonic cells called the *axillary* bud. In perennials, plants which live more than one growing season, the axillary bud left from the previous year undergoes cell division and elongation when the next growing season arrives. Thus a stem growing off at an angle from the original stem is formed. The typical branching pattern of plants is a result of this type of growth (Figure 10.3).

As the cells near the growing tip divide and elongate, the diameter of root and stem increases. As you know, some plants, for instance trees, continue growing in diameter throughout their lives, while others, such as grasses, do not. The continued growth of plants in areas other than the tips of stems and roots is called *secondary growth*. An example is the *cambium layer*, which lies between the bark and the wood of trees and which, as it grows, causes the plant's cylindrical body to become thicker (see Figure 10.4). Most plants have some secondary growth, and elongation occurs at either end as well as an increase in diameter throughout.

Thus far we have considered only the overall pattern according to which a plant grows. The cells forming the various structures we have discussed are not identical, however, and we know they have to become differentiated, that is, different from one another, in order to carry out various specialized functions. The advantages of specialization are obvious: If all the cells were alike, the multicellular organism could perform functions no more complex than those performed by an individual cell. In a similar way, if all human beings were exactly alike and there were no

FIGURE 10.3 (*a*) Stem with dormant buds. (*b*) Terminal dormant bud of the horse chestnut. (*After a photograph by Jean Carel.*)

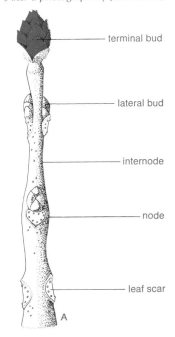

terminal bud

lateral bud

internode

node

leaf scar

A

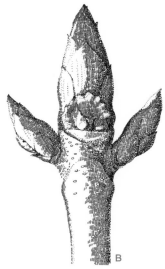

B

FIGURE 10.4 Cross section of a 3-year-old woody stem. (*J. Limbach, Ripon Microslides.*)

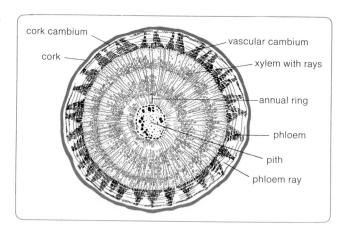

cork cambium

cork

vascular cambium

xylem with rays

annual ring

phloem

pith

phloem ray

specialization or division of labor, our economy would be exceedingly limited. Each man would still be pursuing a small deer with a rock held tight in his fist. The total economy would be no more complex than that of an individual.

In Chapter 1, we described how the living world can be organized into various levels of complexity built up through growth and development. Cells specialize into tissues which join to form organs; organs cooperate as an organ system within the next higher level of organization, the organism. In development, one fertilized egg divides repeatedly to form millions of cells which differentiate into special tissues, organs, and organ systems.

GROWTH AND DEVELOPMENT OF A VERTEBRATE ANIMAL

Since there are over 1 million species of animals, it would be impossible to describe in any detail features of growth and development which would hold true for all of them. We shall review the development of the frog and make occasional reference to other types of animals. More embryological experiments probably have been done on frogs than on any other species of animal, with the possible exception of sea urchins. Much of what we know about the growth and differentiation of the frog can be generally applied to other vertebrates. A discussion of human growth and development will be found in Chapter 12, where the role of hormones in mammalian development is emphasized.

A SOURCE OF MATTER AND ENERGY: THE YOLK

The life of a frog begins with *fertilization,* the fusion of egg and sperm. Like plant embryos, animal embryos must have a source of food for use during the cell division and biosynthesis which follow fertilization. Some animal embryos have food stored in the yolk of the egg. Others, such as mammals, do not have a yolk, instead absorbing food from the mother's tissues and later, when implanted in the mother's uterus, living on the nutrients in the mother's blood. Animals like frogs, birds, and fish, which pass through a prolonged period of embryonic life during which they develop without taking in any food from an outside source, require large amounts of yolk.

In eggs that have a great deal of yolk it tends to be in one end of the egg, the *vegetal hemisphere*. In the eggs of frogs the vegetal end is usually lighter in color and is at the bottom when the egg is immersed in water, due to the high concentration of dense, heavy yolk particles in the vegetal end. The other end is called the *animal hemisphere*.

In the plant embryo the longitudinal axis of the cylindrical plant body serves as an axis of organization. In a similar fashion, a frog embryo develops an axis of organization one component of which is the vertical axis running between the poles of the animal and vegetal hemispheres. If we picture a plane drawn through this vertical axis and through the point of sperm penetration in the animal hemisphere, we can usually determine the plane of the future frog embryo. Its head generally develops on the side where the sperm penetrated, and the tail develops on the other side. Other factors can affect the determination of the axis of organization of the frog embryo, however, and there are many cases in which the axis does not conform exactly to that predicted by the point of sperm entrance. Some other animals, however, rely exclusively on sperm entrance to determine the axis of organization, and in still others the axis is preset in the structure of the egg before it is fertilized. Whatever the means of establishing the axis of organization, however, it is always determined very early in development because it affects how the various cells of the embryo are to grow.

Within 2½ hours after fertilization the fertilized frog egg (*zygote*) divides with an animal-pole-vegetal-pole cleavage (Figure 10.5). Less than 1 hour later, both daughter cells divide simultaneously, a vertical cleavage plane cutting them at right angles to the first cleavage plane (Figure 10.5). There are now four cells. About ½ hour later each of these four cells divides into eight cells, but this time the cleavage plane is horizontal.

RAPID CELL DIVISION: ZYGOTE TO BLASTULA

These newly formed cells do not grow in size (by growth we mean increase in mass); instead they divide immediately into more daughter cells, which divide again in their turn. The divisions are accomplished by mitosis. Through this process, termed *cleavage*, the cells become smaller while the embryo remains about the same size as the original egg. In the frog embryo, after cleavage has proceeded for about 18 hours, there are thirty-two cells. At this point the smaller cells in the animal hemisphere are dividing faster than the large vegetal cells which contain the yolk. Soon there are many more cells without yolk than with yolk, and this trend continues.

After the embryo has divided into many cells, a space opens up in its center and it now takes the form of an asymmetric hollow ball called a *blastula*. Fluid collects at

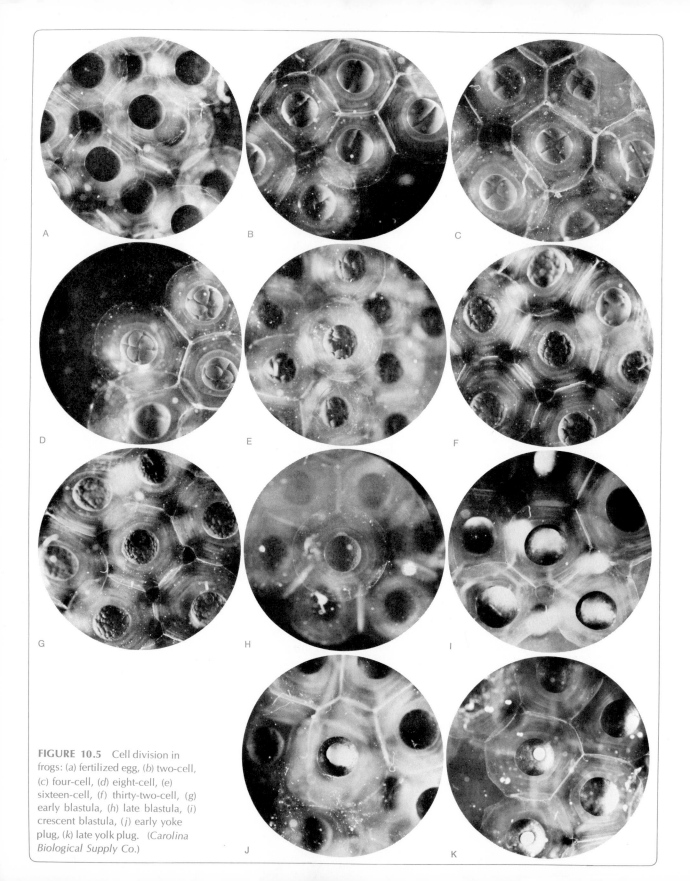

FIGURE 10.5 Cell division in frogs: (a) fertilized egg, (b) two-cell, (c) four-cell, (d) eight-cell, (e) sixteen-cell, (f) thirty-two-cell, (g) early blastula, (h) late blastula, (i) crescent blastula, (j) early yoke plug, (k) late yolk plug. (*Carolina Biological Supply Co.*)

the center of the blastula until a fluid-filled space, the *blastocoel,* is formed (Figure 10.5).

Just above the yolk boundary on one side of the blastula is an area distinguished by a gray pigment called the *gray crescent.* It is usually on the side of the egg opposite where the sperm entered. The blastula stage ends when the frog embryo has about 10,000 cells and some of the cells of the gray-crescent area begin to undergo the movements diagrammed in Figure 10.6. A group of cells on the side bearing the gray crescent begins to move into the interior of the egg (*invagination*), forming a structure which looks like an upper lip, called the *blastopore lip.* These cells now move upward, under the outer surface of the embryo, and form a separate internal cell layer. Thus, a two-layered area is formed on one side of the embryo. Further movements of cells are diagrammed in Figure 10.6; the effect of some of these movements is the formation of the *archenteron,* a cavity that will form the future digestive tract of the embryo. Movement of cells into the interior of the embryo through the *blastopore* meanwhile continues, and the main interior cavity of the embryo, the archenteron, becomes surrounded with a layer of these newly invaginated cells which form the endoderm. The blastopore will become the anus.

The result of these movements is a structure containing three main cell masses called a *gastrula;* the name refers to the formation of the cavity from which the stomach and other parts of the digestive tract will be derived. To picture the process by which a gastrula is formed, push your finger against a soft plastic ball until a portion of it touches the inside of the opposite side of the ball. Now, with your palm facing upward, crook your finger and press upward between the two layers you have formed and you will have a three-layered ball (see Figure 10.7). At the bottom of the embryo surrounding the archenteron are the large, yolk-bearing *endoderm* cells destined to form the gut; the outside of the embryo is now covered by a layer of small *ectoderm* cells; and between the endoderm and ectoderm is the *mesoderm.* The final form of the gastrula is pictured in Figure 10.7. It takes about 34 hours for a frog gastrula to form from a fertilized egg in the common frog, though other species of frog complete gastrulation in as little as one-third this time.

The molecular mechanism by which tissues, organs, and organ systems form from the cells of the three germ layers is not well understood today. The cells undergo different rates of mitosis and migrate either as individuals with ameboid motion or in a group, as moving, folding, and shifting sheets of cells. In the postgastrula stage, the form of the frog embryo changes from an asymmetric spheroid to a cylinder. This process is called *tubulation* because it results in the construction of a series of concentric tissue cylinders, or tubes. The vertebrate embryo is covered with a coat of *epidermis* broken only by a *mouth* at one end and an *anus* at the other (Figure 10.8). A *gut* proceeds through the body from mouth to anus. Above the gut is a solid rod of cells called a *notochord,* derived from special mesodermal cells, and above that is a

FIGURE 10.6 Early development of the frog. (*a,b*) A sperm entering an egg. Repeated cell divisions produce a blastula (*c*). A blastopore forms (*d*) and a sheet of cells folds in (*e,f*) to form a gastrula (*g*) with three germ layers and primitive gut. External views (*h,i*) show neural folds undergoing rapid cell division, moving together, and sinking in as a neural tube. Cross sections (*j,k,l*) show the same elements and also include the notochord which, through inductive interaction, causes the differentiation of the neural tube lying above it. A late frog embryo (*m*) reveals the major outlines of an adult. (Adapted from *Life: An Introduction to Biology*, 2nd ed., by George Gaylord Simpson and William S. Beck, © 1957, 1965, by Harcourt Brace Jovanovich, Inc. Used by permission.)

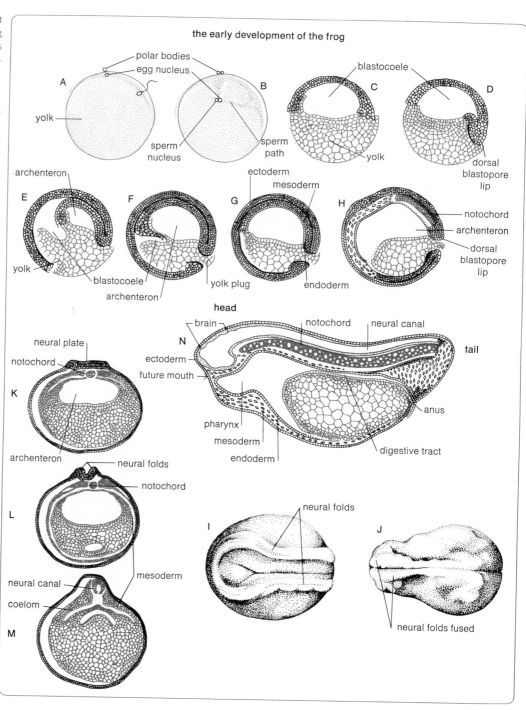

the early development of the frog

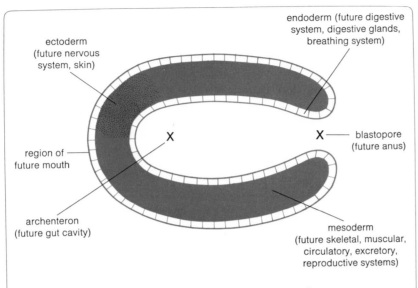

ectoderm
(future nervous
system, skin)

endoderm (future digestive
system, digestive glands,
breathing system)

X ——— blastopore
(future anus)

region of
future mouth

archenteron
(future gut cavity)

mesoderm
(future skeletal, muscular,
circulatory, excretory,
reproductive systems)

structures which develop from germ layer of gastrulation

Ectoderm

Epidermis of the skin, nails, and hair; sweat glands in the skin; all nervous tissue;
receptor cells in the sense organs; epidermis of the mouth, nostrils, and anus.

Endoderm

Epidermis lining the gut, trachea, bronchi, lungs, urinary bladder, and urethra;
liver; pancreas; thyroid gland.

Mesoderm

All muscles; blood; connective tissue (including bone); kidneys, testes and ovaries;
epithelia lining the body cavitites.

FIGURE 10.7 Diagram of the
general structure of a vertebrate
gastrula and the adult organ
systems formed by each of the
primary germ layers. (*Adapted
from Paul B. Weisz, Elements of
Biology, 3rd ed. Copyright
McGraw-Hill Book Company,
1969. Used by permission.*)

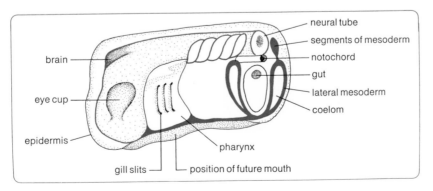

neural tube

segments of mesoderm

brain

notochord

eye cup

gut

lateral mesoderm

coelom

epidermis

pharynx

gill slits —— position of future mouth

FIGURE 10.8 Structure of the
vertebrate embryo.

hollow rod, the *neural tube,* derived from ectoderm. Thus these three cylindrical structures lie, one above the other, in vertebrate embryos. From each side of the notochord, two double sheets of mesodermal cells extend downward around the gut until they meet along the belly side, forming a cylinder of mesoderm surrounding the gut tube. These sheets soon develop open spaces, like an envelope whose two sides are pulled apart, and these spaces become the *coelom,* the vital body cavity containing internal organs. In this way two more cylinders are formed, one directly applied to the gut tube (the inner coelomic mesoderm) and one contiguous to the outer skin, forming the *body wall,* that is, the outer wall of the coelomic cavity (outer coelomic mesoderm). The muscles of these two coelomic walls develop from the two sheets of mesodermal cells. Nerves grow out from the neural tube (Figure 10.9), which, in turn, becomes the spinal cord. Meanwhile, the notochord is replaced by the vertebral column, which not only supports the body but also encloses the neural spinal-cord structures.

FIGURE 10.9 The development of the nervous system in frogs: (*a*) neural plate, (*b*) early neural groove, (*c*) late neural groove, (*d*) neural tube. (*Carolina Biological Supply Co.*)

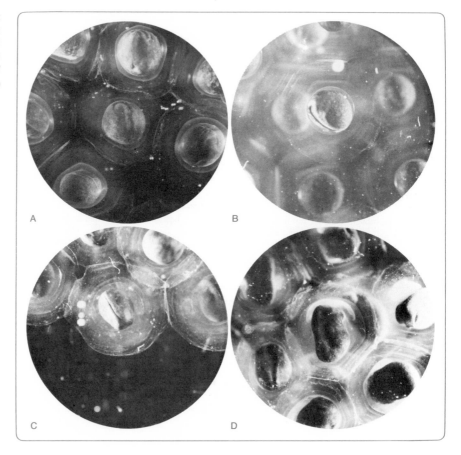

What mechanisms are involved in the transition from single cell to a complex organism such as those we have briefly reviewed? We cannot yet give definitive answers to most of the basic questions about development, but we can describe what happens and attempt some reasonable explanations of how it takes place.

As we learned in Chapter 7, a multicellular organism becomes larger as its cells increase in number and size. Increase in both the total number of cells and the volume of the substances they produce internally and externally causes the size of the organism to increase. However, growth in size does not continue at a constant pace. For example, if *all* the cells doubled with each cell generation in the human embryo, it would reach an adult size 55 days after conception. As we know, this does not happen. Although the rate of cell division is exceedingly rapid during the early embryonic stage, this rate decreases as the embryo continues to develop. Fishes and reptiles continue to grow larger throughout life, but most animals stop growing when they reach an adult size. Plants, however, continue producing new organs throughout their lives.

Within an organism, the rate at which cells lose their ability to divide varies with different types of cells. As we shall see, some cells continue to reproduce throughout the organism's life, while others lose their ability to reproduce. What controls the rate at which cells divide?

Control over growth rate may be determined by various *cell products* which *accumulate* among the cells and inhibit growth. Some cells divide only in response to certain extracellular substances such as hormones. An important factor limiting cell division is the requirements of certain states of *differentiation* of cells. For example, specialized skeletal-muscle cells develop an elaborate contractile apparatus which is essentially permanent. Normally these cells never divide once they have developed this specialized apparatus. Injury may result in the destruction of muscle cells. To repair the injury small cells stored in the muscle tissue and capable of producing daughter cells which can differentiate into new muscle cells are mobilized.

Many of the cell types of your body normally divide only very infrequently or not at all and hence remain as they are until they die, for example, cells of the pancreas, nervous system, skeletal muscles, salivary glands, tooth enamel, kidney filtering units, endocrine glands, and the red blood cells. On the other hand, numerous equally specialized cell types divide continuously, for example, cells of the intestinal lining, skin cells, white blood cells, and wandering connective-tissue cells producing intercellular materials. Thus, merely because a cell is specialized or differentiated does not mean it has lost the power of cell division. In injury repair, furthermore, many cell types which normally divide only very rarely if at all can suddenly burst into active division. A famous example concerns replacement of excised liver tissue; in a rat most of whose liver has been removed 90 percent of the liver can be replaced by cell division in the remaining 10 percent in a few days.

Just as many cells are constantly dividing in an adult organism, many others are constantly dying. Dead cells are continuously being removed from your system. White blood cells live only a few days, red blood cells live about 2 months, and cells lining the digestive tract and covering the surface of the skin are sloughed away so rapidly that their average life is only about 3 days. In certain tissues a reservoir of *stem* cells exists, the division of which serves to replace needed cell populations. An example is bone marrow, the source of new blood cells.

It is possible for normally nondividing specialized cells to suffer a loss of control over mitosis and develop a rapid rate of cell division, thus producing great numbers of abnormal cells, a process common in the abnormal growths we call *cancer* (Figure 10.10). The cause of this often lethal phenomenon remains unknown, though it is the subject of intensive investigation.

Control of the rate of cell division according to the specialization of the cell types in question can be accomplished by means of intercellular control substances or in other ways. Some investigators believe that cellular packing and surface contact in cell types present in closely packed tissues are directly related to control of cell division. Thus when specialized organ tissue is removed from an organism and placed in a nutrient culture, individual cells migrate from the cell cluster and begin to divide. This loss of specialization is thought to be caused by the dilution of cell products which helped the cells maintain their specialization as long as they were encased in the tissue. Once away from the cluster, the cells divide rapidly, until the surface upon which they are living is covered with a sheet of cells. When the cells have occupied all the available space, cell division ceases.

FIGURE 10.10 Urine sediment smear, showing normal cells *left* and malignant cells *right* 600×. (*Courtesy of the American Cancer Society.*)

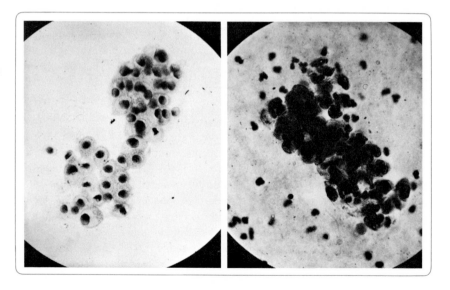

It is obvious that the overall size of a multicellular organism is determined both by the total number and the size of its cells. Cell size is limited primarily by two factors, the surface-to-volume ratio and the nucleus-to-cytoplasm ratio.

The *surface-to-volume ratio* describes the amount of cell-membrane surface area available for transportation of substances in and out of the cell. If the surface area is inadequate, either the food that can be acquired is too little or the waste that accumulates is too great. Because the surface area of a cell increases at a slower rate than volume, there is a limit to the practical increase in volume. This limitation means that a cell cannot continue to grow unless it increases its surface by forming many small extensions of the cell membrane. The highly convoluted surface of cells in tissue culture demonstrates this means of increasing surface area. A skeletal-muscle cell provides a different kind of example: The diameter of a muscle cell is about the size of a human hair and may be several inches long, but it has many nuclei and its extended length provides ample surface area for transport of substances through its cell membrane.

The *nucleus-to-cytoplasm ratio* refers to the size of the nucleus in relation to the volume of cytoplasm in the cell. From the nucleus comes a constant supply of messenger RNA to code for the synthesis of the protein enzymes that regulate the activities of the cell. Like an automobile assembly plant, where cars cannot be assembled any faster than directions are issued from the administrative office, the work of a cell is limited in part by the amount of *m*RNA that is being produced by the DNA in the nucleus. The amount of cytoplasm, therefore, cannot exceed what the nucleus can build and control.

In summary, cell division is controlled by a number of internal and external factors which are only beginning to be understood and which are intimately related to the kind of specialization characteristic of each cell type. Cell size is limited by the capacity of the cell membrane to transport vital substances and of the nucleus to control the cell's activities, as well as by various physical and other factors such as available space. Much still remains to be learned about control of cell size.

A multicellular organism has several means of acquiring its form, including *unequal growth,* imposition of certain *patterns* of cell division, deposition of *extracellular substances,* for example, bone, change in shape of individual cells, and *cell migration.* These processes vary in importance depending on the organism and its particular characteristics. Cells cannot migrate in plants, for instance, which must construct their form without using cell migration.

The form of an individual cell may be influenced by physical contact with its environment. Cells in a fluid environment often assume a spherical shape, in response to the hydrostatic pressures of the fluid in contact with them, like a drop of oil suspended in water. Some single-celled organisms (like the ameba) have continually changing forms while others have fixed shapes (like those moving with

HOW DOES AN
ORGANISM DEVELOP
IN FORM?

flagella or cilia). Cells in multicellular organisms may have many forms, determined by their special functional roles and the details of intercellular contact. Whatever these details in a given case, we can say that the *form of a particular cell results from the expression of its inherited character as that expression responds to the immediate environment*. In cell cultures cells grown on glass with etched grooves respond by extending their pseudopodia along the grooves and assuming elongated shapes. Cells grown on blood clots extend their pseudopodia along the branching fibers of the clot and become star-shaped.

UNEQUAL GROWTH

Growth by cell division not only increases the size of an organism but may also mold its form. Change in form can result from differing rates of cell division in various parts of an embryo (unequal growth). Particular forms often result from certain patterns of cell division which derive from the planes or angles of certain metaphase planes during development (see Chapter 7). The orientation of the metaphase planes determines in what directions the daughter cells will lie after telophase. For example, a spherical embryo growing in only one dimension will become an elongated cylinder; if it grows in two dimensions, it will become a flat sheet; in three dimensions it will become an enlarged sphere. In most plants, for instance, the metaphase planes formed are primarily at right angles to the longitudinal axis of the plant, with the result that plant structures tend to assume the shape of a long cylinder as the cells multiply. Some plants, such as grasses, have only this primary growth and thus are very long and slender. Other plants, especially woody ones, have secondary growth resulting from cell division in tissue arranged in a circle around the long axis of the stem. The cell divisions of secondary growth tend to occur in a plane *parallel* to the longitudinal axis, and thus when the new cells grow in size, the plant increases in girth. In addition, growth of branches, leaves, and flowers occurs by cell division at specific parts of the plant; thus, the form of a plant is due to unequal growth resulting from differing *rates* and *planes* of cell division in various parts of the plant.

MIGRATING CELLS OF
ANIMAL EMBRYOS

Besides unequal cell division, which occurs in the development of all multicellular organisms, both plant and animal, form is developed through the migration of cells from one part of the embryo to another. As we noted above, plants cannot develop shape in this manner since their cells have rigid walls which prevent any sort of movement. Animal cells, however, can move, and the development of form during the very *early stages* of embryonic life in animals is primarily due to migration of cells. Often the cells move individually, by ameboid movement (see Chapter 3). In other cases large masses of cells may move together, in ways that are not yet understood.

During later stages of the animal embryo, unequal rates of cell division cause layers of cells to fold in or out, thus extending organs and appendages. An interesting aspect of the morphogenesis of some appendages is the role of cell death. Saunders has reported that the sculpturing of amphibian limbs is caused by some cells dying in certain areas while other cells are dividing elsewhere (Figure 10.11). Because of the unequal rates of cell death in different areas of the appendage, the upper arm becomes freed from the body wall and separate digits (or fingers) are formed.

In the tadpole, massive cell death occurs as certain tail cells die, the cartilage of the tail is dissolved by special enzymes, and the remains are consumed by phagocytic white blood cells. Meanwhile elsewhere in the tadpole the intestine is shortening, and the gills and other larval structures are disappearing. All these processes involve a controlled pattern of cell death and cell division. In some insects, adult tissues form only after the larval cells have died. Clearly, the form of an organism involves more than the accumulation of additional cells; it also involves the removal of cells through a system of regulated death. Often the regulation agent appears to be a hormone.

While the cells are migrating and dividing in embryonic life, they are also *differentiating*. Thus far, we have emphasized the *growth processes* of development; now we shall consider cellular differentiation.

An interesting example of the appearance of a new, differentiated structure is the formation of the neural tube in frog embryos (see Figure 10.12). The first indication that

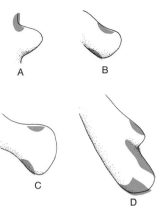

FIGURE 10.11 Cell death in the sculpturing of a limb. (a) to (d) represent successively older limb buds. Areas with color represent regions where cells are dying.

DIFFERENTIATION: NEW STRUCTURES FROM OLD

FIGURE 10.12 The initial development of the nervous system in vertebrates (frogs). (a) Left to right, dorsal views, progressive stages. The anterior ends of the embryos are toward the right. (b) Diagrammatic cross sections corresponding to the stages in (a). (c) Cross sections corresponding to the first and last stages illustrated in (b). Note large amounts of yolk in (c). (*Top and bottom adapted from Roberts Rugh, Experimental Embryology, Burgess Publishing Company. Middle adapted from Paul B. Weisz, Elements of Biology, 3rd ed. Copyright McGraw-Hill Book Company, 1969. Used by permission.*)

the neural tube is forming is a thickening of ectodermal cells along the dorsal midline of the embryo. This thickened strip of cells then bends inward to form a neural groove. The sides of the groove move toward each other and join, to form a tube which sinks below the surface of the epidermis of the embryo. What causes this sequence of events, and what induces the neural tube to begin to differentiate?

THE ORGANIZER CONCEPT

Spemann demonstrated in 1924 that the neural tube of the amphibian embryo will not form if the notochord developing beneath it is removed. The mesoderm from which the notochord develops is known to have migrated into the embryo from the region lying above the blastopore. As the migrating mesodermal cells turn in through the blastopore, they eventually come to lie under the overlying ectoderm, with which they are in close contact.

The region lying above the blastopore of a frog embryo is called the *dorsal lip*. Earlier experiments had shown the cells of the dorsal lip to be responsible for the organization of much of the gastrula, and Spemann believed that the cells of the dorsal lip could cause ectoderm to form a neural tube. To test this idea he transplanted dorsal-lip cells from one embryo into the blastocoel of another so that the cells came into contact with the overlying ectoderm (Figure 10.13). The transplanted cells developed into a notochord as they would have if they had been allowed to develop where they were. What is most important, they *induced a neural tube to form* next to them, and in a most inappropriate place, the embryo's belly. Surprisingly, the area of the second neural tube continued growing and produced a second embryo. These artificially induced Siamese twins were joined at their bellies. Having used dorsal-lip cells from a species of frog colored differently from the host, Spemann could tell that almost all the cells of the secondary embryo were from the host. Thus the dorsal-lip cells had caused the overlying host cells to organize into a secondary embryo. Spemann termed the dorsal lip the *organizer* of the embryo. The interaction between notochord and overlying ectoderm to produce a neural tube is only one of the many interactions which take place during the sequence of changes in development. The term *inductive interaction* is used today to describe phenomena in which certain specialized cells induce other cells to become *differentiated* through some interaction between them.

Inductive interaction is one way in which groups of cells become differentiated, or specialized. Long before the completion of embryonic growth, cells have become differentiated into tissues and organs which perform specific functions in the body. The cells of the blastula are not specialized, but beginning with the onset of gastrulation differentiation begins. The obvious question here is: What is the mechanism by which cells specialize and become different from each other?

We have been discussing development, using whole embryos as our primary frame of reference; let us see what takes place in the individual cells, since it is the properties of individual cells which determine the properties of the organism. One way of studying individual cells from a multicellular organism is provided by cell culturing.

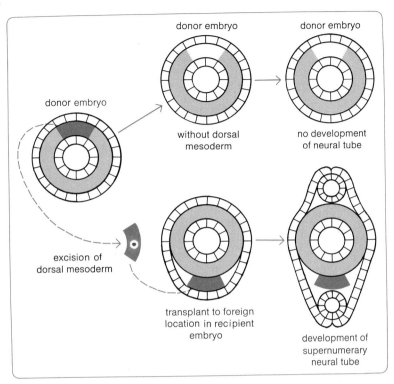

FIGURE 10.13   Neural induction. If the dorsal mesoderm of a
donor embryo is transplanted
under the belly ectoderm of a host
embryo, the transplant induces formation of an abnormally located
neural tube in the host. (*Adapted
from Paul B. Weisz, Elements of
Biology, 3rd ed. Copyright
McGraw-Hill Book Company,
1969. Used by permission.*)

TISSUES TO CELLS AND
CELLS TO TISSUES

Before the beginning of this century, it was found that tissues would break up into
cells if *calcium were removed* from their environment.   During the following years it
was discovered that the addition of trypsin (an enzyme which digests proteins) would
break tissues up into separate cells.   With either of these methods, or other
techniques which have since been discovered, tissues can be transformed into a
population of free cells by dissolving the intercellular cement holding the cells
together.   Such cells can now be studied in a cell culture.

In 1907, Wilson studied the behavior of single free cells derived from the multicellular tissues of a sponge.   He obtained the cells by pressing marine sponges
through a finely meshed silk cloth.   The cells sank to the bottom of the dish and
aggregated into clumps, which later developed into functioning sponges again.   The
cells had apparently attracted each other in certain highly exact ways.   Other scientists later discovered that cells of higher organisms behave in the same way.

Tissues from a bird or mammal embryo treated with trypsin become free cells.
Moscona found that dispersed cells of various tissues of chick and rodent embryos
would migrate over the surface of their culture dish to form clusters of cells with
common specialization.   Thus, kidney cells would always clump with other kidney

FIGURE 10.14 Filter assembly
for studies of induction.

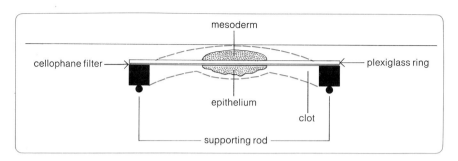

cells, bone cells with bone cells, heart cells with heart cells, etc., even if from different species! For example kidney and heart cells from both mouse and chick embryos were mixed together in culture. When they were allowed to aggregate, it was found that the kidney cells all clumped together with each other and the heart cells clumped together even though the resulting aggregates contained cells from these two very different species. It is clear that differentiated cells are able to *recognize* each other on the basis of their particular specialization even across species lines. The tendency of cells belonging to a single tissue to group together is an important aspect of tissue building in embryonic development.

CELL DIFFERENTIATION AND
CELLULAR ENVIRONMENT

Cell products appear to play an important role in cell differentiation. For example, cell products are known to be involved in inductive interactions. In a number of embryonic induction systems it is known that certain active substances *secreted* by the cells do the inducing; these substances are called inductive agents.

One of the ways this has been demonstrated is the *sandwich technique*. Grobstein set up an assembly which separated mesodermal tissue from undifferentiated embryonic epithelial tissue by a thin, porous, cellophane filter (see Figure 10.14). After about 30 hours of interaction, he found that the epithelium differentiated into such tissues as kidney, pancreas, salivary gland, skin, thyroid, and thymus. The type of tissue the epithelium differentiated into was determined by the particular type of mesodermal tissue used. Grown by themselves in culture, the epithelium cells would not differentiate into these tissues. Interactions between the mesoderm and epithelium tissues were necessary, but direct cell-to-cell contact is not needed, since the inductive interactions occurred across the membrane filter separating the cells themselves. In other words, the inducing tissue, mesoderm, produces certain molecules which can move through the membranes and induce differentiation in the epithelium cells on the other side of the membrane.

This discussion has shown that differentiation can be triggered by means of interactions among cells and by the products of other cells. Through time, descendant cells come to manifest different properties from each other even though the set of genes in all the cells remains the same. What varies is the chemical environment of the cells.

Thus, the *products of a cell vary through time* and have different effects on neighboring cells.

Inductive agents provide an example. To this picture we must add the circulating hormones produced in all higher organisms, which have a multitude of specific differentiation—inducing effects. Sex hormones, for example, induce differentiative changes in the specialized reproductive structures in human beings, such as milk production in the breasts and the preparation of the uterine lining for the support of an embryo.

As we saw in Chapter 9, the type of products a cell will synthesize is controlled by the genetic instructions the cell has inherited. A cursory glance at the processes of differentiation shows that there are also external control factors. The products of one cell may activate switching mechanisms to turn on or off the genes which direct the synthesis of specialized substances in other cells. Thus, a change in the chemical environment may affect the nucleus and its control over the synthesizing activities of the cytoplasm and the structures of the cellular components. The subsequent products of this synthesis may, in turn, alter the chemical environment. This dynamic *feedback interaction* between cell and environment is a fundamental aspect of differentiation.

From the preceding we can summarize the following elements of differentiation at the cellular level: (1) All differentiated cells contain the same set of genes; (2) the particular properties of differentiated cells result essentially from the activities of the genes in these cells; and (3) the *expression* of the particular set of properties characteristic of differentiated cells may be induced by the specific products of other cells, such as hormones or inducing agents. It follows that *differentiation must result from the selective activation of certain genes in each cell type,* in response to the specific environmental factors to which the cell responds. This idea is termed the *variable-gene-activity theory of cell differentiation.* It was first suggested by Morgan in 1934, but its serious consideration dates from the early 1950s, when Mirsky (who had recently discovered that all cells of an organism contain the same amount of DNA except for sperm and eggs, which contain half this amount) proposed that *variation in the activity of the genes is responsible for cell differentiation.* A similar idea was suggested at the same time by the Stedmans, a man-and-wife team who studied the proteins bound to the DNA as it is found in chromosomes.

There is now a great deal of evidence in support of the variable-gene-activity-theory of cell differentiation. First, it is known from both biochemical and biological experiments that all the genes really do seem to be present in almost all the cells of an organism. Biochemical tests have shown that the nucleotide sequences of DNA extracted from different tissues appear to be the same in all the tissues of the organism. A spectacular experiment by Gurdon demonstrated that all the genes must be present in at least one differentiated cell type, the intestinal cell of

THE VARIABLE-GENE-
ACTIVITY THEORY OF CELL
DIFFERENTIATION

a tadpole, since the nucleus of this cell can be implanted into an enucleated egg of the same species and a normal frog can be obtained.

If selective activation of certain genes in each cell type is responsible for differentiation, then in each cell type most of the genes must be inactive. This deduction is also supported by much direct evidence. Thus if chromatin (DNA plus proteins) extracted from cells is compared with the pure (deproteinized) DNA of the same cells for its ability to support RNA synthesis, it is found to be only about 10 to 15 percent as active as is the pure DNA. This proves that the proteins attached to the DNA in life *repress* most of the DNA genes; that is, they prevent them from being used for the synthesis of RNA. Furthermore, direct tests for the nucleotide sequences represented in the RNAs of each cell type have shown striking differences; this represents direct evidence that different genes are in fact functional in each of the cell types examined.

What we still do not know is the molecular mechanism by which the pattern of gene activity characteristic of each cell type is imposed on the genetic apparatus carried in the cell nucleus. How the external agents which serve as triggers for differentiated patterns of cell activity function remains mysterious, as does the whole process of *regulation of gene activity*. This is now a crucial central point of biological investigation. In the solution to this problem may lie major insights into phenomena as diverse as how an egg grows into an organism and how a normal cell can turn into a lethal cancer cell.

REVIEW QUESTIONS
1 Describe briefly the growth and development of a flowering plant.
2 Describe briefly the growth and development of a frog.
3 How is form developed in plants?
4 How is form developed in animals?
5 How do cells become specialized into tissues?
6 Describe briefly growth and development as a society of cells that changes through time as a result of the changes occurring within itself.

SUGGESTIONS FOR
FURTHER READING
* Available in paperback.

Ebert, J. D.: *Interacting Systems in Development*, Holt, Rinehart and Winston, Inc., New York, 1965. Technical but the best book available for generalized models describing what happens in growth and development.

Grobstein, C.: *The Strategy of Life*, W. H. Freeman and Company, San Francisco, 1965. Life processes, including growth and development, presented in a superb fashion; very thought-provoking.

Kennedy, D. (ed.): *From Cell to Organism*, W. H. Freeman and Company, San Francisco, 1967. Twenty-four articles chosen from *Scientific American* and introduced by the editor.

Kerr, N. S.: *Principles of Development,* Wm. C. Brown Company Publishers, Dubuque, Iowa, 1967. A good concise and inclusive presentation of the mechanisms of growth and development.

Saunders, J. W., Jr.: **Animal Morphogenesis,* The Macmillan Company, New York, 1968. Develops generalizations from descriptive evidence in an interesting fashion.

Spratt, N. T., Jr.: *Introduction to Cell Differentiation,* Reinhold Publishing Corporation, New York, 1964. Describes how cells are thought to become different from each other during growth and development.

Part 4

Homeostasis:
A Characteristic of Living Things

Living things must be able to respond to changes in their internal and external environments in ways that balance the effects of these changes. These reactions result from nervous responses and hormones. Their effects can be seen in organisms and in ecosystems. The temperature of a human body, a man on a tightrope, the birth and growth of a baby, intertidal organisms on a rock at the seashore, a relatively constant number of organisms in populations, and the behavior of animals—all are examples of how organisms must be able to respond to changes in ways that alleviate their effects.

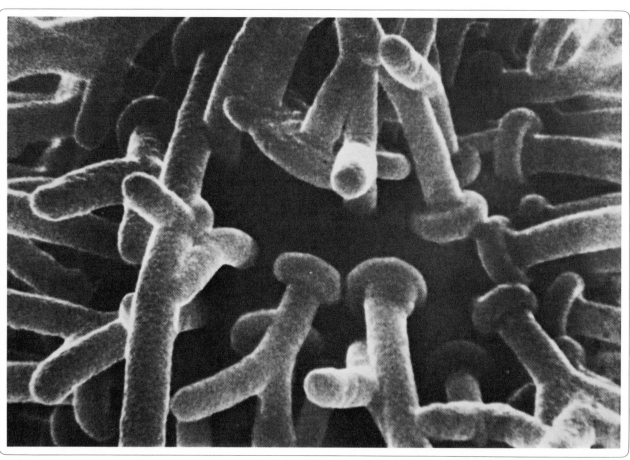

Synaptic knobs of nervous system. (*Courtesy United Press International and E. R. Lewis, Y. Y. Zeeri, and T. E. Everhart, University of California, Berkeley.*)

Chapter 11

Homeostasis in Organisms: How Are Organisms Regulated?

All the vital mechanisms, however varied they may be, have only one object, that of preserving constant the conditions of life in the inner environment.

Bernard

Picture a baby lying in a crib. The baby's structural, functional, and basic behavioral mechanisms were designed by natural selection, coded in its genes, inherited by way of sexual reproduction, and formed by growth and development. Through its inherited mechanisms, the baby is carrying on metabolism, homeostasis, and development in a manner that is characteristic of the human species.

In previous chapters we discussed *metabolism,* the means by which organisms utilize matter and energy, and *development* and *inheritance,* the process by which organisms change in form and function through time. In this chapter, we discuss *homeostasis,* the means by which an organism can maintain itself in a condition that is relatively stable and constant.

WHAT IS HOMEOSTASIS?   A young baby in a crib is often a source of constant concern and worry for its parents, relatives, and baby-sitters. Unlike other newly born mammals, the human baby is almost totally incapable of changing its own relationship with its external environment. Someone else must provide it with food, water, warmth, and protection and must even move it from one position to another. New parents often begin to believe that the baby could not live without their constant attention.

Despite this need for someone else to control its external environment, the baby needs no help with its *internal* activities. Thanks to internal regulatory systems, the baby controls its temperature, blood pressure, pulse rate, breathing rate, replacement of cells, etc. The baby's blood is constantly in a slightly alkaline condition and contains oxygen, carbon dioxide, glucose, and many other chemical compounds which vary only slightly in amount through the day. We may wish to do all we can to comfort the helpless human infant, but most of the vital responses are regulated by the baby's own internal control centers and mechanisms.

As time passes, however, the baby becomes a child and develops more and more intricate processes of interaction with its external environment. We may picture the child feeling the natural urges of a primate and climbing among the branches of a tree. As he starts to fall to the left, he feels muscles pulling him to the right, and as he falls to the right, muscles pull him to the left, so that with an oscillating movement, he is able to weave his way along the limb.

A balance maintained between forces exerting a *push* and a *pull* is an example of homeostasis. Homeostasis is not simply the imposition of a perfectly invariant condition but the regulation of a system which *compensates* in response to a push one way or a pull the other way. For each body process, there is a certain range of fluctuation the body can tolerate, but beyond these limits the organism can lose its balance and be seriously impaired. Homeostasis, in many instances, is what we call *health*.

Homeostasis is all about us and within us. Our tree-climbing child, when he has grown older, gets into his car and drives downtown. He moves along streets and highways turning the steering wheel to the left or right in a manner that prevents collisions with other cars. The pushes and pulls upon the car and its driver-regulator are diverse and complex, but the driver manages to respond to these stimuli and regulate the car's motion. Suppose, however, that upon hearing a loud horn on his left, he overcompensates to the right and drives off the highway and into a tree.

The boy has a slight cut and will lose some blood, but the damaged tissues quickly induce clotting and the blood loss will stop. Red and white blood cells will be released from the bone marrow as replacements for blood cells which have been lost. Some of the white blood cells will flow into the region of the wound and will engulf bacteria and debris, while others may produce antibodies against foreign molecules that have been introduced.

The frightened boy's heart beats faster and his blood pressure rises. He feels stronger, however, since his blood supply to his skeletal muscles is increased and the bronchioles leading to his lungs are dilated. He begins to breathe more rapidly as he gets out of his car and climbs up an embankment to the edge of the highway. It is hard work and his metabolic rate accelerates and provides the necessary energy. Much of the energy is released as heat, and his body temperature begins to rise. This tendency is corrected, however, when he begins sweating and the evaporating liquid causes his skin and its circulating blood to lose heat. His body temperature returns to a more normal range somewhere between 98 and 99°F.

He sits by the roadside and breathes heavily for a time while oxygen is consumed in aerobic respiration and the level of ATP molecules is restored. Soon, his breathing rate, pulse rate, blood pressure, and body temperature return to a normal level. His body has responded to the various pushes and pulls affecting it and has restored the balanced set of conditions that we call normal.

The tree struck by the car also contains homeostatic mechanisms. As a result of the normal growth among the embryonic cells lying between the wood and the bark, a layer of cells will soon grow over and cover the region from which a limb has been lost (see Figure 11.1).

Homeostasis means, then, that for most changes which impinge on an organism counterchanges are available, and the response of the organism tends to alter conditions so that they become more favorable. At times, the alteration may be a restoration to the previous conditions, but at other times the response may consist of a change to an entirely new set of conditions. Either way, the response cannot be said to be homeostatic unless it favors the continued existence of the organism.

The sequence of events in homeostasis usually forms a conceptual *loop,* a circle of agents which act either as receptors or as producers of products. Since homeostatic response is a reaction to a change in the environment, for this to happen, there must be a receptor that can be stimulated by the change. This stimulated receptor must then cause a *control center* to respond in some way. In the best-known mammalian cases the control center responds either by secreting a hormone or by sending on a nerve impulse. Whichever it is, the hormone or the nerve impulse affects the receptor by causing it to continue to be stimulated or to turn off. Thus, this sequence— from receptor to control center to product (hormone or impulse) and back to the receptor—forms a closed loop of events.

HOMEOSTATIC SYSTEMS

A familiar example of a homeostatic loop is the thermostat and furnace system of your home. The thermostat is the receptor that is sensitive to the level of heat. When the heat falls below a certain threshold level, the receptor turns on and causes a flow of electricity in the thermostat, the control center, and on to the furnace. The furnace gives out its product, hot air, and when the temperature builds up to a certain level again, the receptor is turned off by the heat and the electrical output of the control center is temporarily shut down.

In a similar way, there is a region called the *hypothalamus* at the base of the brain which is sensitive to the level of the hormone thyroxin being produced by the thyroid gland in the throat. When the level of thyroxin falls below a certain threshold level,

FIGURE 11.1 Where a branch has been lost from a tree, a layer of cells grows over as a homeostatic response. (*Courtesy of M. Chapman.*)

this receptor is activated and causes the secretion from the adjacent pituitary gland of a hormone called *thyroid-stimulating hormone* (TSH). TSH is carried in the circulating blood to the thyroid gland, which it stimulates to begin producing thyroxin. When thyroxin builds up to a certain level in the blood again, the thyroxin receptor in the hypothalamus is turned off and the production of TSH is temporarily shut down.

In both cases we can identify an *input* (the electrical impulses from the thermostat and the TSH from the hypothalamus) and an *output* (the heat from the furnace and the thyroxin from the thyroid gland). The output product of the system, whether heat, nerve impulse, or hormone, had a *feedback* effect on the homeostatic system. If the system responds to an increasing level of product by increasing the production of that product, the system is said to have *positive feedback* control. In contrast, if the system decreases its output as the product level increases, the system is said to have *negative feedback* control.

Most homeostatic mechanisms utilize negative feedback. Positive feedback would cause the furnace to produce more and more heat as the temperature increases. Likewise, positive feedback would cause more and more TSH to be produced as the thyroxin level increases. Homeostatic responses tend to push conditions back toward the normal range and away from the extremes. The effect of a homeostatic output must therefore be negative in almost all cases.

HOMEOSTATIC FACTORS

In a sense all the morphological and molecular aspects of an organism, from its enzymes to its locomotive appendages, are or can be involved in homeostatic responses. It is not an exaggeration to say that a whole organism is a homeostatic system composed of a multitude of smaller homeostatic systems. On the physiological level at which the activities of tissues and organs are coordinated we are aware of two main homeostatic regulation systems, nervous and hormonal.

Nerves allow rapid homeostatic responses, with nerve impulses traveling on actual physical structures, the nerve-cell membranes, in a fashion somewhat analogous to a telegraph message. The nervous system functions through simple reflexes, whose patterns are inherited, as well as complex responses, which may be learned. Whether learned or not, however, the responses involve a system of nerve cells developed in an embryo according basically to inherited genetic information. Learned homeostatic responses are superimposed on the unlearned mechanisms.

Hormones are molecules that serve as chemical messengers. They are produced by various specialized cells, sometimes belonging to the nervous system and sometimes arranged in masses called glands. The hormones are absorbed directly into the bloodstream or circulated by other means in organisms which lack closed circulatory systems. They are transported to other parts of the organism where they produce their specific effects. Unlike the nervous system, hormonal control systems are "wireless." Interactions between parts of the body can thus be due to molecules dissolved in the water of the blood. Hormones are secreted in response to control signals conveyed to the cells producing them either as nerve impulses or as other hormonal molecules in the blood.

In the following discussion, we shall concentrate on the role of the nervous and endocrine systems in homeostasis in the human organism (*endocrine* glands are hormone-synthesizing glands in which the cells producing the hormones are adjacent to the blood capillaries and secrete directly into them). We shall begin with the nervous system.

NERVOUS CONTROLS IN HOMEOSTASIS

The basic unit of structure in the nervous system is the nerve cell, or *neuron*. There are about 12 billion neurons in the human nervous system, and three-fourths of them are in the brain. The remaining 3 billion are found primarily in the spinal cord but also make up small islands, called *ganglia,* scattered among various tissues and organs.

NEURONS

Neurons in the human may have one, two, or more fibers extending from the *cell body,* the central region containing the nucleus. Usually, these fibers are of two kinds, dendrites and axons (see Figure 11.2). *Dendrites* receive impulses from other nerve cells and conduct impulses toward the cell body. *Axons* conduct impulses away from the cell body. There may be many dendrites on a neuron, and, except for sensory neurons, most dendrites are rather short. Usually there is only one axon leading away from the cell body. Axons are usually covered with a sheath (or *neurilemma*) made of special cells called *Schwann cells,* which not only supply nutrition to the long nerve fiber but provide a tube through which a new fiber can grow if the previous one is damaged. Most axons also have a layer of membranous material called *myelin* between the Schwann cell membrane and the axon membrane. It was thought for many years that the myelin was secreted by the Schwann cells or the axon, but this has recently been shown to be false. The electron microscope has revealed that myelin is not a secretion product at all but a tightly packed sheath deriving from the cell membrane of the Schwann cells (see Figure 11.3). A sequence of regularly spaced nodes is formed where one Schwann cell ends and another begins.

NERVE IMPULSE

The physical chemistry of the nerve impulse was discussed in Chapter 3. We learned that cell membranes contain *ion pumps,* which pump sodium ions to the outside of the cell where they are concentrated. The result is a polarization of the membrane with a positively charged outside region and a negatively charged inside region. Nerve cells are specialized to pump sodium out of their cells. Their sodium pumps are easily stalled by various nerve-stimulating agents. When a region of the membrane has been stimulated and its ion pumps have been stalled, the adjoining region of cell membrane is affected in its turn and a wave of ion-pump stalling moves down the length of the neuron very rapidly. The stalling is temporary, and the ion pumps are restored within 1/1,000 second. The nerve is now ready to carry another impulse. An analogy is often made between a nerve impulse and a burning fuse, for in both cases the impulse is propagated by the fiber itself, but it would be a most unusual fuse which could repair itself immediately and be capable of burning again and again at millisecond intervals.

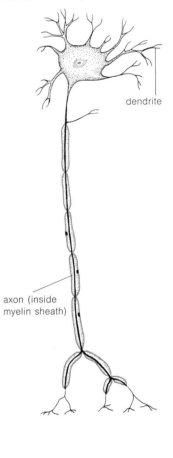

FIGURE 11.2 Dendrite and axon of a motor neuron, with the axon enclosed in its myelin sheath.

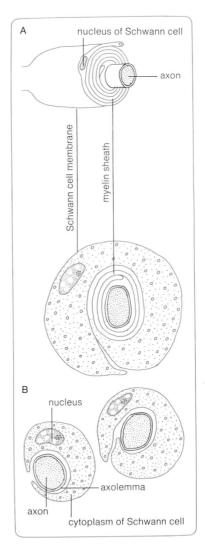

FIGURE 11.3 (a) Myelinated axon, three-dimensional lateral view. (b) Development of myelin sheath from Schwann cell membrane. Note how membrane grows in concentric circles to form sheath around axon.

SYNAPSE A nerve impulse can travel in either direction from the point of stimulation on the nerve-cell membrane, but it can be passed on to another neuron only at the endings of the axon. As a result nerve impulses can travel in only one direction, from the axon of one neuron to the dendrite of the next. The connection between axon and dendrite is called a *synapse*. The reason for this one-way partiality at the synapse is that only the axon is capable of secreting the substance *acetylcholine*, which stimulates the cell membrane of the dendrites of the next neuron. Dendrites cannot secrete this substance, but they do synthesize *cholinesterase*, an enzyme which destroys the acetylcholine. Without this enzyme, the acetylcholine would persist and would continue to stimulate the dendrites. Most nerve gases and insecticides inhibit the secretion of cholinesterase. As a result, the nervous system is uncontrolled and tremors, spasms, and death result. Cholinesterase is secreted only in response to acetylcholine and provides an excellent example of a homeostatic negative feedback.

Acetylcholine is secreted by the endings of axons and induces new nerve impulses where it contacts the dendrites in the synapse (see Figure 11.4). The substance must diffuse from axon to dendrite, and for this to occur in rapid fashion the two nerve fibers must be fairly near each other. The electron microscope reveals that axon and dendrite are very close but are separated by a *synaptic cleft,* a very narrow space about 200 angstroms or about 0.00002 centimeter wide.

Axons branch repeatedly at their terminal ends, each branch terminating in a swelling called a *synaptic knob.* It is the association of these knobs with the membranes of dendrites which makes up what we call synapses. Synaptic knobs

FIGURE 11.4 (a) Synapses between axons of association neurons (shown in color) and the cell body and dendrites of a motor neuron and (b) a detail of a synapse.

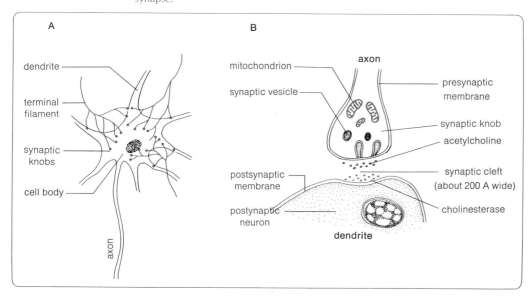

contain energy-generating mitochondria and large numbers of secretion vesicles containing acetylcholine. The arrival of a nerve impulse at the synaptic knob causes the vesicles to move to the surface and empty their contents into the synaptic cleft, across which the acetylcholine then diffuses.

Synapses offer various degrees of resistance to the transmission of nerve impulses along a series of neurons. Usually a dendrite is stimulated only by the action of many synaptic knobs and in many cases seems to require the combined actions of several axons. Sometimes in synapses containing multiple axons, the stimulation of many of them has an inhibiting effect on the transmission of an impulse. Thus, joining several axons in a synapse with a dendrite may result in a cooperative *summation* of their effects as an *inhibition*. Added to these complexities is the fact that acetylcholine and cholinesterase are not the only chemical substances produced by nerve-cell synapses. An understanding of the synapse is fundamental to an eventual understanding of the nervous system and the workings of the mind.

THE EFFECTS OF NERVE IMPULSES

Synapses are the junctions between axons and dendrites in a series of nerve cells. Eventually, a nerve impulse may reach the point where an axon connects with a muscle cell. Again, just as in synapses, a junction exists between the axon and the object to which it can transmit an impulse. Instead of calling the connection between axon and muscle cell a synapse, the most commonly used term is *neuromuscular junction* (see Figure 11.5). When an impulse reaches the end of the axon, it releases acetylcholine, as it would in a synapse, which produces an effect on the membrane of the muscle cell just as it did on the membrane of the dendrite. An impulse moves along the membrane of the muscle cell and causes the filaments of the contractile units in the myofibrils to contract and slide past each other.

A nerve impulse can also travel along a series of nerve cells terminating in a secretory gland. The gland may be nervous tissue, or it may be specialized tissue of another source, such as mesoderm. Either way secretions by the ending of the axon cause the tissue to secrete its substance. We shall learn later in this chapter that the rate at which many endocrine glands function is under direct control of the nervous system. Nerve function is affected by many controlling factors, and hormones can in turn affect the functioning of the nervous system. This control loop is clearly a major mechanism of homeostasis in complex animals.

REFLEX ARCS

Neuron impulses can originate with the stimulation of a sense receptor sensitive to factors inside or outside the body. These impulses may lead into the brain, where they may spread through various neuronal circuits for a brief time before action is taken or they may bring about immediate involuntary action. Many of the immediate actions are called reflexes, and the pathways linking the receptor neuron with the neuron that brought about action are called *reflex arcs* (see Figure 11.6).

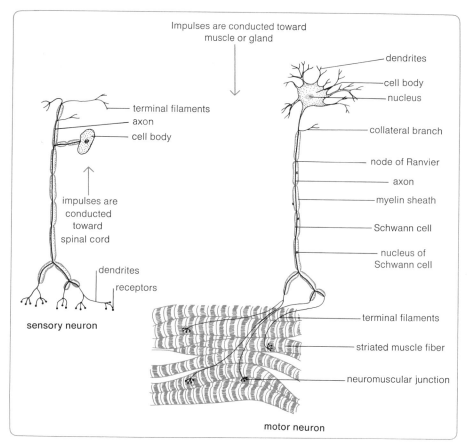

Impulses are conducted toward muscle or gland

dendrites
cell body
nucleus

terminal filaments
axon
cell body

collateral branch

node of Ranvier

axon

myelin sheath

Schwann cell

nucleus of Schwann cell

impulses are conducted toward spinal cord

dendrites
receptors

terminal filaments

striated muscle fiber

neuromuscular junction

sensory neuron

motor neuron

FIGURE 11.5 A comparison of a motor neuron and a sensory neuron. The cell body of the motor neuron lies in the spinal cord, and the cell body of the sensory neuron lies just outside the spinal cord in ganglia.

The minimum number of neurons in a reflex arc is two, a *sensory neuron,* which brings the impulse in from a sense receptor, and a *motor neuron,* which carries the impulse out from the brain or spinal cord to an effector such as a muscle or gland. Most reflex arcs, however, consist of more than two neurons. One or more *association neurons* in the brain or spinal cord afford connections between sensory and motor neurons. Association neurons form complex pathways up and down and within the spinal cord and brain and make up most of their bulk.

Sensory neurons leading to, and motor neurons leading from, the brain and spinal cord do not freely branch around in the tissues: They are collected into bundles called *nerves.* Nerves are similar to telephone cables in that they are made of axons and dendrites arranged in parallel lines separated by the fatty myelin acting as an insulation which prevents nerve impulses from short-circuiting.

An example of a reflex arc is what happens when you step on a tack. The tack stimulates special endings of sensory neurons called *sense receptors* and causes a

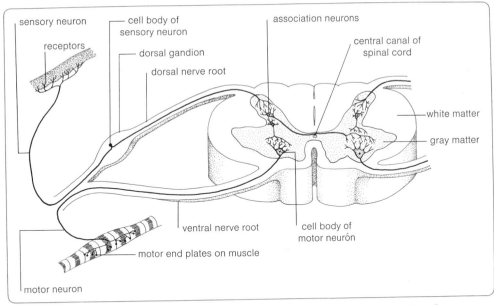

FIGURE 11.6 The reflex arc. Cross section of spinal cord showing motor, sensory, and association neurons.

nerve impulse to travel up the sensory neurons, ascending via a nerve in your leg to the spinal cord near the small of your back. Here the impulse is transmitted to one or more association neurons for transmission on to one or more motor neurons in the spinal cord. The axons of the motor neurons extend outward in nerves leading to the muscles. The muscle cells contract, and the foot is withdrawn from the source of the stimulus. This homeostatic response is almost immediate, involuntary, and not consciously directed. Following the reflex, conscious reflection upon possible sources of the tack in your foot may occur, but these phenomena require the combined action of many neurons in the brain.

THE BRAIN

The control center for both nervous and hormonal control of homeostasis in the vertebrate organism is the brain and the pituitary gland attached to its lower side. The vertebrate brain develops as an extensive overgrowth of the front end of the neural tube. Into the human brain are packed 9 billion neurons, and it is their activities which endow us with typical human potentialities. The cell bodies of these neurons are gray and make up the brain's *gray matter*. The *white matter* consists of the axons and dendrites which branch about in the brain's interior and form an almost infinite number of intricate connections between the vast numbers of neurons. The brain consists of several major areas, but we shall concern ourselves with only the *cerebrum, cerebellum, medulla,* and *hypothalamus* (see Figure 11.7).

The cerebrum, largest part of the human brain, forms a domelike cap over the end of the spinal cord. It is the center for receiving sensory information, associating new

FIGURE 11.7 (a) The left half of
the brain viewed from the outside
with functions of the labeled parts
indicated in parentheses. (b) The
left half of the brain viewed from
the inner, cut side. (c) Various
parts and their functions. (c detail
drawn after model designed by D.
J. F. Mueller, Ward's Natural
Science Establishment, Inc.)

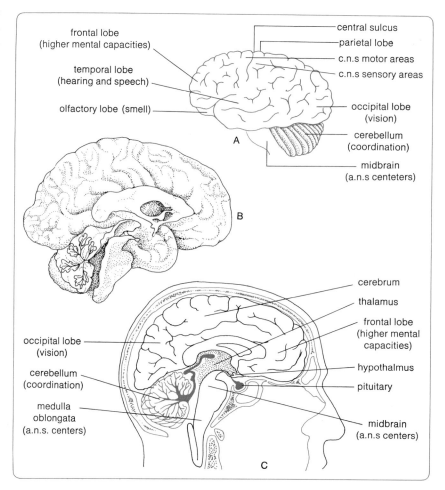

sensations with old, and dispatching motor impulses to the muscles for action. The
gray matter of the cerebrum is found primarily on the outer surface, called the
cerebral cortex. The cerebrum has a division of labor among its regions,
specializations being identified with localized areas in the cerebral cortex. Thus
there are sensory areas, motor areas, and association areas operating as a mosaic of
various specialized operations but each with a major role in addition to its minor
roles.

The primate brain has conspicuous development of the cerebrum into four lobes.
The *occipital lobe* at the rear of the cerebrum contains the greatly expanded visual

cortex. Forward lies the *parietal lobe*, containing the *sensory area*, into which come impulses from the sense receptors in the skin. The localization of function in the motor and sensory areas of the cerebal cortex is show in Figure 11.8.

Below the parietal lobes lies the *temporal lobe*, the large size being another characteristic of primates. This increase in size must have great significance, but the functions of the temporal lobe are not well understood. It is known that part of the temporal cortex is auditory, and it is believed that visual memories may be stored there. If so, a primate may profit from visual experiences from previous times by recalling scenes from this "movie bank." Studies of the anatomy of the temporal lobe reveal connections which seem to allow it to receive impulses from other areas of the cortex. It is possible that integration of the results of activities of the entire cortex takes place on the temporal lobe.

The *frontal lobe* lies forward of the parietal lobe and is separated from it by the central sulcus (a deep crevice in the cortex of the brain; see Figure 11.7). Just in front of the sulcus lies the *motor area* in the frontal lobe. Motor impulses which cause contractions of skeletal muscles originate in the motor area. The frontal lobe has the reputation of possessing the highest level of cortical activity, but this is proba-

FIGURE 11.8 Localization of motor and sensory areas of the human cerebral cortex. Section on the left is through the sensory area just back of the central sulcus and the section on the right is through the motor area just in front of the central sulcus. The cortex is indicated by the heavy black line, and is broken into sections to indicate local functions. The drawings on the outside of the heavy line indicate the body region serviced by that portion of the cerebral cortex. (*Adapted from G. G. Simpson and W. S. Beck, Life: An Introduction to Biology, 2d ed., 1965, Harcourt Brace Jovanovich, Inc. Adapted from W. Penfield and T. Rasmussen, The Cerebral Cortex of Man. Copyright 1950 by the Macmillan Company. Used with permission.*)

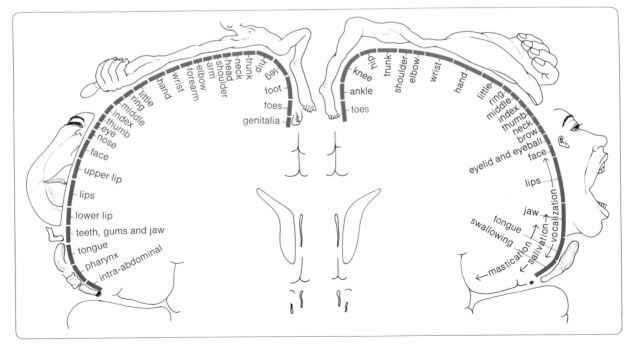

bly not correct. Although its functions are complex and not well understood, the lobe seems to have as its most important function the means of focusing and concentrating mental processes on a particular item of concern. The frontal lobe seems to be the primary site of what we call *consciousness*. In the progression from monkeys to apes to man the frontal lobe gains larger and larger proportions, as is evidenced by the vertical forehead in man. This lobe is the primary reason for man's highly developed ability for *conscious thought*.

The *cerebellum* reveals an increase in size and complexity evolved in direct partnership with the increasing complexity of the cerebrum. This inference of a close functional relationship between cerebrum and cerebellum is shown to be valid by an intricate network of axons and dendrites connecting the cerebellum to most areas of the cerebral cortex. Motor impulses arising in the cerebral cortex pass to the cerebellum before being sent on to the voluntary or skeletal muscles in a coordinated way. With an impaired cerebellum a primate lacks coordination. The cerebrum is sometimes compared to an executive and the cerebellum to his secretary.

It is of interest to note that if the entire cerebral cortex is removed from a dog or cat, he will be able to stand and walk almost as well as a normal animal. Apparently, in these nonprimates control over movement of voluntary muscles lies in parts of the brainstem rather than the cerebrum or cerebellum. Removing the cerebrum from a primate renders it almost completely paralyzed. By developing cerebral dominance, primates have achieved a high degree of muscular coordination but are more vulnerable to potential injury.

The *medulla oblongata* is the part of the brainstem to which the spinal cord is attached. It is the center for vital reflexes, that is, the nerve impulses responsible for the rate at which the heart beats, the lungs fill and empty, the arteries transport blood, and the pupils of the eyes open and close.

The *hypothalamus* is located at the central part of the lower side of the cerebrum just back from where the optic nerves cross in connecting the right eye with the left rear of the cerebrum and the left eye with the right rear of the cerebrum (see Figure 11.7). Leading off from the hypothalamus is the pituitary gland, whose hormones control the rate at which all the other hormone-secreting glands function. The hypothalamus has been determined to be the center of emotions and from its immediate proximity to motor and sensory areas it becomes more apparent how nerves, hormones, and behavior are related. We shall have more to say about this later.

Returning to a discussion of the nervous system in general, we find it to be organized into two basic subdivisions, *central nervous system* and the *autonomic nervous system*. Table 11.1 points out the primary differences between the two.

CENTRAL NERVOUS SYSTEM: EXTERNAL HOMEOSTASIS

The central nervous system consists of the brain, spinal cord, and sensory and motor neurons associated with *conscious voluntary activities*. Involuntary reflex arcs may

CENTRAL NERVOUS SYSTEM	AUTONOMIC NERVOUS SYSTEM
Primarily responsible for external homeostasis	Primarily responsible fo internal homeostasis
Conscious control over skeletal muscles	Unconscious control over smooth muscles
Controlled by brain centers cerebrum and cerebellum	Controlled by brain centers medulla and hypothalamus

TABLE 11.1 The two subdivisions of the human nervous system

occur within this framework, as described above, but the same muscles moved in the reflex may be also moved by voluntary action. The muscles controlled by the motor neurons of the central nervous system are the skeletal muscles.

Learned behavior involves the central nervous system. Crawling, walking, speaking, writing, reading, and all activities which we voluntarily control have their control centers in this part of the nervous system. The sequences of neurons making up the circuits concerned with these activities are formed through gene action as well as in response to environmental demands. Performance of these activities causes development and maturation of the areas of the brain involved. The left side of the brain is dominant in most people (most of us are right-handed) and controls the right side of the body. Because of the demands put upon it, it is larger than the right side of the brain. Thus, the brain causes behavior, but behavior in its turn affects the brain.

The autonomic nervous system has its control centers in the medulla and hypothalamus of the brain and differs from the central nervous system in that it controls *involuntary, unconscious activities*. Reflexes occurring in this system cause smooth or cardiac muscles to contract instead of skeletal muscles. We are not consciously aware of autonomic reflexes as we may be of a skeletal muscle reflex, and we cannot repeat the same muscular movement by voluntary direction. We cannot consciously direct such activities as heartbeat, contractions of intestines, and release of digestive enzymes from the pancreas.

AUTONOMIC NERVOUS SYSTEM: INTERNAL HOMEOSTASIS

We can consciously regulate our rate of breathing, but this usually amounts to meddling with a natural process, resulting in breathing too much or too little. We can hold our breath and faint, but at this point the autonomic center in the brain takes over and a normal breathing rate ensues. Normally our rate of breathing is controlled by sense receptors sensitive to levels of carbon dioxide in the blood.

The autonomic nervous system is actually made up of two subdivisions, the *sympathetic* and *parasympathetic* systems (see Figure 11.9). The control centers lie in the brain and spinal cord, and the axons and dendrites extend out so that every vital organ is connected to both parts of the autonomic system. The rate at which the vital organs function is a result of the balance between the two systems. The sym-

FIGURE 11.9 *Some of the motor pathways of the autonomic nervous system. The column to the left of the spinal cord represents sympathetic chain ganglia. Each neural path shown occurs pairwise, one on the left and one on the right of the body. Similarly, sympathetic chain ganglia occur to both the left and the right of the spinal cord, but for simplicity only one side is shown in each case. (Adapted from Paul B. Weisz, Elements of Biology, 3rd ed. Copyright McGraw-Hill Book Company, 1969. Used by permission.)*

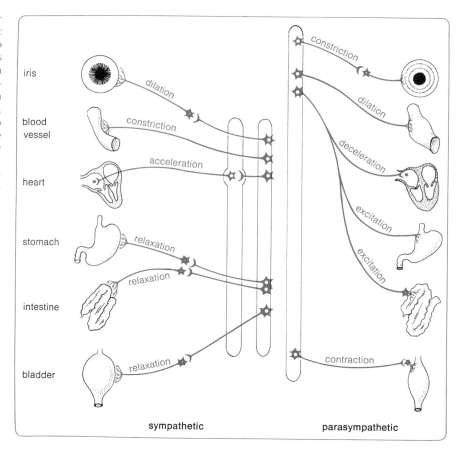

pathetic system is *antagonistic* to the parasympathetic system. Both send impulses to each organ, but the rate of function in the organ is determined by the relative rate at which impulses arrive.

The sympathetic system has an effect on vital organs which, if it got the upper hand, would prepare your body for stress; its action is sympathetic to you. It causes dilation of the pupils of the eye, constriction of blood vessels leading to the intestines, relaxation of the stomach, intestines, and bladder, and acceleration of the heart. The boy in the tree at the beginning of this chapter had these stress reactions: His sympathetic system was temporarily dominant.

The *parasympathetic* system has the opposite effect, and if the brain sends more impulses through it, the pupils of the eye contract, blood vessels to the intestines dilate, the stomach and intestines become excited, the bladder contracts, and the heart slows down.

Normal body operation requires a proper balance between the sympathetic and parasympathetic systems. The balance is accomplished through homeostatic responses. Responses, however, require receptors which perceive information in the internal or external environment.

Your hands don't really feel, your eyes can't see, your ears can't hear, your nose can't smell, and your tongue can't taste. All these structures contain specialized *sense receptors* whose function is to translate environmental information into nerve impulses which travel to the brain and spinal cord. In the brain the sensory information is interpreted as feeling, sight, sound, smell, and taste.

The five senses of vision, hearing, smell, taste, and touch are quite familiar, but sense receptors for these sensations are only a few of the many kinds providing the input for both central and autonomic nervous systems. Mammals can sense pain, pressure, heat, and cold. They also have sense receptors in their ligaments and muscles informing them of the positions of their limbs and receptors detecting changes in blood pressure and blood carbon dioxide content. They can sense mechanical equilibrium and motion of their bodies with their eyes closed. In addition, they can perceive genital sensations, tickling, hunger, thirst, and sleepiness. These last sensations we are aware of since they penetrate into our consciousness, but unconscious sensing occurs with regulation of blood pressure, breathing, heartbeat, etc. Do we and the other mammals possess even more unconscious sensors which have yet to be discovered?

Hormones can be defined as specific secretions which cause an effect elsewhere in the organism, often in a target gland. Secretion of hormones in endocrine glands is stimulated either by other hormones or by nerve impulses.

HORMONE CONTROLS IN HOMEOSTASIS

The nervous system brings about rapid, local reactions of short duration while, in contrast, at least some hormones cause slower reactions of longer duration. We have previously called them the wire and the wireless communications systems in an attempt to describe their mode of transmission, but this implies that the two operate independently of each other. Actually they are very closely related. Each is dependent on the other for proper homeostatic regulation.

NERVES AND HORMONES

The old way of studying the functioning of endocrine glands was to remove the organ, observe effects, prepare an extract of the gland, inject the extract, and observe whether symptoms disappeared. Modern techniques do not require drastic surgery in which entire organs are removed; instead, an organ may be altered surgically so that its products cannot be released into the blood. If symptoms appear, the alteration can be removed so that products suspected to be there can be released into the

METHODS OF STUDY

blood. The symptoms are observed to see whether they disappear. Direct chemical analysis of the blood may reveal the presence or absence of the suspected products. Another technique involves placing electrodes in the organ in question. Analysis of blood following electrical stimulation may reveal an increase in a particular hormone. Changes in either metabolism or behavior may indicate a rise in level of hormones following excitation of the gland. Such techniques allow identification of the site of hormone production.

THE TWO GENERAL TYPES OF HORMONES
Hormones in mammals are molecules of two general types, derivatives of *amino acids* or of certain fatty carbohydrates. Hormones of the first category are peptides, proteins, or amino acid derivatives. The animal hormones derived from fat precursors are complex compounds called *steroids*.

A detailed description of all the hormones produced in man would require far too much space. Some of this information is provided in Figure 11.10, which shows the location of the endocrine glands, and Table 11.2, which lists their hormones, chief functions, and the symptomatic effects of either a deficiency or an excess of each hormone. We shall consider in detail only a few kinds of hormonal regulation in order to illustrate the role of hormones in homeostasis.

FIGURE 11.10 The endocrine glands. (*Adapted from Paul B. Weisz, Elements of Biology, 3rd ed. Copyright McGraw-Hill Book Company, 1969. Used by permission.*)

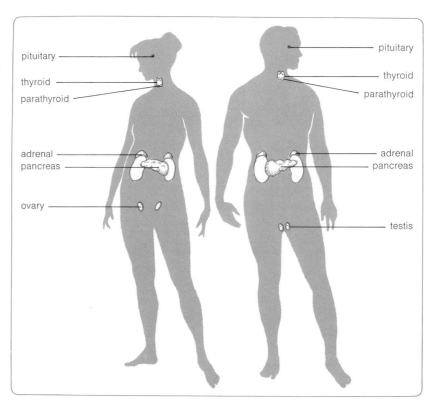

TABLE 11.2 Sources and functions of principal vertebrate hormones

GLAND	HORMONE	MAJOR FUNCTIONS	EFFECTS OF DEFICIENCY OR EXCESS
Pituitary, anterior lobe	Adrenocorticotrophic hormone (ACTH)	Stimulates adrenal cortex to synthesize and secrete its hormones	Abnormal production of hormones by adrenal cortex
	Thyroid-stimulating hormone (TSH)	Stimulates thyroid to synthesize thyroxin	Thyroid diseases
	Melanocyte-stimulating hormone (MSH)	Stimulates production of melanin, brown skin pigment	Causes fishes and amphibians to become darker or lighter
	Growth hormone (GH)	Increases cell metabolism and cell-membrane permeability to amino acids	Simmonds' disease in man
	Follicle-stimulating hormone (FSH)	Stimulates development of follicles in ovary and sperm in testes	Irregularities in egg or sperm production
	Luteinizing hormone (LH); interstitial-cell-stimulating hormone (ICSH)	LH causes ovulation and production of estrogen; ICSH causes production of testosterone	No LH, no ovulation; no ICSH, no sperm since testosterone is necessary for sperm maturation
	Prolactin	Causes production of milk in mammary glands	No milk in absence of prolactin
Pituitary, posterior lobe	Vasopressin	Constricts small arteries and raises blood pressure; influences rate of reabsorption of water in kidneys	Diabetes insipidus; high or low blood pressure.
	Oxytocin	Increases contractibility of smooth muscle in uterus and mammary glands	Problems in birth or nursing
Adrenal medulla	Adrenalin	Converts glycogen to sugar; increases heart rate and blood pressure; dilates bronchioles—part of the response to *stress*	Absence of adrenalin results in inability to cope with stress
Thyroid	Thyroxin	Regulates number of mitochondria and their respiratory enzymes	Cretinism or myxedema; simple goiter or exophthalmic goiter; high or low metabolic rates
Parathyroid	Parathyroid hormone	Releases calcium from bones; raises blood calcium; causes phosphates to be excreted	Absence causes tetanus and convulsions, brittle bones, bone tumors, kidney stones
Pancreas	Insulin	Causes amino acids and glucose to move into cells; increases pinocytic activity of cells	Affects protein metabolism; affects level of sugar in blood; diabetes mellitus.
Stomach and intestines	Eight or more gastrointestinal hormones, e.g., secretin.	Released by small intestine upon stimulation by acid, fat, or bile; causes secretion by pancreas and bile secretion in liver	Improper digestion
Adrenal cortex	Aldosterone	Causes sodium retention by the kidneys	High blood pressure; edema; sodium and water loss
	Cortisone	Affects metabolism of carbohydrates and proteins	Inability to cope with stress; low resistance to disease
Testes	Testosterone	Causes rapid growth of male sex organs, development of male secondary sexual characteristics; causes increase in protein synthesis; sexual libido	Improper development and maintenance of male reproductive structures and behavioral characteristics
Ovary	Estrogen	Causes growth of female sex organs; stops bone growth; makes female secondary sex characteristics develop	Improper development and maintenance of female reproductive structures and behavioral characteristics
	Progesterone	Inhibits LH and ovulation; reduces sensitivity of uterus; increases metabolic rate; causes salt and water retention	Low levels of progesterone during pregnancy cause abortion

Why do you eat? Why are you hungry, and why are you more irritable before you eat than after? What causes animals to have a drive for food, to act out their ecological roles in the food webs described in Chapter 5?

Research during this century has demonstrated that appetite and hunger are controlled by the *hypothalamus*. This vital region on the lower side of the brain contains two regions which regulate feeding, a *hunger center* and a *satiety center*. The two regions have cells with different specializations, those of the hunger center being activated by a low concentration of glucose in the blood and those of the satiety center being activated by a high level of blood sugar. The presence or absence of an appetite, a drive for food, is determined in part by the glucose level in the blood. Since a low level of blood sugar may also cause an irritable emotional state, you may be both hungry and irritable when you get up in the morning.

In a similar fashion, control centers for emotion, body temperature, and such drives as thirst, sex, and aggression, have been identified and studied in the hypothalamus. The hypothalamus is also the center of regulation for most of the hormones secreted by the anterior and posterior pituitary. Since the hypothalamus is affected by cerebral activities as well as by its various sensors and receptors, its role as one of the vital links between emotions and the state of the body is therefore evident. The hypothalamus is one of the most important bridges between mind and body by virtue of its role in integrating the activity of the central nervous system and the endocrine system.

Emotions may also interfere with your hunger drive, and you may eat much more food than your blood sugar level dictates or you may eat too little. Culture and other learned behavior can alter the hunger drive so that you are not even interested in the foods of other cultures and may even lose your appetite at the sight or smell of them. Food preferences of animals other than man may or may not be of a more unlearned nature; in any case their development is little understood.

Once glucose is absorbed from the intestine, its level in the blood is regulated by at least five hormones. Of the five, only one, insulin, causes the level of blood sugar to decrease. Insulin increases the permeability of cell membranes to the passage of glucose into cells (other than those of the brain and liver) and increases the respiration of glucose as well as its conversion to glycogen, the animal equivalent of the starch of plants. People suffering from diabetes have a low level of insulin and a high level of blood glucose since it is not entering their cells. Therefore, their cells lack this vital chemical energy source and such people can die in a diabetic coma, caused by excess blood glucose, or from the effects of insufficient intracellular glucose.

Four hormones cause the level of blood glucose to rise. Adrenalin causes glycogen to convert to glucose. Cortisone and its relatives cause fats and proteins to be converted to glucose. Pituitary growth hormone seems to oppose the actions of insulin but mimics cortisone in causing the conversion of fats to sugars. Thyroxine also causes the level of blood sugar to rise, but the mechanism in this case is still unknown.

This is just one example of how hormones act in concert. One can safely generalize that all hormones act at the cellular level by affecting various aspects of cellular metabolism. With an awareness of the delicate balance that exists in feedback interactions between the endocrine glands and their products, it is easy to see how improper functioning of one endocrine gland can upset the homeostasis of the other glands and the health of the entire organism.

Hunger is the drive causing us, like other animals, to pursue the prey of our food web. From the foregoing discussion we can see that hunger is a result of a complex interplay between the various endocrine glands which raise or lower the level of blood glucose. Hypothalamic regulators monitoring the levels of blood sugar in the hunger and satiety control centers respond homeostatically to the changing status of nutrients, controlling the function of endocrine glands and by means of the nervous system producing the behavioral responses of hunger or satiety. The various components of a highly organized living system like you are thus very tightly integrated, from the cellular to the behavioral level.

REVIEW QUESTIONS

1 Describe how sitting in a chair is an example of homeostasis.
2 Describe briefly how a nerve impulse occurs.
3 Compare the functions of the central nervous system and the autonomic nervous system.
4 Describe how the antagonistic roles of the sympathetic and parasympathetic systems regulate the internal functions of your body.
5 Using glucose metabolism as an example, discuss why you might say that many hormones act in concert or by committee.

SUGGESTIONS FOR FURTHER READING
* Available in paperback

Katz, B.: *Nerve, Muscle, and Synapse,* McGraw-Hill Book Company, New York, 1966. The clearest and most authoritative book on this topic.

Langley, L. L.: *Homeostasis,* Reinhold Publishing Corporation, New York, 1965. Describes many homeostatic mechanisms in man with a minimum of words.

Turner, C. D.: *General Endocrinology,* 4th ed., W. B. Saunders Company, Philadelphia, 1966. A widely used text.

Woolridge, D. E.: *The Machinery of the Brain,* McGraw-Hill Book Company, New York, 1963. A classic that draws comparisons between electronic computers and the brain and presents brain research on structure, memory, reasoning, and other topics in a lucid manner; highly recommended.

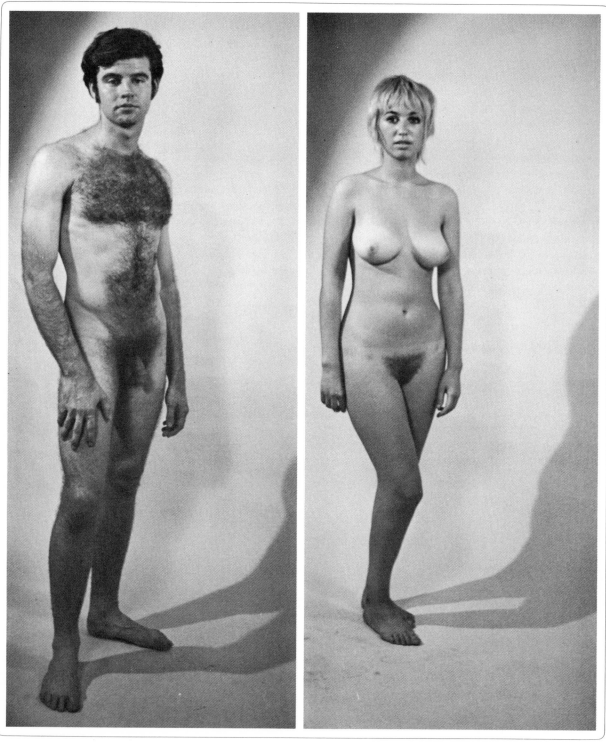

Man and woman. (*Courtesy of M. Chapman.*)

Chapter 12

Homeostasis in Organisms: Hormones and Human Reproduction

A hen is only an egg's way of making another egg.

Butler

Hormones have a role in all aspects of reproduction. In mammals gonadotrophic hormones from the pituitary gland not only induce sex organs to differentiate but also induce them to produce gametes. Various hormones affect human fertilization, development, birth, and milk production, and hormones are responsible for behavioral changes associated with puberty, the onset of reproductive maturity. Mating and sexual behavior too are influenced by hormones by means of their actions on the central nervous system.

We recall that in man, sex is determined by the chance event of whether it is an X-bearing or a Y-bearing sperm that fertilizes the X-bearing egg. A zygote with two X chromosomes is genotypically female, and a zygote with an X and a Y is genotypically male. The process by which these genotypes get expressed as female and male phenotypes is a story of hormone action.

REPRODUCTIVE STRUCTURES

DEVELOPMENT OF EXTERNAL REPRODUCTIVE STRUCTURES

After about 1 month of development the human embryo shows the first sign of external reproductive structure in the form of a *genital swelling*. At the top of this area during the fifth week, a slight elevation, or bump, forms called the *genital tubercle* or *genital papilla*. Within the genital swelling two parallel ridges called *genital folds* form and extend down from the tubercle. Further development causes these features to differentiate in one of two ways, *depending on the sex of the embryo*. The reproductive system is unique among the organ systems in that the organs differ so greatly between the sexes.

If the embryo is genetically male, the genital papilla grows in length and diameter and becomes the *penis*. If the embryo is female, the genital papilla becomes the

FIGURE 12.1 (a) Undifferentiated stages in the development of the external genitalia and (b) differentiation of the external genitalia. (*After Otis from Little, Structure of the Vertebrates, Farrar and Rinehart, Inc., 1937.*)

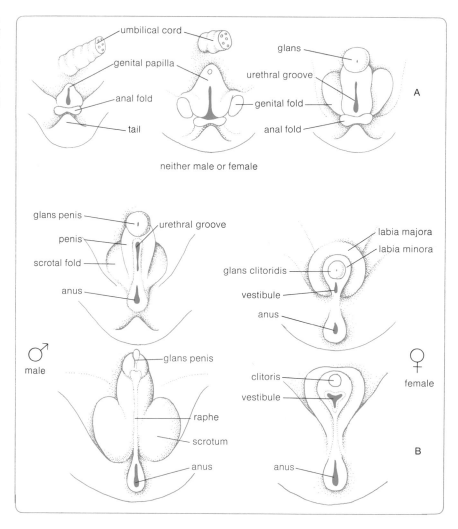

clitoris. The male penis and the female clitoris are *homologous structures;* that is, they have the same embryological origin (see Figure 12.1). Both consist primarily of spongy erectile tissue which fills with blood and becomes erect during sexual excitement. The clitoris, however, remains about the size of a pea in the adult human female, while the penis ranges from 4 to 8 inches in length in the adult male. As the penis grows, it incorporates the urethra (the excretory duct), so that the opening in the penis serves as an exit for both sperm and urine. The clitoris lies above the urethral opening and is separate from it.

In the male, the genital folds form the *prepuce,* which grows over the penis and encloses it except for the *glans,* the head of the penis. The prepuce, often called the foreskin, is frequently removed in a minor surgical operation called circumcision. The genital swellings enlarge in the male to form the *scrotum,* and the testes descend into this sac during the eighth month (see Figure 12.2).

If the embryo is female, the genital folds form *labia minora* (from the Latin words for lips and small), which lie on each side of the opening to the vagina. The genital

FIGURE 12.2 The male reproductive system. (*After Nelsen, Comparative Embryology of the Vertebrates, Copyright 1953. McGraw-Hill Book Company. Used by permission.*)

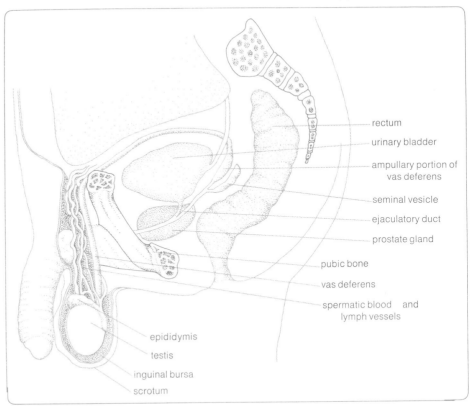

rectum

urinary bladder

ampullary portion of
vas deferens

seminal vesicle

ejaculatory duct

prostate gland

pubic bone

vas deferens

spermatic blood   and
lymph vessels

epididymis

testis

inguinal bursa

scrotum

FIGURE 12.3 (a) Diagrammatic representation of the female reproductive organs. (*After Nelsen, Comparative Embryology of the Vertebrates, Copyright 1953. McGraw-Hill Book Company. Used by permission.*) (b) The ovaries and uterus, posterior view. (*After Schaeffer (ed.), Morris' Human Anatomy, Copyright 1953. McGraw-Hill Book Company. Used by permission.*)

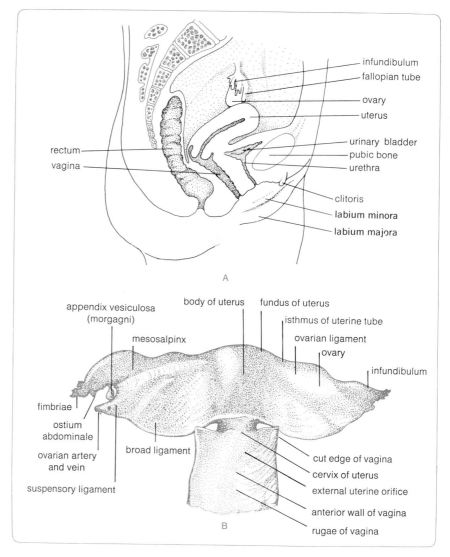

swellings give rise to *labia majora* (lips, large), which extend from above the clitoris to the anal urea. Under the labia majora in descending vertical sequence are the clitoris, urethra, and vagina (see Figure 12.3).

DEVELOPMENT OF INTERNAL REPRODUCTIVE STRUCTURES

The internal male and female reproductive structures have similar origins just as the external structures do. The basic structures of the early embryo later differentiate according to sex. Some embryonic structures specialize further in one sex but remain rudimentary in the other. For example, the duct which drains the embryonic kidney (which is replaced later by another type of kidney) becomes the duct which carries sperm from the testes to the urethra in the penis. In the female, this duct is nonfunctional. In female vertebrates, a duct forms which extends from the lower coelomic cavity to the genital area. In the human female, this duct becomes the oviduct and uterus, and forms most of the vagina. This duct does not form in males.

An obvious example of development of homologous internal structures in males and females is the testes and ovaries. The gonads contain germ cells which give rise to sperm or eggs. The germ cells are stored in a tissue called *germinal epithelium*, which covers the ovary or lines the tubules of the testis (see Figure 12.4). The germ cells take up this position during early embryonic life after leaving their source in part of the endoderm of the yolk sac and migrating to the part of the germinal ridge of mesoderm which later becomes either testis or ovary. Under the influence of hormones, these germ cells may begin meiosis and give rise to sperm or eggs.

Ovaries remain in the abdomen, but testes, under the influence of the male sex hormone, descend into the scrotum, where they are maintained at a temperature about 4°F lower than the body temperature. At body temperature, the sperm will not mature.

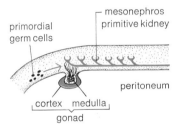

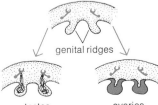

FIGURE 12.4 Germ cells originate in endoderm and migrate to the mesodermal gonadal ridge, where they are incorporated onto the surface of ovaries or in the tubules of testes. A gonadal ridge is composed of a medulla and a cortex. A medulla develops into a testis, which drains by way of a former kidney duct. A cortex forms an ovary, which releases eggs into the coelom. The coelom drains by way of a special duct, which becomes oviduct, uterus, and vagina. (*Adapted from Paul B. Weisz, Elements of Biology, 3rd ed. Copyright McGraw-Hill Book Company, 1969. Used by permission.*)

Starting with a basic pattern, the two sexes develop as variations on a theme, thanks primarily to the effects of sex hormones. Some structures grow and specialize while others degenerate or remain rudimentary. Normally, rudimentary structures remain in that condition and do not affect normal functioning of the dominant organ system. Mistakes in sexual differentiation may happen, however, and the resulting abnormalities may interfere with the duct system or with mating. If the gonads are involved, true *hermaphroditism,* in which both male and female reproductive systems are functional, may occur. Some cases of supposed hermaphroditism are not valid but are cases in which a female's clitoris has overgrown to the extent that it looks like a penis. Aberrations of ducts, glands, and structures may be harmless, but they may interfere to the extent that sterility results.

Genetic mutations may also cause abnormalities in the development of the reproductive system. As mentioned earlier, an extra X chromosome is known to cause Klinefelter's syndrome in males, while a single X chromosome causes the abnormality named Turner's syndrome in females; people with either of these abnormal genotypes are sterile and have undeveloped reproductive systems.

Probably the commonest abnormality of male reproductive tracts is that in which one or both testes fail to descend into the scrotum. This condition, called *cryptorchism* (from words meaning hidden and testes), may cause sterility if both testes do not descend since the body temperature in the abdomen will not allow sperm to mature.

HOW ARE REPRODUCTIVE
FUNCTIONS REGULATED?

So far, only the formation of reproductive structures has been discussed. At this point we begin a discussion of how these structures function. Because homeostatic control mechanisms with feedback responses always involve processes arranged in a circular sequence, or loop, the choice of where to begin is arbitrary. We shall start with the interaction between the pituitary gland and the ovary or testis.

PITUITARY

The pituitary gland is located below the hypothalamus of the brain and is almost completely enclosed in a pocket of bone on the floor of the cranium. It is attached to the brain by a stalk called the *infundibulum*. The pituitary consists of anterior and posterior lobes and the stalk attaching them to the hypothalamus. The anterior lobe forms from the roof of the mouth in the embryo, and the posterior lobe is a small downward extension of the brain. Thus, one lobe is endodermal while the other is ectodermal in embryonic origin. All the hormonal products of both parts are proteins.

Although the anterior lobe of the pituitary has been referred to as the "master gland" of the body, this is misleading since it suggests that it *gives* orders without *receiving* them. Actually, the anterior lobe is not autonomous but is under the control of the central nervous system, particularly the hypothalamus. The central nervous system in its turn is influenced by pituitary secretions. The pituitary should not be considered as a master gland nor as a "leader of the endocrine orchestra" but as the "concertmaster," the first violinist who is a member of the orchestra and may lead it while at the same time reacting to it (see Figure 12.5).

Hormones of the anterior lobe are called *trophic* hormones because they affect the *growth* of other structures. Thus, removal of the anterior lobe of the pituitary results in a decrease in size of the gonads, the thyroid, and adrenal glands, and a marked decrease in body growth. We shall concentrate on the effects of pituitary hormones on testes, ovaries, and other reproductive structures.

PITUITARY AND TESTIS

The testis has two jobs: It carries on meiosis in production of sperm cells, and it produces the male sex hormone *testosterone*. A testis consists of many tiny tubules where sperm are produced. Masses of cells lie between the tubules. In cases of cryptorchism, described previously, testosterone is produced but no sperm. Examination of the undescended testis reveals that the tubules have broken down but the masses of cells between the tubules are still functioning. Sperm and hormone production in testes are carried on by two separate groups of cells.

The two separately functioning groups of cells in testes are regulated by two separate hormones from the anterior pituitary. The hormone that stimulates cells to produce testosterone is called *interstitial-cell-stimulating hormone* (ICSH) and the hormone that controls sperm production is called *follicle-stimulating hormone* (FSH), a name

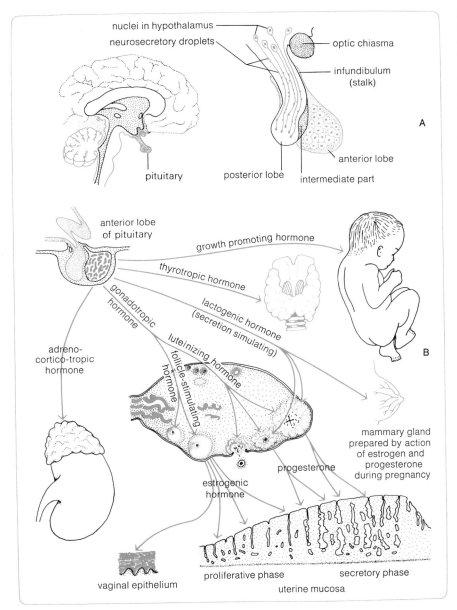

FIGURE 12.5 (a) The pituitary
gland and its relation to the brain
and (b) some of the regulatory
effects of anterior pituitary hormones with emphasis on the
female reproductive organs. ((b)
*After Patten, Human Embryology.
Copyright 1953. McGraw-Hill
Book Company. Used by permission.)*

given first to a hormone in females which turned out to be identical in males.
Actually, both ICSH and FSH have a role in sperm production since FSH is necessary
for meiosis and ICSH causes testosterone to be produced, which is necessary for
sperm cells to mature.

Feedback mechanism between
pituitary glands and testosterone
levels through the body.

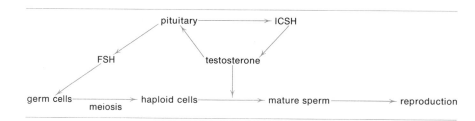

Feedback mechanism between pituitary glands and testosterone levels through the body.

The level of testosterone has a feedback effect on the pituitary and affects production of FSH and ICSH. Thus, as the testosterone level drops, the pituitary produces more FSH and ICSH, causing the testis to produce more testosterone, which then makes the pituitary cut down production of FSH and ICSH. Though production of sperm and testosterone may oscillate somewhat, their levels stay relatively stable compared to similar products in the female.

The *primary effect of testosterone* is in the rapid growth of primary male sex organs, those concerned with production and transport of gametes. Secondary effects of testosterone are much more widespread. For example, testosterone affects the distribution of body hair, causes enlargement of the larynx or voice box, thickens skin, increases melanin production, increases activity of oil glands in the skin, and affects protein metabolism. The protein effects are probably due to the effects of testosterone at the gene level, for it is known to stimulate the synthesis of new *m*RNAs. As a result of testosterone action males have larger muscles and longer bones than females. Pituitary growth hormone (GH) also causes increases in protein mass, but testosterone adds to these effects in a fashion characteristic of males. It is also interesting to note that the prostate gland, which secretes much of the fluid of semen, depends on testosterone to promote the cell division which replaces lost cells. Prostate glands may develop cancerous growths. Administering the female sex hormone estrogen to a male will cause a feedback reaction from his pituitary which decreases ICSH, causing a decrease in testosterone synthesis; the result of this therapy is cessation of growth of the cancerous prostate cells. Surgery may not be required.

PITUITARY AND OVARY — The ovary is similar in function to the testis in that the ovary also performs two roles, production of hormones and production of gametes. The ovary differs from the testes in producing *two* hormones, *estrogen* and *progesterone*. Since progesterone is produced only at certain times, we postpone discussion of its effects until later. *Estrogen* is the female sex hormone responsible for the maturation of female sex organs and development of female secondary sexual characteristics. The metabolic rate is accelerated by estrogen, causing women to have a higher pulse rate and temperature than men. This female hormone also slows the growth of bones earlier than in men and affects fat synthesis, amino acid uptake, and protein synthesis in certain cell types. Estrogen too acts at the level of *m*RNA synthesis in the cell nucleus. As a result of estrogen action, women are generally shorter and tend to have less muscle mass than men. Further effects of estrogen are seen in the light growth of body hair in women and the comparatively large amount of fat deposited under the skin, which gives females their rounded contours. Estrogen also increases mitosis in the skin, which eventually can result in wrinkles.

The gametes produced in the ovary are *eggs,* which are produced through meiosis in germ cells while the human female is still a fetus in the womb. An ovary of a human embryo contains about 7 million primitive germ cells at about 5 months of pregnancy, but by seven years of age the number has declined to about 300,000. These usually mature at such a rate that only one egg is released from one of the two ovaries every 28 days. Thus, during a woman's reproductive life, she releases only about 400 of these eggs. Pregnancy means that the number of eggs released will be proportionately less.

Germ cells are arranged around the outer portion of the ovary (see Figure 12.6). Each germ cell becomes surrounded by groups of follicle cells, which contribute nutrients to the germ cells they enclose. After the onset of puberty at the age of

FIGURE 12.6 Schematic diagram of ovary showing development of the ovum and its release from the follicle. (*After Patten, Human Embryology. Copyright 1953. McGraw-Hill Book Company. Used by permission.*)

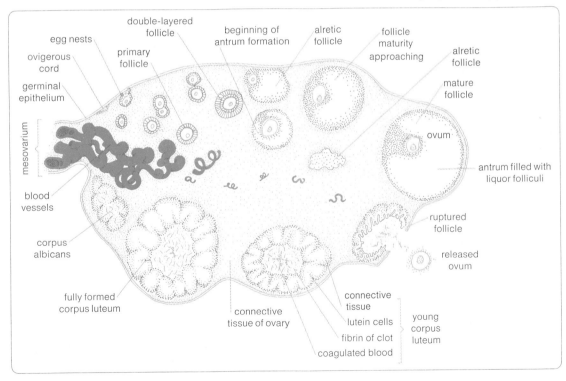

about twelve to fourteen, one or more of these germ cells will become an egg every 28 days.

Eggs develop from germ cells in fluidfilled multicellular spheres called *follicles,* which become larger as they mature. The follicle begins enlarging and continues developing as a result of FSH from the pituitary. FSH stimulates the follicle to begin its development, which is why it is called follicle-stimulating hormone. Cells around the follicle secrete *estrogen,* which stimulates the pituitary into releasing more FSH, and this, in its turn, stimulates the follicle into secreting more estrogen. This is an example of positive feedback, and it continues for about 14 days. At the beginning of the cycle, there is little LH being secreted along with the FSH, but as the follicle gets larger and the positive feedback cycle produces increasingly more FSH and estrogen, the rising estrogen level causes a sudden shift in the ratio between FSH and LH. Above a certain estrogen level positive feedback switches to negative feedback and causes a decrease in FSH. (As will be described on a later page, this inhibition by estrogen is one of the two ways in which birth-control pills may function.) The dominance of LH which now ensues causes the follicle to burst open through the surface of the ovary, releasing the egg into the coelom, where it can enter the oviduct. This process is called *ovulation* (see Figure 12.7).

OVARY AND UTERUS The ruptured follicle now becomes a tiny endocrine gland, the *corpus luteum* (body, yellow), which secretes *progesterone.* (Luteinizing hormone, LH, gets its name because it causes ovulation and the formation of a corpus luteum.) Since progesterone first appears only at the onset of ovulation, its appearance is a signal that an egg has been released. It is relatively simple to determine when progesterone is released, since progesterone causes body temperature to rise about 0.5°F. A woman can chart her daily temperatures for several months and note the point at which it seems to rise each month. Typically, ovulation takes place on about the fourteenth day following the onset of menstruation. It is upon this assumption that birth control by the *rhythm method* is based. Unfortunately, however, most women are not regular enough to render this method of birth control reliable.

Progesterone has two main roles in reproduction.

1   It has an inhibitory effect on the production of LH by the pituitary and prevents further ovulation while the newly ovulated egg is traveling along the oviduct. This is the second negative-feedback relation between an ovarian hormone and a pituitary hormone in the menstrual cycle. Just as rising estrogen causes shutoff of pituitary FSH secretion, so rising progesterone causes shutoff of pituitary LH secretion. In this way a cycle is established, for when the corpus luteum ceases to produce progesterone and degenerates, the estrogen-progesterone balance again reverts to dominant estrogen, and the pituitary begins the secretion of FSH all over again. Birth-control pills contain artificial hormones which duplicate either the estrogen inhibition of FSH or the progesterone inhibition of LH. Some pills contain both types of hormones. Either way, birth-control pills inhibit

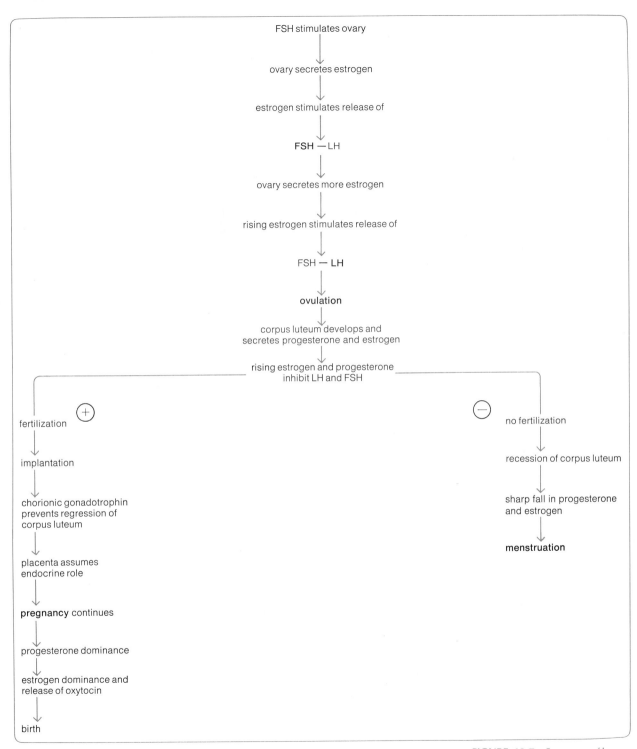

FSH stimulates ovary

ovary secretes estrogen

estrogen stimulates release of

FSH — LH

ovary secretes more estrogen

rising estrogen stimulates release of

FSH — **LH**

ovulation

corpus luteum develops and
secretes progesterone and estrogen

rising estrogen and progesterone
inhibit LH and FSH

(+) fertilization

implantation

chorionic gonadotrophin
prevents regression of
corpus luteum

placenta assumes
endocrine role

pregnancy continues

progesterone dominance

estrogen dominance and
release of oxytocin

birth

(−) no fertilization

recession of corpus luteum

sharp fall in progesterone
and estrogen

menstruation

FIGURE 12.7 Summary of hormonal control of ovulation, menstruation, and pregnancy. (*From J. Tepperman, Metabolic and Endocrine Physiology, Year Book Medical Publishers, Inc.,* 1962, p. 74.)

TABLE 12.1 Methods of
birth control

CONTRACEPTIVE	RATING*	TYPE OF CONTROL	PROCEDURE	DOCTOR INVOLVED?
Sterilization	0	Mechanical barrier	Vas deferens severed in male; fallopian tubes tied or uterus removed in female; does not affect virility	Yes
Combination pill	0–1	Chemical (prevents ovulation)	Combination pill of estrogen and progestin taken from day 5 of menstrual cycle to day 25	Doctor prescribes; cost of follow-up visits
Sequential pill	0–1	Chemical (prevents ovulation)	Estrogen pill taken from day 5 through 19 of menstrual cycle, then combination pills taken day 20 to 25	Doctor prescribes; cost of follow-up visits
Intrauterine device (IUD)	1–3	Believed to cause egg to reach uterus at wrong time to implant	Doctor inserts IUD in uterus at doctor's office; patient checks periodically to see it is still in place; doctor removes IUD if pregnancy desired	Yes
Condom	5–15	Mechanical barrier worn by man	Worn on erect penis; must be used all times penis is in vagina, including foreplay, and removed before penis loses rigidity or rating will be raised	No; choice of many kinds at drugstore
Diaphragm	5–15	Mechanical barrier worn by woman	Fitted by doctor who will instruct how to insert it; covers the cervix of the uterus; used only with special jelly or cream; may be inserted as long as 6 hours before intercourse and *must* remain in place 6 hours after intercourse; new fitting necessary after birth of each baby	Yes; a doctor must fit diaphragm properly
Foam	10–30	Chemical (spermacide) and mechanical barrier	Insert *two* applicators as directed into vagina under cervix not more than 1 hour before intercourse; don't walk around before intercourse	No; buy at drugstore without prescription
Creams and jelly	20–40; unreliable	Chemical and mechanical	Inserted as directed on package shortly before intercourse	No; buy at drugstore
Foaming vaginal tablets	20–40; unreliable	Chemical and mechanical	Tablet is inserted into vagina under cervix; waiting period of 10 minutes required for tablet to dissolve and foam up; some secretion must be present to dissolve tablet	No
Rhythm	20–40; unreliable	No intercourse during time pregnancy can occur	If intercourse is avoided 3 days before and 3 days after ovulation, pregnancy should not occur	Yes

* Rating signifies the number of women out of 100 women using the particular method who will probably be pregnant at the end of 1 year.   As an example, 5 to 15 women out of 100 women for whom the condom was the contraceptive choice will be pregnant at the end of 1 year.   They may be pregnant because the condom was not put on until just before orgasm or because the condom was not removed before the penis lost its rigidity, allowing some sperm to escape around the edges.   Postcoital douche; *very unreliable* because some sperm have entered the *uterus* within 90 seconds after ejaculation.   The douche washes sperm only out of the vagina.   Abortion is gaining acceptance in many countries as a method where others have failed.   In the United States, however, though attitudes and laws are gradually changing, this is generally not a legal method.   In California the law has been broadened to legalize abortion when the pregnancy would gravely impair the physical or mental health of the mother or when the pregnancy resulted from rape or incest.

ovulation. Table 12.1 lists various methods of birth control and contrasts their
relative effectiveness.

2   To understand the second effect of progesterone we must transfer our attention to
the uterus. The uterus of mammals undergoes great changes each month. The
estrogen level rises during the first 14 days following menstruation and causes the
endometrium, the lining of the uterus, to become greatly thickened with blood
vessels. Under the influence of the surge of progesterone at ovulation, the
endometrium becomes even thicker (up to 5 millimeters thick) and becomes
secretory, that is, soft, spongy, and covered with mucus. If an embryo arrives in
the uterus at this point, it sinks into the endometrium and continues developing.
If no embryo arrives, however, the uterus again undergoes change.

In Old World monkeys, apes, and man, menstruation occurs if the ovulated egg is
not fertilized. In the human female, menstruation occurs on about the twenty-
eighth day following the onset of the preceding menstrual period and continues
for about 3 to 7 days (see Figure 12.8). *Menstruation* consists of a sloughing off

FIGURE 12.8   Diagram of menstrual cycle. (*After Johnson,
Laubengayer, De Lanney, and
Cole, Biology, 2d ed., Holt, Rinehart and Winston, Inc., 1966.*)

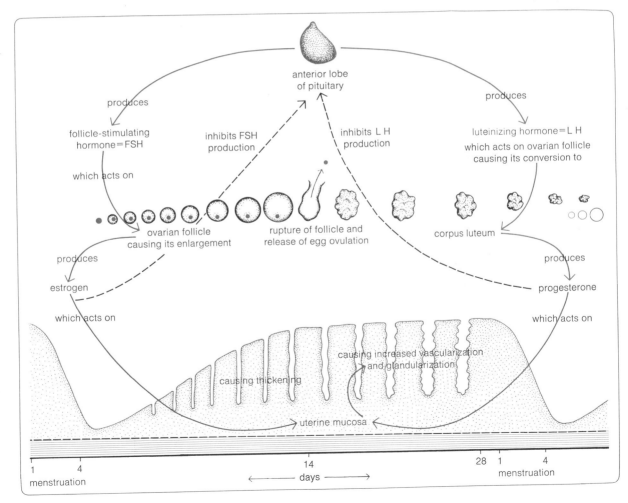

of the outermost layer of the endometrium accompanied by a bloody discharge through the vagina. Between 20 to 200 milliliters of blood is lost with each menstruation, and a woman may lose 40 quarts of blood during her life. The word menstruation comes from the Latin word for moon, since one menstrual cycle approximates a lunar month of 28 days.

Why does the endometrium slough away after 28 days? The answer lies with progesterone, since it is responsible for maintaining the endometrium. The corpus luteum may last only about 14 days after ovulation, and its deterioration, a result of the shutoff of LH synthesis by the pituitary, ends the production of progesterone. Without progesterone the endometrial mucosa cannot be maintained and is sloughed off as the menstrual discharge (see Figure 12.9).

FIGURE 12.9 Diagrammatic summary of the menstrual cycle. (*After Schroeder. From Patten, Human Embryology. Copyright 1953. McGraw-Hill Book Company. Used by permission.*)

OVARY, UTERUS, AND EMBRYO

During sexual intercourse, about 3 milliliters of semen containing about 300 million sperm cells may be deposited at the end of the vagina, the *cervix*, the portion of the uterus which protrudes slightly into the vagina. Following ovulation, an egg may

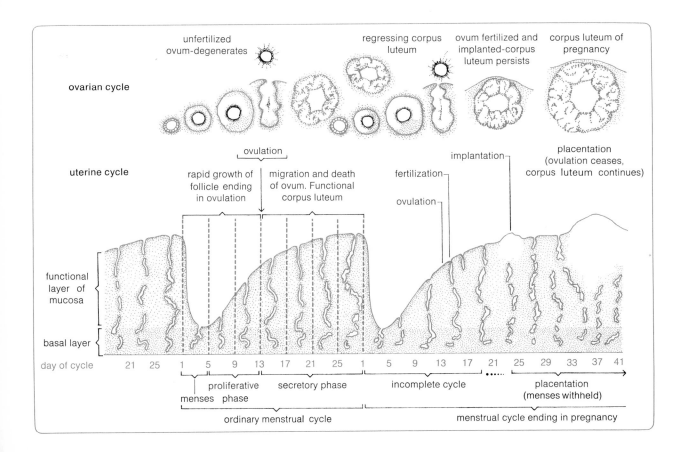

live 24 to 48 hours and is propelled into the oviduct by currents caused by cilia in the oviduct and by muscular movements of the oviduct. If fertilization is to occur, it must take place in the first inch or so of the oviduct, but how do the sperm get there? Sperm are found in the oviducts of rats in less than 1 minute and in cow's oviducts in about 2½ minutes after mating. Sperm cannot swim that far that fast. The sperm are transported by *contractions of the uterus and oviducts,* probably caused by *oxytocin,* a hormone from the posterior lobe of the pituitary which also causes contractions of the uterus during birth and of the milk glands after birth. (It is known that in cows and women producing milk, milk is ejected from the mammary glands during the act of mating, which apparently sends nerve impulses to the posterior lobe of the pituitary by way of the hypothalamus and causes the release of oxytocin.) If the egg is not fertilized within about 24 hours after ovulation, it disintegrates, but if the egg is fertilized, the embryo begins developing while it is swept along in a current of mucus down the oviduct to the uterus. The trip takes about 8 days, and the embryo arrives in the form of a *blastocyst,* a mammalian form of blastula. The embryo *implants,* or sinks, into the endometrium (see Figure 12.10). As growth and differentiation progress, the embryo forms four membranous sacs, *yolk sac, amnion, chorion,* and *allantois* (see Figure 12.11). We shall hear of these membranes again in Chapter 21.

The *yolk sac* of a mammal bears no food supply and, to survive, the embryo becomes parasitic on the mother. The embryo is enclosed in the fluid of the *amnion* and is protected against dehydration and physical damage by this fluid. Around the amnion is another membrane, the *chorion,* from which projects a mass of fingerlike projections called *villi.* On the side of the chorion where it makes contact with the endometrium, the villi grow and branch extensively as they erode tunnels through the maternal tissue.

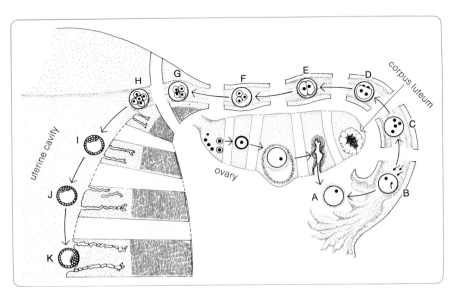

FIGURE 12.10 A schematic representation of the development of the oocyte in the follicle of the ovary. The follicle ruptures, and the mature ovum (*a*) passes into the oviduct, where it is fertilized (*b*); various cleavage stages are shown as the ovum passes down the oviduct (*c–g*); the morula (*h*); the blastocyst in the cavity of the uterus (*i, j*); the beginning of implantation in the wall of the uterus (*k*). (*Adapted from Hamilton, Boyd, and Mossman, Human Embryology, W. Heffer & Sons, Ltd., 1945.*)

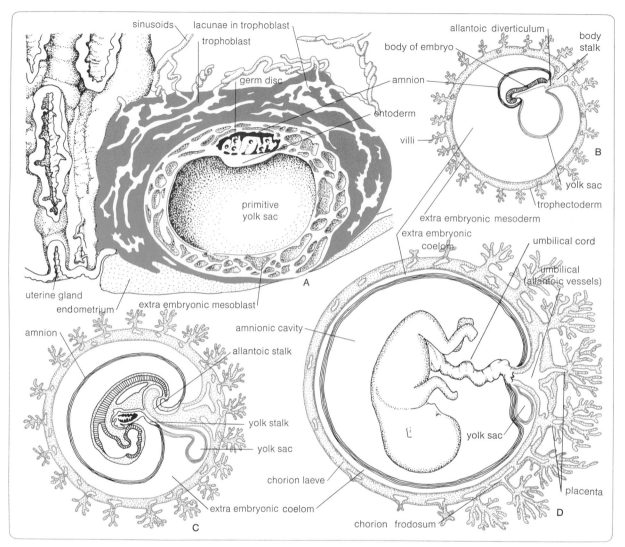

FIGURE 12.11 Extraembryonic membranes in human embryo: (a) Diagrammatic representation in embryo of about 12 days. (*Redrawn and modified from Hertig and Rock, Carnegie Contributions to Embryology, vol. 29, 1941.*) Embryo of about (b) 16 days, (c) 28 days, (d) 12 weeks. (*After Nelsen; Comparative Embryology of the Vertebrates, Copyright, 1953. McGraw-Hill Book Company. Used by permission.*)

The mammalian *allantois* is a collapsed membraneous bag lying within the chorionic villi and ascending into the embryo. The yolk sac of mammalian embryos is also a collapsed bag, but it seems to have no function. The embryo gains nutrients by way of capillaries in its circulatory system, which branches throughout the allantoic membrane. Blood from the mother lies in microscopic pools around the villi, so that nutrients can diffuse from the mother's blood into the embryo's capillaries, while wastes from the embryo diffuse in the opposite direction. This structure, consisting of capillaries, chorion, and allantois from the embryo and expanded endometrium of the mother, is called a *placenta*. In the placenta, the circulatory systems of mother and baby must come into contact, but their *bloods do not mix*. Instead, foods, wastes, gases, and hormones diffuse between the two bloodstreams across a membrane barrier, the chorion.

The embryo's capillaries in the placenta function as a web connecting two arteries with a vein descending from the embryo. The amnion grows over the arteries and vein in the allantois, and incorporates the chorion and vestigial yolk sac into an *umbilical cord*. Even though this structure is disengaged from the embryo at birth, it leaves lasting evidence of the point where the arteries and vein entered the body of the embryo, the *navel*.

Progesterone is necessary for retention of the endometrium, and normally the corpus luteum stops producing progesterone about the twenty-eighth day of the menstrual cycle. If this happened in pregnancy as well, the embryo would be lost about 1 week after implantation. Clearly, the corpus luteum must continue producing progesterone if the placenta is to be retained. This is accomplished through a feedback mechanism: The embryo produces a hormone called *chorionic gonadotrophin* which causes the corpus luteum in the ovary to enlarge and continue producing progesterone for 3 months, rather than disappearing after a few more days in response to a renewed synthesis of FSH in the pituitary as the next cycle begins. The placenta enlarges and differentiates during the first 3 months of pregnancy into an endocrine gland capable itself of producing sex hormones, including progesterone. Thus after 3 months the placenta produces progesterone, which maintains its position in the uterus. This shift from ovary to placenta as a source of progesterone is a delicate one. It is a time when miscarriages occur at a higher frequency.

Progesterone appears at the time of ovulation and can be used as an indicator that an egg has been released. Chorionic gonadotrophin (CG) appears only if pregnancy has occurred, and by detecting its presence it is possible to tell whether a woman is pregnant. Various simple tests have been developed for the presence of the CG hormone, one being the frog test. Pregnant females excrete CG in their urine. This urine causes a male frog or toad to release sperm or a female to release eggs if the urine containing CG is injected into it. The appearance of sperm or eggs in the cloaca following the injection indicates that the woman is pregnant while the absence of sperm or eggs indicates that she is not.

BIRTH

During the 9 months of pregnancy, the uterus does not expel the *fetus* (as we call the human embryo after the third month, when it can first be recognized as human). The uterus does not contract during that time because its state is dominated by progesterone, which decreases the ability of the uterus to contract. At the end of 9 months the uterus does contract, and birth results. Three main factors are responsible for the onset of birth.

1   There is a sudden drop in the level of both estrogen and progesterone due to some change in the placenta. Both hormones drop in level, but progesterone drops farther and *estrogen becomes dominant*. Estrogen, instead of decreasing the contractibility of the uterus as progesterone does, increases it.
2   The shift to estrogen dominance and the nerve impulses from the uterus with its heavy fetus both stimulate the posterior lobe of the pituitary to release *oxytocin*, a hormone which increases the ability of smooth muscle to contract. Oxytocin may be injected by a doctor to induce labor, but if it is administered before the joint holding the two bones together in the pubic arch has been softened, the vagina cannot expand adequately to allow passage of the baby.
3   The increasing weight of the fetus stretches the uterus and causes contractions. This is a *mechanical effect*. All these factors, plus others which are not known yet, cause the onset of what is called *labor*.

MILK   Mammary glands, one of the unique features of mammals, are discussed in Chapter 21. In all placental mammals, milk glands appear somewhere along two parallel *milk lines* extending along the chest and abdomen. In primates, elephants, and sea cows the mammaries are located on the chest part of the milk line, but they are located on the abdomen in pigs, groin in cows, goats, and sheep, and all three in the rat. Rudimentary extra mammaries are occasionally found in human beings.

Milk glands are highly modified oil glands of the skin. *Estrogen* causes epithelial cells to grow inward and form a branching network of tubules. *Progesterone* causes grapelike clusters of sacs to form at the terminal ends of the tubules. The epithelial cells forming the walls of these sacs are made to synthesize milk by the action of *prolactin,* an anterior pituitary hormone. Milk, with its fat globules, sugars, calcium, and other nutrients, is secreted in the Golgi complexes of these cells before extrusion into the tubules of the gland. Here it is stored until released.

The ducts in the mammary glands empty to the outside through an elevated structure called a *teat*. For milk to be released, two things must happen: (1) The ducts in the teat must be opened, and (2) the milk in the tubules must be forced out and into the teat. The first is accomplished through suckling (or milking by hand or machine in cows). The second, the ejection of milk, is accomplished through contraction of special smooth muscles, called *myoepithelial cells,* around the ducts and the secretory sacs. These smooth muscles contract as a result of oxytocin being released into the blood in the posterior pituitary.

The sucking action stimulates sense receptors in the teat of the mammary and sends nerve impulses to the hypothalamus of the brain, causing it to release oxytocin.

From the hypothalamus, the oxytocin moves down the pituitary stalk and into the posterior lobe, where it is absorbed into the blood. The blood carries oxytocin to the mammaries and causes a letting down of the milk. It also carries oxytocin to the uterus and causes it to contract. Usually, a mother can feel her uterus contract at the same time that milk is let down. At first an unpleasant experience, it aids in restoring the uterus to its condition before pregnancy. Eventually it may turn into a pleasant experience and become associated with the mother's love for the infant.

The production of milk usually has an inhibitory effect on the production of FSH and LH in the pituitary. Many couples mistakenly consider this to be a "safe period" for sexual relations, but the inhibitory effect does not always happen and ovulation may occur.

ADRENAL CORTEX AND SEX HORMONES

Endocrine glands which develop from embryonic mesoderm produce hormones which are *steroids;* they are all variations on a common theme, the basic steroid molecule (see Figure 12.12). The adrenal cortex, although it is mesodermal in origin, produces not only the steroids cortisone and aldosterone but estrogen and testosterone as well, which are also steroids. The adrenals produce both sex hormones regardless of whether you are male or female: Each sex has some hormones of the opposite sex.

FIGURE 12.12 Steroid molecules. All are variations on basic four-ring steroid molecule.

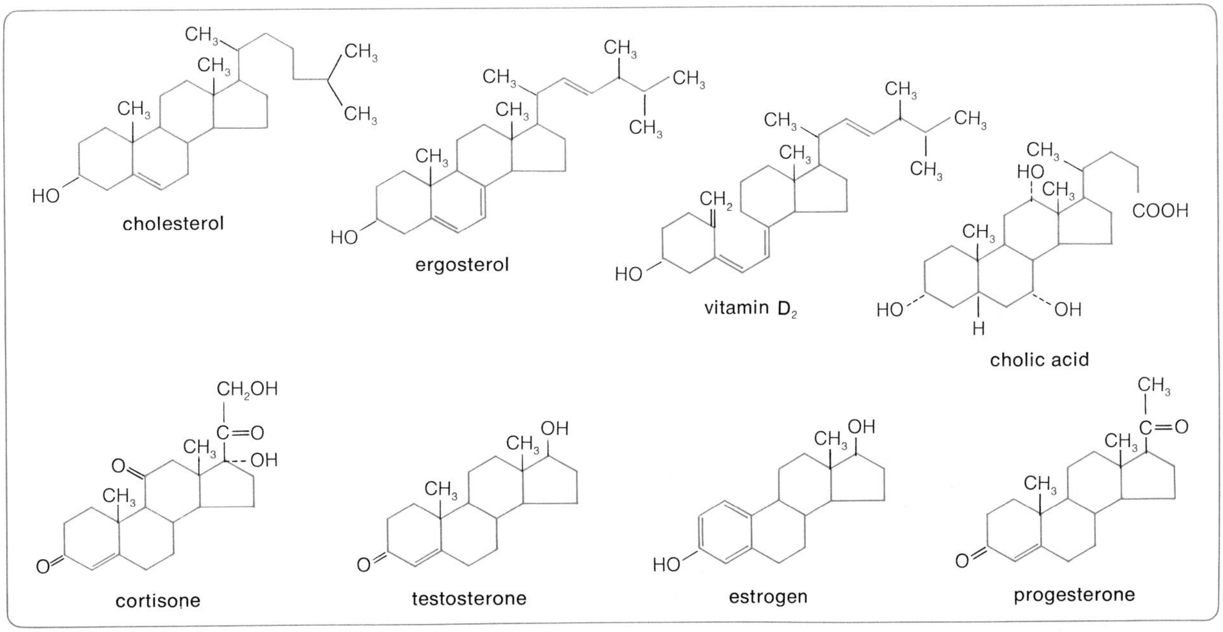

The role of steroid sex hormones produced in the adrenal cortex is relatively unknown. Evidence has shown that adrenal sex hormones cannot maintain sexual characteristics in human beings if testes or ovaries have been removed. Their level must be low in comparison to the sex hormones produced by the gonads. The role of estrogen in a male is thought to be insignificant, but the effect of adrenal testosterone in females is thought to play an important role in causing the growth of axillary and pubic hair; it is thought by some to be the cause of sex drive in women, as well as in men. Sex drive continues in a woman without ovaries but not if the adrenals have also been removed.

Errors in embryological development or formation of a tumor in the adrenal cortex can cause production of adrenal sex hormones in higher quantities. If this happens in babyhood, it may cause *precocious puberty,* a maturation of reproductive structures at a very young age. (About 1940 a girl in South America gave birth to a baby at the age of seven!) Adrenal tumors in mature women may cause high levels of testosterone, resulting in a reversal of secondary sexual characteristics, a disease called *hirsutism.* Most bearded ladies of the circus suffer from tumors of the adrenal cortex.

A CAPSULE REVIEW
OF HOMEOSTASIS,
HORMONES, AND
REPRODUCTION

Homeostasis is the maintenance of relatively constant conditions within or between organisms as a result of self-regulation. Without these processes, disorder would result, and any environmental change could push an organism into an extreme condition. Basically, homeostatic controls are the result of negative feedback responses which inhibit the production of enzymes, nerve impulses, or hormones when these products reach certain levels. In this chapter, the hormones of human reproduction were used as an example of feedback controls. We saw how the pituitary gland causes many other glands to function but is in turn controlled in its own actions by the levels of hormone produced by the very same glands it causes to function.

Responses in an organism may be the result of stimuli outside the organism's body, and these external stimuli may result from the actions of other organisms. The subject of our next chapter is the means by which homeostasis is maintained in interactions between the organisms forming an ecosystem.

REVIEW QUESTIONS

1 How are male or female geonotypes expressed as phenotypes?
2 List the homologous structures in the male and female reproductive systems.
3 Discuss the role of pituitary hormones in the production of sperm.
4 Review briefly the function of testosterone.
5 Discuss the role of pituitary hormones in the production of eggs.
6 Contrast the mechanisms by which sperm and eggs are produced.

7 Describe the process of ovulation.
8 Describe briefly the interactions of hormones and structures in pituitary, ovary, and uterus.
9 What is menstruation and what causes it?
10 What are the functions of yolk sac, amnion, chorion, and allantois?
11 Describe and compare the various methods of birth control.
12 Why is a baby born?
13 Describe the roles of nerves and hormones in the secretion and release of milk.
14 Discuss pregnancy from fertilization to birth as an example of homeostasis.

Corner, G. W.: *The Hormones in Human Reproduction,* Princeton University Press, Princeton, N.J., 1942.

Corner, G. W.: *Ourselves Unborn,* Yale University Press, New Haven, Conn., 1944. Although these two books are old, their content is still fascinating and largely accurate.

DeCoursey, R. M.: *The Human Organism,* 3d ed., McGraw-Hill Book Company, New York, 1968. The section of human growth and development should be clear to a beginning student.

Hardin, G.: *Population, Evolution, and Birth Control: A Collage of Controversial Ideas,* W. H. Freeman and Company, San Francisco, 1969. Part 3 of this fascinating book describes reactions to the idea of birth control.

Tanner, J. M., G. R. Taylor, and the Editors of Life: *Growth,* Time-Life Books, New York, 1965. Contains beautiful photographs of human embryos and a clear explanation of human growth and development.

Tepperman, J.: *Metabolic and Endocrine Physiology,* Year Book Medical Publishers, Inc., Chicago, 1962. Although technical, it describes the role of hormones in human reproduction clearly and concisely.

SUGGESTIONS FOR
FURTHER READING
* Available in paperback.

Octopus vulgaris. (Courtesy of the American Museum of Natural History.)

Chapter 13

Homeostasis in Ecosystems: Animal Behavior

Reasoning at every step he treads,
Man yet mistakes his way,
Whilst meaner things, whom instinct leads,
Are rarely known to stray.

Cowper

Behavior can be defined as the way an organism reacts when exposed to some environmental or internal stimulus. The ability to react to stimuli is a general property of homeostasis.

LEVELS OF BEHAVIOR
PHYSIOLOGICAL BASIS OF
ANIMAL BEHAVIOR

In the more advanced animals the reaction to a stimulus is brought about by the action of the nervous and endocrine systems. Of the two, the nervous system is more directly involved in behavior. Nervous systems vary in complexity among animal groups, and since the complexity and behavior of animals is limited by the complexity of their nervous systems, we can generalize that simple animals have simple behavior and complex animals have complex behavior.

A primary function of the nervous and endocrine systems is to control the contraction of *muscles* and the secretions of internal *glands*. Control over muscular movement is very important since complex behavior requires the contraction of muscles in an intricate and highly integrated fashion. Sensory input of information about current conditions is associated with memories of past events, and responses are produced through both the autonomic and voluntary nervous systems. With vertebrates and many other organisms, the endocrine system is also involved in response. Behavior of organisms is the result of changes at *every level of biological organization*—from molecule to cell to organism to ecosystem.

TYPES OF BEHAVIORAL ACTS

The behavior of one-celled organisms and of many invertebrates may be considered relatively simple because a particular stimulus will cause the animal to respond in the same way every time. Such repeated, highly predictable responses are called *stereotyped behavior.* A second type of behavior makes its appearance to a limited degree in worms and insects and increases to a high level in the vertebrates; this type of behavior may be called *acquired* since the behavioral patterns are affected by experience and learning (see Figure 13.1). Much of the behavior of the lower vertebrates is stereotyped, but as the taxonomic ladder to primates is ascended, the mode of behavior becomes mixed. In more complex vertebrates and particularly in primates the stereotyped mode is finally replaced with acquired behavior. Man's behavior is almost entirely acquired.

STEREOTYPED BEHAVIOR

If a particular stimulus always elicits the same response in a fixed way and the response is apparently due to inherited neural mechanisms, the behavior is called *stereotyped.* Three aspects of stereotyped behavior have been identified, taxes, reflexes, and instincts; they are inseparably associated.

Taxes is the plural of *taxis,* a simple form of behavior involving *orientation of an animal* to some factor in its environment. For example, orientation of a fish so that it points upstream is due to certain environmental information, namely, the water pressure, which stimulates sense receptors in the lateral line canals extending down each side of the fish's body. The fish responds by adjusting its position so that pressures are equal on each side of the body. A *constant stimulus*, water pressure, guides the behavior throughout the response. Taxes are involved in the orientation of animals to such environmental factors as light, heat, gravity, oxygen, and carbon dioxide.

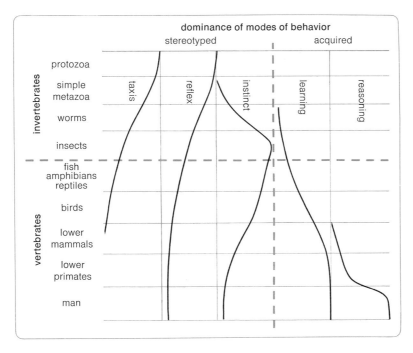

dominance of modes of behavior

stereotyped ⋮ acquired

invertebrates: protozoa, simple metazoa, worms, insects

vertebrates: fish amphibians reptiles, birds, lower mammals, lower primates, man

taxis | reflex | instinct | learning | reasoning

FIGURE 13.1 Complexity of behavior is a function of the complexity of the nervous system. Reflexes and taxes are quite important in invertebrates but have a minor role in vertebrates, where acquired learning is dominant. Instinct seems to have a role in both groups. (*Modified after V. G. Dethier and E. Stellar, Animal Behavior: Its Evolutionary and Neurological Basis, 2d ed., © 1964. By permission of Prentice-Hall, Inc., Englewood Cliffs, N.J.*)

Many insects orient either directly at light or at some angle to it. Moths, for example, are attracted to the lights at night, which they circle for hours at a time. A man leaning into the wind is demonstrating a taxis, an orientation to a constant external stimulus.

A taxis is a response involving the entire organism and is usually a combination of several reflex responses. A *reflex* typically involves only a certain part of the body. In Chapter 11 we discussed simple reflex arcs, which involve the central nervous system and peripheral nerves. Simple organisms without such complex nervous systems display reflexive behavior and, in fact, rely almost entirely on reflexes. A few years ago some psychologists believed that all behavior consisted of a mosaic of reflex units. By this scheme a reflex response would act as a stimulus for a second reflex response, which would act as a stimulus in a continuing chain of reflexes forming a behavioral act. Such chaining of simple reflexes into complex behavior seems theoretically possible but has not yet been demonstrated.

Instinct or *innate behavior* signifies that a behavior pattern is inherited and is not a learned response. The difficulty lies in knowing for certain whether or not a behavioral mechanism has been partially learned. For example, recent studies have shown that kittens raised with mice do not kill them. Until this time, though, it was thought that cats *instinctively* eat mice. Clearly, each behavior pattern must be carefully studied before its innateness is actually known.

The complex behavioral mechanisms of instinctive behavior are attracting greater attention, and direct experimental investigations of instincts have yielded some fascinating clues. Two general approaches have been utilized, one primarily by American psychologists studying the behavior of rodents in the laboratory and the other primarily by European zoologists studying the behavior of lower animals in the field. At present investigators using all approaches are working in both Europe and America.

THE STUDY OF
LABORATORY RODENTS

The so-called American school of behavioral psychologists has concentrated on developing an understanding of the physiology of unlearned behavioral mechanisms. For example, investigations into the neurophysiological basis of hunger, thirst, temperature regulation, sleep, rage, fear, and sexual behavior of rodents have been particularly rewarding. From this approach has developed the concept of instinct as a pattern of *drives* which direct an organism toward *goals*. The attainment of goals is considered to have a feedback response, called *satiation*, in which the drive is reduced. For instance, a hunger drive is satiated when food is eaten, and sex drive is satiated with the mating act.

The hypothalamic portion of the brain has been investigated in an attempt to define the areas responsible for regulating instinctive behavior, and it has been found to be the primary brain center controlling instincts. The regulation of a species' innate behavior patterns is accomplished through two centers, each antagonistic to the other. One *excites* and the other *inhibits*. For example, stimulation of electrodes implanted in the hunger center of the hypothalamus causes a rat to continue eating so that its weight is tripled, and stimulation of electrodes in another part of the hypothalamus causes a rat to starve. Food in the stomach bringing the blood-sugar level to normal stimulates the *satiety* center and removes the feeling of hunger. Similar pairs of counterbalancing centers in the hypothalamus have been found for thirst, sexual behavior, emotional behavior, sleep, and maternal behavior. Endocrine secretions also affect the centers. For example, injection of small amounts of sex hormones into fine pipettes implanted in the *mating* center of the hypothalamus causes immediate and vigorous sexual behavior, showing that this center is sensitive to the level of sex hormones in the blood.

Such supposedly instinctive drives as mating and hunger appear to be largely regulated by inherited instinctive mechanisms. If, however, rodents, carnivores, and man are compared, we find an increasing dependence on learning in the regulation of these drives. For example, a rat raised in isolation mates just as successfully in its first experience as a rat raised with others. A monkey raised in isolation past puberty, however, may not be able to perform the mating act because without experiencing close social relations with other monkeys and without having witnessed mating, the monkey cannot imitate it.

THE STUDY OF BEHAVIOR UNDER
NATURAL CONDITIONS

The European school of behaviorists has traditionally conducted its work in the field for the most part. This type of work is called *ethology,* the study of animal behavior.

The discoveries of ethologists have produced many important new generalizations concerning innate behavior. One interesting fact is that whole patterns of responses are programmed in the nervous system of organisms and the entire pattern is displayed by the presence of the correct stimulus which acts as a *trigger* or, as it is usually termed, a *releaser*. Once initiated, the entire pattern of acts constituting the instinctive behavior occurs without repetition of the original stimulus.

An excellent example of a chain-reaction behavioral response to a series of releasers is seen in the mating behavior of the three-spined stickleback fish (Figure 13.2). Each movement by the male is a releaser stimulus which elicits stereotyped movement from the female, and her actions, in turn, stimulate the male. The male, stimulated by the sight of the female's belly swollen by eggs, performs a zigzag dance. The dance exposes his red belly, which attracts the female to the male, and she assumes a vertical position in the water. This stimulates the male to swim toward his igloo-shaped nest, and the female responds by following him. The male puts his mouth into the nest entrance and rolls on his side, an act which stimulates the female to enter the nest. The male trembles and thrusts himself against the female at the base of her tail, and she responds by laying eggs. She leaves the nest, and the male enters and fertilizes the eggs. The fertilized eggs seem to serve as a repressive stimulus which causes a decrease in further sexual behavior, but the male continues to defend the developing embryos and fans them with fresh oxygen-laden water by movement of his fins.

Mating behavior of turkeys has also been found to follow a chain-reaction pattern. The sight of the female turkey causes the male to fan his feathers and strut. (A stereotyped pattern of showing off in the male bird is called a *display*.) Upon seeing this, the female crouches, and her lowered head acts as a releaser, causing him to climb up onto her back and tread his feet. Treading causes the female to raise her head and lower her wings, a posture that causes the male to now tread on her back at the base of the wings. She is stimulated by this to lift her tail and lower her head; the male lowers his tail and thrusts his cloaca forward against the female's cloaca, and she responds to the touch by extending her oviduct. This causes the male to ejaculate. The sequence of events is diagrammed in Figure 13.3.

Postures, colors, general configurations, and motion are very important in releasing mechanisms. The responses of sticklebacks and turkeys in mating behavior are primarily unlearned. All members of the particular species respond in a similar way, and very little of the behavior in taxes and reflexes is modified by experience.

The leaves of some plants undergo sleeplike movements, being elevated during the day and drooping at night. At first, this behavior was thought to be a response to the day-night light changes in the environment, but when bean seedlings were kept in constant darkness and temperature, the daily rhythm was found to persist. These movements are repeated with such *beatlike* regularity that the pattern can be referred to as a rhythm. Like many similar phenomena in the biological world, this pattern is

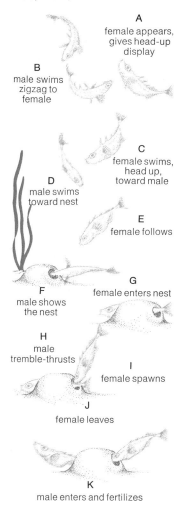

FIGURE 13.2 Courtship behavior in the three-spined stickleback. (*Modified from N. Tinbergen, The Study of Instinct, Oxford University Press,* 1951.)

A
female appears, gives head-up display

B
male swims zigzag to female

C
female swims, head up, toward male

D
male swims toward nest

E
female follows

F
male shows the nest

G
female enters nest

H
male tremble-thrusts

I
female spawns

J
female leaves

K
male enters and fertilizes

BEHAVIOR WITHOUT EXTERNAL CLUES: BIOLOGICAL RHYTHMS

FIGURE 13.3 Chain reaction of releasers and responses in mating behavior of turkeys.

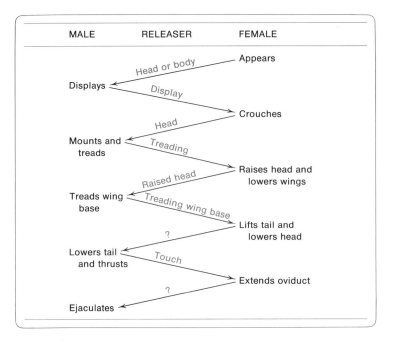

thought to be controlled by a biological clock geared originally to the length of a day. Anyone who has flown across the country in a jet has experienced the effects on his biological clock. If a person flies from California to New York City, his watch, still operating on Pacific standard time, will indicate that it is only 9 o'clock in the evening when his friends in New York are yawning and suggesting that it is midnight and time for bed. Needless to say, he will have difficulty getting to sleep and will be quite tired the next morning. Traveling salesmen have known for years that if they have an important client in a distant city, they do better to arrive a day or two ahead of time and adjust to the local time as their biological clocks require this long to be reset to the new time zone. There are many examples of biological-clock-controlled processes; we can mention only a few here.

Fiddler crabs become dark during the day and blanch at night, even in conditions of exposure to constant light. Fruit flies emerge from the pupa at dawn, and some flowers open and close in a 24-hour cycle, even in constant dim light. Even the potato, maintained in constant conditions, has shown both a daily rhythm and an annual one. The potato reaches its peak of metabolic activity during the day and, on an annual basis, during April.

Each cell of a multicellular organism is thought to contain its own biological clock. Enzyme activity, osmotic pressure, respiration rate, membrane permeability, growth rate, sensitivity to light and temperature, and mode of reaction to drugs are all examples of processes known to change rhythmically in individual cells. The actual mechanisms of biological clocks are not understood, but many people believe that they must stem from biochemical oscillators whose period closely parallels the rhythms of days and seasons. Obviously, a great deal of research must be done before biological clocks are understood. The behavior of organisms is affected by their biological clocks, another example of innate, or *biologically programmed* behavior.

ACQUIRED BEHAVIOR

Taxes, reflexes, and instincts are stereotyped behaviors in which the same stimulus always elicits the same response. When the repetition of a stimulus brings forth variable responses, such behavior can be said to have been *modified by experience;* it has been *acquired.* Acquired behavior can be subdivided into learning and reasoning. *Learning* is a lasting change in behavior, and *reasoning* is problem solving.

Learning is a broad concept which includes a spectrum of behavioral actions extending from very simple modifications and innate behavior to the complex processes by which man uses abstract symbols. The study of learning is difficult because it is not always certain that behavior has actually been modified in a lasting way, and if behavior has been changed, it must be proved that the change was not merely caused by growth and maturation. Traditionally, learning is studied through techniques which attempt to associate a change in behavior with a specific, deliberate *training* procedure to which an animal is subjected.

The simplest form of modification of stereotype behavior by environmental stimuli, called *imprinting,* has been observed primarily in birds and young mammals. Soon after hatching or birth, at a stage called the *critical period,* a young bird or mammal learns to follow the *first* large object which *moves.* In nature, the first moving object would, of course, be the mother. However, by walking slowly near artifically incubated newly hatched geese and making quacking noises, Konrad Lorenz, the great German ethologist, caused young geese to imprint on him and follow him around as they would follow a mother goose. Young ducklings, goslings, and chickens have been made to follow such artifical objects as wooden decoys and balloons. The critical periods for imprinting seem to be related to the rate of development. For example, young mallard ducks are susceptible to imprinting 13 to 16 hours after hatching, while the moose calf will develop a heeling, or following, response to its mother around 4 days after birth. As the animal gets older it will follow strange objects less and less frequently. Imprinting behavior is apparently an adaptation among organisms whose young are born or hatched in an advanced or highly mobile form. Thanks to imprinting, they follow the mother and the flock or herd rather than wandering off by themselves.

Imprinting during critical periods is also demonstrated by the manner in which newborn mammals are accepted or rejected by the mother. Apparently the mother must be in contact with the young for a few minutes following birth. Immediately following birth, and for a few hours thereafter, a sheep or goat will accept *any* young lamb or kid as her own but in a few hours will reject all newcomers. The sensory information in imprinting in mammals relies as much on smell as on vision. The role of sound is also important in imprinting in birds and mammals.

Modification of behavior in learning may depend on either a gain or loss of responses to stimuli. In the development of an organism, losses of response can be just as important as gains. Otherwise, organisms would continue through their lives responding in the same way they had when they matured. Shedding responses which have lost their significance is a type of learning called *habituation*. Gaining responses is usually called *conditioning,* of which there are basically two types, *classical* and *operant* (see Figure 13.4).

Classical conditioning is a simple type of learning in which the original stimulus or response is substituted by another. This process was discovered in the nineteenth century by the Russian biologist Pavlov. He noticed that dogs salivated when meat powder was in their mouths. He then rang a bell each time he fed a dog meat powder, and after time discovered that the dog salivated at the sound of the bell alone. The stimulus to salivate had been transferred from the meat powder to the sound of the bell. Pavlov called the response of salivation to the bell a *conditioned response* and the sound of the bell a *conditioned stimulus.* Since the animal already possessed his reflex pattern before the new conditions were set up, he considered the

FIGURE 13.4 Classical and operant conditioning. These are two types of learning.

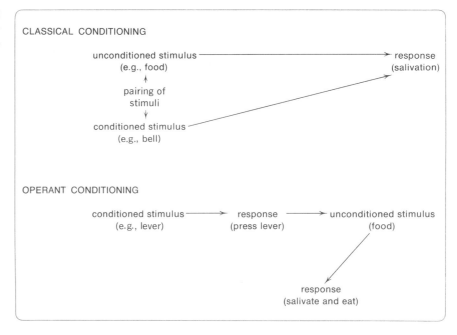

meat powder an *unconditioned stimulus* and the salivation upon tasting of the meat an *unconditioned response.*

Operant conditioning is a type of learning first studied extensively by B. F. Skinner, a psychologist at Harvard. He developed the *Skinner box,* a contraption in which an animal is placed and confronted with a variety of stimuli to which he can respond. The operator selects one of the responses and attempts to strengthen it. For example, whenever the animal responds to the stimulus with the preferred response, it receives a reward, usually food. The response may be an act such as standing up, turning right or left, rolling over, or pressing a lever. At first the animal does not relate the pressing of a lever with the appearance of food, but if the animal chances to press the lever and food appears and it repeats this a few more times, it will soon be actively pressing the lever to gain more food. The act of pressing a lever is *reinforced* each time by the reward of food. Actually, this is the way most people train babies and young children as well as domesticated and circus animals. In natural conditions, preferred behavior is that which makes the animal successful in his many activities, and it is the environment that chooses which responses are best adapted. By trial and error an animal makes various responses to a stimulus, and when the animal begins to increase the rate of a particular response which is gaining him greater rewards in that particular environmental situation, the animal can be said to have *learned.* Classical and operant conditioning differ in several ways, but the basic difference is that in classical conditioning stimuli are paired by an *agent* outside of the organism, while in operant conditioning the organism itself associates the two stimuli: The animal is the operator.

EVOLUTION OF LEARNING

No behavioral changes can be observed in organisms less complex than flatworms. Apparently, a certain concentration of neural material must be present before the process of learning can take place. An ability to learn is possessed by animals that have a head and move from place to place. Flatworms, earthworms, arthropods, mollusks, and vertebrates have shown an ability to learn.

Earthworms can be trained to turn right in a T-shaped maze and enter a dark, moist chamber rather than turn left and receive an electric shock. Flatworms such as planarians (Figure 13.5) can be conditioned to contract when a light is turned on by first pairing the light stimulus with an electric shock. Bees can be trained to go only to feeding dishes on blue paper. Ants and cockroaches can learn routes through simple mazes, ants being the faster learners of the two. Octopuses and squid (Figure 13.6, and the photograph at the beginning of the chapter) seem to be the most efficient learners of all invertebrates, which is in line with the extremely large accumulation of brain cells these animals have in comparison with all other invertebrates. Learning in the octopus has been studied extensively. The higher vertebrates, however, are the quickest learners of all animals. In all the animals studied

FIGURE 13.5 A planarian (phyllum Platyhelminthes).

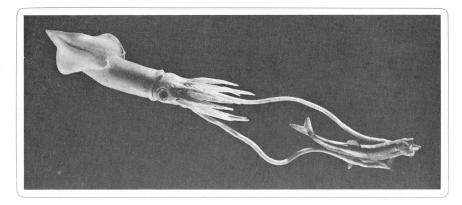

there is generally a high correlation between ability to learn and the degree of evolution of the central nervous system.

PHYSIOLOGICAL BASIS OF LEARNING

The location of functional areas used in learning has been investigated primarily by surgically destroying parts of the nervous system and observing the changes in behavior. During the early years of this work, much attention was directed to the cerebral cortex since it was believed to be the center of learning. More recently it has been found that vertebrates other than primates can learn even if they are missing a cerebral cortex; in its absence, however, their senses are impaired.

Learning may be *short-term* (forgotten within a few minutes) or *long-term* (retained throughout the life of the individual). There are at least two major theoretical models of how memory takes place.

One idea of how learning takes place is by *cell assembly:* a loop of neurons functioning in a continuous closed circuit. Each neuron in sequence activates the next cell, and the impulse continues around full circle until the first neuron is reached and stimulated again. By this method, an impulse could be perpetuated for a long time.

A second major model of learning invokes biochemical means. It is believed that nerve impulses may cause a nerve cell to produce *m*RNA; this then causes particular kinds of protein to be formed which in some way function as memory-storage units. Perhaps these proteins have a role in the cell membranes, as enzymes or hormones that cause the neurons to ''fire'' under certain conditions. The entire picture of the biological basis of memory is still extremely obscure, and the basic principles of nerve-cell integration in learning remain to be discovered.

REASONING

The second type of acquired behavior is *reasoning,* or the ability to solve problems. Reasoning in man is the ability to form abstract generalizations and concepts from information in the present or past. Traditionally, reasoning in man and less complex

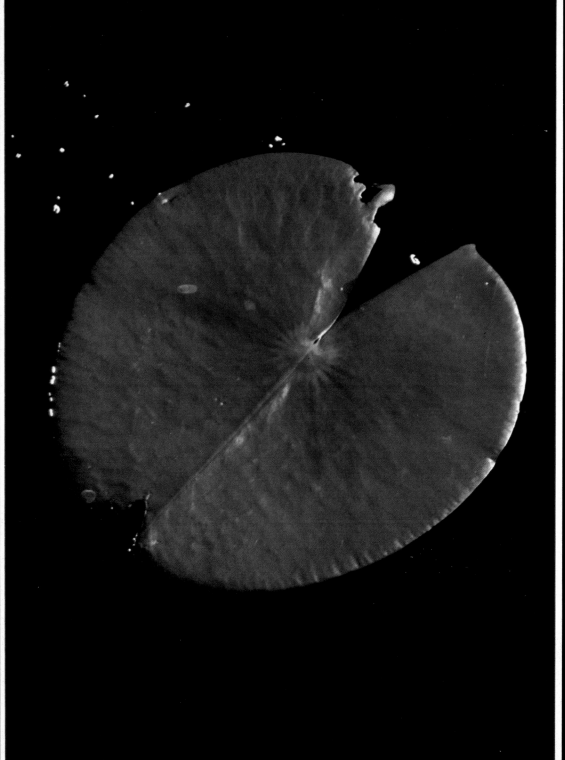

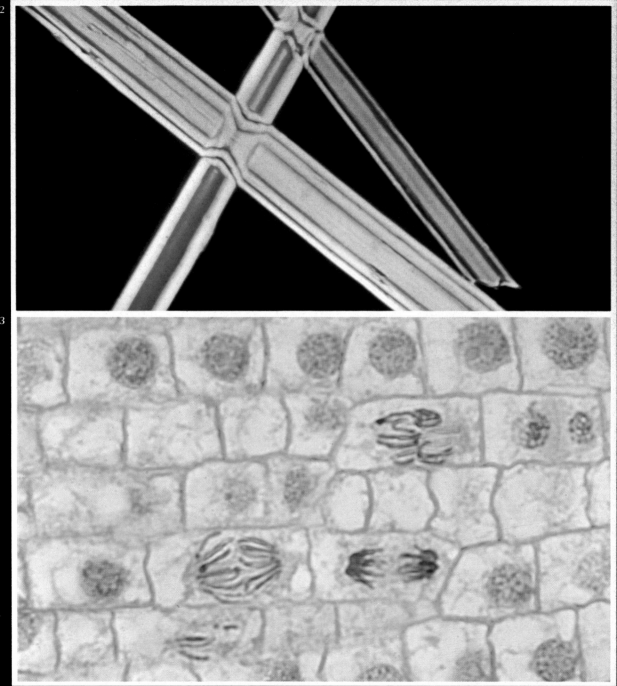

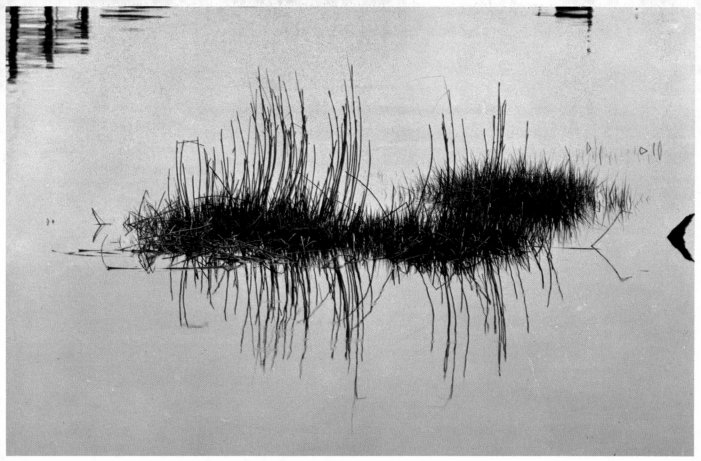

Plate 5 The spider and her eco-system as seen through a fish-eye lens. (*Courtesy of J. Paul Kirouac.*)

5

Plate 6 Lichens need little or no soil and grow abundantly in rocky areas with a minimum of rainfall. (*Courtesy of J. Paul Kirouac.*)

Plate 7 Floating aquatic plants grow rapidly to cover the surface of ponds and still lakes. (*Courtesy of J. Paul Kirouac.*)

Plate 9 Mating behavior of
sheep.
(Courtesy of J. Paul Kirouac.)

Plate 10 A highly developed
sense of parental care is shown
by members of the cat family.

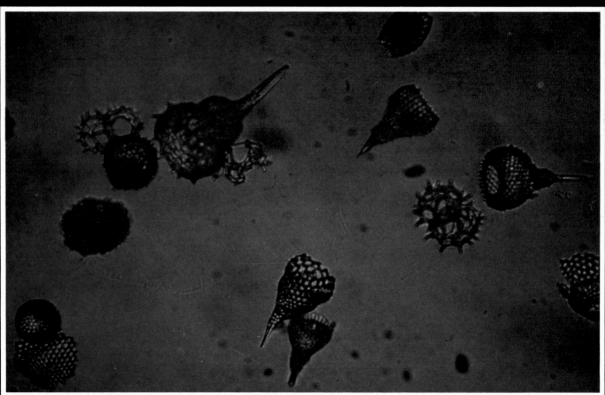

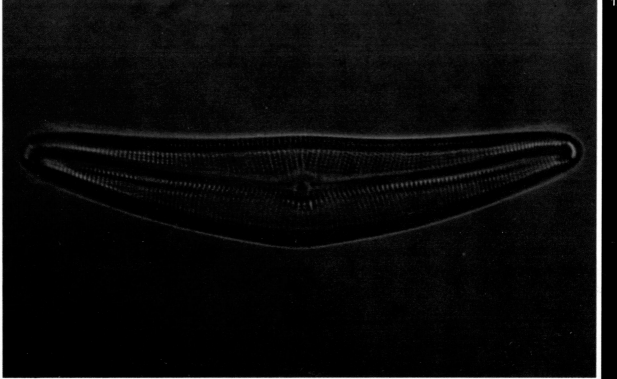

Plate 14 Fungi.
(*Courtesy of Howard A. Miller, Sr.*)

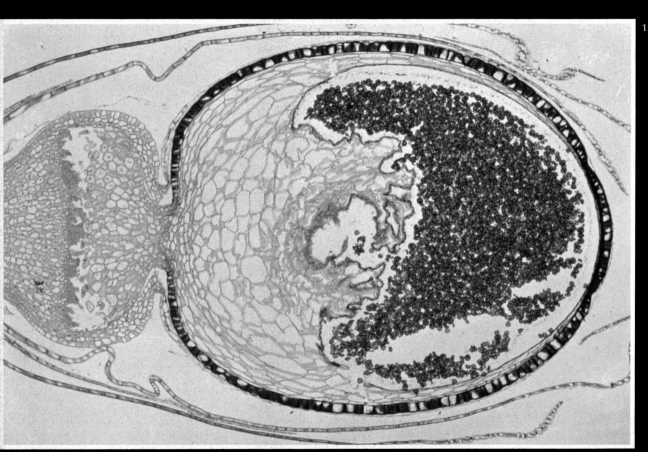

Plate 15 Meiosis occurs in the sporophyte or diploid form of particular mosses, here the sphagnum.

Plate 17   The anemone often have brightly colored bodies and appear to sway freely in the current.
(Courtesy of George Lower from The National Audubon Society.)

Plate 18   Penguins in Antarctica.
(Courtesy of Michael C. T. Smith from The National Audubon Society.)

with *Cladophora*, an alga which
thrives on pollution materials.
(*Courtesy of Zvonko Glyck.*)

Plates 20 and 21 Air pollution
over Manhattan, a daily
phenomenon. On some days it is
worse than shown here.
(*Courtesy of J. Paul Kirouac.*)

Plate 22
(Courtesy of J. Paul Kirouac.)

22

animals has been studied by confronting them with problem situations and observing their attempts at solving the problem.

By way of example, in *detour problems* the animal can see or smell food but cannot reach it because of a barrier. To reach the food, he must take a detour, a path around the barrier. Usually, only primates can solve such a problem on the first exposure; other vertebrates try again and again before discovering a path around the barrier, and others never find it. Of the invertebrates, thus far only an octopus can solve detour problems and then only under certain conditions.

The ability of higher primates to solve detour problems during the first try is called *insight*. This type of problem solving was first observed in chimpanzees, who had the insight to stack up three boxes to reach a banana suspended from the ceiling. The chimpanzees also fitted several pieces of wood together to reach food far beyond their arms' reach outside the cage. They are apparently able to solve problems *without previous trial-and-error experiences*.

There are many other ways investigators have challenged vertebrates to reason their way out of problems, but there is not space in this book to describe them. The main reason for describing the physiological basis of behavior in this chapter has been to understand, in broad outline, the processes of behavior in an individual organism. In the following pages we shall find that behavior responses are essential to survival of the individual and the social group of which he is a part. Behavior is *adaptive*, evolutionarily speaking, as much as a leg or a heart: It permits life to continue under the pressures of the environment. Now we shall see how animal behavior allows not only an organism but the population of which it is a member to continue existence.

ANIMAL BEHAVIOR

Animals are all social beings to some extent. All animals that reproduce sexually must get together at least for mating. This is the minimum amount of contact, for at least one species of mammal it is actually the full extent of social contact. The males and females of the little eastern chipmunk of North America are antagonistic to each other at all times except the few minutes of mating. The mother and young are associated only while in the nest and for 1 week afterward. Most mammals have more interaction than this, and their interactive behavior falls into two classes, *aggression* and *cooperation*.

AGGRESSIVE BEHAVIOR

The social bond which forms between parents and offspring and between young animals generally weakens as the young animals get older. The young learn to distinguish between individuals of their species and begin to demonstrate one of the most common patterns of interaction, *aggressive behavior*. Aggressive behavior consists of two opposing drives, *attack* and *escape*. Some behavioral acts are strictly one or the other, but others are combinations of the two. Actions which seem irrelevant to the situation confronting the animal are called *displacement activities* and are believed to be an expression of conflict in the animal whether to attack or escape. In this state of behavioral conflict, many birds and mammals scratch themselves, look here and there, yawn, stretch, and eat. They often redirect their frustrations by attacking a tree or some inanimate object. Thus dogs may attack a bone or a piece of wood or a neighbor. A man frustrated at his job may come home and "take it out on his wife and family."

Aggressive behavior has several components, including *territoriality* and *social dominance*. The communication allowing this behavioral structure in a population consists of *visual displays, sound, smell, taste,* and *touch*. Through these different means of communication animal populations delimit boundaries around their territories and social rank within their group. It is from aggressive behavior that competition for *food, space,* and *mating,* the three basic drives of all animals, develops. The result is a regulation of population size and distribution (see Plate 9).

TERRITORIALITY
A territory is a geographic region *defended* against competing members of the same species. The many types of territories—mating, nesting, feeding, etc.—are usually characterized by being defended by males through threatening *displays* or *actual fighting* (see Figure 13.7). A population of animals demonstrating territoriality usually contains three structural components: (1) The *home* is the nest or the shelter to which land animals return for sleeping, hiding, or reproducing. (2) A *territory* includes a home and an area around it which is defended. Home and territory may include a single individual, a mating pair, or parents and offspring. (3) *Home range* is the area over which an animal habitually travels in its search for food and other diverse activities. The home range may be the same as the territory, but it is usually larger and most of it is not defended against other members of the same species. Several home ranges may overlap without giving rise to conflict. Usually, *signposts* are used by mammals to mark their home ranges. Secretions of skin glands, urine, piles of dung, barked trees, and other signposts are used to mark trails and other features of home ranges. Probably the main advantage of home range is that it ensures the individuals in it a supply of daily food and a quick marked pathway to their territories at home.

Home ranges of mammals do not always involve set territories. Many species of mammals travel in groups, which they defend instead of a geographic territory. When animals feed and reproduce with the entire social group as a unit, the concept of individual territoriality does not strictly apply. Instead the group is organized into a hierarchy of social dominance.

SOCIAL DOMINANCE
When animals travel as a group, two opposing forces are at work in an interacting system of attraction and repulsion. Animals have varying degrees of attraction for

FIGURE 13.7 Two Alaskan moose fighting over territory. *(Courtesy of Charles J. Ott from The National Audubon Society.)*

each other, but they also have reactions against crowding. Population size affects behavior since aggressiveness increases with population growth and related crowding. Because of the forces of competition and aggressiveness, a hierarchy of social rank is established in a social group. Each individual occupies a position of social rank in the hierarchy based on *dominance* and *submissiveness*. Through fighting, bluffing, and threatening, pairs of individuals determine which is to be dominant or submissive, and this relationship may remain unchanged for long periods of time.

Chickens provide a good example of how social rank is established and are, in fact, the group in which social rank was first discovered. It was well known that hens cackled and fussed a great deal and that roosters crowed, but it was not until 1913 that Schjelderup-Ebbe noticed that one hen in a barnyard flock acts as a tyrant, pecking and threatening the others. He saw that in repeated encounters between certain pairs of hens the same hens always seemed to be able to peck the other hens without being pecked by them. One, he said, was *dominant*, and the other *submissive*. Further studies of other hens made him realize that there was a hierarchy of "who could peck whom" in the flock. He called this social hierarchy a *peck order*. Hen A could peck hens B and C, hen B could peck C, but not A, and C could peck neither A nor B. This is called *straight-line dominance order*. Other investigations revealed that dominance relationships in groups of vertebrates can be quite complex and can assume the nature of a triangle or web as well as a straight line. Since the work with chickens in 1913, social-dominance systems have been found in all classes of vertebrates and in many arthropods as well. Social hierarchies have been studied in fishes, amphibians, reptiles, and birds and such mammals as rats, sheep, lions, baboons, chimpanzees, dolphins, and sled dogs.

Social rank, once established, is maintained in a habitual way by both dominant and submissive animals, but an occasional threat or punishment may be used to maintain the relationship. Such relationships in groups of animals is an adaptation that reduces the *destructive fighting* within a group. Thus competitive relationships are kept stabilized without continual fighting and waste of energy.

COOPERATIVE BEHAVIOR

Some animals show no dominance at all among individuals in a group. Ants, termites, and bees are examples of cooperative societies with division of labor and an order of dominance established through competitive behavior. Prairie dogs serve as an example of a vertebrate in which there is no aggression among the members of the colony and no division of labor.

SOCIAL DOMINANCE AND LEADERSHIP

Leadership has been studied relatively little. It is usually defined as the ability of an animal to move ahead, with the rest of the group following, without the use of force. From what we have previously learned, it would seem reasonable that a group leader would be an animal at the top of the dominance order. This is not necessarily the case, for dominance does not seem to be involved in the development of leadership in most groups. For example, while it was commonly believed that flocks of birds are led by an old and experienced individual, actually the leadership changes from bird to bird. Primates seem to be unique in the way group leadership is organized, usually being based on social units led by dominant males. Some *baboon* groups are led by one dominant male, while others are led by several. *Gorilla* groups are composed of a dominant male plus all females and young; the extra males roam around several hundred feet away. The dominant male gorilla determines the distance traveled, the location of rest stops, and nests. In contrast to the closed social system of baboons and gorillas, *chimpanzees* have open systems, in which individuals move from group to group. Chimpanzee groups show evidence of neither dominance nor social hierarchies and do not have permanent leaders (see Figure 13.8). Several investigators argue that this is also true of baboons. The contradiction emphasizes that the study of primates has only begun.

FIGURE 13.8 Some animal groups show no evidence of dominance-submission among their members. (*Penguins, courtesy of Michael C. T. Smith; chimpanzees, courtesy of Arthur W. Ambler, both from The National Audubon Society.*)

REPRODUCTIVE BEHAVIOR

Obviously, the continuation of population requires reproduction; males and females must mate, and the offspring must live at least until they can mate. We have seen that animals have aggressive components in their personality. How are the barriers of territoriality and social dominance overcome or utilized in interactions between males and females? It is difficult to generalize, since there are large behavioral differences among the vast numbers of animal species, and so we shall limit our discussion to vertebrates.

If there is territoriality, as in gulls, males will defend their territories against all other members of their species, usually with gestures and threatening motions. Invading males or unreceptive females often put up a mock battle but will usually leave. If the invader is a receptive female, she will be threatened by the male and may show a mixture of fight and flight for a while, but she will eventually assume a submissive role which reduces or inhibits the aggressiveness of the male. They will pair and begin courtship behavior characteristic of their species.

Courtship displays are mechanisms for attracting females to males, or vice versa, and, as we have seen, decrease or inhibit aggressiveness so that mating can take place. Since mating occurs as the culmination of a sequence of instinctive courtship acts, courtship behavior is vitally important in preventing mating with the wrong species (see Figure 13.9).

FIGURE 13.9 Courting behavior in the sage grouse and Laysan albatross. In the grouse note the expanded neck sacs of the male as he struts. In the albatross pictures, the male (on the right) seems to be threatening the female, but in a moment or two, if she is receptive, she will assume a submissive role. (Laysan albatross courtesy of D. S. Pettingill, Jr.; sage grouse courtesy of Cameron Thatcher, both from The National Audubon Society.)

Courtship and mating behavior are stereotyped in most species of animals but is learned among primates. For example, monkeys raised in isolation do not know how to mate and try to mount the female from the side or make other unsuccessful attempts. Young monkeys and apes must observe adults mating and imitate them before they can be successful.

If there is a social dominance instead of territoriality, reproductive behavior is usually polygamous. Depending on the species, receptive females may mate with any males in the group or mate at a higher frequency with dominant males than with subordinate males. Nonhuman primate females in estrus (*heat,* a period of receptivity) will mate with any adult male of their species. Human females do not undergo periodic estrus and are sexually receptive throughout the year.

COMMUNICATION IN BEHAVIOR

Some of the stimuli which elicit behavior patterns are endogenous, but many come from external sources in the physical and biological environment. Stimuli coming from other individuals in the population are called *signals* and constitute a definite form of communication between organisms. Signals used in animal communication are chemical, such as odors, or physical, such as light, sound, or touch.

Since man relies primarily on his senses of sight and hearing when observing other animals, he is much more aware of signals of sight and sound than of any other kinds used by animals. The role of smell and touch has been studied only slightly.

VISUAL SIGNALS

Mammalian communicative signals are well known to us, as we are mammals and can draw on our own experience. A dog offers other familiar examples: *threat,* baring of fangs, curling of lips, direct look, erection of ears and tail (see Figure 13.10); *submission,* hiding of fangs, lowering of eyes, laying back of ears, and curling of tail between legs.

Monkeys, apes, and man are all active during the day and rely predominantly on sight and sound for communication. Colors, postures, and movements of the entire body are important, but the most important body part in visual signaling in monkeys and apes (and in man?) is the face. In the face, the *eyes* and *mouth* seem equally important. *Threat* is communicated usually with a *direct* gaze in monkeys and apes (see Figure 13.11). One cannot help wondering about the psychological state of these primates in zoos, where they are under the direct gaze of hundreds of other visiting primates every day. *Submission* is signaled in primates by *looking* away or anywhere but at the other animal. Gorillas carry this to the extreme of shaking their heads from side to side. (When encountered by a wild gorilla, you can save yourself by looking at the ground and shaking your head.)

Monkeys and apes seem to signal with their *mouths* by forming it into various shapes. The mouth is used as a signal when in one of three positions, mouth threat, grimace,

FIGURE 13.10 A coyote and a wolverine. Note the bared fangs and direct look. *(Courtesy of Edward Cesar from The National Audubon Society.)*

FIGURE 13.11 A look of threat and a direct gaze in a gorilla. *(Courtesy of Maurice E. Landre from The National Audubon Society.)*

and lip smacking. In the *open-mouth-threat* signal the mouth is open and the corners are drawn forward, but the lips are pressed tight against the teeth, which do not show. Submission is signaled with a grimace, which looks like a frightened grin as the corners of the mouth are drawn back and the teeth are exposed. (Perhaps this is the beginning of the evolution of the smile in man, since a smile is certainly not a signal of threat.) Neutrality or pacific intentions are signaled by lip smacking, in which the corners of the mouth are brought forward, the teeth are held slightly apart, and the lips make kissing movements.

SOUND SIGNALS

Sounds can serve as signals even if they are not formed by a vocal apparatus. Locomotion and common occurrences cause sounds that supply a great deal of information to the rest of the population, informing them of the presence of animals and their activities. Cessation of these sounds constitutes a dramatic signal of alarm to animals. For example, the sounds of breathing are sufficiently noticeable for an alarmed mammal to hold its breath in an attempt to conceal its position. Intentional breath holding can also serve as a signal of alarm to other members of the population.

Many monkeys and apes threaten one another by rattling branches and striking the ground with hands or feet. Chimpanzees "drum" on trees, and gorillas beat their chests with partially cupped hands. Branch shaking is a threat of local nature, but drumming and chest beating can serve as communication over a distance.

Local sounds made by nonhuman primates may be used to direct the response of the listener to visual signals or to make listeners respond to certain preferred objects or act in a certain manner prescribed by the sounds. Moods can also be communicated by primates and provide a very important source of interaction in the dominance hierarchy of the group.

SIGNALS WITH ODORS: PHEROMONES

We have seen that animals produce chemicals which act as internal messengers, but an increasing mass of evidence indicates that they also produce substances which are discharged externally and perceived by other animals, usually members of the same species. *Pheromones* means external secretions that serve in the integration of individuals in the group. In insects, pheromones act as sex attractants, trail substances, and alarm substances. Female *Cecropia* moths can attract males from several miles away with their odors (see Figure 13.12). Ants follow trails of pheromones secreted by themselves and their scouts, and if their trail is wiped away with alcohol, this means of finding their way home is destroyed.

With mammals, musky secretions are believed to be involved in sex recognition, marking of home ranges and territories, defense of territories, and sensing of population densities. Most of the chemical studies of such secretions in mammals have in-

FIGURE 13.12 A pair of *Cecropia* moths. *(Courtesy of The American Museum of Natural History.)*

volved the musk deer, muskrat, and civet cat since their musky secretions are used in the manufacture of perfume. Most mammals mark their territories and home ranges with urine and feces, but primates such as apes and monkeys urinate and defecate anywhere, even in their nests. Carnivores use anal glands for sexual attraction, marking territories and home ranges, and defense. In general, among mammals signals transmitted by means of odors are as important as vision and hearing.

There is evidence that pheromones of one mammal may affect the endocrines of another mammal. If female mice are caged together, their periods of heat are disrupted. This effect does not result if the part of the brain concerned with smell is destroyed. If a male mouse is placed in a cage with a group of female mice, the females all come into heat on the third day after his arrival. The odor of a male mouse will terminate the pregnancy in a mouse if the odor is introduced while the embryos are still in the oviducts. The pheromones are probably in the urine of the male mouse, and in order to explain these effects it is necessary to assume that the male pheromones actually alter the endocrine secretions in the females.

SIGNALS WITH TOUCH
Man's sense of touch is highly developed. While our sense of touch, as used in communication, is centered in our hands, most other mammals touch nose to nose or nose to anus when first meeting. They communicate aggression through touch by biting, kicking, clawing, etc., and they convey appeasement and harmony through licking each other's skin. In primates, the most universal signal of harmony and social ties is through stimulation of the skin by *grooming*, a behavior pattern in which one primate manipulates the fur of another. Such interactions occupy much of the time of monkeys and apes and are vital in promoting social cohesion and peace. Chimpanzees in the wild spend a great amount of time slapping each other's backs, fondling and patting each other, and even holding hands.

ADAPTIVE BEHAVIOR
Behavior is adaptive since it is indispensable in animals for such activities as orientation, nest building, feeding, defense, parental care, etc. Within a population, behavior mechanisms establish division of labor, territories, dominance hierarchies, and modes of communication which allow peaceful expression of these social patterns. Behavioral processes affect births and deaths and determine the distribution of animal species. In short, behavior is a key factor in the maintenance of populations. The characteristics of populations are due to the behavior of the component organisms. Thus behavior is vitally important in the success of populations in evolution by natural selection, the topic of Chapter 16.

REVIEW QUESTIONS
1 Contrast stereotyped and acquired behavior.
2 Contrast taxes, reflexes, and instincts.
3 Discuss drives and instincts.
4 What is a chain reaction in behavior?
5 Contrast learning and reasoning.
6 What is habituation?
7 Contrast classical and operant conditioning.
8 Contrast short-term and long-term learning.
9 Contrast attack, escape, and displacement in aggressive behavior.

10 Describe the various expressions of territoriality.

11 What is the adaptive value of a social hierarchy?

12 Discuss visual and sound signals in primates.

13 Discuss the use of odors and pheromones by various animals.

14 Describe the evidence that pheromones of one animal can influence the endocrines of another animal.

15 What is the social significance of grooming in primates?

16 Argue briefly that behavior has adaptive value in the homeostasis of an ecosystem.

Ardrey, R.: *African Genesis, Delta Books, Dell Publishing Co., Inc., New York, 1961. A controversial interpretation of the nature of man as revealed by fossil evidence and animal behavior.

Ardrey, R.: *The Territorial Imperative,* Atheneum Publishers, New York, 1966. A sequel to *African Genesis* that goes much farther as a personal inquiry into the animal origins of property and nations; controversial but fascinating.

Coopersmith, S. (ed.): *Frontiers of Psychological Research,* W. H. Freeman and Company, San Francisco, 1966. Forty-four readings selected from *Scientific American* introduced by the editor.

Dethier, V. G., and E. Stellar: *Animal Behavior,* 2d ed., Prentice-Hall, Inc., Englewood Cliffs, N.J., 1964. An outstanding synthesis of the evolutionary and neurological basis of animal behavior; highly recommended.

Fraenkel, G. S., and D. L. Gunn: *The Orientation of Animals, Kineses, Taxes, and Compass Reactions,* Dover Publications, Inc., New York, 1961. A classic, first published in 1940; the categories of orientation it describes are still in current use.

Hinde, R. A.: *Animal Behaviour: A Synthesis of Ethology and Comparative Psychology,* McGraw-Hill Book Company, New York, 1966. A technical but very authoritative and successful attempt to synthesize the discoveries of psychologists and animal behaviorists.

Lorenz, K. Z.: *King Solomon's Ring,* Thomas Y. Crowell Company, New York, 1952. A charming and amusing account of a leading animal behaviorist and his animals.

Lorenz, K. Z.: *On Aggression,* Bantam Books, Inc., New York, 1967. A leading animal behaviorist attempts to understand human aggression by applying the generalizations learned by studying other animals.

Marler, P. R., and W. J. Hamilton, III: *Mechanisms of Animal Behavior,* John Wiley & Sons, Inc., New York, 1966. An excellent but rigorous text on animal behavior.

SUGGESTIONS FOR
FURTHER READING

* Available in Paperback.

McGaugh, J. L., N. M. Weinberger, and R. E. Whalen (eds.): *Psychobiology: The Biological Bases of Behavior,* W. H. Freeman and Company, San Francisco, 1967. Forty-five articles from *Scientific American* selected and introduced by the editors.

Smith, R. L.: *Ecology and Field Biology,* Harper & Row, Publishers, Incorporated, New York, 1966. An introductory text in ecology containing several chapters on the role of animal behavior in the homeostasis of populations.

Tinbergen, N.: *Curious Naturalists,* Basic Books, Inc., Publishers, New York, 1958. An autobiographical sketch and account of adventures in the study of animal behavior; very readable.

Tinbergen, N.: *The Herring Gull's World,* Doubleday Anchor Book, Garden City, N.Y., 1960. A study of the social behavior of birds.

Tinbergen, N., and the Editors of Life: *Animal Behavior,* Time-Life Books, New York, 1965. Clearly written by a great behaviorist and beautifully illustrated.

Swamp and cattails. (*Courtesy of Grant M. Haist.*)

Chapter 14
Homeostasis in Ecosystems: Changing Populations

One cannot step into the same river twice.

Heraclitus

A population is a group of organisms all of the same species. Populations have properties which are unique and are not characteristic of individual organisms. A population, for example, has a *birth rate, death rate, age ratio, sex ratio,* and the *ability to migrate,* which gives it a *distribution.* In responding to the physical forces of the environment, a population has a life history similar to an individual organism: It *grows, diversifies,* and *maintains itself* to some extent. Some biologists like to think of a population as a superorganism in which the organisms are the cells which may specialize into various ecological niches, the "tissues."

REGULATION OF POPULATION SIZE

FIGURE 14.1 Predator-prey relationships are demonstrated in these experiments by Gause, a Russian biologist. An increase in prey population allows an increase in predators, which in turn causes a decline in prey. Since the food has decreased, the numbers of predators decrease, and this allows the numbers of prey to increase. (*Adapted from Simpson and Beck, Life, Harcourt Brace Jovanovich, 1965.*)

Births cause an increase in population size, and deaths cause a decrease. The rates at which these opposing statistical forces operate affect the *density* of a population. Density increases when birth rates are higher than death rates and vice versa.

The relative rates of births and deaths may vary through *time,* and if these rates are graphed, they will portray the *growth form* of a population. The growth form of a population of *microorganisms* such as bacteria or protozoans in a culture flask shows geometric progression (1, 2, 4, 8, 16, . . .) up to a point where the growth levels off, and then, frequently as a result of accumulation of toxic metabolic products liberated from the organisms, a period of rapid deceleration may occur. Eventually a steady-state population is attained in which the rate of death equals the rate of reproduction and the total number of organisms in the culture remains the same (see Figure 14.1).

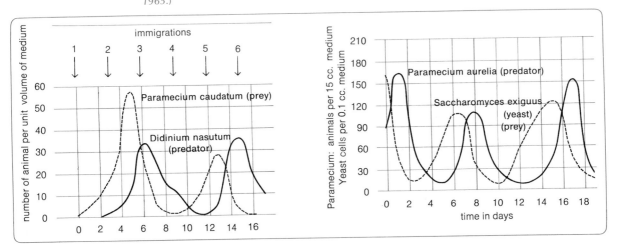

Insect populations are regulated in a variety of ways. The fruit fly *Drosophila,* the classic organism studied in genetics, has some sort of homeostatic mechanism by which it decreases egg laying as population density increases. Flour beetles may practice cannibalism and begin puncturing eggs as a response to crowding. Frequency of mating also decreases as crowding increases. Some species of flour beetles release a gas which kills larvae and decreases the mating activities of adults. Production of this gas increases with crowding and serves as an effective control over population size.

Similar control in mammals was for many years thought to be caused by interaction between predators and prey (see Figure 14.2), by analogy with certain famous cases known from studies of lower organisms (see Figure 14.3). Records kept since the

FIGURE 14.2 Predator-prey relation in action. The frog is about to eat a tiger swallowtail. (*Courtesy of Trent Davidson from The National Audubon Society.*)

Eighteenth Century describe 4-year cycles in population size not only of the small Alpine field mice called lemmings, but also their predators, foxes, mink, and weasels (Figure 14.4). Ledgers of the Hudson Bay Company of Canada show 10-year cycles in the abundance of lynx pelts (Figure 14.5), and these seem to match the oscillations in abundance of snow shoe hares, the lynx's primary food (Figure 14.6). A reasona-

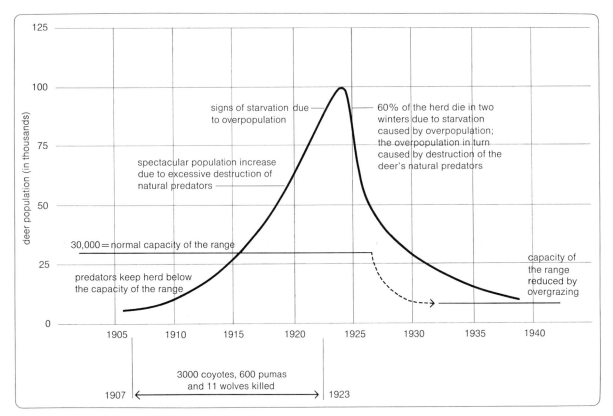

FIGURE 14.3 The history of the Kaibab deer indicates that many populations are regulated in size by pressure from predators. When the predator pressure is removed, the limiting factor becomes food and many starve. During overgrazing by the large population the carrying capacity of the range was reduced, so that the survivors barely eke out a marginal existence. (*Adapted from Simpson and Beck, Life, Harcourt Brace Jovanovich,* 1965.)

A

FIGURE 14.4 (a) The prey, a lemming (Alpine field mouse). Two of its predators, (b) fox and (c) weasel. (*Courtesy of The Museum of Natural History; weasel photography by H. T. Middleton.*)

B

C

FIGURE 14.5 Lynx. *(Charles J. Ott, Photo Researchers, Inc.)*

ble explanation for these cycles seemed to be that the rodents and hares were able to reproduce rapidly while predator pressure was low, and that this period of population increase in prey was followed by a corresponding increase in predators, which began again to extend their influence on the prey and cause the rapid, sudden increase in predators. Studies in the first half of the century revealed, however, that many cycles occurred *without* a proportionate increase in predators.

A Russian biologist, A. F. Gause, proposed that the predators involved in the population cycles were actually *disease* organisms and not the large food consumers. This idea stimulated a search for pathological reasons for the deaths of lemmings, hares, and other mammals whose populations underwent cyclic changes. The results of these studies were disappointing in that no correlation could be found between the incidence of microbes and the population crashes.

In 1862, the Norwegian naturalist Robert Collett observed the bizarre migration of lemmings and remarked that ''life quickly leaves them, and they die from the slightest injury . . . it is constantly stated by eye witnesses, that they can die from their great excitement.'' About 80 years later, the following clinical report[1] was made on the disappearance of Minnesota snowshoe hares during the population decline of 1939:

[1] From Hudson Hoagland, ''Cybernetics of Population Control, *Bull. Atom. Sci.*, February, 1964, p. 1.

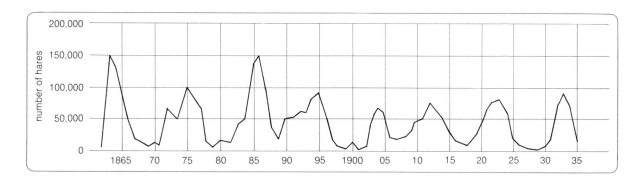

FIGURE 14.6 Population perio-
dism in the snowshoe hare of
Canada. The cycle reaches its
maximum about every 10 years.

This syndrome was characterized primarily by fatty degeneration and atrophy of the liver with a coincident striking decrease in liver glycogen and a hypoglycemia preceding death. . . . [Brain] hemorrhages, and congestion and hemorrhage of the adrenals, thyroid, and kidneys were frequent findings in a smaller number of animals. The hares characteristically died in convulsive seizures with sudden onset, running movements, hind-leg extension, retraction of the head and neck, and sudden leaps with . . . seizures upon alighting. Other animals were typically lethargic or comatose.

These symptoms were familiar to biologists who have worked with laboratory rabbits, and they named the disorder *shock disease*. The highly overcrowded conditions apparently caused internal stresses which resulted in the death of the organisms.

Studies by John J. Christian concluded that the mechanisms of shock disease were centered in the adrenal and pituitary glands. In 1950 he wrote:[1]

[1] *Ibid.,* p. 2.

We now have a working hypothesis for the die-off terminating a cycle. Exhaustion of the adreno-pituitary system resulting from increased stresses inherent in a high population, especially in winter, plus the late winter demands of the reproductive system, due to increased light or other factors, precipitates population-wide death with the symptoms of adrenal insufficiency and hypoglycemic convulsions.

Thus one theory suggests that the Minnesota snowshoe hares were victims of their own hormonal regulation systems. Normally, homeostasis is maintained as a result of responses to a certain input of information from the various sense receptors. According to the stress theory, at a certain crucial population size the stress induced by crowding would cause an input of sensory information and an accumulation of stressful problems which would trigger responses that are no longer homeostatic. The hypothalamic region of the brain, which must deal with this set of problems, is connected to a control center regulating emotions as well as the rate of pituitary hormone secretion. The reaction to overcrowding would be an abnormally large secretion of ACTH by the pituitary, causing in turn a proportionate increase in activity of the adrenal gland, with widespread effects on levels of blood sugar and salts as well as decreased resistance to infection. With such an improperly balanced condition, a slight stimulus, such as a loud noise or the sight of the opposite sex, could tip the scales, causing the adrenal medulla to release large quantities of adrenalin. The effect of adrenalin is to direct sugar away from the blood and brain and into the muscles. The result could be shock disease with its bizarre nervous behavior. The actual reason for population cycles in hares and other mammals remains obscure, and the stress theory is simply one plausible explanation.

An obvious question now arises: Is man also subject to stress disease; will he react to overcrowding like rabbits, rats, and lemmings? Some people argue that "give-up-itis" demonstrated by some American prisoners during the Korean War falls into this category. Scores of American prisoners became very drowsy or drifted into comas, and some even died in sudden convulsive seizures. The spectre of an increasingly overcrowded world with human beings housed in the equivalent of rabbit warrens makes research on the nature of stress disease one of the most vital enterprises of man. For a fascinating account of "pathological togetherness" read Calhoun's article listed in the Suggestions for Further Reading.

CHANGING POPULATIONS: ECOLOGICAL SUCCESSION

Ecosystems do not remain unchanging and static. Physical factors in the habitat may change because of changes in climates, and the like, and the organisms themselves alter the habitat in which they live. Changes may be so drastic that the ecosystem is altered to a condition in which none of the previous resident organisms can persist. Plants and animals that are dominant at one point in time are not dominant at a later time. These shifts in dominant types follow an orderly temporal progression called *ecological succession*.

SUCCESSION OF PONDS IN SAND DUNES

One of the first studies of ecological succession was carried out at the sand dunes at the southern end of Lake Michigan in 1899, where H. C. Cowles studied plant succession and Victor Shelford studied animal succession. Lake Michigan once had a level 60 feet higher than it has now, and as it receded toward the north, younger and younger sand beaches were exposed. Depressions in the new beaches gave rise to a series of 95 narrow, shallow ponds which parallel each other in arcs leading south for several miles from the present lakeshore. The age of a pond is a function of its distance from the lakeshore—the further south, the older the pond. Life in the sequence of ponds differs as increasingly older ponds are encountered. Studies of these ponds of varying ages therefore allow ecologists to reconstruct a detailed study of the evolution of a single pond through time. We have space for only a brief and general description of how ponds undergo the process of ecological succession.

When a beach pond is first formed, its bottom is sandy and lacks plants and animals. Such a condition is called the *bare-bottom stage*. A *pioneer* stage begins with the influx of bacteria, protozoans, algae, and small animals. Black bass, bluegills, and catfish may build nests on the bare bottom, which they share with snails, caddis fly larvae, clams, and other organisms which not only tolerate the sandy bare bottom but require it. As the years pass, the pioneering organisms of the pond contribute their debris, causing a buildup of humus on the bottom of the pond. Eventually, enough humus will have accumulated to allow chara, a green alga commonly called stonewort, to grow and contribute its organic matter to the buildup of humus. Since chara does not extend above the surface of the water, this stage is called the *submerged vegetation stage*. Hiding or resting among the chara are dragonfly and mayfly nymphs, small crayfish and other crustaceans, and other organisms which live on chara rather than on the sandy bottom. Plankton becomes dense enough to support larger animals, which may emigrate from other ponds or streams during flooding or by some other means. Dominant animals include fishes which lay their eggs on chara, gill-breathing snails which eat food living on chara, and caddisworms which build their tubes out of humus and sand grains. All these organisms add to the accumulation of humus on the bottom, and after a few years it becomes thick enough to support rooted plants and their associated animals.

The pioneering chara is replaced by pondweeds, cattails, and bulrushes at the edges and, perhaps, water lilies at the center of the pond (see the photograph at the beginning of the chapter and Figures 14.7 and 15.11). Most of these plants have their roots in the bottom while their leaves are either at the surface or extend above it. This new ecosystem is called an *emergent vegetation stage*. Dominant animals of this stage are small bivalved mollusks which burrow in the humus, dragonfly nymphs and other aquatic insects, lung-breathing snails, diving spiders, and annelid worms, including the leeches. All these diverse organisms add their contributions of matter to the bottom, causing it eventually to build up to the point where it lies above the groundwater level. When a pond has become so shallow that its bottom lies above the groundwater level, it usually dries out during the summer. This new ecosystem is called a *temporary pond*. Conditions are hazardous in such a pond, for water disappears completely in summer and may freeze solid in the winter. The adaptations which permit plants and animals success in such conditions are equally dramatic. Drying and freezing are escaped by bacteria, protozoa, molds, yeast, and algae through the formation of resistant, heavy-walled *cysts* and *spores*. Snails, amphibians, and crayfish escape drying and freezing by burying themselves in the muddy bottom. Some forms, such as the tiny crustacean called a fairy shrimp, have resistant eggs which can withstand summer, fall, and winter hazards and hatch in the spring.

Life in a temporary pond is not as luxuriant as that in earlier stages, but the organisms continue to add their debris to the bottom until it is so shallow that it is wet only during the rainy months in the spring. During the rest of the year, the former pond is dry and occupied by plants and animals of the land.

Meadow grasses invade the dried-up pond and form a marsh meadow in forests or a prairie in a grassland zone. In temperate forests alders, willows, and various bushes

FIGURE 14.7 Snakeweed
growing in a pond. (*Courtesy of
Henry Mayer from The National
Audubon Society.*)

FIGURE 14.7 Snakeweed growing in a pond. (*Courtesy of Henry Mayer from The National Audubon Society.*)

are the pioneers which colonize the site of a former pond. Eventually these plants change the soil so that aspen, elm, maples, and white pines outcompete the colonizers and become dominant. As time passes, the fallen trunks and roots of these trees add their substance to the accumulating soil and change its nature. Trees get taller and thicker, so that their crowns form a canopy which shades the ground. Seeds of many forest trees cannot germinate in the semidarkness on the dry forest floor, but seeds of sugar maple, beech, hemlock, spruce, and cedar can tolerate low light intensities. Flourishing in the dense shade, these trees grow tall and replace their parents as they die, so that the community finally becomes stable. This stable condition in an ecological succession is called a *climax community*, one which will endure until some catastrophic factor such as disease, fire, or flooding disrupts the balance so that the area reverts to an earlier stage in the succession.

Bare rock is the original source of soil. Soil formation is a story of ecological succession which begins with the weathering of rocks under the combined effects of temperature, water, and winds (see Figure 14.8). Water seeps into cracks and crevices, and as it freezes, it expands with such force that it cracks rock apart, ex-

SOIL FORMATION AS AN
ECOLOGICAL PROCESS

FIGURE 14.8 Rock eroding into soil. *(Courtesy of G. E. Kirkpatrick from The National Audubon Society.)*

posing a great amount of rock surface to the actions of further weathering. Carbon dioxide from the air or from respiring organisms can combine with water to form carbonic acid, which slowly dissolves rock surfaces. Pioneer plants such as lichens, mosses, and liverworts are especially adapted to maintain a foothold on bare rocks, and their products further dissolve the rocks. Small rock particles fall off and gather and eventually enough material is accumulated so that rooted plants can gain a foothold and begin growing in the humus and other organic material which the pioneering plants are accumulating. Roots probe into cracks and crevices of the rocks and break them into even smaller pieces. When the plants die, their roots, stems, and leaves decompose and add organic nutrients to the forming soil so that earthworms, roundworms, fungi, and many other forms of life can live in the soil and form humus to leave to posterity.

Ecological succession demonstrates three striking generalities: (1) It is an *orderly* process, in which ecosystems form and replace each other in a sequence often predictable (see Figure 14.9). (2) The causes for this replacement lie in the ecosystems themselves, since the activities and products of each assemblage of organisms in the sequence alter the habitat to the extent that another assemblage of organisms becomes more successful. (3) The organisms in the changing ecosystem must be able to control the environment to some degree if an orderly succession is to occur. If the physical environment undergoes frequent and drastic changes, the organisms cannot modify their environment and succession cannot occur.

SUCCESSION IN THE OCEAN

The ocean is teeming with microscopic bacteria, algae, protozoa, and immature animals which will settle down and take up residence wherever they can find space and proper living conditions. Man-made beaches, wharf pilings, ship hulls, newly exposed rocky outcroppings, and newly stirred-up sea bottoms all become populated by willing pioneers. In some cases, organisms occupy the areas in sequences similar to those in ecological succession in lakes and ponds.

If an object with a hard surface is placed in the ocean, a *bacterial slime* forms on it within a few hours. Before the day is over, diatoms and protozoa are found in the slime. By the second or third day, colonies of coelenterate polyps are growing there. Within a week, dense clusters of algae and barnacles and a few mussels have replaced the polyp colonies. During the second month, a climax stage is reached, in which mussels have become dominant and only a few barnacles remain. Intertidally, climax stages consist of the various assemblages described in Chapter 15. The exact sequence leading to the climax stage depends greatly on the physical conditions in the region itself.

Some ecologists argue that succession is not very common in the ocean. They argue that limiting factors in the ocean are primarily physical and that organisms cannot alter physical factors to any significant degree in most of the regions of the ocean. It

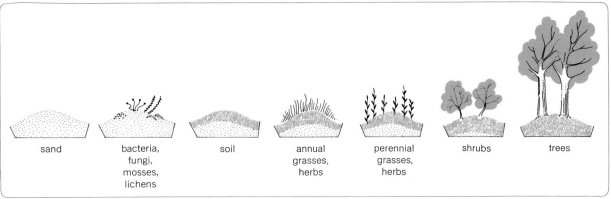

sand | bacteria, fungi, mosses, lichens | soil | annual grasses, herbs | perennial grasses, herbs | shrubs | trees

FIGURE 14.9 Ecological succession in sand dunes: left to right, a sequence of ecosystems from virgin land (sand) to climax (trees). (*Adapted from Paul B. Weisz, Elements of Biology, 3rd ed. Copyright McGraw-Hill Book Company, 1969. Used by permission.*)

SUCCESSION IN MAN'S ECOSYSTEM

is clear that a great deal more is known about freshwater habitats and their dynamics than about the massive seas and their ecological processes.

We shall have a great deal more to say about man and his ecosystem in Chapter 22, but at this point it seems appropriate to ask: What is man doing to his ecosystem? Is he altering his habitat to the extent that it will become more suitable for some other organism? Is he altering the soil, water, and air to the extent that it will no longer support his needs? Will man be forced to change his way of living to conform to the habitats he is creating? If these questions are to be answered with yes, what will be the manner of life in the future?

We do not know how man will respond to the changing demands being put upon him by the ecosystem he is creating, but we do know that at least some groups of human beings have in the past managed to change customs cherished for long periods in response to changing conditions. Man must understand that he is a biological organism functioning in an ecosystem. He must realize that the ecosystem needs to function naturally. Man cannot completely control ecosystems. He must learn his role in the drama of his ecosystem and play it accordingly.

REVIEW QUESTIONS

1 Discuss how population sizes are regulated.
2 Describe shock disease in lemmings, rabbits, rats, and man.
3 Describe the changes occurring in the transition of a bare-bottom pond to a maple and beech forest.
4 Describe the ecological succession in the ecosystem of urban man.

SUGGESTIONS FOR
FURTHER READING
* Available in Paperback.

Buchsbaum, R., and M. Buchsbaum: *Basic Ecology,* Boxwood Press, Pittsburgh, Pa., 1957.   Simple explanation of ecological principles.

Calhoun, J. C.: "Population Density and Social Pathology," *Scientific American,* February, 1962.   A fascinating account of the effects of crowding.

Odum, E. P.: *Ecology,* Holt, Rinehart and Winston, Inc., New York, 1963.   More general than the larger text.

Odum, E. P.: *Fundamentals of Ecology,* 2d ed., W. B. Saunders Company, Philadelphia, 1959.   A widely used introductory text.

Smith, R. L.: *Ecology and Field Biology,* Harper & Row, Publishers, Incorporated, New York, 1966.   Several excellent sections deal with the ecology of populations.

Tree. *(Courtesy of M. Chapman.)*

Chapter 15

Homeostasis in Ecosystems: Habitats and Organisms

The foxes have holes, and the birds of the air have nests. . . .

Matt. 8:20

In Chapters 11 and 12 we discussed homeostasis of organisms and found that an organism controls its internal environment by interactions between its cells and their products. In this and the following chapters, we shall see how an ecosystem (a natural unit consisting of living organisms plus their environment which interact to produce an enduring system) also maintains somewhat constant conditions and how this stability is due to the interactions between organisms and their environments, both living and nonliving. The study of how organisms interact with their environment is called *ecology*.

ECOLOGICAL NICHES
AND HABITATS

Two concepts basic to ecology are the *habitat* and the *ecological niche*. Each organism lives in a specific portion of the environment called its *habitat* (see Plate 4). Habitats include such regions as under the bark of trees, the surface of a lake, the litter on the soil of a prairie, the intestine of man, etc. The *ecological niche* of the organism is its role and status within its ecosystem. Using man as an example, the neighborhood where he lives and works would be his habitat, while his type of employment and community service would be equivalent to his niche. Two different species do not usually occupy the same ecological niche in the same habitat. If they do, their coexistence will not last long, as one will outcompete the other and take over the niche entirely.

The daily life of an organism is affected by many factors, both nonliving and living, in its environment, for example, temperature, light, water, oxygen, carbon dioxide, salts, wind, soil, and predators. All organisms must be *adapted* to the variable conditions of their environment in order to survive in a particular habitat. For instance, consider the adaptations of the *Uma* lizard, which has overlapping eyelids, membranes covering the eyes, barbed feet, blending coloration, the ability to withstand high external temperatures, and a system that can extract all the water from urine and feces. With such adaptations you can probably guess that the ecological niche of this animal belongs in a desert habitat.

There are limits to how well the organisms tolerate an environmental factor. Each species has a different *range of tolerance* for each environmental force, and within this range there is usually a certain point that is an optimum, a value at which the organism performs best. As values of an environmental force deviate more and more from the optimal, they become detrimental and eventually lethal for an organism, requiring it to abandon a particular habitat or perish. For example, an orchid thrives at tropical temperatures but cannot exist in the Arctic; man requires drinking water for life, but cannot live under water; and so on. Too much or too little of a good thing can become intolerable. When an environmental force ranges so far away from optimal value that it becomes detrimental to the existence of species in a particular habitat, it is termed a *limiting factor*. In other words, the effect of a single environmental force on an organism may be optimal, suboptimal but tolerable, or lethal.

PHYSICAL FACTORS IN
WATER AND ON LAND

Life exists in three major regions on the earth, the *sea, fresh water,* and the *land.* Each environment has some single factors which are different, though the majority are quite similar. We shall discuss the most important of these factors in each of the three major habitats so that at a later point we can discuss the adaptations organisms have evolved as solutions to their environmental problems.

THE PHYSICAL ENVIRONMENT
OF THE SEA

If an explorer from outer space parked his flying saucer on the moon to take a look at our planet before coming down for a visit, he would be struck with the observation that almost three-fourths of the earth's surface is water. On a cloudless day the planet appears as a blue sphere with large patches of green here and there. The ocean contains 330 million cubic miles of water, a volume 18 times greater than the volume of the land above sea level. If the land areas were eroded to the point where the earth became a smooth sphere, the ocean would cover the earth uniformly with 12,000 feet of water.

The sea has been called the *cradle of life,* since life probably originated there and then evolved into the myriad forms which have existed up to the present. The earliest living forms generated in the sea gradually gave rise to descendants, and through the passage of immense periods of time and continuous biological change these descendants invaded all parts of the ocean, moved on into fresh water, up onto the land, and into the air. The invading organisms were confronted with a variety of new environmental problems which had to be solved before new ecological niches could be formed.

The dominant factor in both the sea and freshwater habitats is, of course, water in the *liquid* state. No other planet in our solar system has surface temperatures which permit water to remain in the liquid state. If neighboring planets do contain water, it is present only as vapor or ice.

The properties of liquid water permit life to exist. Nutrients must be in solution before they can enter a cell, and so must wastes before they pass out. Almost all the chemical reactions in the cell take place in water. Cells are therefore quite water-laden. As the biologist Haldane once said, "even the Archbishop of Canterbury is 60 percent water."

Water also has an unusually high capacity for storing *heat.* Bodies of water serve as heat reservoirs, absorbing heat during the day and giving it off at night. Such large bodies of water as the sea store up heat during the summer and release it during the winter, causing lands near the oceans to have relatively less variable climates. The British Isles, for example, would have the climate of Greenland if the Gulf Stream stopped bringing warm water from the Gulf of Mexico.

In addition to heat, water carries dissolved *gases* and *salts.* The amount of salt dissolved in the ocean is about 3.5 grams in each 100 cubic centimeters of water or, in the words of oceanographers, 35 parts per thousand. Stated another way, if all the salt were removed from the ocean, it would cover the land with a layer 500 feet thick. Different parts of the ocean have different amounts of salt. For example, areas with high rates of water loss by evaporation have high concentrations of salt. Waters with high amounts of salt are heavier than more dilute waters and sink. The importance of this will be seen when we discuss ocean currents.

The solubility of gases in water increases as the temperature decreases. A glass of water placed in a cold refrigerator takes on the taste of the exposed foods because gases from the foods dissolve in the cooling water. Also, a glass of cold water from a refrigerator left standing will form air bubbles around the inside of the glass as it warms up. As the temperature rises, the solubility of gases decreases, and they come out of solution. Bodies of water therefore contain more dissolved gases when they are cold than when they are warm. Surface temperatures of the oceans vary from freezing in the Arctic and Antarctic to 80°F or higher at the equator. The waters below a depth of 600 feet, however, range from 32 to 40°F, with deep waters usually just above freezing, even at the equator. Since the oceans are primarily cold water, they normally have an adequate supply of oxygen for all the living things they contain. In addition, dissolved gases are carried to all parts of the seas by currents. Oxygen has been found in the deepest waters, where no light from the sun penetrates, and aerobic life exists at depths of several miles. All of this oxygen has been produced by organisms living near the surface which use sunlight for photosynthesis. In fresh waters, however, varying temperatures, plus the consumption of oxygen by bacteria which decompose organic pollutants, sometimes cause ponds and streams to be deficient in oxygen to the extent that many forms of life cannot be supported.

Currents are caused in water by density, gravity, winds, and rotation of the earth. Water may become denser either by getting colder or by getting saltier. Water that is warmer or is less salty rises and moves over layers of heavier water. Bottom water may rise to the surface in what is called *upwelling,* bringing with it a rich supply of nutrients, which allow the surface waters to support a diverse and plentiful assortment of plants and animals. Upwelling of cold bottom water along coasts causes overlying air to cool down and form the fogbanks associated with many of the world's coastlines.

Rotation of the earth toward the east causes the overlying ocean waters to move toward the west at the equator. As a result, the major currents in the Northern Hemisphere flow clockwise (counterclockwise in the Southern Hemisphere) (see Figure 15.1). The rotation of the earth causes the air to move in a similar way, and the prevailing winds thus set up cause water to pile up not only at the centers of the oceans but against the coastlines of the continents. The piled-up water sinks, and additional currents are formed. Clearly, the ocean is not a homogeneous mass of water but a gigantic freeway system of rivers, great and small, which carry nutrients to all parts of the oceanic habitat and play a vital role in the regulation of the environments in the ocean as well as on the land.

Thus the water of the earth, in many respects, is quite similar in function to the water of the body fluids of organisms. It bears foods, waste, gases, and salts, and its resistance to temperature change renders its various habitats livable. Is it any wonder that the oceans are teeming with life?

FIGURE 15.1 Rotation of the earth toward the east causes overlying ocean waters to move westward.

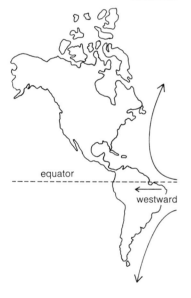

equator

westward

PHYSICAL FACTORS IN FRESH WATER

The environmental variables in fresh water are basically the same as in the ocean, most important being temperature, transparency, currents, dissolved gases, and salts. Since the migration of organisms took place primarily (though by no means exclusively) from the ocean into fresh water, we shall compare this more recently settled world with the older biological world, the ocean.

Temperature fluctuates much more in fresh water than in the ocean since the mass of water is much less and the water has more contact with surfaces which can absorb or add heat. As pointed out above, water resists temperature change, so that freshwater habitats are thermally stable, compared, for instance, to sand or rock. The actual temperature depends, of course, on the location of the body of water and the rate of flow. Another property of water expresses itself in the colder regions of the world, where the temperature of the water reaches or goes below the freezing point. Water is unique in that it reaches its greatest density at 39°F (4°C) instead of the freezing point, 32°F (0°C), when it becomes a solid. As a result, water becomes *less dense* as it freezes, and ice floats. The ice layer thus forms an insulating barrier over the surface, preventing larger streams, lakes, and ponds from freezing solid and destroying all the life contained in them.

The *transparency* of water determines the amount of light which can reach photosynthetic algae and aquatic vascular plants. The degree to which light can penetrate through the water may be affected by suspended materials in the water and by small organisms in the surface layers.

The primary cause of *currents* in freshwater streams, lakes, and ponds is gravity. The rush of fresh water down the slopes to the sea results in a flushing action that freshwater organisms must resist or be carried to the sea. We shall discuss later in this chapter some of the adaptations of freshwater organisms that prevent this from happening.

Oxygen is necessary for aerobic respiration and *carbon dioxide* for photosynthesis by green plants. As a result of photosynthesis, ocean water is saturated with oxygen, and the surplus passes into the atmosphere. Essentially all the oxygen now present on the earth is a result of plant photosynthesis. Wave action and other turbulent factors cause some of the atmospheric oxygen to redissolve in unsaturated water. Unlike the ocean, freshwater habitats may become deficient in oxygen through the needs of oxygen-consuming bacteria, which metabolize organic pollutants irresponsibly dumped into the water by man. The same is true of harbor areas and bays on the shore of the ocean, where water circulation is limited by geographic factors. While certain bacteria can use refuse as a source of nutrients and thus consume it, their respiration exhausts the oxygen dissolved in the water and renders the region unfit for other forms of aerobic life. Often a low concentration of oxygen is accompanied by a high amount of carbon dioxide if respiration has been the cause for the consumption of the oxygen. A high concentration of carbon dioxide is advantageous for plants and their photosynthesis, and the bottom of polluted lakes and rivers often becomes covered with green mats of slippery algae.

The amounts of dissolved *salts*, though small, play an important role in the freshwater habitat because certain salts are necessary for life. An important salt present in minimum permissible amounts often becomes the weakest link in an aquatic habitat and therefore the most important limiting factor. Nitrates and phosphates are often limiting in freshwater ecosystems. The overall concentration of all salts in the freshwater habitat introduces a problem which is not present in marine ecosystems: Most marine animals have a body salt concentration approximately equal to that of seawater and therefore exist in relative osmotic balance with their environment, but freshwater animals (having evolved from marine ancestors) have a body salt concentration greater than that of the external medium, and this creates a tendency for water to move into their bodies. This must be prevented, and the osmotic mechanisms freshwater organisms have developed to handle these problems constitute some of the primary physiological differences between marine and freshwater animals.

PHYSICAL PROPERTIES OF THE
TERRESTRIAL ENVIRONMENT

The conditions in large regions of the ocean are fairly constant while, in contrast, freshwater habitats tend to be in a state of change. Neither of these watery habitats, however, is as variable as many habitats in the terrestrial environment, for conditions on land change drastically over brief periods of time and short geographical distances. *Habitats on land tend to be much more rigorous than those in water.*

All organisms are actually creatures of water, for this substance makes up the largest percentage of their protoplasm. Before aquatic organisms invaded the land, adaptations had to be evolved which would prevent the evaporative loss of their internal solutions in the dry air. Dehydration is still a prime problem of organisms living on land.

Unlike water, air quickly gains and loses heat, and unless a large body of water is nearby, temperatures will vary greatly in the air through each day and season. Terrestrial organisms must possess adaptations permitting wide ranges of tolerance for variations in temperature. Sometimes they must conserve heat, and at other times they must lose it. Often the organisms must be able to move from place to place and seek an environmental temperature which they can tolerate.

Body support is not much of a problem to organisms enjoying the bouyant effect of water. Many organisms living in water have the same density as the surrounding water and are therefore virtually weightless. Air, however, offers much less buoyancy, and plants and animals must possess strong supporting structures to remain erect. Animals require an additional supporting framework for locomotion.

On land, because the gases of the atmosphere are constantly mixed by the wind, the concentration of gases is remarkably constant. There is, of course, increasingly less air as one rises in altitude above the earth. At the tops of the highest mountains the low quantities of air become limiting. No matter how thick or thin the air is, however, the relative proportions of its gases remain the same: about four-fifths nitrogen, one-fifth oxygen, and less than 1 percent other gases. Carbon dioxide and water vapor, together with the so-called *rare gases,* amount to about 1 percent of the total. The concentrations of carbon dioxide and water vapor, however, tend to vary within this small range from habitat to habitat. Man's pollution of air, however, introduces a new array of limiting factors, and we are only beginning to understand their effects.

Soil not only offers a surface upon which animals can move and to which plants attach; it also serves as a source of minerals upon which both plants and animals depend. Soil also serves as a home where countless organisms spend all or part of their lives. For example, 95 percent of insect species, the most prevalent organisms on the face of the earth today, live in soil during part of their life cycles. Soil is a habitat occupied by many organisms, and many of them have a role in the ecosystem of man, for the soil is the indirect source of some of the materials from which man is made.

Earlier in this chapter we saw that the ecosystem can be subdivided into different habitats, each inhabited by organisms with different roles determined by their specific ecological niches. Ecosystems can also be divided up into geographic regions called *zones,* each defined by the physical properties of their environment and the unique species distribution of the area. Because of the sharply contrasting physical conditions between zones, which serve as barricades, organisms residing in one zone seldom venture into another. Within each zone are many habitats, and each is usually occupied by its unique assemblage of organisms.

ZONES: A FURTHER SUBDIVISION OF THE ECOSYSTEM

All the major biotic regions of the earth—the sea, fresh water, and land—are divided into zones. We shall begin our discussion with the vertical and horizontal zonation of the sea.

The sea is divided into four major zones, each with its own set of variable factors (see Figure 15.2). Most visitors to the sea are familiar with the *intertidal zone,* the border where land and sea meet and the shoreline is periodically washed by the tides. Below the tidal area and extending out over the continental shelves is the *zone of*

ZONATION IN THE SEA

FIGURE 15.2 The four zones of the sea.

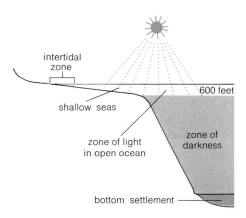

shallow seas, a region seldom deeper than 500 feet or over 100 miles in width. It is in the intertidal zone and shallow seas, the narrow ribbon bordering the continents, that the majority of marine life is found. Beyond the shallow sea lies the deep ocean, and its enormous mass can be divided up into two regions, the *zone of light* (photic zone) and the *zone of darkness* (aphotic zone) (see Figure 15.3). Depending on the transparency of the water, light may penetrate to a depth of 1,000 feet or to just 50 feet or less, the average depth of penetration being about 600 feet. Beneath this zone lies the realm of eternal darkness, where there are no seasonal changes and the temperature remains just above the freezing point.

Marine creatures are placed into major categories according to their location in the sea. The *plankton* includes the microscopic algae, protozoa, and small animals which float and drift, essentially at the mercy of the currents. *Nekton* comprises swimming organisms, such as fishes, whales, and squid, which can make their own way despite the currents. *Neuston* consists of those organisms which rest or swim on the surface. *Benthic organisms* are bottom-dwelling and attach, rest, or burrow into the bottom settlements (see Figure 15.4 and 15.5).

THE INTERTIDAL ZONE

The most challenging problems to life in the intertidal zones are the degree of *wave shock,* the *type of bottom,* and the periodic *tidal exposure.* The action of wind blowing across the surface of the sea rolls the water into waves, which crash against the shore and dislodge organisms not adapted to hold fast. *Rocky shores* provide firm foundations for attachment, while *sand and mud shores* provide burrowing substrata. Intertidal organisms are subjected to alternating periods of inundation and exposure to air, as a result of the ebb and flow of the tide. Clearly, organisms living in the intertidal zone must have adaptations which allow success in this habitat of rapidly changing characteristics.

FIGURE 15.3 (*Adapted from Paul B. Weisz, Elements of Biology, 3rd ed. Copyright McGraw-Hill Book Company, 1969. Used by permission.*)

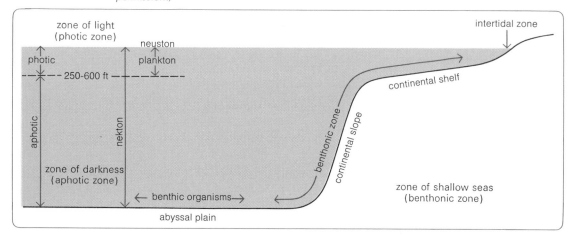

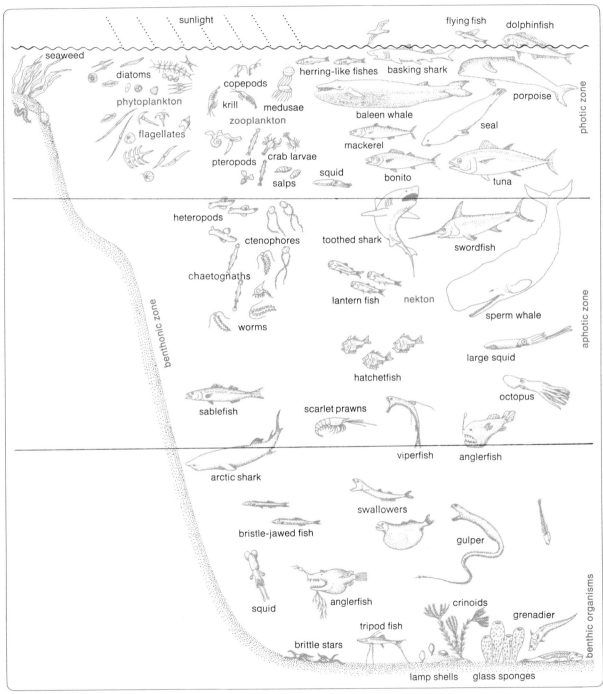

FIGURE 15.4 Marine food web (organisms not drawn to scale). (*Adapted from Scientific American, September,* 1969.)

FIGURE 15.5 Two kinds of oceanic angler fish inhabiting the deepest water. The beard on the fish is probably luminous, to attract prey in the dark water. Horrendous as they look, angler fish are usually small enough to fit into one's palm. (*Courtesy of The American Museum of Natural History*.)

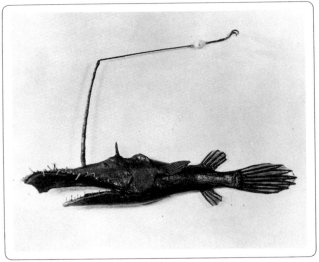

Representatives of almost every phylum of plants, animals, and microbes are found in the intertidal zone. The shore exposed during very low tides is found to be divided into distinct zones of plant and animal associations. The late E. F. Ricketts (immortalized by John Steinbeck as Doc of *Cannery Row*) was a pioneer marine ecologist who described the four major habitat zones existing in the intertidal zone.

He numbered them 1 to 4, but many people now refer to them as the *splash zone, high-tide zone, midtide zone,* and *low-tide zone* (see Figure 15.6). We shall briefly describe them as they occur along the California coast.

On rocky shores, the *splash zone* is characterized by the appearance of very small barnacles (crustaceans), periwinkle snails (mollusks), lichen (see Plate 6) and occasionally green algae (see Figure 15.7). On sandy beaches this zone is inhabited by sand hoppers and beach fleas feeding upon material that has washed ashore.

The *high-tide zone* on rocky shores is characterized by brown algae, known as *rockweeds,* grazed upon by rock snails and black turban snails (mollusks) and the active striped shore crabs (crustaceans). On sandy mud flats this zone would contain the ghost shrimp and mud shrimp, crustaceans which build tubes into the bottom sediments. Bent-nose clams and sand clams also live in this area. The high-tide zone of the sand beach is a relative biotic desert with very little life.

The *midtide zone* of rocky shores has enormous numbers of mussels (mollusks), leaf barnacles and purple shore crabs (crustaceans), and brown turban snails. Starfish (echinoderms) are voracious predators in this zone, feeding upon mussels, barnacles, and other prey (Figure 15.8). Sea anemones (coelenterates) may form solid colonies like carpets or isolated soft cylinders of slowly waving tentacles searching for food. The midtide zone of sandy beaches often has burrowing red worms (annelids) and sand crabs (crustaceans). Within the shelter of bays, sandy and muddy shores may have predatory snails such as the moon snail, basket whelk, or the purple olive. Along rocky shores, the lower boundary of the midtide zone may be indicated by the presence of the feather boa kelp (algae), a long straplike seaweed with fringed blades and small olive floats. The midtide zone is exposed twice a day.

The *low-tide zone* is exposed only during the lowest tides. On rocky shores the region is inhabited by broad-plated brown kelp (algae) and the flowering plants called *surf grass*. The purple sea urchin (echinoderm) is abundant there. In the low-tide zone, only occasionally exposed to air, is found an assemblage of living creatures equalled in variety of phyla by no other habitat. Sponges, coelenterates, tunicates, and annelid tube worms adhere to the rocks. Worms of many phyla, crus-

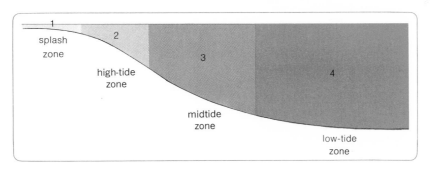

FIGURE 15.6 The four major habitat zones in the intertidal zone. The splash zone is just above high-water line. The high-tide zone and the midtide zone are exposed twice a day. The low-tide zone is exposed only during the lowest tides.

splash zone

high-tide zone

midtide zone

low-tide zone

FIGURE 15.7 Intertidal zonation on three types of shores. (*Adapted from J. W. Hedgpeth, Introduction to Seashore Life, University of California Press,* 1962).

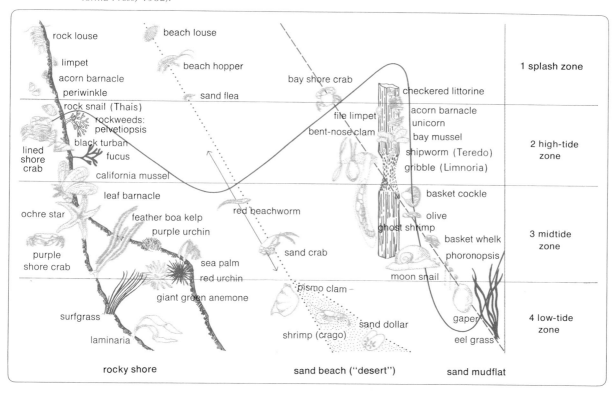

rock louse
beach louse
limpet
beach hopper
acorn barnacle
periwinkle
sand flea
bay shore crab
checkered littorine

1 splash zone

rock snail (Thais)
rockweeds: pelvetiopsis
black turban
fucus
california mussel
lined shore crab
file limpet
bent-nose clam
acorn barnacle
unicorn
bay mussel
shipworm (Teredo)
gribble (Limnoria)

2 high-tide zone

leaf barnacle
ochre star
feather boa kelp
purple urchin
red beachworm
basket cockle
olive
ghost shrimp
basket whelk
phoronopsis
purple shore crab
sand crab
moon snail

3 midtide zone

sea palm
red urchin
giant green anemone
surfgrass
laminaria
pismo clam
sand dollar
shrimp (crago)
gaper
eel grass

4 low-tide zone

rocky shore   sand beach ("desert")   sand mudflat

FIGURE 15.8 (a) Barnacles are splash-zone creatures, and starfish are midtide-zone creatures. Both are shown exposed here at low tide, predator and prey. (*Courtesy of Dorothy M. Compton from The National Audubon Society.*) (*b*) Shells of mussels, snails, scallops, and barnacles. (*Courtesy of Gordon S. Smith.*) (c) Wave action in midtide zone. (*Courtesy of Gordon S. Smith.*) (*d*) Sandpipers feeding on shore in midtide zone. (*Courtesy of M. Chapman.*)

A

B

C

D

tacean crabs and shrimp, and assorted mollusks move over the rocks. Eel-like fish slither among the crevices between the rocks, while perchlike fish swim freely in the water. On sand and mud bottoms of this zone various clams are found. The habitats in the low-tide zone are many.

THE SHALLOW SEAS
AND THE OPEN OCEAN

The zone of shallow seas begins at the outer margin of the low-tide zone. Close to shore grows eelgrass (a flowering plant) and further out large kelp beds (algae), which may be so dense that they form a breakwater for the shore. The tips of the kelp float on the surface while the other end is anchored to the bottom, and the blades may be more than 100 feet long.

The continental shelves, under which the shallow seas lie, extend from a few to several hundred miles into the ocean and may be several hundred feet deep. Light penetrates through most of the water of the shallow seas and allows lush growths of algae to flourish. The algae are eaten by a variety of animals, including protozoa, larval shrimp, squid, and hosts of other small animals which drift with the current. Collectively, because of their feeding role, these animals are called *consumers.* The microscopic suspended algae which are consumed are collectively called *phytoplankton* and along with other plants are called *producers,* since their photosynthetic activity is continually producing new living material from sunlight and raw matter. A single organism is called a *phytoplankter.* Phytoplankton photosynthesis also produces great quantities of oxygen, which saturates the ocean water and escapes into the atmosphere. Man is very much dependent upon this supply of oxygen, since relatively little comes from terrestrial plants.

The collective terms for members of the plankton that are animal is *zooplankton,* and of these the *copepods,* a type of microscopic crustacean arthropod only slightly larger than their food, are the most numerous (see Figure 15.9). Copepods in turn are the primary source of food for thousands of varieties of larger animals. For example, herring, which feed on copepods, are in turn eaten by larger fish, which may then be eaten by something as large as a whale. It has been calculated that a single whale meal may consist of several hundred herrings which have consumed 5,000 to 10,000 copepods which in turn would have eaten over 100,000 phytoplankters. Thus, 400 billion tiny algae are indirectly necessary to keep a medium-sized whale full for several hours. This example of "eat or be eaten" portrays the necessity of death in supporting life and the basic concept of the *food chain.* Producer organisms are eaten by consumers which are eaten by other consumers, and the protoplasm is passed on and on to consecutively higher feeding levels.

Bacteria are found in every part of the ocean, even the deepest samplings of sediment on the ocean floor. Bacteria serve along with the plankton as a source of food for filter feeders, organisms that feed by straining tiny organisms out of seawater by very specialized collecting adaptations. Bacteria also have as their primary

FIGURE 15.9 A copepod from the zooplankton. (*Courtesy of N. E. Beck, Jr., The National Audubon Society.*)

ecological role the decomposition of organic material into the basic nutrient building blocks. For this reason they are collectively called *decomposers.*

The ocean is fascinating for studies of habitats and adaptations. It also shows some promise as a source of food for the rapidly increasing human population. Many marine ecologists argue, however, that increasing man's take from the sea by more than two or three times may seriously upset the food chains of the sea. An understanding of the sea and its potential is therefore vital to man's future.

Habitats in fresh water vary a great deal between the headwaters and mouth of a river. Swift streams may slow down to form small pools and then rush on to flow into lakes which may empty by way of several small sluggish streams. The extremes are evident: Standing water and running water form the two most easily identified ecological systems.

ZONATION IN FRESH WATER

FIGURE 15.10 Zonation in fresh water lakes.

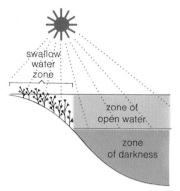

Lakes and ponds are primary examples of *standing-water habitats* and have many of the same properties as oceans. A lake that is large enough has three of the four zones of oceans, lacking, of course, the intertidal zone, for there are no tides in lakes (Figure 15.10). Lakes and ponds have a *zone of shallow water* (littoral zone) of a depth such that light can penetrate to the bottom, where the plants grow. Beyond this is the *zone of open water* (limnetic zone), which extends to the maximum depth that light will penetrate. Beneath the lighted zone in deep lakes is a *zone of darkness* (profundal zone), where only consumers and decomposers can live.

Along the shore of lakes and ponds vegetation grows in distinct zones. As the depth of the water increases, aquatic vascular plants, which grow only if they are able to emerge from the water, are replaced by plants that live completely submerged. The sequence is from cattails, to bulrushes, to arrowhead, water lily, pondweed, and muskgrass (Figure 15.11). Muskgrass and pondweed live only if they are completely submerged in water. Animals of the shallow regions of lakes and ponds are primarily aquatic insects and the immature stages of fish and amphibians.

Organisms of the open water consist primarily of algae (see Plate 7), plankton, fishes, and surface waterfowl. As in the ocean, the phytoplankton and zooplankton are the major producers and herbivores, respectively. With the awesome problems which will soon confront man in his search for food to supply his increasing numbers, the food chains and productivity of lakes and ponds will demand greater attention.

FIGURE 15.11 Zonation of fresh water plants.

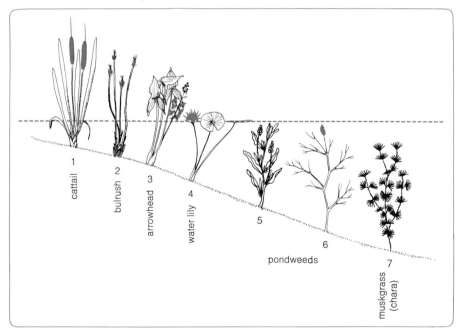

Running-water habitats include streams of various sizes. Small streams contain two zones with contrasting environmental conditions. A *rapid zone* is shallow and has a current which is usually too swift to allow sediments to build up. The bottom is usually rocky and contains many organisms specifically adapted to adhere to the rocks. A *pool zone* is deeper and has a current slow enough to permit silt and other suspended materials to settle out on the bottom. Burrowing forms such as worms and clams inhabit this zone and form an ecological assemblage quite different from that of the rapids.

ZONATION ON LAND

The success of an organism in a particular habitat is determined by the effectiveness of its adaptations against the limiting factors confronting it (see Figure 15.12). The most important of the limiting factors on land are desiccation and the vagaries of temperature. The nature of the terrestrial habitat is determined by its climate, soil characteristics, and interactions between organisms.

Soils, temperatures, and rainfall vary around the world's land masses, and combinations of these factors constitute a multitude of local conditions in which well over a million different species of terrestrial organisms have evolved. Rigorous environmental pressures have selected for increasingly greater complexities and specializations. As a result, the most complex forms of life are land-dwelling forms. At present the seed plants, insects, and warm-blooded vertebrates are the dominant land forms.

MAJOR TERRESTRIAL ZONES

It is often possible to identify a specific habitat by the presence of a few dominant plants or animals (sometimes called *indicator species*) enjoying success there. Adaptations of the organisms living in a habitat serve as valid indicators of the environmental pressures exerted there. Of these pressures, the most important are *temperature* and *annual rainfall* (see Figure 15.12). With these two criteria we can divide up the terrestrial environment into six major kinds of zones: *desert, grasslands, rain forest, deciduous forest, taiga,* and *tundra.*

Deserts average less than 10 inches of rain a year, precipitation falling in occasional heavy rainfalls or cloudbursts. By necessity desert plants must be adapted to such erratic supplies of water. These adaptations are of several kinds. Some desert plants have enormously long root systems extending deep into moist areas far beneath the surface. Others are able to flower, pollinate, and form seeds within a few days following rain. The plants which grow from the germinated seeds must have very brief growing seasons as well, for growth also depends upon the scanty rainfall. Desert plants are generally smaller than those in wetter habitats, and to decrease evaporative water loss many have greatly reduced leaves. Cactuses, for example, have leaves reduced to spines and thorns, and photosynthesis is carried on by the green succulent stems.

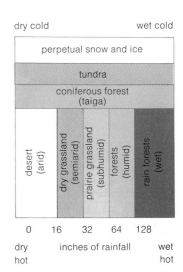

FIGURE 15.12 Zonation on land. Organisms fail or succeed depending on their adaptation to such limiting factors as humidity and temperature, soil characteristics, and interactions between organisms.

Desert animals are also relatively small and usually escape the hot rays of the sun by burrowing into the ground or hiding under rocks. Reptiles are plentiful in the desert because their lower metabolic rate does not produce much internal heat and because alterations in body temperatures are not damaging to them, within limits. Furthermore, they are covered with a tough integument which prevents water loss (see Figure 15.13). Birds and mammals get rid of excess body heat mainly through evaporation of water, but also "dump" their heat directly from their body surfaces. Mammals in the desert are mostly rodents, which stay in underground chambers during the day where the moisture of their breath is not lost to the warm surface airs. They do not drink, instead gaining all their water from the seeds they eat. They lose little water by excretion since their urine is excreted mostly as a solid.

Grasslands are characterized by intermittent rains providing an annual total of 10 to 30 inches. Temperatures, as well as rainfall, may vary widely among grassland habitats in the northern regions. Tropical grasslands vary no more than 10 or 15°F on either side of the average, 80°F; in contrast, the northern plains may have an annual temperature range of −50 or −60°F to 120 or 130°F.

Grasses, the dominant organism of this habitat, may vary from bamboo and elephant grass to the short buffalo grass, but they all have the ability to cope with alternating wet and dry periods. The success of grasses in meeting the pressures of their environment is matched by the success of the mammals living upon the grasses: There are many more species of mammals in the grassland than in any other habitat. Many of man's early civilizations arose in grassland regions, where he cultivated both the grazing mammals and forms of grasses called grains (Figure 15.14).

Rain forests experience almost daily rains for part or all of the year. Many inches of rain a day may fall. Throughout the year temperatures average 80°F and may vary only 10°F from the average. As a result of all this rain, combined with high temperatures, plant growth is continuous throughout the year and the plants may become exceedingly large and crowded together, so crowded in fact, that they do not fall over if cut. Rain forests are marked by an extreme *diversity of species* of both plants and animals. There may be 200 different species of trees in a few acres, and it has been found that three-fourths of all bird species live in the rain forest. The rain forest is a very productive habitat for vegetation, but it has been abused by men who have attempted to superimpose upon it types of agriculture not adapted to its special requirements. Corn, for example, will flourish for a few years and then completely deplete the soil of its nutrients because forest floor decomposes quickly and consumes the organic material present. Rain forests have only a thin layer of rich humus. Over a billion people populate the humid tropics, living in close proximity to rain forests. The complex ecosystem represented by the rain forests must be better understood so that more effective agricultural methods for these ecosystems can be devised (Figure 15.15).

Deciduous forests have about 30 to 40 inches of precipitation per year, which usually falls as well-spaced rains or snows. Cold winters and warm summers

A

B

FIGURE 15.13 (a) Tough integument of the whiptail lizard. (*Courtesy of The American Museum of Natural History.*) (b) Its habitat in the desert of the southwestern United States. (*Courtesy of Lola Beall Graham from The National Audubon Society.*)

FIGURE 15.14 Bison, mammals that graze on grasslands. (*Courtesy of Leonard Lee Rue from The National Audubon Society.*)

FIGURE 15.15 Rain-forest plants. Rain forests are characterized by a diversity of species of plants and animals, coexisting in dense formations. Note moss plants hanging from tree branches. (*Courtesy of Charles J. Ott from The National Audubon Society.*)

characterize this habitat. Daily temperature variations are not as great as seasonal variations, which are themselves not very dramatic; still temperatures usually go below freezing in the winter. Cold winters halt plant growth, and the plants are adapted to this limitation. Most of the trees are deciduous; that is, they drop their leaves in the autumn and are photosynthetically inactive in the winter. In contrast to the dense rain forests with their hundreds of species of trees, there may be only one or two dozen species of trees in a deciduous forest; typical deciduous trees are maple, beech, oak, elm, ash, and sycamore. Through the trees roam such characteristic animals as deer, black bear, racoons, foxes, and squirrels. Most of the deciduous forests of North America have been cut by man and replaced by farmlands and cities.

Taigas are coniferous forests distributed across northern Canada, northern Europe, and Siberia. Typically, one species of conifer, usually spruce, makes up a forest extending for miles. Taigas are characterized by long, severe winters alternating with short growing seasons limited to a few months in summer. Moose, wolves, and bears are the typical animals of the taiga, which is often called the spruce-moose biome because of the common appearance of this plant-animal relationship (Figure 15.16).

Tundras, like taigas, are found almost exclusively in the northern parts of the Northern Hemisphere since very little land projects that far south in the Southern

FIGURE 15.16 Taiga landscape with caribou and a moose feeding. Note the predominance of a single tree species in this coniferous forest. (*Caribou courtesy of Charles J. Ott; moose on page 330 courtesy of W. J. Schoonmaker, both from The National Audubon Society.*)

FIGURE 15.16

Hemisphere.   Because a great deal of the tundra lies in the Arctic Circle, its climate is characterized by cold temperatures, continuous night in winter, and continuous daylight in summer.   There may be some thawing of the surface layer of the soil in summer, but it extends down only a few feet to the permafrost, a level at which the ground remains permanently frozen.   Since most of the water remains locked in a frozen state, it is as limiting a factor here as in the desert, and plants in the tundra are small and adapted to conserve water.   Lichens, mosses, shrubby conifers, and herbaceous flowering plants make up most of the plant life.   Mosquitoes and other flies are present in great hordes, and ingest blood from such mammals as caribou, Arctic hares, lemmings, foxes, musk-oxen, and polar bears.   Most birds of the tundra are migratory and leave for warmer climates in the south with the approach of winter (Figure 15.17).

MINOR TERRESTRIAL ZONES   The six zones we have examined occupy vast regions of the surface of the globe. Four other zones cover large but less extensive areas of land in isolated parts of the world.

The thorn forests of Africa, Australia, and Brazil form the *tropical shrub forest zone,* while certain of the monsoon forests of tropical Asia form the *tropical deciduous forest zone.* Both zones have two seasons, wet and dry, of equal length. The rainy season has a rainfall approaching that of a rain forest, while in the dry season the amount of rainfall is similar to that in a desert. The striking differences between wet and dry seasons are as contrasting as winter and summer in a temperate region in the United States.

Savannas are grassland zones in the tropics with scattered trees or clumps of trees. These warm regions have long dry seasons interspersed with 40 to 60 inches of rainfall. Over half of Africa consists of savanna, and large regions of South America and Australia also contain this zone. Plants of a savanna must be able to resist extended drought and frequent fire. Animals of this zone include the famous African big game mammals.

FIGURE 15.17 Most of the tundra lies in the Arctic Circle and consists of small plants, lichen, mosses, shrubs, conifers, and herbaceous flowering plants. Animal life includes mosquitoes, musk-oxen, and polar bears. (*Courtesy of The American Museum of Natural History.*)

The *chaparral zone* consists of shrubs and small trees, with hard, thick evergreen leaves which will withstand the long periods of hot, dry weather. Frequent fires prevent large trees from becoming dominant over the shrubs. Chaparral is found in California from the San Francisco Bay region south, in Baja California, in the narrow strip along the Sierra Nevada and Southern Rocky Mountains, around the shores of the Mediterranean Sea, and along the southern coast of Australia.

Five to six million acres of California's hills and canyons are covered with chaparral. The rainy season, which is also the growing season, extends from October or November to May and averages 15 to 20 inches of rainfall. California chaparral can be recognized by such dominant shrubs as manzanita, sagebrush, greasewood, wild lilacs, and coyote bush. Separating the patches of chaparral are open hills and slopes covered by wild oats, a European plant introduced during the days of the California missions well over a century ago. In May the wild oats ripen and turn the slopes from green to light brown, which appears golden to optimistic Californians.

ZONATION IN BOTH LATITUDE AND ALTITUDE

A jet pilot traveling from the equator to the North Pole might notice that the six major zones we have discussed fit roughly into broad bands across the lands from east to west. Rain forests are found primarily in the tropical latitudes, grasslands and deciduous forests in the middle latitudes, and taiga and tundra successively closer to the poles (Figure 15.18). Clearly, the horizontal zonation is due to the fact that temperature and rainfall decrease as latitudes approach the poles.

A mountain climber on a high mountain at the equator would find himself passing through the same six zones in climbing from the base to the top. The climber's clothing would have to be adaptable, for he might pass through rain forest, grassland, deciduous forest, coniferous forest, and into a region at the snow line where low shrubs, mosses, and lichens grow. At the very top, snow and ice would present conditions quite similar to those encountered by the jet pilot at the North Pole. From a helicopter traveling up the face of the mountain one could see all six zones faster than the jet pilot streaking from equator to pole, for each 400 feet of altitude usually equals 1 degree of latitude, or 60 miles of horizontal travel. If the hiker climbs other mountains further north, he will find that the more northerly zones are lower on the mountains and that more southerly zones are missing. For example, a mountain in a deciduous forest region has coniferous forests above the deciduous forests and tundra and polar regions at the top.

Surely we can get more out of living if we learn to understand and appreciate the forces that formed this world. . . .

Bates

We see from this discussion that zonation is a universal characteristic of ecosystems. There is vertical zonation from the depths of the ocean to its intertidal splash zone, from the bottom of a lake to its shoreline, from the short trees to the tallest trees of a forest, from a valley to the top of a mountain, and from the equator to the North Pole. These zones describe the differing environmental systems to which organisms have been adapted in the process of evolution.

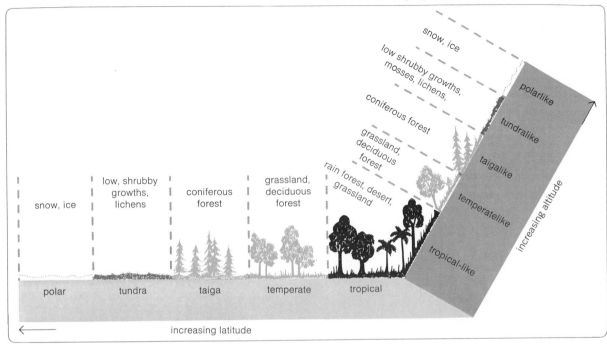

FIGURE 15.18 The sequence of habitat zones between equator and pole is repeated vertically between the foot and the top of a mountain. (*Adapted from Paul B. Weisz, Elements of Biology, 3rd ed. Copyright McGraw-Hill Book Company, 1969. Used by permission.*)

increasing latitude

REVIEW QUESTIONS

1 Compare and contrast the limiting factors of the sea, fresh water, and land.
2 Describe the limiting factors of the zones of the ocean and some adaptations of their residents.
3 Describe the limiting factors of the zones of fresh water and some adaptations of their residents.
4 Describe the limiting factors of the zones on land and some adaptations of their residents.

SUGGESTIONS FOR FURTHER READING

* Available in Paperback.

Benton, A. H., and W. E. Werner, Jr.: *Principles of Field Biology and Ecology*, 2d ed., McGraw-Hill Book Company, New York, 1966. An easily read text on introductory ecology.

Carson, R.: *The Sea around Us*, Oxford University Press, New York, 1951. A remarkable book as noteworthy for its beauty as scientific accuracy.

Odum, E. P.: **Ecology*, Holt, Rinehart and Winston, Inc., New York, 1963. More general than the larger text.

Odum, E. P.: *Fundamentals of Ecology*, 2d ed., W. B. Saunders Company, Philadelphia, 1959. A widely used introductory text in ecology.

Smith, R. L.: *Ecology and Field Biology*, Harper & Row, Publishers, Incorporated, New York, 1966. Well written and beautifully illustrated.

Part 5

Evolution: Process and Product

Populations of organisms change through time because the environment allows some variant forms to reproduce more effectively than others. Populations may change to the degree that they become new species. Descendants of new species may also give rise to new forms through time. The result of evolution is the multitude of diverse forms in the fossil record and living today. This diversity seems overwhelming, but patterns of order can be recognized.

Lion, *Panthera leo.* (*Stan Vogel, Photo Researchers, Inc.*)

Chapter 16
What Is the Process of Evolution?

We can never have enough of Nature. We must be refreshed by the sight of inexhaustable vigor. . . .
We are cheered when we observe vulture feeding on the carrion . . . and deriving health and strength from the repast. . . . I love to see that Nature is so rife with life that myriads can be afforded to be sacrificed and suffered to prey on one another. . . . The impression made on a wise man is that of universal innocence.

Thoreau

When Darwin published his *Origin of Species* in 1859, the reactions were lively and mixed. To most people it seemed a bold, new, and perhaps ominous idea. Though Darwin was not the only thinker of his time to deal with the concept of evolution by natural selection (see Chapter 2), debate over the consequences of the theory intensified greatly with the publication of his book. Among the uncomfortable conclusions drawn from the theory were the idea that man's time on earth has been only a brief flash compared to the length of time other life has existed on earth;

the idea that man is related to, and shares common ancestors with, other organisms; the idea that man's origin is a part of the same natural process which had created the present diversity of life from a sterile, barren earth in the dim past. Man's nature, purpose, and place in the timeless, shifting, and impersonal world introduced by Darwin had to be reinterpreted. Many clung emotionally to past dogma and refused to discuss the issue rationally. Others accepted Darwin's arguments as a working hypothesis and began looking for evidence with which to bolster it.

EVIDENCE FOR EVOLUTION

Since Darwin's time there has accumulated an overwhelming mass of evidence supporting the idea that evolution has taken place. Students of comparative anatomy, physiology, and embryology studying organisms living today together with those represented in the fossil record have discovered that organisms can be classified into groups reflecting likenesses and differences in structure, function, and behavior. For example, all vertebrate embryos, including the human, show striking similarities during development: possession of a yolk sac, segmentation, gill slits, aortic arches, and common processes of development of heart, kidneys, brain, and tail. Within this group of animals, the more closely the organisms are related, the greater the similarities during development. Physiologists have found carbon in certain combinations with hydrogen, oxygen, and nitrogen as fundamental components of all organisms. The geographic distribution of plants and animals indicates that, in many cases, closely related organisms are also closely distributed. All these observations can be explained on the basis that organisms share common structures and functions because they have a *common evolutionary ancestry.*

DARWIN'S MAJOR
POINTS REVISITED
COMPETITION

Darwin observed the competition which resulted from the tendency among organisms to overreproduce and used the phrase "struggle for existence" to describe this competition. Unfortunately, some of his contemporaries interpreted natural selection to be based on combat and widespread carnage as exemplified by Tennyson's phrase, "Nature, red in tooth and claw." From such understandings and attitudes arose the doctrine of "social Darwinism." This distorted view of the process of natural selection, never accepted by Darwin himself, was advanced as a "law of nature" which justified ruthless competition in the business world and wars in the international world. It was pictured as a victory of the "strong" over the "weak," the "good" over the "bad," the "more perfect" over the "less perfect." The human aggressors could decide for themselves whether their side was the strongest, best, and most perfect. Ruthlessness and power were accepted as the "law of the jungle" and a *natural* mechanism of progress. John D. Rockefeller, for example, declared in a Sunday school class:

The growth of a large business is merely a survival of the fittest. . . . The American Beauty rose can be produced in the splendor and fragrance which bring cheer to its beholder only by sacrificing the early buds which grow up around it. This is not an evil tendency in business. It is merely the working-out of a law of nature and a law of God.[1]

[1] From Richard Hofstadter, *Social Darwinism in American Thought,* The Beacon Press, Boston, October, 1965, p. 45.

Despite the prominence of its advocates, there is no justification in Darwin's theory of natural selection for the doctrines or abuses of social Darwinism. *Competition* does certainly exist in the interactions between living things, but seldom is it expressed as actual physical combat. After all, plants don't fight, and neither do most living things. Man is one of the few organisms functioning as a predator upon his own species. There is actually a great deal of *cooperation* between species, as seen in mutualistic symbiosis, and within a species, as seen in social organization. The competition existing in natural selection is much more subtle than open combat; it is the testing of adaptations, not only against individual organisms but against the total environment as well. Evolutionary success is determined by the ability of a species to leave behind it offspring which are able to reach maturity and reproduce in greater numbers than a different species attempting to occupy the same ecological niche. Natural selection is defined today as *differential reproduction;* that is, some genotypes produce phenotypes which are slightly more successful in reproducing their type than others. Even the slightest advantage in reproductive success, with the passage of time and many generations, means evolutionary success.

Darwin would have been overjoyed to have seen a heading like this, for the problem of explaining the source of variations within a population plagued him all his life. The answer to this question is emerging from modern genetics. As we recall from earlier discussions, heredity is encoded in the nucleotide sequences of DNA molecules carried in the chromosomes. Variations in the DNA, that is, differences in the genes, arise from mutations. Gene mutations result from changes in the sequence of purines and pyrimidines in the DNA of the gene itself, while chromosome mutations arise from deletions, duplications, or changes in sequence or arrangment of lengths of DNA greater than a single gene.

THE SOURCE OF VARIATIONS
IN A POPULATION

Variation in the genotypes of a population of organisms is the product both of the changes which may occur in the DNA of the individual genomes (*genome* means the *total complement of genes,* or the genetic apparatus present in any one cell of an organism) of the reproductive cells and of the production of new *combinations* (recombination) of genes in the genomes of the reproductive cells. Recombination is far more frequent than the molecular events leading to new DNA sequences. We have already discussed meiotic recombination as a source of variation in genotype in Chapter 8 and only touch on the subject by way of review here.

Recombination produces different assortments or combinations of the various types of new chromosomes produced by *mutation.* Variation due to recombination results from two processes: (1) crossing-over and (2) the chance assortment of paternal and maternal chromosomes which goes into each gamete of an organism. Crossing-over (see Chapter 8) differs from chromosome mutations in that the end product is merely an equal exchange of segments between two members of a homologous pair of chromosomes, resulting in a different combination of alleles of genes already present. This differs from mutation, which produces entirely new genes or alleles or eliminates them. The process of crossing-over nevertheless results in variation in gametes, which will be reflected in variation among the individuals of a population if the gametes combine successfully in sexual reproduction.

The second source of variation from recombination in gametes is the chance distribution of maternal and paternal chromosomes which occurs in meiosis.

Chromosomes occur in pairs in sexually reproducing organisms. One member of each pair was originally derived from the male parent, and one from the female parent of the adult organism undergoing meiosis. The gametes produced by meiosis contain only one member of each pair. It is a matter of chance, for each pair of chromosomes, whether the original maternal or paternal chromosome is included in a given gamete. Figure 16.1 in which meiosis is diagrammed in a simplified way, illustrates this process. In this case, an organism with only three pairs of chromosomes can form eight different gametes with respect to the various possible combinations of maternal and paternal chromosomes of each pair. The formula for deriving the possible number of different kinds of gametes is 2^n, where n is the number of pairs of chromosomes. Thus, in the example given in Figure 16.1, there are three pairs: $2^n = 2^3 = 8$ combinations. Obviously, the number of combinations increases with the number of pairs of chromosomes. A human male, for example, may form 2^{23}, or 8,388,608, different combinations of paternal and maternal chromosomes in his gametes.

What are the chances of your parents producing another offspring genetically exactly the same as you? This would require the chromosomes in one cell in each of your parents' gonads to line up again exactly the same as the gametes which produced you lined up. Further, no crossing-over could occur. Ignoring the possibility of crossovers, the chance of obtaining the same combination of maternal and paternal chromosomes in one egg and one sperm is 1 in $2^{23} \times 2^{23}$, or 1 chance in 70,368,744,177,664. This does not take into account the further chance involved in fertilization, in which the 1 gamete in 8,388,608 from the male parent would be only 1 in about 2 billion spermatozoa released in a single ejaculation, all with an equal chance of fertilizing the egg! As a result, unless you have an identical twin, the odds are overwhelmingly against your having an exact double existing somewhere in the world today or in the past. Probably you and every other organism produced

FIGURE 16.1 Homologous pairs of maternal and paternal chromosomes have four different possible ways of aligning themselves and produce eight different kinds of gametes.

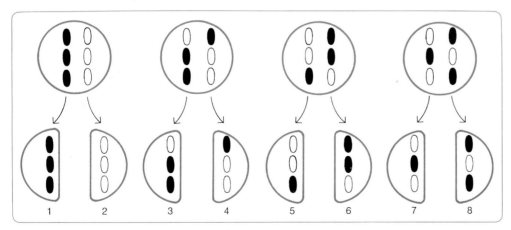

through sexual reproduction are unique. This is a reflection of the variability possible within a population, and it is this variability which provides the raw material for natural selection.

Populations evolve, not individuals. It is true that each individual produced by sexual reproduction is genetically unique and differs from other individuals in the population, but evolution cannot be said to have occurred unless there has been a shift in frequency of hereditary characteristics of the population as a whole. *The population is the evolutionary unit,* and to develop a workable picture of this evolutionary unit we would have to count all the alleles of all genes present in the population and determine their ratios and percentages. The abstract quantity representing all the genes present in a population is called a *gene pool.* In this pool, genes pair up within individual organisms and form various phenotypes which are tested against the environment before being passed on to the next generation with varying success through sexual change in the gene pool.

POPULATIONS EVOLVE

Let us daydream for a moment about a passenger liner steaming through the South Seas. Suppose that it sinks and its 200 passengers swim ashore on a deserted tropical isle. Among this unusual group there are 100 men homozygous for brown eyes (*BB*) and 100 blue-eyed women (*bb*). They soon pair up into mates and within a year 100 offspring are born. All the children will be hybrids (*Bb*) and, since brown-eyedness is dominant, all the children are brown-eyed. In this gene pool, the 100 fathers contain 200 genes for brown eyes (*B*), and the 100 mothers have 200 genes for blue eyes (*b*). Thus, the gene pool of the parental generation is 50 percent *B* and 50 percent *b*. Since the children are all hybrids (*Bb*), the gene pool of the children is 50 percent *B* and 50 percent *b*. When these hybrid children mate, the possible combinations of genes are *BB, Bb, bB,* and *bb*. From these combinations you will see that there are four *B*'s and four *b*'s, again, 50 percent *B* and 50 percent *b*, this time in the grandchildren (see Figure 16.2). Perhaps an easier way of picturing this is by considering gametes in the gene pool. They will be continuously 50 percent *B*-bearing and 50 percent *b*-bearing. This 1 : 1 ratio of genes *B* and *b* in the gene pool will continue generation after generation as long as certain requirements are met. This concept of unchanging gene frequencies is called the *Hardy-Weinberg law* and might well be called *genetic homeostasis.* The requirements for its expression are:

1 No mutations of genes or chromosomes.
2 No migration of types in or out of the population.
3 The population must be relatively large.
4 There must be random mating.
5 The environment cannot favor any phenotype.

THE GENETIC BASIS
OF EVOLUTION
SHIFTS IN GENE FREQUENCIES

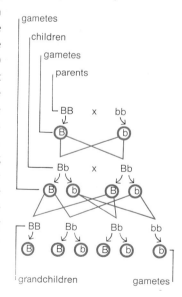

FIGURE 16.2 Hardy-Weinberg law. The persistence of gene frequencies in large randomly mating populations with neither natural selection, mutations, nor migrations. Note that in each generation the ratios of *B* to *b* remain the same, 1 : 1.

When Hardy in England and Weinberg in Germany independently derived this law during the first part of this century, they assumed that these five factors were present in most populations. If this were true, gene frequencies would not change and evolution would not occur, but if any of these factors are missing from the population, there will be a shift in genetic homeostasis and evolution will occur. As a matter of fact, it is most probable that, in natural populations, the requirements for a Hardy-Weinberg equilibrium are never met, because of exceptions to one or more of these five requirements. For this reason, a description of these five conditions for *equilibrium* is most useful for our discussion of the process of *evolution*.

Mutations have already been discussed as a source of variations in a population. The requirements for a favorable mutation are restrictive since the delicate balance of interactions in cells and among them is easily upset. Some traits may vary quite a bit, and mutations affecting them may be relatively severe, but such a structure as a heart, for example, could not function adequately if severely altered. Many mutations are thus dangerous to some degree, but some are so small in their effects that the bearer is not adversely affected by them. A few mutations will contribute some slight degree of increased reproductive efficiency to the bearer of the new gene when it is expressed as a phenotypic trait. After all, you and I and all other living things represent an assemblage of mutant genes accumulated and tested by our ancestors down through time.

Migration into or out of the population will cause shifts in frequencies of the genes carried by the migrants. If organisms migrate into the population bringing alleles new to the gene pool, the effect is the same as if a mutation had occurred in the native population. If some of the people left our fictitious tropical isle, or if another ship sank and more people swam ashore, the gene frequency would be affected.

Population size has a great deal to do with the equal opportunity for all types of gametes to be involved in fertilizations. To illustrate this point, a coin may be used to represent a hybrid organism. The heads and tails of the coin represent the alleles on a pair of chromosomes, and the types of gametes would be determined by the way the coin falls. Tossing the coin several hundred times should produce results approaching a ratio of 1:1 heads and tails. Thus, a large population should allow equal chances for eggs and sperms bearing both types of alleles to be involved. What is likely to happen if the coin is tossed only ten times? Chance might bring up nine heads, one tail or one head, nine tails, or any other combination, even including the possibility that there would be no gametes bearing a particular allele. In other words, *in small populations, large shifts in gene frequencies can occur due to the small sampling of gametes.* The random shifting of gene frequencies due to chance in small populations is called *genetic drift.*

Random mating means that any individual may mate with any other individual in the population. This ensures that it is purely random chance which is involved in the fertilizations of the gametes formed by a population. Random mating could be

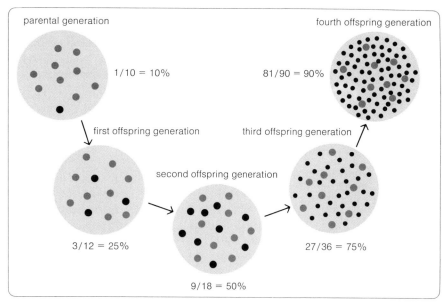

symbolized by a bucket full of nickels (males) and a bucket full of dimes (females). Suppose the buckets are dumped on the floor together and the sides of the coins represent gametes, and wherever a nickel and a dime have landed side by side a fertilization is said to have occurred.   The association of the coins would be purely random.   On the other hand, we know that in actuality there is a selection of mates based on a multitude of preferences in many living things.   Also, it is obvious that the factor of distance will interfere with the chances that *any* male can mate with *any* female.   Selection of mates due to behavior, odors, visual displays, sounds, cultural preferences, and so forth, will cause a shift in frequency of genes.   If the favored phenotypes are not just due to environmental effects but are due to genotypes, such nonrandom mating will cause a shift in frequency of genes toward those gene complexes causing the favored phenotypic traits *if the favored types* have a greater number of successful offspring than the less favored types (see Figure 16.3).

Natural selection implies that the forces in the environment favor some phenotypes over others.   The result of this favoritism is that some gene complexes are passed on to the next generation in a higher frequency than others; i.e., some parents have more offspring than other parents.   This favoritism causes a shift in frequency of those genes and causes the process called evolution.

Darwin's book is commonly referred to as *Origin of Species,* but its full title was *On the Origin of Species by Means of Natural Selection, or the Preservation of Favoured Races in the Struggle for Life.*   Darwin was aware that the process of evolution could

FIGURE 16.3   The effect of differential reproduction, or natural selection. Assume that a variation arises in one individual of a paternal generation (black dot) and that the variant organism is able to leave three offspring, which eventually reproduce. Each nonvariant organism (colored dot), on the other hand, manages to leave only one offspring. The complexion of the population will then change as shown during subsequent generations. That is, the variant type will represent a progressively larger fraction of the numerical total. Such spreading of variations, brought about by differential reproduction, constitutes natural selection. (*Adapted from Paul B. Weisz, Elements of Biology, 3rd ed. Copyright McGraw-Hill Book Company, 1969. Used by permission.*)

SPECIES

simply mean a change in appearance in groups of organisms, but he also argued that these changes could accumulate through the years in these groups to the point where a new species of organism was present. These local groups of organisms within a species were usually referred to as *races*, and Darwin described a process by which he thought they could become separate species.

What is a species? Living things appear as a chaos of variability and none seem completely alike. Yet it was realized many years ago that organisms fall into discrete groups. Man has for countless years referred to these kinds of organisms by group names such as cat, lion, tiger, jaguar, and puma (mountain lion or cougar), etc. In the eighteenth century Linnaeus called these kinds *species* and assigned the species known to him to the groupings he had devised. In ascending order of inclusiveness, they were genus, family, order, class, phylum, and kingdom. The name for each kind was the genus and species. Thus, the names for each of the members of the cat family (Felidae) mentioned above were, respectively, *Felis maniculata, Felis leo, Felis tigra, Felis onca,* and *Felis concolor.* Linnaeus believed that each species could be represented by a single *type specimen* which could be preserved in a museum as the example of that species. The characteristics which identified a species as being different from other species were considered to be morphological, namely, the shape, the structure, and the appearance. (Whom would you have sent to Linnaeus as a type specimen of man?) Linnaeus, in his *Systema Naturae* of 1758, defined a species as follows: "A species is a group of individuals or populations with the same or similar morphological characters." This definition of over 200 years ago ignored the multitude of other behavioral and physiological traits which provide biological success and did not recognize the significance of variation. To Linnaeus, species were specially created. This opinion was explicit in his famous dictum: "Species are as many as were produced at the beginning by the Infinite." By 1758 Linnaeus had named and described 4,235 species of animals, most of which were from northern Europe. During the next 200 years the total number of animal species known and described rose to about 1 million and plant species to about 265,000, and the list still continues to grow.

The use of the word "about" in the last sentence is important since it is often unclear whether two populations are members of the same species or should be considered as two separate species. Often there are forms which are intermediate between two species. In 1859 Darwin said: "In determining whether a form should be ranked as a species or a variety, the opinion of the naturalists having sound judgment and wide experience seems the only guide to follow." The naturalists of his day were, of course, concerned only with phenotypes, since the concept of the gene was undeveloped.

After the rediscovery of Mendel's paper, a geneticist named Lotsy produced in 1918 a concept of species which rested on a purely genetic basis: "A species is a group of genetically identical individuals." Today we know that only identical twins can have identical genotypes. Not only do populations differ from each other in genotypes, but each individual member differs. Well before 1920, biologists realized that phenotypic traits are products of both the genotype and the environment and that *selection pressures act upon phenotypes.* In 1919, Stresemann stated: "Forms which have reached the species level have diverged physiologically to the extent that, as proven in nature, they can come together again without interbreeding." This definition does not rest upon artificial or hypothetical criteria but upon the very practical test of whether two populations can interbreed. It does not, however, take into account the fact that many populations are not in contact and an observer has no way of determining whether they can interbreed. Often, representatives of the two populations can be placed in a tank or cage and observed, but the conditions are artificial and are not valid for the natural populations. For example, the lion and the tiger may interbreed in captivity, yet, in nature, they do not.

A practical species definition which combines the valid parts of the previous definitions is as follows: Species are groups of interbreeding natural populations reproductively isolated from other such groups.[2] The members of a species are seen as participants in a gene pool closed to other species. The closed nature of the gene pool may be due to infertility or inviability of hybrid forms or may rest simply upon geographical separation or structural or behavioral differences which make interbreeding impossible. The important part of this definition of a species is not that separate species cannot interbreed but that in nature, for various reasons, they usually do not interbreed. This definition must be qualified, however, for hybridization between plant species is common, and hybridization has been observed in insects, fish, amphibians, birds, and some mammals.

[2] From *Principles of Systematic Zoology* by Ernst Mayr. Copyright 1969 by McGraw-Hill, Inc. Used with permission of McGraw-Hill Book Company. (p. 26)

If the two populations are in contact, the question of the ability to interbreed is settled by observation. But if the populations are not in contact or are fossils, whether they are one species or two can be settled only by an expert on the groups.

Evolutionary change was once thought by the Dutch biologist de Vries to take place by "big" mutations which would cause drastic phenotypic effects and allow the mutants greater success in natural selection. Since the macromutation would not allow interbreeding with the ancestral type, a single mutation could cause the formation of a new species. Geneticists have since found that it is only very rarely that a single mutation can cause a new population to form (on the other hand speciation *has* been a rare event, compared to reproduction). The prevailing opinion today is that *speciation is a gradual process in which small variations among the members of a population may give slight reproductive advantage or disadvantage under the pressure of natural selection.* We know now that these variations arise by recombination of genes which originally arose by small, nondrastic mutations in the gene pool. To produce a new species, genetic change must be coupled with a decrease in interbreeding between the emerging species and the genetic pool of the old species from which it is diverging. Furthermore at present we cannot rule out the idea that

SPECIATION

occasional large changes such as the replication of large amounts of the genome are an essential aspect of speciation.

Mutation, sexual recombination, migration, chance variations in gametes in small groups of organisms, and natural selection act in concert in populations to cause shifts in gene frequency. With each generation, the various phenotypes are pitted against the pressures of the environment. The environmental pressures were referred to in Chapter 15 as *limiting factors* and include variable amounts of temperature, light, water, oxygen, carbon dioxide, salts, wind, soil, predators, and the like. Each phenotype, or trait, has a *range of tolerance* for each of these factors, and the degree to which the organisms are adapted will determine the success of the genotypes which caused the phenotypes. Traits or characteristics of an organism or species which serve to promote its general welfare under the pressures of the environment are called *adaptations*. Much of the work done in biology is the pursuit of understanding adaptations of organisms in various environmental situations.

In the process of natural selection we can describe two opposing elements: (1) the environment, with its limiting factors, and (2) the sum total of the adaptations of the species inhabiting the environment. The nature of the environment changes through time, and a population must always contain some adaptations which will be successful in new conditions if the species is to be perpetuated. As an overall view, we may say that a species possesses ranges of tolerance in the form of variations in its adaptations, which may be selected and become dominant through the pressures of a changing environment. If environmental change results in the accumulation of a multiplicity of new adaptations in a population of a species, and if reproductive isolation follows, *speciation* may result.

The genetic variations involved in adaptations to a changing environment are probably small, and the time required is immense. To visualize this elusive concept resurrect all your ancestors back to the first cell and stand them before you in ranks according to their order of occurrence in time. Your father and mother would stand facing you, your grandparents behind them, great-grandparents behind them, and so on into the distance and over the horizon. For your hypothetical line of ancestors choose only one male and one female from succeeding generations and arrange them in a line extending over the horizon and on into the distance. Here, geographical distance substitutes for the immensities of time. If a generation is taken as 20 years, you would have to walk past 1,000 couples before you were looking at your caveman ancestors who lived 20,000 years ago. If you had placed your ancestors a little over 5 feet apart, you would have walked about 1 mile before seeing the cave dwellers of about 21,000 years ago, and if you walked on and on mile after mile, you would be struck by the observation that there is no more difference between parents and offspring of any of the succeeding generations than there is between your parents and you. But if you had jumped in a car and driven down the line several miles and then looked at the line again, you would have seen more striking differences. In a way, it is like a growing youngster. If you live with him, you are not aware of daily changes, but if you are a relative who visits every year, the changes are much more apparent.

Most people have difficulty in picturing the immense amount of time through which the processes of evolution operate. The following excerpt should help:[3]

VISUALIZING GEOLOGIC TIME

[3] From Paul Ames Moody, *Introduction to Evolution*, 2d ed., pp. 140–141. Copyright © 1962 by Paul Ames Moody. Reprinted by permission of Harper & Row, Publishers, Incorporated.

Unavoidably our ideas of time are conditioned by the length of the human life span and its subdivision into periods (infancy, youth, etc.) and years. The term "one million years" is so far outside our experience as to be meaningless to us. Multiples of a million years are, if anything, even less meaningful. We may have the vague impression that a million years is "a very long time," and that a thousand million years is "a very, very long time." But in other connections a thousand years also seems "a very, very long time." Indeed, all periods longer than a human lifetime or two have a tendency to fade into "a-very-long-time" vagueness for us.

But we can grasp the meaning of the length of a year and of its subdivisions into months, weeks, days, hours, minutes, and seconds. Consequently James C. Rettie . . . rendered a signal service by picturing geologic time in subdivisions of a year. He imagined a moving picture taken of earth by inhabitants of another planet, using a super-telephoto lens and a time-lapse camera. This imaginary film was taken at the rate of one picture per year for the last 757 million years. When it is run on a projector at normal speed (twenty-four pictures per second) twenty-four years of earth history flashes by each second. Since the author has the film run continuously twenty-four hours a day, about two million years of past history are shown on the screen each day. To show the entire 757 million years requires running the film continuously for one full year. The author starts the show at midnight of one New Year's Eve and runs it without interruption until midnight of the next New Year's Eve.

For many fascinating details of this movie readers are referred to the original article or to the reprint of it in Coronet *magazine (March, 1951). We have space for but a few high spots.*

Throughout January, February, and March the movie runs on without showing any signs of life upon the earth. Single-celled organisms appear early in April, many-celled ones later in that month. Late in May come the first vertebrates. It is the middle of July before the first land plants begin to pave the way for animal life on land. Late August arrives before the first land vertebrates, the amphibians, put in an appearance. The first reptiles appear by the middle of September. Among these the dinosaurs dominate the scene through the remainder of September, through October and much of November, about seventy days. In the meantime the first birds and first mammals appear. The raising of the Rocky Mountains near the end of November signals the end of the great era of reptilian domination.

As the movie runs on into December we see the mammals dominant; they undergo their great evolutionary developments. Christmas arrives: The movie shows us the

Colorado River beginning to cut its Grand Canyon. We have the vaguely uneasy realization that the year is nearing its close, yet we have seen no signs of man. Day follows day until we reach the last day of the year. Suddenly about noon of December 31 the movie shows us the first men. During the afternoon the glaciers push southward from the polar regions, and then retreat, four successive times. By suppertime man is still not much in evidence. By about 11 o'clock in the evening varied "Old Stone Age" men become quite prominent in the picture, and by 11:45 men who make more refined stone implements and cultivate the soil appear. Five or six minutes before the end of the picture we see the dawn of civilization. One minute and seventeen seconds before the end the Christian era begins. Twenty seconds before the end Columbus discovers America. Seven seconds before the end the Declaration of Independence is signed.

Many aspects of this wonderful imaginary movie are worth pondering. Life has existed on earth for some eight months of the movie's year; man has been here for about twelve hours of that year. The dinosaurs dominated the movie for seventy days; man has dominated it for about half of one day, so far. (Yet sometimes we look condescendingly upon the dinosaurs as "unsuccessful" animals! If the movie continues into the future, will it show us here seventy days from now?) Man has been in existence for about twelve hours of the movie, but for only about five or six minutes has he had any civilization which we consider worthy of the term. This is sometimes a comforting thought when we become impatient with the "slow" progress made by mankind in adopting various desirable reforms—such as the abolition of war. In speaking of this progress as "slow" we are using human lifetimes as our yardstick. Any progress made since the dawn of civilization has been dazzlingly swift, measured in terms of man's total existence on earth.

HOW ARE NEW SPECIES FORMED?
SEQUENTIAL AND DIVERGENT EVOLUTION

Population gene pools continue through time, changing slowly in response to the changing environment. The gene frequencies change, and if the organisms could be mated with distant ancestors, the success of the cross would decrease with the amount of time and the degree of variation. The more distant the ancestry, the more difficult the hypothetical cross. Even though a gene pool has been continuous through time, descendants may differ from their remote ancestors so much that they must be considered separate species. Change through time in a given gene pool results in *sequential evolution* since it involves a linear, continuous sequence of changes in the nature of the gene pool and hence of the population of organisms. Speciation may occur as a consequence of genetic change through time in a single population.

Gene pools often break up into smaller pools. If sequential evolution now takes place in each independent population, two gene pools can be formed which are significantly different both from the ancestral population and from each other.

There is ample proof in the fossil record that this has happened over and over again; this is a major aspect of the process by which the fantastic multitudes of living things have arisen. The term for evolutionary processes of this kind is *divergent evolution*.

Divergent evolution results from either a gradual or sudden decrease of interbreeding between parts of a population. The parts may then evolve separately, and if enough time and variation is available, the two gene pools may become separate species. The factors which decrease interbreeding between organisms are called *isolating mechanisms*. Natural selection causes gene frequencies to change in populations of organisms, and *isolating mechanisms can cause a given species to give rise to other species.*

At this point it is worthwhile to summarize the material discussed in this chapter, since we have covered the major processes which make up the various parts of the modern theory of evolution. This theory differs from Darwin's original statement, primarily in its explanation of the source of variability, which Darwin was unable to account for in his theory:

1   Various kinds of mutational changes and genetic replicative events, plus *recombination*, provide intrinsic *variability* in an interbreeding population of organisms. As a result, variability in phenotypic traits may occur in the population.
2   Pressures of the *environment*, acting through *natural selection*, provide evolutionary direction to the variability in the population by favoring the reproductive success of organisms which possess favorable traits.
3   Populations which become differentiated by accumulation of new adaptive traits may be separated from their original gene pool by *reproductive isolation*. Isolation can take the form of actual barriers to interbreeding, such as geographical or structural, or can take the form of isolation of an altered gene pool from its original form simply by the passage of time.

Thus the basic processes of evolution are the *generation of variability, natural selection,* and *reproductive isolation*. Reproductive isolation, which is necessary for natural selection to result in the formation of a new species, is so important that we shall devote more attention to it as well as to other aspects of speciation in the remainder of this chapter.

There are basically five types of mechanisms which result in reproductive isolation. The most obvious and probably most effective one is demonstrated when gene exchange between populations is decreased by space and distance. Such *geographic isolation* is almost always involved in divergent evolution. Obviously, if two populations of field mice or petunias are separated by a distance of several miles, there will be little or no gene exchange between them. Separation may occur quickly, as a result of drastic changes in climate, volcanic action, or man-made con-

ISOLATING MECHANISMS

structions, or it may occur slowly by geological processes, such as the rising of the Rocky Mountains or the formation of the Bering Strait.

The second type of isolating mechanism is *environmental isolation*. As mentioned earlier, populations have ecological niches within their habitats. If mating takes place between populations with divergent gene complexes, the result is a hybrid with a genotype producing a phenotype that is usually not suited for the habitat of either parental population. A hybrid usually "falls between the chairs" (on the other hand, many plant hybrids are very successful). Yet since most hybrids formed from occasional matings between two populations are not successful, at least in animals, they do not contribute to either gene pool. Hybridization in this case does not form a bridge between the two gene pools since the hybrids are adapted to neither of the habitats of the two gene pools.

A third type of isolating mechanism is *structural* isolation, a situation in which, even if the organisms of two populations are occupying the same environment, successful interbreeding is made impossible by the appearance of adaptations in the anatomy of reproductive structures which prevent copulation or pollination. Related to this is *behavioral* isolation, in which differences in mating behavior, courtship displays, or odors associated with sexual attraction make interbreeding unlikely. For example, some organisms reproduce simply by discharging their gametes into the water of the environment. Cross-fertilization between two such species inhabiting the same

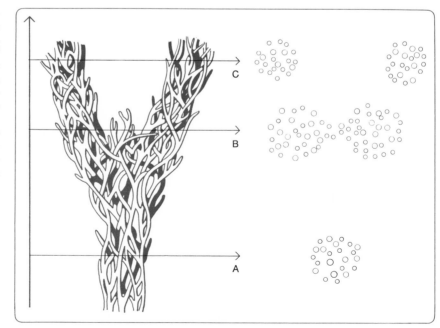

FIGURE 16.4 Divergent evolution of one species into two species through time. At time level *A* there is a single species made up of many populations or races symbolized as strands making up a bundle. As time continues, the races may be seen to diverge into new races or blend into one. An isolating mechanism arises at time level *B*, and by time level *C* the two gene pools have diverged to the point that they are separate species. (*From T. Dobzhansky, Evolution, Genetics, and Man, John Wiley & Sons, Inc., 1955.*)

region of the water environment may be prevented because the gametes do not chemically attract each other in the water. If mating does take place between different species, reproductive isolation may still occur because of sterility or inviability of hybrids; the result would be faulty embryonic growth. This isolating mechanism is termed *developmental isolation*. All the isolating mechanisms listed— *geographic, environmental, structural, behavioral,* and *developmental*—act to prevent the formation of fertile offspring between separate or diverging species. In this way, mixing of gene pools is prevented.

The term *race* often has unfortunate social connotations, and it is important that its biological significance be understood. Each and every person today should know that the terms *race* and *subspecies* are synonymous and describe *populations which differ in the frequency of genes from the other population groups within the species.* Races are gene pools which have diverged genetically in detectable amounts, but they may still interbreed with other races and produce viable offspring. If races are isolated from each other for many generations, their gene pools can become increasingly different to the degree that they would be reproductively isolated and would form separate species. Obviously, the concept of race and subspecies formation is part of the process of speciation (see Figure 16.4).

Evolution is opportunistic in that populations take every chance to spread out and fill the available habitats with as many reproducing organisms as possible. The fossil record shows that there have been many instances in which populations with a novel complex of adaptations have entered and become dominant in habitats which were previously either empty or occupied by less well-adapted organisms. A reconstruction of the evolutionary record would show portions of the invading population entering the various habitats, becoming reproductively isolated, and diverging into separate species with different body structures and ways of life. From one ancestral population there would develop different lines of evolution diverging first into races, and with the passage of time and the establishment of isolation, these races would diverge into separate species. For example, the dog genus, *Canis,* has radiated from a common ancestral population to produce the coyote of the western plains, the timber wolf of the northern forests, the jackal of Asia, and several others (see Figure 16.5) Within the domestic dog species there has been adaptive radiation into many races, not to fill habitats of the environment in *natural selection* but to fill habitats defined by the needs of men who have used *artificial selection.*

The role that environmental opportunities play in adaptive radiation is clearly shown by the animals and plants on the Galapagos Islands, 600 miles off the coast of Ecuador. This compact group of islands is volcanic in origin and has never had a connection with the mainland. The animals and plants on the islands today represent an extremely spotty sampling of organisms on the South American coast. It is obvious that they are immigrants from the mainland, and it is likely that they got there by riding wind currents or on floating islands, depending on the nature of the organism and its habitat. Portions of a riverbank may have broken away and floated out to sea as a floating island bearing plants and animals as passengers. Such natural rafts are commonly seen in the ocean and help explain how oceanic islands get populated. If the immigrants can fly, they may simply have been carried to islands by air currents. Once plants have been established on the islands, immigrant animals can take up residence in whatever habitats in the new environment their adaptations permit.

Darwin was greatly impressed by a group of small land birds on the Galapagos Islands. He realized that they were all finches and reasoned that the fourteen species present there had all descended from a small ancestral finch which had im-

FIGURE 16.5 Two domesticated dogs and two wild timber wolves. Both pairs have common ancestors. (*Courtesy of The American Museum of Natural History.*)

A

B

migrated from the mainland. Darwin believed the original immigrant finches to have been ground-dwelling and to have fed on vegetation and seeds. Adaptive radiation is believed to have taken place among the descendants of these immigrants, and some populations of descendant finches moved into trees, others took up residences in cactus, and others on the ground. The diverging populations became either seed eaters or insect eaters. Their bills evolved so that seed eaters had short, blunt bills and the insect eaters had longer, thinner bills. One population evolved a behavioral trait enabling it to perform as a "woodpecker," but instead of probing out insects from a tree with a long tongue, it pries them out with a tool, a cactus spine held in its bill.

As the populations of finches immigrated to new islands of the group, geographic isolation caused immediate reproductive isolation and rapid speciation (see Figure 16.6). A population of finches arriving on a new island had a variety of habitats open to it, and adaptive radiation occurred on each island, so that a habitat on one island was filled by one species and the same habitat on another island became occupied by a different species. This situation was unusual in the lack of competition faced by each diverging species in its new habitat. The Galapagos Islands are a natural laboratory of evolution in which adaptive radiation can easily be demonstrated.

CONVERGENT EVOLUTION

When the first settlers reached Australia, they saw what they thought were moles,
wolves, mice, cats, anteaters, flying squirrels, and groundhogs. Closer observation
revealed, however, that these were not really what they seemed to be, for they were
all marsupials, mammals with a pouch in which the young spend most of their
embryonic and early lives. The marsupials had evolved such striking similarities to
their distant cousins, the placental mammals, because both groups had lived in very
similar habitats with almost identical selection pressures. Similar selection pressures
tend to select for similar adaptations. For example, selection pressures exerted on
the marsupial mole and the placental mole would evolve similar adaptations if the
appropriate small variations appeared in both groups.

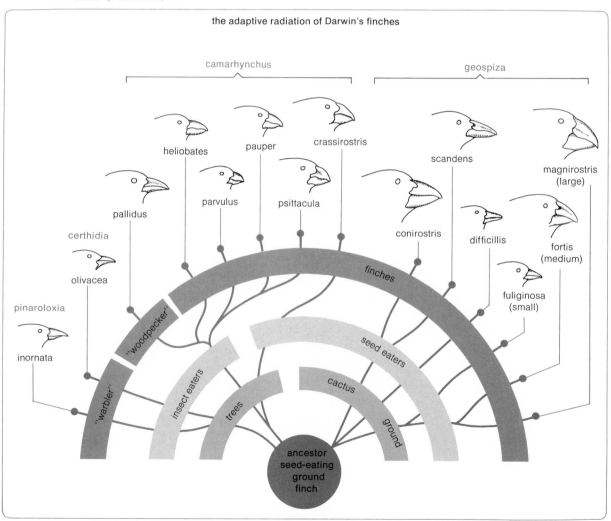

When the four-legged ancestor of whales and dolphins left its home in swamps and marshes and entered the ocean, selection pressures were exerted against the protruding limbs. After many generations of variations within populations of primitive whales and selection pressures from the marine environment, a more streamlined body plan evolved, which closely resembled that of fishes. Similarly, invasion of the air and its selection pressures has caused parallel adaptations to evolve in the wings of insects, bats, and the flying reptiles of antiquity. Evolution of similar adaptations because of the requirements of similar ecological niches is called *convergent evolution*.

The splitting of gene pools in divergent evolution through the past 2 billion years has resulted in the fantastic diversity of organisms living today and is recorded in the fossil record of the past. Divergent evolution has produced over a million kinds of living things making their living in over a million different ways. To understand their many lives, their ecological niches, it is helpful to have a method by which organisms can be named and categorized. This is called *classification,* and the study of the classification of living things is called *taxonomy*.

DIVERSITY FROM DIVERGENCE

In Chapter 2, the Great Chain of Being was described as an attempt by people, from the Middle Ages back to the Greek philosophers, to perceive a pattern of order in the overwhelming diversity of kinds of things around them. They believed that everything had been *specially created* to be of a certain complexity and to have a certain purpose and that the degree of complexity and purpose decided whether the species would be placed *higher* or *lower* in the ladder of life. Later, Linnaeus designed a plan which was not a straight line from lower to higher organisms but a system of categories in a hierarchy indicating likenesses and differences. Names were applied to the categories to indicate the degree of likeness. By this scheme, members of a genus would have more in common than the members of a family, and the members of a family would have more in common than those of an order. In proceeding "from the top down," from kingdom to species, the groups became increasingly *exclusive*.

CLASSIFICATION OF THE LIVING WORLD
THE SYSTEM OF CLASSIFICATION

At present the hierarchy in use, as mentioned in Chapter 2, is made up of the following seven major groups:

Kingdom
  Phylum (plural, phyla)
    Class
      Order
        Family
          Genus (plural, genera)
            Species (plural, species)

There is actually no reason in nature for deciding on seven levels of classification, and conceivably the number might just as well have been forty or fifty. Seven seemed an ample number to work with 100 years ago, but as the groups of organisms have been studied intensively through the years, a number of new subgroups have been added to the basic seven (see Figure 16.7 for examples of family members of the order Carnivora).

FIGURE 16.7 In the order Carnivora are many families. Shown here are five members of the family Felidae. Domestic cat, lynx (note relative size), tiger, lion, cheetah. Also shown are members of the family Canidae (the fox), the family Ursidae (brown bear), the family Mustelidae (skunk). (*Bear courtesy of Leonard Lee Rue from The National Audubon Society; lions courtesy of M. Chapman; all others courtesy of The American Museum of Natural History.*)

The *species* is the basic unit in this system of classification, and the process of speciation, or divergent evolution, is the underlying reason why a hierarchial classification system works. It is somewhat ironic that when Linnaeus, the supporter of *special creation,* described his system of classification, he was introducing a *map* of the paths of *evolutionary divergence* which speciation had taken in the past. Ideally the description of a phylum is a general description of the ancestral population, which diverged into the various populations now placed in the category of classes. The description of each category, from kingdom to species, is a description of an ancestral population which diverged into populations characterized by the description of the next lower category.

For example, a group of animals existed an extremely long time ago which had many of the characters, in a primitive form, which we now associate with the entire phylum Chordata. This group, through divergent evolution, gave rise later to various species with characteristics which we now associate with the various classes of vertebrates. One of these species had the characteristics which we relate to mammals, and its gene pool split into many divergent lines, which in turn gave rise to many species of mammals, some of which had traits which we associate with the *orders* of mammals. This story could continue on through family, genus, and species, but the point is clear: *Species indicate actual populations or gene pools, and the categories from genus through kingdom indicate the points in evolution when divergence occurred within a species which then existed.*

In a direct line of evolution, the higher the category, the more ancient the population and the divergence. For example, two genera in a certain family diverged more recently than two families in its order. It is important to note, however, that at the time of divergence of a new order, family, or any other higher category, the group of organisms which actually gave rise to the new evolutionary line was a *species.*

It is also important to realize that you cannot picture the evolution of a species living today as a sequence of species which are also alive today. For example, the evolution of man cannot be pictured as a sequence of shark, frog, lizard, shrew, ape, and man. There are two basic mistakes in this idea: (1) *Modern species cannot have evolved from modern species,* and (2) *evolution is not a straight-line ladder or scale.* The pattern of evolution is accurately described as a *bush* with a fantastic number of branches. Each fork in the bush represents a divergence, and, just as in actual bushes, the closer a fork is to the main stem, the more ancient the divergence and the higher the category in classification. The word higher as used in these categories of classification may now be seen to actually mean older (see Figure 16.8).

A reconstruction of the patterns of divergence which evolution has in fact taken is a difficult undertaking because it rests upon spotty and often inadequate fossil evidence, which may be interpreted in a variety of ways. Since a system of

THE MEANING OF THE
CLASSIFICATION SYSTEM

FIGURE 16.8 The pattern of evolution resembles a bush. The tips of the branches at the top represent species living today, and those terminating at a lower point represent extinct species. Forks in the bush represent points where the gene pool diverged from a common ancestor. Gene pool *A* is most ancient and is ancestral to the following divergent gene pools. Point *B* is more ancient than point *C* and would have a higher rank in classification. An isolating mechanism would have existed at each fork in the bush. (*Adapted from Paul B. Weisz, The Science of Biology, 3d ed. Copyright McGraw-Hill Book Company, 1967. Used by permission.*)

MAJOR PATTERNS OF DIVERGENCE

classification should represent the patterns of divergence and these patterns are constantly being reevaluated and reconstructed, the classification of the living world is also constantly being changed. At the risk of being somewhat presumptuous, we shall consider that the evolution of life followed the scheme which follows. Most biologists today would agree that this model fits the evidence fairly well as it is now perceived.

The overall major patterns of evolutionary divergences are shown in Figure 16.9. Notice the designations of kingdoms by letters and major groups within the kingdoms by numbers. Following this diagram is a description of each of the kingdoms and their component groups which are *commonly seen* by you, the student. Over twenty phyla of seldom seen organisms have been ignored. The diagram is intended to be a road map from which the student can form a concept of the pathways evolution has taken and an idea of the evolutionary relationships existing between organisms in the living world, past and present. It is a map of the highways by which life has traveled down to the present.

In the following chapters, we shall briefly discuss the major features of the prominent groups of microbes, plants, and animals. We begin, in the next chapter, with discussion of some of the leading ideas about how the living world began and some of the experiments which support these hypotheses.

REVIEW QUESTIONS

1   Discuss the modern interpretation of competition and natural selection.
2   What is the source of variation in a population?
3   What is the Hardy-Weinberg law, and what are its conditions?
4   Describe how mutations serve as the raw material for evolution.
5   How does migration affect the frequency of genes in a population?
6   How does population size affect the shifting of gene frequencies?
7   How does nonrandom mating affect the shifting of gene frequencies?
8   What is a species?
9   How is a new species formed from an existing species?
10   Describe the means by which isolating mechanisms function.
11   What is a race?
12   Describe the process of adaptive radiation.
13   What is convergent evolution?
14   Why are certain assemblages of organisms associated with certain geographic regions?
15   What is the source of the diverse forms of living things?
16   Why are we able to classify the living world into categories?

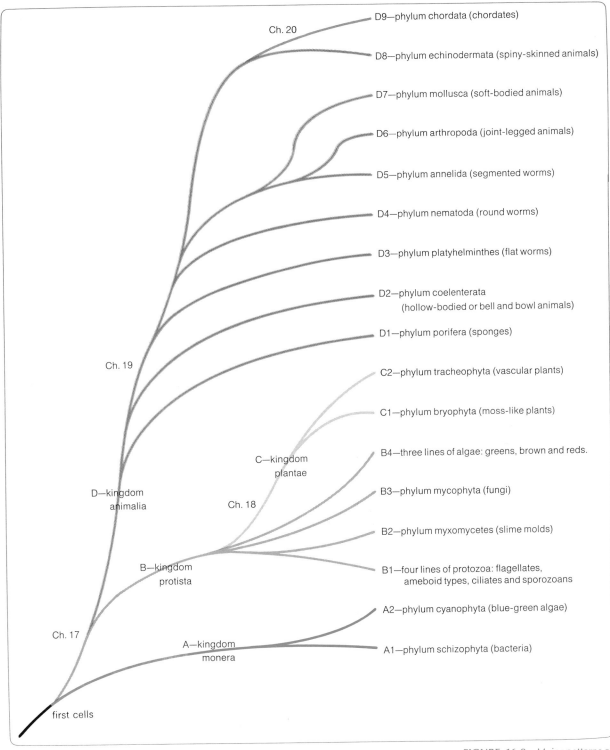

D9—phylum chordata (chordates)

D8—phylum echinodermata (spiny-skinned animals)

D7—phylum mollusca (soft-bodied animals)

D6—phylum arthropoda (joint-legged animals)

D5—phylum annelida (segmented worms)

D4—phylum nematoda (round worms)

D3—phylum platyhelminthes (flat worms)

D2—phylum coelenterata
(hollow-bodied or bell and bowl animals)

D1—phylum porifera (sponges)

C2—phylum tracheophyta (vascular plants)

C1—phylum bryophyta (moss-like plants)

B4—three lines of algae: greens, brown and reds.

B3—phylum mycophyta (fungi)

B2—phylum myxomycetes (slime molds)

B1—four lines of protozoa: flagellates,
ameboid types, ciliates and sporozoans

A2—phylum cyanophyta (blue-green algae)

A1—phylum schizophyta (bacteria)

Ch. 20

Ch. 19

C—kingdom
plantae

D—kingdom
animalia

Ch. 18

B—kingdom
protista

Ch. 17

A—kingdom
monera

first cells

FIGURE 16.9 Major patterns of divergence.

SUGGESTIONS FOR
FURTHER READING

* Available in paperback.

Ehrlich, P. A., and R. W. Holm: *The Process of Evolution,* McGraw-Hill Book Company, New York, 1963. A technical and authoritative text on the mechanisms of evolution.

Hamilton, T. H.: *Process and Pattern in Evolution,* The Macmillan Company, New York, 1967. Briefly describes the mechanisms of evolution.

Mayr, E.: *Principles of Systematic Zoology,* McGraw-Hill Book Company, New York, 1969. The most authoritative text available.

Moody, P. A.: *Introduction to Evolution,* 2d ed., Harper & Row, Publishers, Incorporated, New York, 1962. An easily understood text.

Solbrig, O. T.: *Evolution and Systematics,* Prentice-Hall, Inc., Englewood Cliffs, N.J., 1966. Describes how the rate and direction of evolution depend upon the interactions between populations and their environment.

Wallace, B., and A. M. Srb: *Adaptation,* 2d ed., Prentice-Hall, Inc., Englewood Cliffs, N.J., 1964. A brief description of the process of evolution and an expanded account of the role of adaptations in this process.

Parasol mushroom, kingdom Protista, phylum Mycophyta. (*Courtesy of Jeanne White, from The National Audubon Society.*)

Chapter 17
Patterns of Diversity in the World of Microbes

There is grandeur in this view of life, with its several powers, having been originally breathed into a few forms or into one; and that, while this planet has gone cycling on according to the fixed laws of gravity, from so simple a beginning endless forms most beautiful and most wonderful have been, and are being, evolved.

If throughout evolution life has come only from previously existing life, the stream of life still must have had at least one beginning, far back in the early history of the earth. In this chapter we discuss how life may have originated on earth and then examine some of the various forms of microscopic life, the microbes.

Darwin

GENESIS: HOW MIGHT
LIFE HAVE BEGUN?

In 1924, A. I. Oparin of the Soviet Union published the statement that there is no basic difference between a living organism and lifeless matter. Oparin presented arguments that the properties characteristic of life must have arisen in the course of the evolution of matter.

Soon after Oparin's first statement of this theory Haldane independently presented similar conclusions:

Now when ultraviolet light acts on a mixture of water, carbon dioxide, and ammonia, a vast variety of organic substances are made, including sugars and apparently some of the materials from which proteins are built up. Before the origin of life they must have accumulated until the primitive oceans reached the consistency of hot, dilute soup.

These ideas of Oparin's and Haldane's stimulated many scientists to propose processes by which life might have developed through a synthesis of larger and larger organic molecules. This has continued to be an active field of biological research, and we are now able to imagine a plausible sequence of events to explain the origin of the first systems displaying the characteristics of life.

ORIGIN OF LIFE: AN OVERVIEW

The ability of carbon to form covalent bonds with itself and other atoms was a central factor in the first appearance of life on this planet. Complex molecules formed by combination of carbon with hydrogen, oxygen, and nitrogen were also essential. As the earth was cooling down about 5 billion years ago, carbon, C, hydrogen, H, oxygen, O, and nitrogen, N, bonded together to form a variety of small molecules. Hydrogen is chemically active and bonded with itself to form *hydrogen* gas, H_2, with carbon to form *methane*, CH_4, with oxygen to form *water*, H_2O, and with nitrogen to form *ammonia* NH_3. The atmosphere became a mixture of at least four gases, hydrogen, methane, water vapor, and ammonia. Note that the molecules of these gases contain the atoms we have designated as being vital to living organisms, methane as a source of carbon, ammonia as a source of nitrogen, and water as a source of oxygen. Hydrogen, of course, is present in all these gases.

Water vapor cooled, condensed, and fell as rain, only to rise again as steam when the rain hit the hot rocks below. As the steam rose, cooled, and fell again from clouds which undoubtedly covered many regions of the earth, the downpour of rain eroded the mountains and valleys. Torrents of water carried dissolved minerals into the earth's basins, and primitive oceans were formed—warm, salty, and containing dissolved compounds of carbon, hydrogen, oxygen, and nitrogen.

Most scientists agree that the energy required for synthesis of complex organic molecules from these primordial gases probably came from electrical discharges during storms, ionizing radiation from the sun, and heat from the earth. Some scientists, however, argue that this synthesis could not have taken place without the regulative control of enzymes; on the other hand enzymes could not have appeared until the evolution of molecules had gone on for some time. This would be placing the cart before the horse before the cart had evolved! This line of reasoning brings up the question whether enzymes are really necessary for the early evolution of life. Of course no one was there to watch the series of events, and the only way to demonstrate that enzymes were not necessary in the early evolution of organic molecules is to retrace the hypothetical steps of evolution, by testing for spontaneous synthesis of such molecules in an artificially arranged environment imitating that of the primitive earth and containing only methane, water, ammonia, and hydrogen, plus a source of energy.

In 1953, Stanley Miller, working with Harold Urey at the University of Chicago, set up a system which approximated the conditions of the primitive earth. Miller devised an apparatus in which water vapor was circulated along with methane, ammonia, and hydrogen past a source of energy, an electric spark representing the effects of lightning (see Figure 17.1). The water vapor and other gases circulated through a cooling condenser and collected as a watery solution in a trap at the bottom of the apparatus. Tests revealed that this watery mixture contained several simple amino acids, and this had happened in the absence of enzymatic controls! In

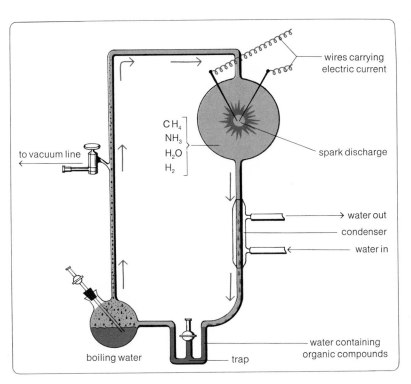

FIGURE 17.1 Diagrammatic representation of apparatus used by Stanley Miller for the synthesis of amino acids by electric discharge.

the years since Miller's pioneering experiments other investigators, using mixtures of gases in which methane was the only carbon source plus an energy source, have synthesized a great variety of organic molecules, including simple sugars and the precursors of nucleic acids.

Sidney Fox was intrigued with Miller's synthesis of amino acids, and he and his colleagues decided to determine whether amino acids would bond together to form proteins if they were simply heated. The addition of heat, they thought, should add a source of energy for bonding as well as a means of dehydration. They found that heating several amino acids, such as aspartic acid and glutamic acid, caused the formation of molecules containing all twenty amino acids! The amino acids formed into chains similar to those in proteins, and Fox called them *proteinoids*. He went further. When he allowed the supersaturated solutions of proteinoids to cool down, tremendous numbers of microscopic, gel-like spheres were formed. He named them *microspheres*. When they were analyzed, they were found to contain minute quantities of guanine, a component of DNA and RNA.

Recently, C. Ponnamperuma irradiated a mixture of methane, water, ammonia, and hydrogen with a high-energy electron beam, simulating the energy which might have been released on the primitive earth from potassium 40, a radioactive isotope. He and his colleagues also studied the effect of ultraviolet light on hydrogen cyanide, HCN, another simple compound which could have been formed spontaneously in the prebiotic period. Both experiments produced adenine. Apparently, adenine is the most easily synthesized of the five types of nitrogenous bases found in DNA and RNA. This is important since adenine is a component of many important biological molecules such as the energy-carrying adenosine triphosphate (ATP). In fact ATP synthesis was also demonstrated in these experiments. Thus, like amino acids, adenine and guanine, the two purines, can be formed by a relatively simple process without enzymes or living cells. What about the sugars of DNA and RNA? In 1951, Melvin Calvin irradiated water and carbon dioxide in a cyclotron and produced formaldehyde. When formaldehyde was irradiated with ultraviolet light, a variety of sugars was produced, including ribose and deoxyribose.

With a supply of energy from ultraviolet light, lightning, and other sources, DNA and RNA could have formed from the sugars, phosphates, and nitrogenous bases previously synthesized and present in the ocean. In order for a self-replicating unit we could recognize as a primitive cell to be formed, *membranes* would also be needed, so that the cell contents could be selected, concentrated, and kept separate from the environment. The nucleotide bases from which DNA and RNA could be formed, for example, probably would have to be sequestered and concentrated before the reactions leading to nucleic acid formation would be likely.

Recently, separate investigations of de Jong and Oparin have shown how early cells might have formed. Each man carried on experiments in which he simply mixed solutions containing various proteins and a few other large molecules and found that small droplets called *coacervates* were formed. Further investigation revealed that the internal environments of these droplets are quite different from their external environments. These experiments also showed that certain organic substances are selectively absorbed from the environment of the coacervate droplet and concentrated inside. Because of the physical characteristics of the droplet, a layer of water molecules is formed on the surface of the coacervate which acts much like a selectively permeable membrane. Thus, for example, the structural components of DNA could be absorbed and maintained inside the droplet at a higher concentration than in the surrounding medium. In this more concentrated form, the possibility of chemical interaction is increased with the resultant possibility of incorporation into a nucleic acid.

Chance dictates that different coacervates will contain different internal substances. Some absorb greater quantities of material from the surrounding medium, and others have greater internal organization and stability. Coacervates which have increased to a large size are likely to fragment, and the small droplets which result, if internally stable, absorb the same materials as the parent droplet and grow large. In this manner, natural selection could have acted in shallow shoreline ponds at the edge of the primordial seas to produce coacervates with the characteristics of a primitive form of growth and reproduction.

A selective advantage would be gained if a system could be included in the droplets to ensure that fragments would retain the structural configuration of the ''parent'' droplet. In this way, nucleic acids may have entered the picture as a molecule stabilizing the chemical system in the droplet because of their capacity for self-replication. Once a nucleic acid control system arose in the coacervate system, mutations were possible. By selection of mutations which relieved the coacervate system of dependence on the surrounding medium for nutrients, systems could have become established to allow synthesis of component molecules internally, until synthesis of all the needed components was made possible from simple organic precursors. Somewhere along the line photosynthetic reactions, enabling light to be used as an energy source, must have also appeared in the system. Along with the evolution of these synthetic capabilities, structural modifications, such as the presence of true membranes, would have provided a selective advantage for the coacervate in the promotion of greater internal stability. In the course of the gradual acquisition of this greater complexity, the characteristics of the system changed from coacervate-like to cell-like, and with this change, what we call life can be said to have appeared on earth.

The photosynthetic reactions which appeared early in the evolution of cellular life resulted in the release of oxygen into the environment through the splitting of water. This by-product of photosynthesis caused a dramatic change in the surface of the earth, its crust, and its life. As oxygen was released into the atmosphere, it combined with methane to form carbon dioxide and water and with ammonia to form nitrogen gas and water. Thus the advent of photosynthesizing cells changed the atmosphere of the earth. The effects of oxygen on the nature of the atmosphere were equaled by its effects on the crust of the earth, for the oxygen combined with the metals and salts of the earth's surface to form most of the minerals common today.

Photosynthesis and its production of nutrients and oxygen not only changed the atmosphere and the earth's crust but allowed life to progress on earth. The earth was converted from a *closed-energy system,* in which the store of chemical energy was being depleted, to an *open-energy system,* in which there was a constant addition to the earth's supply of chemical energy. A new form of respiration also evolved, in which oxygen was a necessary factor, a respiration many times more effective in releasing energy than the oxygenless form. Thus photosynthesis not only trapped the sun's energy and stored it in nutrients but provided the oxygen which allowed a more effective release of energy from the nutrients it produced.

FOUR KINGDOMS, TWO KINDS OF CELLS

From the first primitive cellular forms of life, two major lines of evolution diverged and continued through the subsequent billions of years. One line of evolution is represented today by the blue-green algae and bacteria, the kingdom Monera. The other line of evolution is represented today by the kingdom Protista and the kingdoms Plantae and Animalia, which descended from the primitive protistans.

Some biologists do not separate the monerans and the protists into two separate kingdoms, but to others the differences are so striking and so fundamental that it has even been suggested that they might have had separate origins. Regardless of the answer to this question, the living world can be classified into four kingdoms, and we shall begin our discussion of diversity with the kingdom Monera.

THE KINGDOM MONERA

The kingdom Monera includes bacteria and blue-green algae, organisms with characteristics which mark them as remote relatives of the rest of the living world. Monerans lack separate membrane-bound cell nuclei. Instead of having pairs of chromosomes, each moneran cell contains a single strand of DNA.

Cytoplasm of moneran cells does not stream but apparently remains almost static. Surrounding the cytoplasm of a moneran cell is, of course, a cell membrane, but outside the membrane is a rigid cell wall made not of cellulose, as in higher plants, but of polysaccharides, proteins, and sometimes fat. Many moneran cells are photosynthetic, but they lack the highly organized chloroplasts of higher cells. Instead, the photosynthetic units are tiny disks called *chromatophores.* They resemble the individual grana of chloroplasts described in Chapter 6.

Monerans hold a vital place in all ecosystems since their enzymes act upon almost all organic compounds thus far discovered. As nitrogen fixers and decomposers, they produce nutrients for plants and serve as a source of food for many animals. Because of their high reproductive rate and their wide ranges of tolerance, monerans have become adapted to a variety of environmental conditions.

There are about 2,000 known species of bacteria, which, under the modern system of classification, compose a single phylum, Schizophyta. Bacteria are the smallest cells known but have the widest distribution. Some bacteria are capable of locomotion because they are endowed with flagella. Bacterial flagella are not like those of higher cells, however, for they lack the "9 + 2" arrangement of fibers. Instead, bacterial flagella are tiny threads containing two or three long molecules of protein twisted around one another. Flagella may be restricted to one or both ends of a bacterial cell, or they may occur all over the surface.

Bacteria can reproduce either sexually or asexually. Asexual reproduction takes place by fission, that is, the cells seem simply to constrict and form two cells. In either case replication of the bacterial DNA strand precedes fission of the cell. This process may be very rapid, and if conditions are good, the cells may divide every 20 minutes. In 6 or 7 hours, at this rate of reproduction, one bacterial cell would become 1 million, and in 24 hours a layer of bacteria 2 feet thick would cover the entire earth.

Sexual reproduction occurs when two bacterial cells form a junction and genetic material is inserted from one cell (the "male") into the other (the "female"). The genetic material is in the form of a single strand of DNA. The transfer of this thread is often interrupted before completion, so that the "zygote" has all the "female" genes but only part of the injected "male" genes. The fragment of the male DNA strand injected pairs with the female strand in some way, so that recombination can occur between the regions of the female strand and the male fragment which are homologous. In this manner, variability due to recombination is added to variability originating from mutations in bacterial populations.

Bacteria are often very resistant to environmental pressures. In many bacteria, a *capsule* of mucoid or slimy material is secreted on the outside of the cell wall which increases the resistance of the bacterial cell to drying or other limiting factors in the environment. Because the capsule appears to provide resistance to the defense mechanisms of host organisms, many of the agents of human diseases are capsulated forms.

Some kinds of bacteria respond to an unfavorable environment by forming *endospores,* a process by which cytoplasm containing genetic material becomes surrounded by a thick and impervious wall. Since a single bacterial cell can produce only one endospore, it is clear that this process is not a form of reproduction. Instead it is an adaptation which allows the cells to live through an unfavorable environment. Once the environment becomes favorable again, the endospore germinates into a functioning cell. Endospores are little short of fantastic in their ability to withstand stresses. For example, some endospores can germinate even after a 3- to 4-hour immersion in boiling water.

Bacterial cells come in three shapes, spheres, rods, and spirals. The spheres are called *cocci* (singular, coccus), rods are *bacilli* (singular, bacillus), and spirals are called *spirilla* (singular , spirillum) (see Figure 17.2).

BLUE-GREEN ALGAE

FIGURE 17.2 The three forms of bacteria: spheres (cocci), rods (bacilli), and spirals (spirilla). Bacteria are unicellular microorganisms that lack nuclei and chlorophyll. The phylum includes some of the smallest forms of life. Shown enlarged is *Proteus vulgaris,* a bacillus.

There are about twenty-five known species of blue-green algae, forming a single phylum called *Cyanophyta* (see Figure 17.3). This group includes not only bluish-green forms but others of various hues and containing various kinds of pigments. Blue-greens occur in virtually all environments containing water and have even been found in hot springs at temperature of over 190°F!

Blue-green algae are similar to bacteria but differ in that they are surrounded by a sheet of slime, their cell walls lack fat and contain cellulose, and they often contain crystals of phosphate. Also, they lack flagella and have no means of locomotion ex-

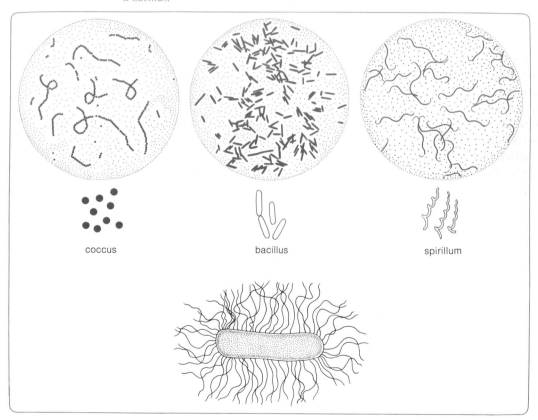

coccus   bacillus   spirillum

cept for a peculiar gliding or jerking motion which is not understood. There is no evidence that blue-greens can reproduce through sexual means. They appear to reproduce only by fission.

Bacteria and blue-green algae carry on the same roles on land as they do in fresh water and in the ocean. The algae and some bacteria are photosynthetic, and, as we all know from experience, some bacteria are parasitic. Actually, however, most bacteria are decomposers. Some bacteria live in nodules on the roots of legumes, such as beans and clover, and convert the inert and useless nitrogen of the air into nitrates, which are of vital necessity to plants if they are to produce amino acids and proteins. Some blue-green algae also fix nitrogen. Through decomposition and nitrogen fixation, bacteria supply to green land plants the nutrients necessary for the formation of plant protoplasm, the material which also serves as the food of animals.

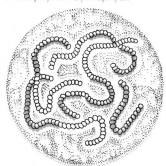

FIGURE 17.3 A blue-green alga of the phylum Cyanophyta.

THE KINGDOM PROTISTA

The kingdom Protista includes the protozoa, algae, fungi, and slime molds. Many of the species in this kingdom exist as independent single-celled organisms; others develop into multicellular structures of various sizes. Protistan cells are representative of the idealized cell type we have described in previous chapters because, within this group, internal membrane systems are present in the cytoplasm and surrounding the nucleus. Thus, the chromosomes, which exist in pairs in many Protista, are separated from the cytoplasm by a nuclear membrane; a nucleolus is present in the nucleus; and complex membrane systems in the cytoplasm form mitochondria, chloroplasts, endoplasmic reticulum, vacuoles, and small vesicles. Their flagella have the "9 + 2" plan, and they carry out cell division by mitosis. A centriole is found in association with the spindle, that is, the fiber system on which the chromosomes become arranged in mitosis and meiosis. The cytoplasm of protistan cells is usually in constant motion.

PROTOZOA

Protozoa are protistans which lack chlorophyll and must rely upon foods in their environment as sources of nutrition. Many protozoa actively pursue their prey and exhibit other characteristics of organisms in the animal kingdom. For this reason, some classification schemes place the protozoa as a phylum in the animal kingdom. It is difficult to determine the ancestors of the protozoa, but some authorities believe that both the algae and protozoa descended from a flagellated algalike ancestor which had the ability to carry on photosynthesis. Almost all protozoa exist as single cells, but a few species form colonies (see Figure 17.4 and Plate 11).

Most biologists consider that the protozoa include four phyla, representing four main lines of divergence. The four phyla can be recognized on the basis of their *means of locomotion*. The most primitive protozoa move by means of flagella and are called the *flagellates*. Some species of flagellates are capable of losing their flagella and

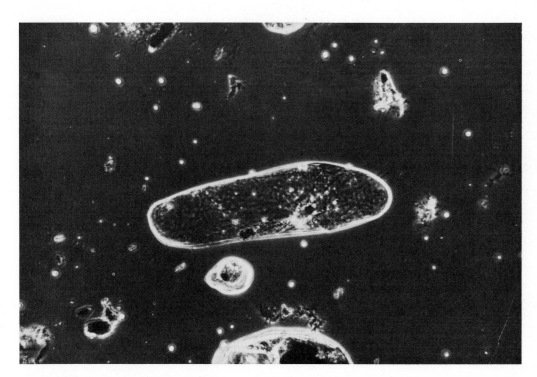

FIGURE 17.4 A protozoan, showing the nucleus in the lower right center supported by cytoplasmic strands. Protozoans are one-celled protists which lack chlorophyll and usually pursue their prey. (*Chas. Pfizer & Co., Inc.*)

becoming ameboid, and it is believed that the other three lines of protozoa, the ameboid forms, the ciliates, and the sporozoans, diverge from an ancestral flagellate protozoan stock.

The *flagellates* (Figure 17.5) are the most diverse of the protozoa, and since many of the algae are flagellated cells, it is often difficult to decide whether you are observing an alga or a protozoan. If you examine a text on algae or protozoa to find an answer, you will see that some of the same organisms are often included in both. The best criterion for a decision of this kind is nutrition. If a single-celled organism has chlorophyll, call it an alga, and if it lacks chlorophyll, call it a protozoan. If certain algae are kept in the dark, however, they lose their chlorophyll and begin functioning nutritionally as protozoa, by capturing and ingesting bacteria.

Ameboid forms share an ability to form pseudopodia, but many have little else in common (see Figure 17.6 and Plate 11). They differ in color, size, and general appearance. Some consist of flowing, mobile protoplasm, while others produce shells outside their cell membranes and extend their pseudopodia through holes in the shell. Protoplasm does not fossilize, but the shells formed by these ameboid forms accumulate on the floor of the ocean and form vast deposits, like the chalky white

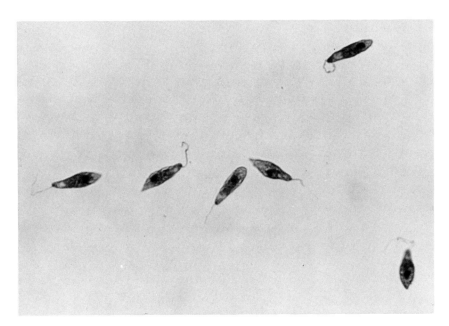

FIGURE 17.5 *Euglena*, a flagellated alga. (*Carolina Biological Supply Co.*)

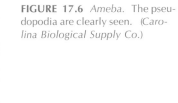

FIGURE 17.6 *Ameba.* The pseudopodia are clearly seen. (*Carolina Biological Supply Co.*)

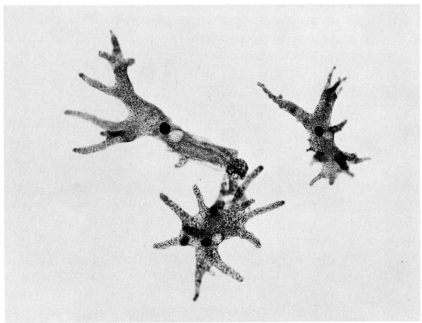

cliffs of Dover.   Fossil shells of this type have been found in rock deposits over half a billion years old.

Ciliates are usually the most intriguing of the protozoa to most observers.   They are continually active and possess intricate structures with complex functions in a single cell.   Most of the ciliates secrete material outside the cell membrane called the *pellicle* which gives support to the cell and provides many ciliates with a somewhat fixed shape and appearance (see Figure 17.7)   The cilia project through the pellicle and move in rhythmical waves, a function requiring coordination supplied by fibers

FIGURE 17.7   Ciliated protozoa: (a) *Vorticella*, (b) *Stentor*, and (c) *Paramecium*.   All show the cilia with which they move their body. (*Carolina Biological Supply Co.*)

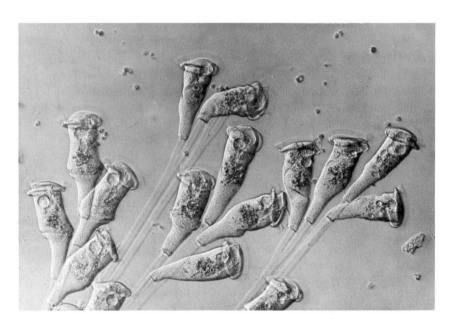

A

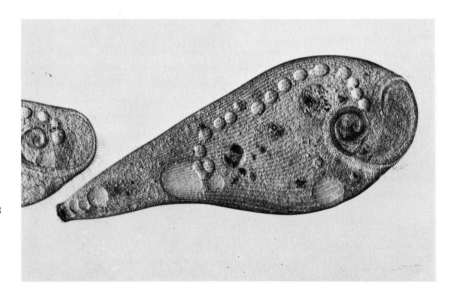

B

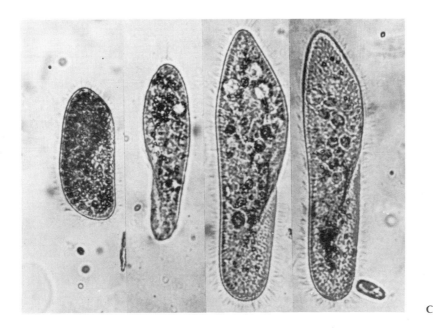

C

connecting the cilia beneath the pellicle. The cilia provide not only a means of locomotion but also bring food to the mouthlike structure found in most ciliates.

The diverse and intricate activities carried on by ciliates reflect an exceedingly complex macromolecular organization in the cytoplasm of these organisms. This degree of organization ultimately rests on directions for the biosynthesis of proteins and other molecules originating in the nucleus, which in the ciliate group is subdivided into two structures. This subdivision is related to the two major roles of the nucleus in all cells, expression of genetic information for synthesis and reproduction of the hereditary material. The two subnuclei between which these functions are divided in the ciliates vary in size. The larger nucleus, the *macronucleus,* carries out the transcription of genetic information into directions for the cytoplasmic synthesis of proteins involved in nutrition, metabolism, growth, regeneration, and all the other activities of the cell. The smaller nucleus, the *micronucleus,* is concerned only with the replication of DNA in preparation for cell division. Some ciliates even have a method of offense and defense, for many of them contain *trichocysts,* tiny structures containing toxins which immobilize predator or prey.

Sporozoans include a wide variety of organisms with only a few traits shared by all. They are *all parasitic* and have highly complex life cycles. The hosts for these parasites include almost every species in the animal kingdom, and the life cycles of some include several different animals as hosts. This group is able to propagate by forming vast numbers of spores through multiple fission at some point in the life cycle. Some stages in the life cycle of a sporozoan may have flagella, some glide, and some move like a slug, but none of this activity takes place free in nature. Sporozoans always live inside the body of a host.

We have seen that the protozoa are a diverse and widespread group. Many authorities say that there are around 15,000 species of protozoa, but this is admitted to be a serious underestimation. When consideration is given to all the various habitats in which protozoa live, it is clear that there must be a fantastic number of different species. In addition to the free-living forms there are also the parasitic forms, and since the parasitic protozoa usually parasitize only one host or a few hosts, there may well be almost as many species of protozoa as there are animal hosts. There may be over 100,000 species of protozoa.

SLIME MOLDS

The *slime molds* of the phylum Myxomycetes (see Figure 17.8) are an interesting group which, although placed in the kingdom Protista in our classification, have so many baffling characteristics that they have been variously classified by experts as protists, plants, or animals, and most often as fungi. The group has two subgroups, the *true slime molds* and the *cellular slime molds,* which are so different from each other that some taxonomists feel they are not closely related and should be in separate phyla. The *true slime molds* spend most of their life cycle in the form of an ameboid cell which grows in size as it ingests nutrients from moist decaying vegetation. As the cell grows, its diploid nucleus divides until many diploid nuclei are formed in the single large cell, which may attain a size of several inches in length and take the form of a branching mass of naked protoplasm, easily visible to the naked eye. At maturity, this mass of protoplasm, called a *plasmodium,* sends up a *fruiting body,* in which meiosis takes place, giving rise to haploid spores, which, when they germinate, form haploid flagellated gametes. Two of these fuse to form an ameboid diploid cell, and the cycle is repeated.

FIGURE 17.8 *Stemonitis fusca,* phylum Myxomycetes, a slime mold.

The *cellular slime molds* are quite different. In these organisms, which are apparently haploid during all parts of their life cycle, the small ameboid cells do not grow markedly in size but remain as amebas living in the soil, each with a single haploid nucleus. Cell division occurs at this stage, with production of multiple numbers of ameboid cells which remain separate from each other. Under certain conditions, great masses of individual ameboid cells collect together and form a sluglike *pseudoplasmodium,* which moves about as a unit until a *fruiting body* is formed. Inside the pseudoplasmodium the separate cells retain their membranes, in contrast to the plasmodium of the true slime molds, where many nuclei all occupy a common cytoplasm. Meiosis does not occur in the fruiting body of cellular slime molds; the haploid cells simply bud off into haploid spores, which, if the environment is favorable, germinate into individual amebas. Cellular slime molds have been of considerable interest to embryologists, because *differentiation* of the mass of cells of the slug into the base, stalk, and cap of the fruiting body resembles differentiation of the cells of multicellular organisms during development, but the extremely simple form lends itself readily to study in the laboratory.

The *fungi* of the phylum Mycophyta are very diversified protists and are represented in every habitat on earth. Some fungi live on dead organisms or on organic material, and others live as parasites inside or on living organisms. Some fungi are aquatic and produce flagellated reproductive cells, and others are terrestrial, distributing their reproductive cells by wind, water, or animal carriers. In some fungi, the nonreproductive part of the body, made of filaments called *hyphae,* has many nuclei but lacks cell membranes between the nuclei. Other fungi, including the larger and better-known varieties, such as mushrooms and toadstools, are made up of hyphae which have walls and membranes between the nuclei and are thus multicellular. The vegetative part of the body of a fungus, consisting of a mass of individual hyphae, is called a *mycelium;* most of the mycelial mass in toadstools and mushrooms is below the surface of the soil and is not visible. The mycelium and reproductive parts may contain rigid cell walls composed of cellulose or *chitin,* a material found commonly in animals (the exoskeletons of insects are formed primarily of chitin). The fungi may possibly represent a separate offshoot from a common ancestor which gave rise to both the protozoa and the algae (see Plates 13 and 14).

Algae are photosynthetic protists which make up 90 percent of the producer organisms of the ecosystems of the world. They vary in size from single-celled organisms to the enormous multicellular kelp which lie just off the shores of the Pacific Coast of North America. Kelp may reach 100 feet long and are among the longest organisms in the world. Algae, the "grass of the sea," are browsed by countless numbers of animals. Four types of chlorophyll are found among the algae, and this feature, plus differences in the stored food substances and in cell-wall construction, permit the algae to be grouped into three main lines of divergence, the green algae, the brown algae, and the red algae.

The *green algae* contain chlorophylls *a* and *b,* store carbohydrate nutrients in the form of starch, and usually have cellulose cell walls. The *brown algae* contain chlorophylls *a* and *c* and store nutrients as fats, starch, and more exotic compounds such as leucosin, laminarin, and mannitol (see Figure 17.9). If cell walls are present in brown algae, they are made of cellulose. The *red algae* have chlorophylls *a* and *d,* store their food in a special form known as floridean starch, and also have cell walls made of cellulose.

Algae reproduce both sexually and asexually. Asexual reproduction may be vegetative and involve a mere breaking away of fragments, which drift off to develop into another organism, or it may involve the formation of spores. Spores of many algae are called *zoospores* since they have flagella which allow the rapid locomotion typical of an animal sperm.

Sexual reproduction, of course, involves gametes, but the gametes are not always easy to recognize as being male or female. Even though some species of algae have

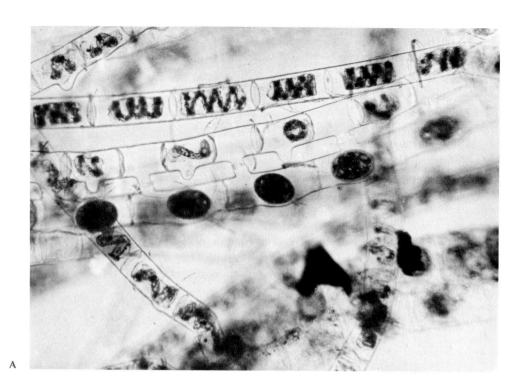

A

FIGURE 17.9 (a) Green algae, (b) brown algae, and (c) red algae. (*Courtesy of Hugh Spencer from The National Audubon Society.*) (d) *Chlorella vulgaris,* a one-celled green alga (*Chas. Pfizer & Co., Inc.*)

B

C

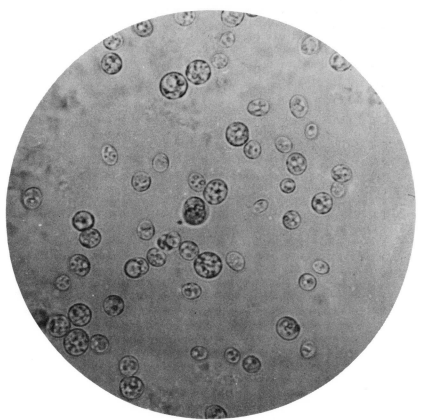

D

*Amoeba is an entire organism
in just the same sense that man
is an entire organism. . . .
From a physiological point of
view, the Protista are very
complex.*

Dobell

gametes which look identical, they must have a "chemical sex" since the gametes, called *plus* and *minus* recognize each other and migrate together to fuse in fertilization. On the other hand, many species of algae have gametes which are of different sizes and abilities to move. Often, one gamete is large and incapable of movement and is designated the egg. The opposite type of gamete is smaller and capable of movement and is designated the sperm. The various species of algae demonstrate so many variations on the theme of sexual and asexual reproduction that a separate chapter or book would be required to present an adequate sampling.

REVIEW QUESTIONS

1 Describe briefly how life might have evolved as a result of synthesis of larger and larger compounds including some that could reproduce themselves.
2 What are the characteristics that separate the kingdoms Monera and Protista?
3 Why are bacteria and blue-green algae so successful?
4 Describe the roles of bacteria, blue-green algae, slime molds, fungi, and algae in ecosystems.
5 Contrast the four types of protozoans.

SUGGESTIONS FOR
FURTHER READING
* Available in paperback.

Alexopoulos, C. J., and H. C. Bold: *Algae and Fungi,* The Macmillan Company, New York, 1967. Compares and contrasts the algae and fungi.

Hall, R. P.: *Protozoa: The Simplest of All Animals,* Holt, Rinehart and Winston, Inc., New York, 1964. Brief and well written by a noted authority.

Jahn, T. L.: *How to Know the Protozoa,* Wm. C. Brown Company Publishers, Dubuque, Iowa, 1949. A pictured key to common freshwater, marine, and parasitic protozoa.

Kudo, R. R.: *Protozoology,* 5th ed., Charles C Thomas, Publisher, Springfield, Ill., 1966. A widely used advanced text on protozoa; excellent for identification.

Manwell, R. D.: *Introduction to Protozoology,* St. Martin's Press, Inc., New York, 1961. A text that stresses principles.

Prescott, D.: *How to Know the Fresh-water Algae,* Wm. C. Brown Company Publishers, Dubuque, Iowa, 1954. A pictured key to common freshwater algae.

Smith, G. M.: *Cryptogamic Botany,* 2d ed., vol. I, *Algae and Fungi,* McGraw-Hill Book Company, New York, 1955. A technical and authoritative textbook.

Stanier, R. Y., M. Doudoroff, and E. A. Adelberg: *The Microbial World,* 2d ed., Prentice-Hall, Inc., Englewood Cliffs, N.J., 1963. An excellent text on microbiology.

Tree branches. (*Courtesy of M. Chapman.*)

Chapter 18
Patterns of Diversity in the World of Plants

To see a World in a Grain of Sand,
And a Heaven in a Wild Flower,
Hold Infinity in the palm of your hand,
And Eternity in an hour.

Blake

The dominant color of the land on this planet is green, a fact testifying to the success of the invasion of the land by the members of the kingdom Plantae, the green, multicellular, terrestrial plants. The land plants are believed to have evolved from freshwater green algae. We begin our discussion of land plants by comparing them to their ancestors.

THE ORIGIN OF
LAND PLANTS

There is abundant circumstantial evidence to support the idea that land plants evolved from freshwater green algae. The strongest evidence is that both land plants and green algae have chlorophylls *a* and *b*, have cellulose cell walls, and store their food as starch. On the other hand, land plants differ from green algae in several basic ways. Reproductive parts in land plants are *multicellular;* after fertilization of the female gamete in the female reproductive organ, an *embryo* forms inside the parental structures; *centrioles* are absent in the cells of the most highly evolved land plants, and a waxy *cuticle* is present which protects the surfaces of the plant from drying. In the most highly evolved land plants, an increase in size has been accompanied by development of a system of *transport* of nutrients within the plant. The transport system consists of two types of tissue, *xylem* and *phloem.* Because of these conductive elements, the more highly evolved land plants are often termed the *vascular* plants.

These specializations possessed by land plants are clearly adaptations which allow plant life to exist on land, where dehydration, air currents, gravity, and other limiting factors are prominent. Their ancestors, the primitive green algae, lived in a watery world where buoyancy made them almost weightless, where the algal cells were in contact with surrounding water containing nutrients and gases, and where reproduction was accomplished through the direct release of spores and gametes into the watery environment, which served as the medium of transfer. These points are summarized in Table 18.1.

Alternation of generations is the rule in land plants. The life cycle begins with a diploid form which produces spores through meiosis. The spores germinate to form haploid plants. These haploid plants produce gametes mitotically, and at fertilization the gametes fuse to form a diploid spore-forming plant once again. The gamete-forming plant is the dominant form in mosslike plants, and the spore-forming plant is dominant in higher plants. Alternation of generations is diagrammed in Figure 18.1.

The evolution of land plants probably took place along the shores of ponds or streams, where the level of water constantly rose and fell. This caused selection

TABLE 18.1 Similarities and differences between plants and algae

A Loss of water environment caused problems
   requiring new adaptations to deal with
   1 Spore germination
   2 Sperm transfer
   3 Dehydration
   4 Body support
B Freshwater green algae and land plants both
   1 Have chlorophylls *a* and *b*
   2 Have cellulose cell walls
   3 Store foods as starch
C Land plants but not green algae have waxy cuticle

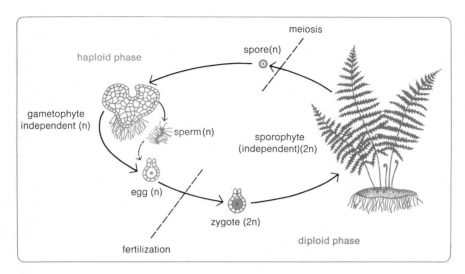

FIGURE 18.1 Summary of the life
cycle of ferns, showing alternation
of generations. (*Adapted from
Paul B. Weisz, Elements of Biology,
3rd ed. Copyright McGraw-Hill
Book Company, 1969. Used by
permission.*)

pressures for survival out of water. The first forms could probably stand only brief
exposure to the air, but variant descendants could stand more prolonged exposure.
As time and many generations passed, some forms evolved which required immersion in water only during reproduction and other forms no longer required immersion at all.

Two major lines of plant evolution diverged from the ancestral green algae and are
represented today by two phyla, the *bryophytes* or *mosslike* plants, and the
tracheophytes, or *vascular* plants. The evolution of the major plant groups is summarized in Figure 18.2.

FIGURE 18.2 Evolution of bryophytes and tracheophytes.

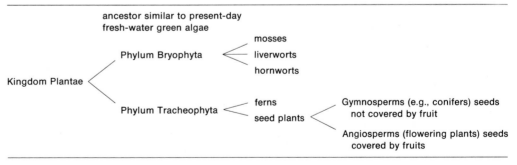

BRYOPHYTES

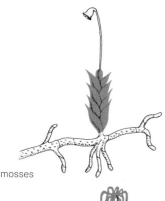

mosses

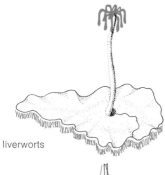

liverworts

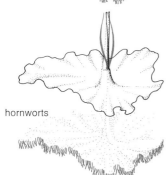

hornworts

Bryophytes include mosses, liverworts, and hornworts (see Figure 18.3) and are found in habitats which are shady and moist. None of the bryophytes have true roots, stems, or leaves. Bryophytes never grow more than a few inches off the ground, and their internal fluids move from cell to cell by diffusion.

Mosses grow as mats of green filaments with rootlike rhizoids extending into the soil and green shoots projecting into the air with tiny, overlapping leaflike blades radiating from the outer surface of the shoots (see Figure 18.4). Sex organs develop at the top of the haploid shoots, and sperm must actively swim from the male organ to the female organ to accomplish fertilization. The fertilized egg germinates into a slender spike containing diploid cells and may project as much as several inches above the green, haploid portion of the plant. Through meiosis, the small, diploid, spiky structure produces haploid *spores*. When the spores are released and land on wet soil, they germinate and again form the more conspicuous branching green plant. Thus, the plant alternates between two styles of life, one, a haploid form which occupies the dominant phase of the cycle, and the other, a diploid form which is much reduced in size and persists like a small parasite on the dominant haploid form only long enough to produce spores. Since fertilization of the egg requires water in the environment, mosses are limited to areas which are often covered with a film of water.

This type of life cycle, in which two different forms of a species alternate with each other, as noted before, is called alternation of generations. The haploid form of the plant, which produces gametes, is called a *gametophyte*. It is important to remember that since this form of the plant is haploid, *formation of gametes occurs without meiosis*. The diploid form, in which meiosis occurs, produces *spores* and is called a *sporophyte* (see Figures 18.1 and 18.5 and Plate 15). Alternation of generations of this type occurs in all the higher plants. As plants evolved greater complexity in their life cycle, they gradually shifted from the gametophyte to the sporophyte. Thus the largest and most conspicuous of modern plants, our familiar trees and flowers, are *sporophytes*.

Liverworts are flattened, sheetlike plants which grow flat upon the ground. Male structures resemble umbrellas, and female structures look like umbrellas with only the ribs remaining (see Figure 18.6). As in mosses, the sperm must swim from the male to the female gametophyte, and spores must germinate on wet soil. Because of their common need for a wet habitat, mosses and liverworts are often found together.

Hornworts are very similar to liverworts except for the appearance of the reproductive structures, which look like horns. The name has arisen from this appearance. Like liverworts and mosses, the hornworts are also limited in their distribution by a need for water.

VASCULAR PLANTS

As we have noted, vascular plants get their name from the possession of two distinctive tissues, the *xylem,* which conducts water and minerals, and the *phloem,* which

TABLE 18.2

BRYOPHYTES	TRACHEOPHYTES
Gametophyte dominant	Fertilization by sperm or sperm nuclei in pollen tubes
Sperm swim from male to female	
Sporophyte grows from fertilized egg, discharges spores, and dies	Motile, swimming sperm in ferns and in certain primitive seed plants, but in most seed plants fertilization by wind or insect-borne pollen
No vascular tissue	
No true roots, stems, or leaves	Has vascular tissue (conductive and supportive)
	True roots, stems, and leaves (organs with vascular tissue)
	Xylem and phloem are tissues which conduct
	Xylem (wood) is supportive as well as conductive

transports water and foods.   They are further characterized by the division of the plant body into three separate organ systems, *roots, stems,* and *leaves.*   Vascular plants first became dominant in the coal forests about 300 million years ago.   The original primitive forms are represented today by fossils in coal and by a few relics still alive, such as club mosses and horsetails.   The dominant modern forms of vascular plants are the large-leafed plants (pteropsids), which include the *ferns,* and the seed plants, the *gymnosperms* and *angiosperms* (see Table 18.2 and Figure 18.7).

Ferns grow as trees in the tropics, but in cooler climates the stems of many species grow horizontally under the ground and the projections above the ground are leaves. At certain times of the year, the underside of older fern leaves of some common species reveal small brown spots which if touched release spores.   If the familiar fern plant is thus a sporophyte, where is the gametophyte?   Careful scrutiny of wet soil in spring may reveal small green cellular plates about 1/4 inch across.   These green plates are gametophyte fern plants.   Ferns are characterized by having gametophytes and sporophytes which are both green and photosynthetic.   Therefore one form is not dependent upon the other for food, as in the bryophytes, where the sporophytes grow as spikes which depend on the tissues of the parent gametophytes.

Ferns require some of the same environmental factors as bryophytes.   Thus transfer of sperm and germination of fern spores must take place in water.   Ferns, however, have xylem and phloem tissues which serve not only in internal transport but give support to the plant body and allow it to achieve a much larger height and size than ever seen in bryophytes.

Seed plants, whose adaptations allow fertilization in the absence of water, are of two major types, the gymnosperms and the angiosperms.   As in ferns, the spore-forming sporophyte is the dominant phase of the life cycle.   *Gymnosperms* are typified by the

FIGURE 18.4 (a) Germinating spore of a moss and (b) recently germinated moss, showing rhizoids, buds, and young shoots. (*Adapted from Paul B. Weisz, Elements of Biology, 3rd ed.   Copyright McGraw-Hill Book Company, 1969.   Used by permission.*)

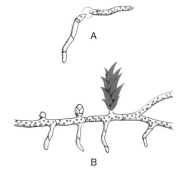

conifers, in which the spore-forming tissues are in special structures called *cones*.
Angiosperms are the flowering plants and contain the spore-forming tissues in structures called flowers.   Both cones and flowers form spores of two sizes, big and small.
The larger spores, which germinate into the female gametophyte, are retained in the
cone or flower.   The female gametophyte consists of only a few cells, one of which
becomes the *egg cell*.   The small spores are released from the cone or flower as
pollen and may be carried by wind or animals to the female gametophyte.   Upon

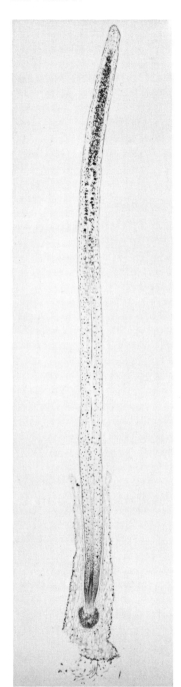

FIGURE 18.5 Sporophyte of moss
(two different magnifications). *(J.
Limbach, Ripon Microslides.)*

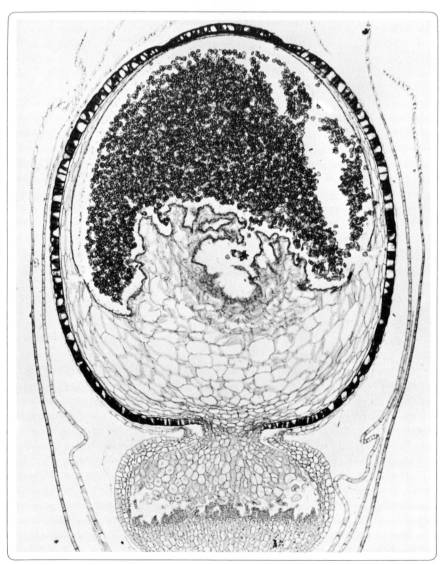

FIGURE 18.6 Sex-organ-bearing stalks in liverwort *Marchantia*. The ones resembling the ribs of an umbrella are the female, and the ones that look more like umbrellas (in lower part of picture) are the males. (*Photograph by Hugh Spencer from The National Audubon Society.*)

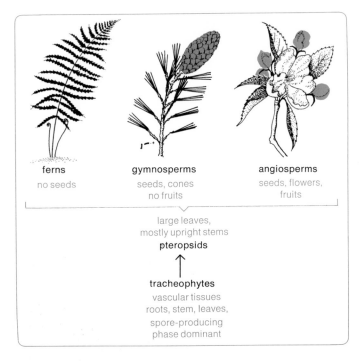

FIGURE 18.7 The subphyla of tracheophytes and the classes of pteropsids. Some of the unique features of each group are shown.

reaching the female gametophyte, the small spores germinate to form the male gametophyte, which grows out of the pollen grain as a slender filament or tube.   This tube
grows and extends through the tissues of the flower or cone until it comes in contact
with the female gametophyte.   The tube contains only a few nuclei, one of which,
called the *sperm nucleus,* fertilizes the egg nucleus within the female gametophyte.
As in the bryophytes and ferns, the fertilized egg becomes a sporophyte.   Thus the
gametophyte generation is reduced to structures which contain only a few nuclei.   In

FIGURE 18.8 Enlarged cross
section of (a) male pinecone and
(b) female pinecone.   (*J. Limbach,
Ripon Microslides.*)

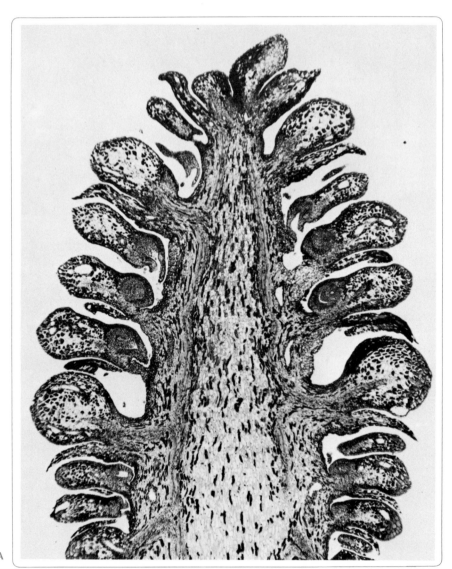

A

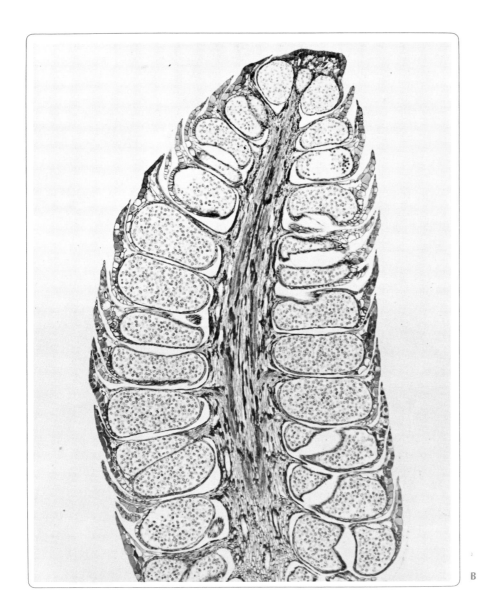

B

seed plants, the embryonic sporophyte ceases its development at an early stage and becomes surrounded by a thickened wall. This specialized embryo with its stored foods and protective coat is called a *seed*.

Gymnosperms are represented today primarily by the cone-bearing plants called conifers. Cones are either male or female; that is, one cone does not contain structures of both sexes (see Figure 18.8). Male cones are small and have pollen-forming structures on the underside of the scales of the cone. Female cones are larger and have spore-forming tissues on the upper side of the scales. Thus, when the pollen is released, it can fall out of the male cones and land on the upper sides of the scales of the female cones or be carried to the female cones by wind.

Angiosperms, the flowering plants, are the most varied and abundant of all plants. Over 200,000 species are known. With angiosperms the *flower* is the reproductive structure and is made of leaves specialized to form a circle of *sepals* which surround a circle of *petals.* The sepals and petals may be pigmented and secrete scents. Many fascinating adaptations in plants cause pollen to be rubbed off on animals as they reach down into the flower to get the nectar secreted there. Flowers of the grasses and other plants which are pollinated by the wind are far less dramatic and colorful in appearance but equally complex in function.

Inside the whorls of sepals and petals the flower has an inner circle of pollen-producing structures called *stamens.* At the center of a flower is the *pistil,* which contains the *ovary* in its base (see Figure 18.9). Inside the ovary, meiosis occurs, giving rise to a spore which forms the female gametophyte. The pistil is extended from the region of the ovary into an elongated *style,* which carries at its tip the *stigma,* a sticky enlargement which traps pollen grains carried to the flower by winds or insects. If pollen from the same or closely related species falls on the stigma, the pollen grains germinate into a pollen tube, which grows down the style and into the ovary. The nucleus of the pollen tube divides and gives rise to two nuclei, one of which is the *sperm nucleus* and will fertilize the *egg nucleus* of the female gametophyte in the ovary. The other nucleus from the pollen tube fuses with *two* secondary nuclei of the female gametophyte to form a triploid nucleus. The additional fusion in fertilization of these secondary female gametophyte nuclei with the male nucleus is unique to the angiosperms. The resulting triploid nucleus, termed the *endosperm nucleus,* divides repeatedly and lays down cell walls, forming a tissue in the seed called the *endosperm.* The diploid zygote nucleus divides also, to produce an embryonic sporophyte which becomes embedded in the endosperm tissue. When enclosed in a protective coat, the embryo and endosperm together constitute a seed. The endosperm will serve as a source of nutrient material to the embryo when the seed germinates at some future time. The endosperm is of utmost importance to man and other consumers of seeds as it is the main source of nutrients in many angiosperm seeds, for example, kernels of corn.

Shortly after fertilization, coverings around the embryo and endosperm derived from the parent sporophyte harden to become a *seed coat.* Most of the rest of the flower withers away. In many angiosperms, the ovary wall, also derived from the parent sporophyte plant, enlarges to become a *fruit.* Some fruits are dry (like nuts), some are fleshy (like apples), but either way, the fruit covers the seeds contained in the ovary. This is the basis for the name angiosperm, which means "hidden seed." Gymnosperms lack expanded ovaries and have naked seeds, the basis of the name.

Angiosperm reproduction has three features not found in gymnosperm reproduction:

(1) the flower, (2) formation of a triploid *endosperm* inside the seeds from fusion of a pollen nucleus with two female gametophyte nuclei, and (3) fruits. Each feature has had a great effect on the *evolutionary success of the angiosperms*. The flower increases the likelihood of pollination by different carriers. The fruit not only promotes dispersal of the seeds by animals but also provides nourishment to the soil if it simply decays upon the ground. Thus, instead of relying upon spores as means

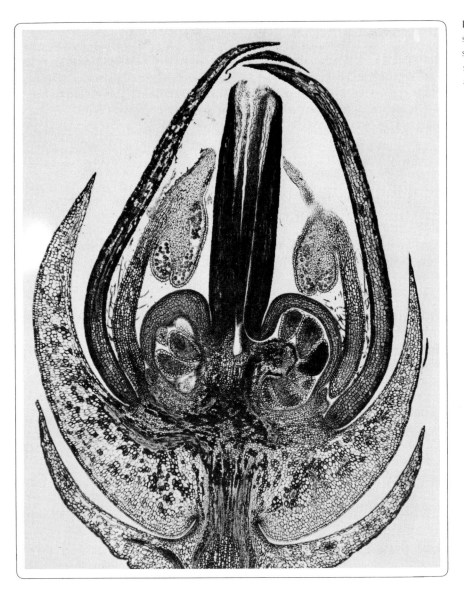

FIGURE 18.9 Enlarged cross section of flower, showing stigma, stamens, pistil, ovary, petal, and sepal. (*J. Limbach, Ripon Microslides.*)

of dispersal, seed plants utilize seeds, dormant embryonic plants supplied with endosperm which can nourish them during their early growth. Furthermore, seed plants have eliminated the necessity for sex organs to be immersed in water during part of their life cycle. Fertilization does not take place by union of swimming gametes; instead, as we have seen, the sperm nucleus is carried to the female gametophyte inside a pollen tube. This pattern is roughly equivalent to the transfer of sperm from the male to the female by a copulatory organ in higher animals in that the gametes are never subjected to the hazards of the environment.

The success of the vascular plants today is a measure of the success of their adaptations to the characteristics of a terrestrial environment. This environment demands *resistance to desiccation, support* of the parts of the plants which rise into the air, and *transport* of materials from one part of the plant to another. Adaptations to meet these requirements have taken place primarily in the *sporophyte,* the dominant form in the alternation of generations in the seed plants.

In discussing reproduction in seed plants, we have seen how *resistance to desiccation* in gametic reproduction has been accomplished by a type of internal fertilization which does not require the reproductive parts of the plant to be immersed in water. Resistance to desiccation of the sporophyte plant, in general, has been accomplished primarily through evolution of a waxy outer covering, the *cuticle,* which allows light to pass but prevents the passage of moisture from the plant to the surrounding air. Gas exchange, severely limited by the presence of the cuticle, takes place through small openings in the epidermis of the plant called *stomata.* These allow oxygen, a by-product of photosynthesis, to escape into the atmosphere and permit the diffusion of carbon dioxide into the plant. These openings also allow a significant loss of water each day through evaporation.

Since exposure to sunlight is necessary for photosynthesis, competition between plants has placed a selective advantage on height, resulting in a trend toward erect posture in land plants, with an accompanying requirement for some means of *support.* Two general types of support are observed in land plants, *turgor* and *tissue.* Turgor is a condition in which cells become swollen and rigid due to the uptake of water. A mass of such cells in the main axis of a plant will produce rigidity and permit the plant to stand erect. Loss of turgor causes wilting. *Tissue* support is provided by the secondary thickening of cell walls with lignin and other materials. The extreme of this condition is seen in the woody plants, where the wood of the trunk and branches consists entirely of xylem which has been largely converted into supportive tissue (see Figures 18.10 and 10.4). Since the conversion of the xylem into woody tissue provides an extremely rigid support for plants, it is no surprise that the largest land plants are woody, while the smaller land plants depend primarily on turgor for support.

The extension of plants into the air has carried with it specialization of the parts of the plant. *Leaves* are specialized as photosynthetic organs and are the regions where gas exchange takes place. The *stem* provides support and houses the main conductive elements of the plant. *Roots* not only anchor the plant to a substrate but also ab-

FIGURE 18.10 Cross section through a fairly young woody stem, showing internal tissues. (*Courtesy J. Limbach, Ripon Microslides.*)

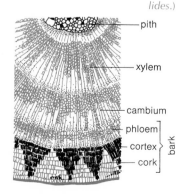

pith

xylem

cambium

phloem

cortex

cork

bark

sorb water and minerals from the soil. *Cones* and *flowers* carry out the reproductive functions of the plant. This degree of specialization, in which the parts of the plant which carry out diverse tasks are located some distance from each other, emphasizes the need for system of *transport* within the plant, supplied by the conductive elements of *xylem* and *phloem.*

A series of adaptations permitting the invasion of land has also occurred in the animal kingdom. The diversity of species among the advanced animals is exceedingly more complex than in the other three kingdoms, for there are over a million different kinds of animals. We shall examine the evolution of diversity among animals in the following chapters.

THE KINGDOM ANIMALIA

1 What would be the problems to be solved by descendants of green algae as they moved farther and farther onto land?
2 Describe the alternation of generations in land plants.
3 Describe briefly the extent to which bryophytes have "solved" the problems of invading the land.
4 How are vascular plants different from bryophytes?
5 How are ferns different from seed plants?
6 Describe briefly the extent to which ferns have "solved" the problems of invading the land.
7 Describe the life cycle of a seed plant.
8 How have seed plants successfully invaded the land?

REVIEW QUESTIONS

Billings, W. D.: *Plants and the Ecosystem,* Wadsworth Publishing Company, Inc., Belmont, Calif., 1964. The role of plants in ecosystems.

Bold, H. C.: *The Plant Kingdom,* 2d ed., Prentice-Hall, Inc., Englewood Cliffs, N.J., 1964. Further information on plants, bacteria, fungi, and algae.

Delevoryas, T.: *Plant Diversification,* The Macmillan Company, New York, 1966. How plants evolved and the adaptations which resulted.

Devlin, R. M.: *Plant Physiology,* Reinhold Publishing Corporation, New York, 1966. An excellent text.

Doyle, W. T.: *Nonvascular Plants: Form and Function,* Wadsworth Publishing Company, Inc., Belmont, Calif., 1964. The last chapter discusses bryophytes.

Salisbury, F. B., and R. V. Parke: *Vascular Plants: Form and Function,* Wadsworth Publishing Company, Inc., Belmont, Calif., 1964. The anatomy and physiology of ferns and seed plants.

Steward, F. C.: *Plants at Work,* Addison-Wesley Publishing Company, Inc., Reading, Mass., 1964. Surveys the major concepts of plant physiology.

SUGGESTIONS FOR
FURTHER READING
* Available in paperback.

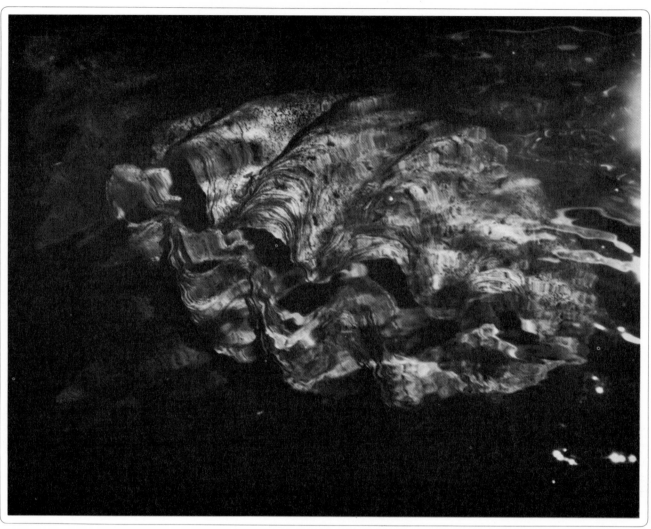

Giant clam. (*Russ Kinne, Photo Researchers, Inc.*)

Chapter 19

Patterns of Diversity in Animals without Backbones

I believe a leaf of grass is no less than the journey-work of the stars,
And the pismire is equally perfect, and a grain of sand, and the egg of the wren,
And the tree-toad is a chef-d'oeuvre for the highest,
And the running blackberry would adorn the parlors of heaven,
And the narrowest hinge in my hand puts to scorn all machinery,
And the cow crunching with depress'd head surpasses any statue,
And a mouse is miracle enough to stagger sextillions of infidels.

Whitman

All members of the kingdom Animalia are multicellular and have characteristics which are clearly "animal," a word stemming from the Latin word *animus,* meaning "vital." Animals differ from their protistan relatives in having tissues, organs, and usually organ systems. Their cells differ from those of plants in the absence of chloroplasts and cell walls.

Unlike the higher land plants, which lack centrioles, the cells of all known animals have them.

The reproductive organs of animals are multicellular, and the stages of embryonic development in animals form a distinct succession, often with forms called larvae. Probably the most noticeable characteristics of animals are their

ability to move by locomotion and their inability to manufacture their own food. Animals are typically involved in an almost constant search for food, in which they are attached to a surface and bring the food to them or are freely moving and pursue it. From these two very different modes of nutrition have evolved two basic architectural plans among animals.

THE GENERAL BODY
PLAN OF ANIMALS

Animals which do not move must meet their food and their predators from all directions. The best body plan places the mouth in a central location and arranges the organs of defense and feeding in a circle around the mouth and the body. This is called *radial symmetry*. If a creature has perfect radial symmetry, it means that no matter how one chooses a diameter to cut it on, the two halves, like those of a pie, will be identical. An example is provided by sea anemones, which consist essentially of a vertical cylinder with a mouth located centrally at the top and tentacles arranged around the rim.

Most animals, however, move actively in pursuit of food. From the appearance of such animals it seems evident that an *elongated, bilaterally symmetrical shape* is best suited for this way of life. In bilateral symmetry there is only one way to cut the animal in two along the longitudinal axis to yield almost identical left and right sides. Only a bilaterally symmetrical animal has a right and a left side. Apparently, equal right and left sides provide the mechanical balance necessary for locomotion. The elongated shape of actively moving animals probably decreases the resistance of the air or water through which the animals walk, swim, fly, or slither.

Active pursuit of food requires that the front end of the animal meet the environment before the rear end (see Figure 19.1). Typically, the front end contains the mouth, sense organs, and brain and the rear end provides an exit for excretory and reproductive products, where they will not interfere with the forward progress of the animal. Actively moving animals have a *head*, a specialized structure which acts as the primary sensor and coordinator of the senses and nervous system as well as the intake for the digestive system.

FIGURE 19.1 The basic structure of a moving hypothetical animal, showing the position and function of various body parts and organs typical of elongated worm-shaped types. (*Adapted from Paul B. Weisz, Elements of Biology, 3rd ed. Copyright McGraw-Hill Book Company, 1969. Used by permission.*)

Hard-and-fast rules cannot be drawn, however, for within several animal groups the type of symmetry found is not clearly related to a motile or nonmotile way of life. Mussels and oysters, although bilaterally symmetrical, spend their adult lives attached to rocks or pilings. Starfish, which have evolved from nonmotile radially symmetrical forms, are motile as adults but still retain their radial symmetry. It is interesting to note that both oysters and starfish have bilaterally symmetrical actively

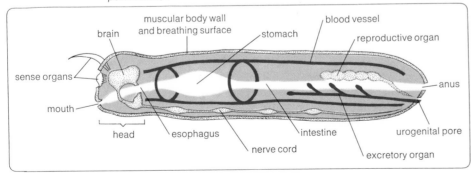

swimming larvae. Squid, furthermore, though highly motile, have excretory and gonadal exits at the forward end of the body. In the animal world variety is so great that there are exceptions to almost any generalization one cares to attempt.

Support of the architecture of animals is provided by a *skeletal system*. Although small animals, primarily microscopic forms, exist without organized skeletal elements, all large animals have a supportive system inside or outside. In some animals, such as the earthworm, structural support is provided by the pressure of fluids inside spaces in the body. An external skeleton limits the size of an animal, which must grow and breathe within it, but the existence of ¾ million kinds of insects (some fossil insects are extremely large, too) demonstrates that the limitation of an exoskeleton is not very restrictive in evolutionary competition.

Movement is accomplished by the contraction of muscles attached to skeletal elements or other muscles. Because of the specialization of animals for rapid movement, their metabolic demands are far greater than those of a plant. To meet these demands, specialization and division of labor are much greater in animals than in plants. Most animals have organ systems which are specialized for support, locomotion, coordination, breathing, digestion, circulation, excretion, protective covering, and reproduction. Usually these organ systems form from embryonic structures which resemble a *tube within a tube within a tube*. Review of Chapter 10 will recall the three embryonic germ layers, ectoderm, mesoderm, and endoderm. In vertebrates, *ectoderm* gives rise to the protective covering and nervous system of the outer tube, *mesoderm* produces the muscles, bones, circulatory system, reproductive system, many of the glandular systems, and the excretory system of an inner tube, while *endoderm* gives rise to the respiratory and digestive systems associated with the innermost tube (see Figure 19.2).

We concerned ourselves in Chapter 10 only with the embryos of vertebrates, and you will recall that the mesoderm in vertebrate embryos comes from derivatives of the original endoderm. The mesoderm forms a hollow called a *coelom*, or body cavity. This space allows independent movement of the muscles of the body wall and the muscles of the intestines and other internal organs. Without it, movement of the abdominal muscles would move the internal organs, and movement of the intestines would cause the abdomen to move. The coelom allows vital internal organs to function independently of the body wall and its muscles of locomotion and support. Not all animals have a coelom, and among those which do a variety of ways of forming it are known. Animals at a very low level of evolution, for example, roundworms, lack coeloms, and others even lack mesoderm. The patterns of mesoderm and coelom formation are associated with specific lines of evolution and will be discussed as the various groups are considered. There are about twenty to thirty phyla of animals, but we shall consider only nine, the remaining ones being relatively inconspicuous.

We shall begin the study of animals by directing our attention and imagination to the ocean, where almost all animal phyla arose. The sea is the cradle of life where the

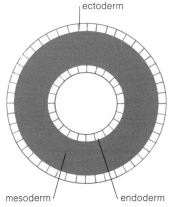

FIGURE 19.2 The three germ layers of an animal embryo. (*Adapted from Paul B. Weisz, Elements of Biology, 3rd ed. Copyright McGraw-Hill Book Company, 1969. Used by permission.*)

first forms of life originated and the major lines of evolutionary divergence took place. Insects and many vertebrates live on land, but most other animals are found only in the ocean. We begin with the simplest of animals and proceed to the most complex, postponing a discussion of the vertebrates until the next chapter. Thus in this chapter we are concerned with the invertebrates, animals without backbones.

INVERTEBRATES WITHOUT COELOMS
SPONGES

Peering at the lower half of rocks on the beach exposed at low tide, you can often see patches, sheets, and lumps of yellow, white, red, and purple. At first glance, you might be misled, just as people in the past have been, into regarding this strange material as a form of plant life or some kind of decaying matter. Sponges were not recognized as living animals until 1825. In 1636, the naturalist Gerard wrote: "there is found growing upon the rocks neer unto the sea, a certaine matter wrought together, of the forme [foam] or froth of the sea, which we called spunges . . . whereof to write at large woulde greatly increase our volume, and little profite the Reader."

Sponges constitute the phylum Porifera, animals which begin their lives as ciliated free-swimming larvae but finish their lives firmly attached to surfaces. Sponge larvae are made up of two layers, ectoderm and endoderm, but the layers are not maintained in any recognizable form in the adult. Instead, the body wall of a sponge has several kinds of cells in the outside, middle, and inside. The middle layer of cells secrete minute particles called *spicules,* which serve not only in protection but also in support. Spicules support the sponge in a way similar to a skeleton and are made of calcium salts or silicates. In some forms spongin, an organic material similar to that contained in horns of mammals, is produced instead of the spicules or in addition to them. On the basis of their skeleton sponges are classified into three groups: calcareous, or chalky, sponges; silaceous, or glassy, sponges; and spongin, or horny, sponges. The sponge in your bathroom is either an artificial plastic sponge or the skeletal remains of a horny sponge taken from the Mediterranean or Caribbean (Figure 19.3).

FIGURE 19.3 Sponges: (a) skeleton of bathroom sponge; (b) and (c) living sponges. ((a) and (b) *Carolina Biological Supply Co.;* (c)*Courtesy of H. W. Kitchen from The National Audubon Society.*)

A

B

C

If you look closely at submerged sponges, you can see a current of water issuing forth from pores along its surfaces. It is because of these pores that sponges are given the name *Porifera,* meaning ''pore bearers.'' As you watch the water coming from the pores, you may wonder how this pumping takes place. Microscopic examination of the inner lining of the sponges reveals the pumping mechanism. Sponges are lined with *collar cells,* a type found only in sponges and in a small group of protozoa, a possible clue to the evolutionary origins of the sponges. Each collar cell bears a flagellum, and the combined effect of their beating causes a current of water to move into the sponge through minute *entry pores* and out through large *exit pores.* The collar cells engulf bacteria and other microscopic foods as the water passes by. After digestion in the collar cells, the nutrients are shared with the surrounding cells (see Figure 19.4).

Sponges have no front or back and lack the specialization of cells into tissues associated with more complex animals. There are no gut cells or nerve and muscle cells. Sperm and eggs are formed, but the process is not well understood. In fact, it is safe to say that the details of most of the processes of metabolism, homeostasis, and reproduction in sponges are still unknown. The wide distribution of sponges in shallow seas and, to a lesser degree, in deep seas and fresh water, indicates that their way of life is quite successful. They have no mouth and no digestive cavity; the entire body structure is built around a unique system of water canals. Apparently the only advances that sponges have made during their many millions of years of evolution have been in the degree of complexity of the branching of the water canals inside the sponge bodies. More advanced sponges have highly branched systems of water canals. In all, about 3,000 species of sponges are living today.

Sponges are very primitive animals believed to have branched off from protozoan

FIGURE 19.4 The organization of a simple sponge (diagrammatic): (*left*) cross-sectional view showing the direction of flow of water; (*right*) detail of a portion of the body wall. (*Adapted from Paul B. Weisz, Elements of Biology, 3rd ed. Copyright McGraw-Hill Book Company, 1969. Used by permission.*)

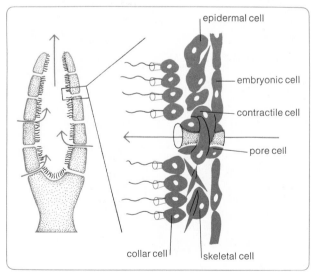

epidermal cell

embryonic cell

contractile cell

pore cell

collar cell

skeletal cell

ancestors. Evolutionarily they constitute a blind alley which has not given rise to any other phyla of animals.

The phylum Coelenterata (also known as the phylum Cnidaria) includes such animals as jellyfish, sea anemones, and coral. The name of the group is based upon the body plan found universally in all members of the group, a cup-shaped body which encloses a hollow (coel-) gut (-enteron). The hollow gut has a single opening, functioning as both mouth and anus. The gut cavity also has two functions: It not only holds the food while it is being digested but also allows circulation of digested food and other substances back and forth within the body. Digestion begins in the gut cavity and is completed in the cells lining the cavity. Undigestible materials are thrown back out of the single opening.

The body plan of coelenterates resembles a bowl with a central mouth surrounded by tentacles on the bowl rim (see Figure 19.5). Arranged along the tentacles are *stinging cells,* a type of cell found only in this phylum and containing poisonous barbs capable of paralyzing or immobilizing predator or prey. The body of the bowl consists of an outer ectoderm containing sensory cells and an inner endoderm containing ameboid cells which engulf food in the gut. There is no mesoderm, but there are individual contractile cells and a material between the ectoderm and endoderm, called *mesogloea,* which has a simple nerve net embedded in it. Thanks to

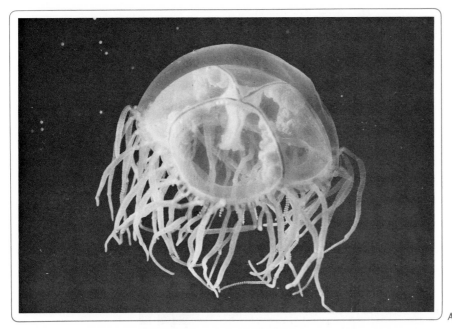

A

FIGURE 19.5 Two coelenterates: (a) *Gonionemus and* (b) *Aurelia flavicula on next page. (Carolina Biological Supply Co.)*

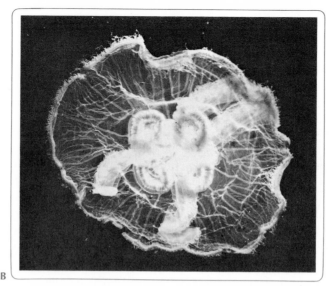

FIGURE 19.5 B

these nerves, the entire organism can perform certain simple responses, such as contraction.

An adult coelenterate is attached to a surface or freely floating, depending upon the species. If it floats, as the jellyfish do, it does so with its mouth down and looks like a bell (Figure 19.5 and Plate 16), but if it is attached, as the sea anemones are, it sits with its mouth up and resembles a bowl (see Figure 19.6). These two coelenterate body plans are termed the *medusa* and the *polyp* (see Figure 19.7 and Plate 17).

FIGURE 19.6 (a) Sea anemone and (b) coral with polyps. (*Carolina Biological Supply Co.*)

A

B

FIGURE 19.7 Sea urchin with medusa body plan. (*Courtesy of Robert Hermes from The National Audubon Society.*)

FIGURE 19.8 Schematic drawing of *Obelia:* (*Top*) A colony of polyps. Note feeding polyps with tentacles and club-shaped reproductive polyps, which produce medusae. (*Bottom*) A medusa. The dark region in the center is the ventral mouth. Note the four sex organs. (*Adapted from Carolina Biological Supply Co.*)

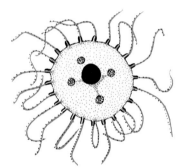

Either way, the tentacles reach out in all directions from the radially symmetrical body in search of food. A hapless organism that comes into contact with the tentacles is stung by the poison cells and brought through the mouth and into the gut for digestion (see Figure 19.8).

Sea anemones and corals have the bowl, or polyp, body plan and differ in that corals are smaller and can secrete calcium salts around their bases. The accumulation of this material, plus the secretions of the coralline red algae, causes the slow buildup of coral reefs in the warm waters of the world.

Jellyfish have the bell, or medusa, body plan, which allows them to swim through the water. To swim, a jellyfish takes up water and then contracts to force the water out in a form of jet propulsion which pushes the organism up higher in the water. The jellyfish then drifts slowly back down through the water with tentacles waving in search of prey. Such jellyfish as the Portuguese man-of-war and the lion's mane can kill men with their stinging cells.

Many coelenterates *alternate generations* in their life cycle. One generation is the free-swimming medusa stage, which is sexual and produces gametes; after fertilization, the gametes give rise to an attached polyp stage. The polyps then form buds through asexual means which break away and swim off in the water as tiny bell-like medusae which reproduce sexually, and the cycle continues. Other coelenterates suppress the polyp stage and exist primarily as medusae (the true jellyfishes) or they suppress the medusa stage and live primarily as polyps (the sea anemones and corals) (see Figure 19.9). Both the medusa and polyp forms in the alternation of generations in coelenterates are *diploid,* in contrast to plants, where the generations alternate between diploidy and haploidy.

Coelenterates are primarily ocean-dwelling, there being only fourteen known species in the fresh water of the United States. Three of the species are freshwater jellyfishes, one is a colonial polyp, one is a rare primitive polyp, and eleven are species of the genus *Hydra.* Hydras are found in clean unpolluted waters where their cylinder-shaped bodies are attached by basal disks to submerged solids. In general, coelenterates are not important in man's economy except as an occasional pest. For example, one large species of *Hydra* may kill small fish in hatcheries, and jellyfish sometimes clog the nets of fishermen.

FLATWORMS

Many of the various phyla are commonly called "worms," a tribute to the spectacularly successful wormlike structure and mode of life. It is accepted by most biologists that a type of flatworm was ancestral to the rest of the animal types discussed in the following pages. This primitive worm is best represented today by the modern flatworms, the phylum *Platyhelminthes.*

All flatworms have bilateral symmetry, have a mesoderm which develops out of endodermal cells, and lack a coelom (see Figure 19.10) The flatworms have evolved

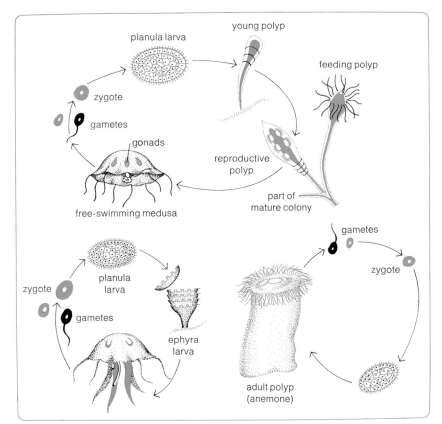

FIGURE 19.9 The life cycles of coelenterates. Polyp and medusa generations alternate in Hydrozoa like *Obelia*; polyp phases are suppressed in Scyphozoa like *Aurelia* and other jellyfish, and medusa phases are suppressed in Anthozoa like sea anemones. (*Adapted from Paul B. Weisz, Elements of Biology, 3rd ed. Copyright McGraw-Hill Book Company, 1969. Used by permission.*)

FIGURE 19.10 Striped flatworm. (*Courtesy of Bucky Reeves from The National Audubon Society.*)

reproductive and excretory *organs,* in contrast to the *tissue* grade of organization found in the coelenterates.

Flatworms include the parasitic *flukes* and *tapeworms* found in the body spaces of animals and free-living forms which can usually be found wherever there is water and a solid surface upon which they can move. Locomotion is a gliding motion caused by movement of cilia in mucus secreted on the lower surface or by waves of muscular contraction moving from front to rear.

The most familiar of the freshwater flatworms are the *planarians,* small worms often confused with leeches as they glide over surfaces of leaves, rocks, or any other submerged object in the search for food. Planarians detect the presence of food by sense receptors in their triangular head. Food is taken into the gut cavity by means of a long, highly muscular tube which is protruded from the mouth. Instead of being on the head, the mouth is on the ventral side midway between the front and rear ends. Soft food is sucked up the tube as in a vacuum cleaner and is digested by cells lining the gut. Undigestible food is expelled through the mouth, which doubles as the anus, a trait shared with the coelenterates. Gas exchange takes place directly through the body wall. *Excretion* takes place by excess water, carrying dissolved waste materials, diffusing into systems of tubules which drain to the exterior. The movement of water out of the tubules is hastened by the beating of cilia in cells at the blind end of the tubules. Since the movement of the cilia in the cells looks like flickering flames, the cells are called *flame cells.* A diagram of the *nervous system* is shaped like a ladder (see Figure 19.11), and the brain consists of two tiny lobes at the front end lying beneath the eyespots. Each eyespot is shaped like a kidney bean and contains light-sensitive cells. The planarian is capable of a sort of primitive learning, but the site of the storage of memory is not just the brain. Planaria can be cut up in pieces which regenerate the missing parts; when experiments of this kind are successful, the regenerated planaria display the memory of the original planarian, even though they may have developed from the half which lacked a brain. Active research is now going on to discover the mechanism of this type of memory.

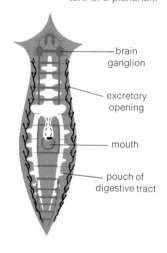

FIGURE 19.11 The internal structure of a planarian.

brain ganglion

excretory opening

mouth

pouch of digestive tract

ROUNDWORMS

Roundworms (see Figure 19.12) are placed in the phylum *Nematoda,* animals in which the mesoderm forms in part from scattered cells arising from the ectoderm but mainly from endoderm. Spaces formed between the patches of mesoderm have the same function as a true coelum, but since the coelomic cavity in nematodes is not completely bounded by mesoderm, these animals are called *pseudocoelomate.* The pseudocoelom functions very like a true coelom, allowing independent movement of the body wall and internal organs. Muscles of locomotion in the body wall are arranged only as longitudinal fibers, and their contraction causes a whipping motion characteristic of the entire phylum. Roundworms have complete digestive systems with a mouth and anus.

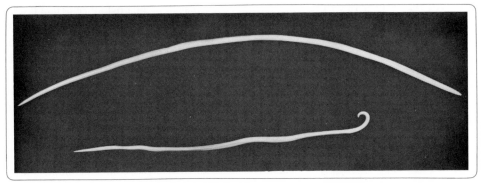

FIGURE 19.12 Roundworms.
(*Carolina Biological Supply Co.*)

Of all the higher animals, only insects have ranges of tolerance equal to that manifested in the roundworms. Often the same species of roundworm has worldwide distribution in habitats varying from arctic to tropical conditions and from deserts to ocean depths. Their eggs are highly resistant, and larvae and adults of some species can be dried out and shriveled and still move actively when returned to water.

Roundworms include free-living forms at the bottom of the ocean and in fresh waters as well as in the soil, where they are important agents in mixing and breaking up the soil. Many forms are parasitic in plants and animals, including those species which cause hookworm, pork roundworm, pinworm, elephantiasis, Guinea worm, and other parasitic diseases of man. Libbie Hyman, a renowned authority on invertebrates, estimates that there are probably 500,000 species of nematodes, but only 10,000 species have been discovered thus far. Except for insects, there are more individual roundworms and species of roundworms than any other animal. In a teaspoonful of mud from the Italian coast, for example, 1,074 roundworms were found, and they were from thirty-six different species. In one rotten apple 90,000 individual roundworms were found. Good farmland, whether in the United States, Austria, or China, contains about 9 billion roundworms per acre.

An important line of evolution diverged from the ancient flatworms, an evolutionary line which gave rise to annelids first, then mollusks and anthropods. In all three of these major phyla, definitive mesoderm of the adult organisms is formed from embryonic endoderm, and from it is constructed a body cavity, the true coelom.

THE ANNELID LINE
OF EVOLUTION

Worms such as earthworms, clamworms, and leeches have bodies made up of a series of compartments called *segments,* which appear externally as rings. The seg-

SEGMENTED WORMS

FIGURE 19.13 Diagram of
various annelids.

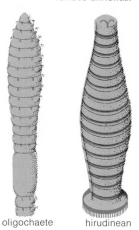

oligochaete   hirudinean

mented worms are placed in the phylum *Annelida* (from *annulus,* the Latin for ring). Each segment is separated from neighboring segments by a membranous partition. Except for the segments at the front end and some reproductive organs, all other segments contain duplicate sets of the same structures and look very much alike. Annelids have a complete digestive tract with a mouth in the first segment and an anus in the last. The annelid nervous system, in contrast to the ladderlike form in flatworms, consists of a single cord located ventrally, under the digestive system. Dissection shows the ventral nerve cord to be made up of two lateral cords which have fused together side by side along the length of the animal. The nerve cord shows swellings in each segment which are concentrations of neurons called *ganglia;* the ganglion in the head, called the *brain,* is very much like the ganglia to be found in each segment and has only limited dominance over the rest of the nervous system. The annelids also have an extensive circulatory system, consisting of a dorsal blood vessel bringing blood forward and a ventral blood vessel taking it to the rear, both vessels providing their force through muscular contractions. The dorsal and ventral blood vessels are connected by five pulsating pairs of tubes, called *hearts,* in the front end and by many small vessels and capillaries elsewhere. Each segment contains a pair of primitive, tubelike excretory organs, called *nephridia,* which collect wastes from the coelom and release them at the exterior surface.

Annelids are of three types, polychaetes, oligochaetes, and leeches (see Figure 19.13 and 19.14). *Polychaetes,* such as sandworms and clamworms, have a pair of fleshy lobes called *parapodia* extending to the side from each segment and fleshy tentacles

FIGURE 19.14 Annelids: (*a*) polychaetes, (*b*) oligochaetes (common earthworm shown here), and (*c*) leech. (*Carolina Biological Supply Co.*)

A

B

C

around the mouth. Many bristles extend from the parapodia and provide the basis for the name of the group (poly-, many and chaeta-, bristles). Parapodia furnish large breathing surfaces and in free-swimming worms also serve as paddles. If the worm lives in a tube, the parapodia cause water to flow through the tube.

Oligochaetes, such as the familiar earthworm, lack eyes, head appendages, and parapodia, but they do have a few bristles on each segment and this provides the basis of the name of the group (oligo-, few and chaeta-, bristle).

Leeches lack bristles and attach themselves during locomotion by suckers at the front and rear ends. They move themselves along like an inchworm, or they swim through the water with an undulating eel-like body movement. Leeches are commonly called bloodsuckers, but only a minority suck the blood of vertebrates; the rest are scavengers and eat organic debris or are predators on small snails, crustaceans, and worms. Leeches are often brightly colored, with mottlings, spots, and stripes. Mature leeches vary in length from minute species to the giant *Haemopis,* the horseleech, which may extend to a length of 18 inches while swimming. *Haemopis* is found in lakes and watering troughs, where it may attack horses, cows, and occasionally people. The medicinal leech, *Hirudo medicinalis,* supported a large industry in the eighteenth and nineteenth centuries when it was used to remove blood from boils, bruises, and infected teeth. Clotting of the host's blood is prevented by a protein which the leech secretes into the wound. Many lakes in the northern United States are infested with bloodsucking leeches, and splashing the water attracts them by the thousands.

ARTHROPODS

Such organisms as insects, crayfish, crabs, spiders, centipedes, and millipedes belong to the phylum *Arthropoda.* All have *jointed appendages* (the meaning of the phylum name), a jointed *external skeleton* made of chitin, *segmentation,* an *open circulatory system* with blood-filled body cavities, a pulsating, open-ended *dorsal blood vessel,* which picks up blood at the rear end and carries it to the front, and a *complete absence of cilia.* This list of attributes, when functioning as a package, has permitted this to become the most successful of all phyla, plant or animal, ever to have lived. Over three-fourths of all species of animals are arthropods, and their distribution extends from the crabs of the ocean depths to insects, the flying arthropods. Their distribution as a group seems to be limited only by the requirement that food be present and temperatures be above freezing long enough to permit breeding.

Divergent evolution within the arthropods gave rise to three major groups, the trilobites, the chelicerates, and the mandibulates. The primary differences between arthropods lie in the way the segments and their appendages are specialized.

Trilobites, known today only as fossils, had a body plan consisting of three parts; each part was segmented, and each segment had appendages which were not specialized. Even though trilobites were plentiful in the primitive oceans, they became extinct millions of years ago (see Figure 19.15).

FIGURE 19.15 Trilobite fossil, an extinct arthropod.

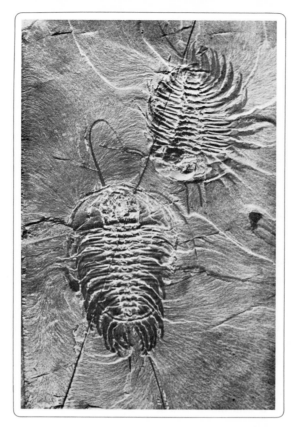

Chelicerates lack antennae but bear pincers, or chelicerae, near their mouths. Instead of jaws, the pincers break up the food before it enters the mouth. The best known chelicerates are the *arachnids,* the spiders (Figure 19.16), scorpions (Figure 19.17), ticks, and mites, but this subphylum also includes sea spiders and horseshoe crabs (Figure 19.18). Many of the arachnids have silk glands with which they produce spider webs and are economically important because they destroy insects. Mites include the chiggers, which irritate the skin, and other forms which destroy crops.

Mandibulates include most of the arthropods and are characterized most dramatically by the specialization of segments and appendages on the head. Instead of pincers on each side of the mouth, mandibulates have *mandibles,* appendages modified so that they rasp together in front of the mouth, much as the knuckles of your fists can be rasped together. The two segments behind the mouth bear flattened mouthpart appendages, known as *maxillae,* which help chewing. Two segments forward of the mouth is located a pair of sensory *antennae.* The nature of the segment in front of the mouth is significant in differentiating between the two main lines of mandibulates. All Crustacea, a predominately water-dwelling form, have a pair of second antennae on this segment, but the terrestrial forms, the insects, millipedes, and centipedes, lack them.

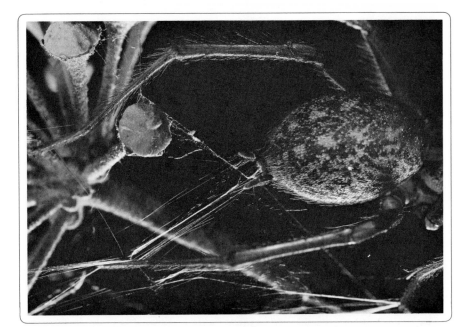

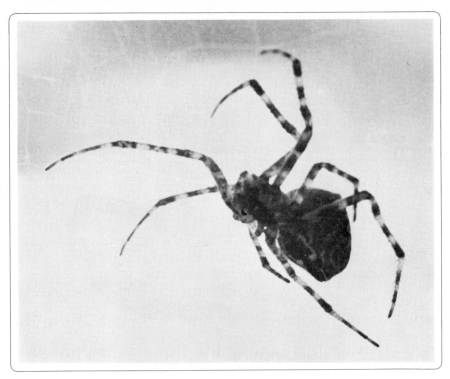

FIGURE 19.16 Phylum Arthropoda, class Arachnida, spiders. *(Courtesy of Stephen Dalton, Jeanne White, and George Porter, from The National Audubon Society.)*

FIGURE 19.17 Scorpion. (Carolina Biological Supply Co.)

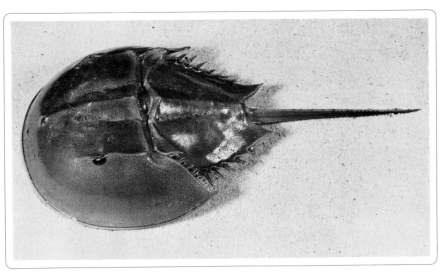

FIGURE 19.18 Horseshoe crab.
(*Carolina Biological Supply Co.*)

Crustacea are almost as influential in the sea and fresh water as insects are on land. Some crustaceans, such as crabs and lobsters (Figure 19.19), get quite large, but others function as the herbivores of the surface waters of the ocean and fresh water and are microscopic. As in all arthropods, the entire body of a crustacean is covered with matter called chitin, but in crustaceans this is impregnated and hardened with calcium carbonate. The arthropod exoskeleton serves not only as a protective armor but also provides sites of attachment for muscles. Crustaceans must breathe through the exoskeleton, and this is accomplished with gills. In crabs, lobsters, and shrimp the gills are attached to the upper parts of the walking legs. Barnacles are crustaceans which swim about as larvae but soon settle down on solid surfaces, where they attach by their backs and use their legs to filter food out of the water. Barnacles secrete a calcium carbonate turret about them and also respire through their legs. Other than temporary land dwellers such as land crabs, pill bugs and sow bugs are the only crustaceans to invade the land, but they must limit their activities to habitats which remain moist, for the breathing surfaces on their lower rear ends must remain constantly damp. There are about 30,000 species of crustaceans.

INVASION OF THE LAND BY INVERTEBRATES

The land has presented a formidable problem for invertebrates to solve. Certain invertebrate groups have found homes in humid places such as the soil. Roundworms, earthworms, and protozoa flourish in damp soil. Snails, a few leeches, and crustaceans such as pill bugs have invaded terrestrial habitats which remain damp and humid. Invertebrate parasites are carried around inside land animals, but of course they are not really facing the hazards of a terrestrial habitat.

FIGURE 19.19 (a) Crab and (b) crayfish. (*Carolina Biological Supply* Co.)

A

B

Of all the invertebrates, only the arthropod groups, *insects, millipedes, centipedes, spiders,* and *mites,* can be described as having been truly successful land animals, for they are found in arid as well as humid habitats.

Millipedes and *centipedes* are usually called the *myriapods* because of their myriad feet. Despite their common names, however, millipedes do not have a thousand legs, and centipedes do not have a hundred legs. Instead, centipedes have one pair of legs per segment, millipedes have two pairs of legs per segment, and the maximum number of legs is always less than 200 (see Figure 19.20). Myriapods have a head and a trunk and have appendages on nearly every segment. They breathe through channels opening into their bodies called *trachaea*. Most millipedes are herbivorous. The centipedes are all carnivores with poison fangs and sharp mandibles. Millipedes prefer to munch on vegetation, and many of them can defend themselves with noxious secretions which in some cases can be ejected for several feet. This repugnant material varies with the species but frequently contains cyanide gas,

MILLIPEDES AND CENTIPEDES

A

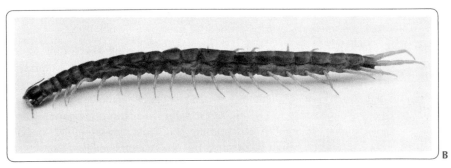

B

FIGURE 19.20 (a) Millipede and (b) centipede. (*Carolina Biological Supply Co.*)

iodine, quinine, and traces of chlorine.   This fluid is very irritating, even to man, and may cause blindness in chickens and other animals which attack millipedes with a meal in mind.   Many millipedes and centipedes are brightly colored as warnings to possible predators that they have poison fangs or gas warfare.   Despite their prowess, however, there are only a few hundred species of myriapods.

INSECTS
The success story of the invertebrate invasion of land is really the story of the insects. In terms of numbers of species and variety of habitats insects are the most successful group of organisms to have evolved.   Over 800,000 species of insects have already been identified, and the number grows larger every day.   Some biologists talk of assigning them numbers rather than names.   No other type of organism offers man as much competition for his food, clothing, and shelter.   Man's ecological niche is extremely broad, but in almost every part of man's spectrum of physical needs some type of insect is offering competition, not on a direct physical basis but through an attack on man's possessions and food.   Man has waged a continual war upon the insects and their fantastic adaptations for thousands of years, but so far has never won, except at costs unacceptable to himself.

A percentage of the insect population has always been resistant to every weapon used by man.   The resistant group then takes over and becomes the dominant group, so that a new population of insects—now all resistant—appears.   Then man devises further chemical weapons, but each time with only temporary results.   This is the Age of Mammals but it is also the Age of Insects, for these organisms have been the dominant land animals for at least the past one-third billion years!

Insects have been found in the deepest caves, and at the other extreme termites have been collected from airplanes flying at 19,000 feet.   The Arctic and the Antarctic regions contain insects which are limited in their dispersal only by the distribution of the plants and animals upon which they feed.   Some insects have been subjected to temperatures as low as −30°F and recovered; others live in hot springs with a temperature of 120°F.   Larvae of some insects live in brine that is almost a saturated solution of pure salt, while the petroleum flies inhabit pools of oil around oil wells in southern California.   Other insects can endure high concentrations of carbon dioxide for hours or can get along without an external source of water for days by retaining water released internally as a by-product of their own metabolism.

The success of insects is not due to large size, for their average size is quite small. Insects vary, however, from some forms which are smaller than large protozoa to other forms which are larger than the smallest mammals, the shrews.   Some beetles are so small they can crawl through the eye of a needle, but at the other extreme the Atlas moth of India measures 12 inches from wingtip to wingtip.   Some moths were shot by early explorers in South America in the belief that they were birds or bats. Modern insects, however, would be dwarfed by some which lived in the past.   For example, an ancestor of the dragonflies had a wingspan of 30 inches.   Most insects, however, are relatively small and compete with *numbers* and *not size* as their weapon. It is the combined effect of an insect *population* which is overwhelming.

The remarkable success of insects is due primarily to six features: flight, adaptability with respect to food and habitats, exoskeleton, small size, metamorphosis, and a specialized system of reproduction.

1   The *ability to fly* occurs in most orders of insects other than primitive forms and those in which wings have been secondarily lost and allows insects to travel over wide distances in search of food, water, and safety.

2   A wide *range of adaptations* permits insects to survive, feed, and reproduce in an astonishing variety of habitats. Insects feed on grain, paintbrushes, carpets, corks, dead museum specimens, tobacco, opium, pepper, blood, every kind of higher plant, and an almost endless list of other kinds of foods.

3   The *exoskeleton* of insects forms as a hardening of the outer skin and is made of chitin. This tough, outer armor protects the animal as a shield and also serves as a means of support for such structures as spines, wings, stingers, and jaws.

4   The *small size* of insects means that the niche they occupy may also be quite small, each individual requiring only a speck of food, a droplet of water, and a crevice for shelter. Usually, the insect finds food and shelter together in a tiny, unnoticed spot.

5   The pattern of development known as *metamorphosis,* in which the body plan changes in a sequence of egg, larva, pupa, and adult, allows each stage to specialize with adaptations for different habitats. The larva usually has a different ecological niche than the adult and does not compete with it.

6   The *system of reproduction* in insects is further specialized in that some females can store sperm for as long as they live following mating. This enhances fertilization of eggs and reduces the required frequency of matings, thereby contributing significantly to the overwhelming reproductive potential of the insects.

These six features underlie the fantastic success enjoyed by the insects ever since they diverged from an arthropod ancestor 300 to 400 million years ago. The insects are placed in the arthropod class *Insecta,* distinguished by three divisions of the body (head, thorax, and abdomen), three pairs of legs, a single pair of antennae, and usually wings. Fossils from which we could deduce the early history of insects have not yet been discovered. The earliest known insect fossils have wings and appear in a variety of forms, but millions of years of evolution had to have occurred in insects before the stage represented by these fossils. Until such time as earlier fossils are found, the evolutionary origin of insects will have to be inferred. Most biologists believe that insects, millipedes, and centipedes diverged from a common ancestor.

The most primitive insects living today are bristletails and silverfish. They are wingless, and it is not difficult to picture them as having diverged from centipedelike arthropods with many body segments, each with a pair of stubby legs. From this basic plan the generations of insects which followed changed so that legs were retained only on the three segments behind the head. The *thorax* became a locomotion center, and legs with the associated musculature were lost from the more posterior segments. These segments became specialized into an *abdomen* containing reproductive, digestive, and excretory organs, heart, and sometimes a stinger.

Like the myriapods, insects breathe through *tracheal tubes*. The tubes diverge into smaller and smaller branches, and no part of the body is without a direct means of gas exchange. An insect's blood carries only foods and wastes, since oxygen is transported by the tracheal system. This means of breathing seems to work remarkably well in air but cannot work under water. For this reason there are no insects in the ocean and only about 40,000 in fresh water. Most aquatic insects spend only their larval lives in the water and fly about in the air as adults. For example, dragonfly nymphs breathe under water, but upon becoming adults, the dragonflies live in the air. Larvae of aquatic beetles and most flies breathe with tracheal tubes and must rise to the surface to breathe. Thus, mosquito larvae have a type of snorkel tube through which they breathe at the surface of the water. Many other aquatic insect larvae, however, exchange gases directly through their body walls or through specially formed gills. Only two groups, bugs and beetles, have aquatic forms which remain as adults under the water. Since they have tracheal tubes, they must rise to the surface periodically and trap air bubbles under their wings or on other parts of their bodies.

By the time the evolution of vertebrates had reached the Age of Reptiles, some 200 million years ago, all the major features of insects had already evolved; all the orders of insects were present, and dragonflies, grasshoppers, crickets, cockroaches, cicadas, leafhoppers, beetles, and many others abounded. The butterflies, moths, bees, wasps, and the higher flies had not yet evolved, appearing only with the flowering plants which they pollinate. During the last period of the Age of Reptiles, some 130 million years ago, the flowering plants and their insect partners flourished.

MOLLUSKS   The mollusks exhibit a group of adaptations different from those of the annelid-arthropod line but almost as successful in the number and variety of species which exist today. The name of this group, the phylum *Mollusca,* means "soft body." Octopus, squids, and slugs readily convey what is meant by this term. Although snails, clams, oysters, and mussels are not obviously soft-bodied, the shell, which is really external to the body, encloses and protects the soft-bodied mollusk inside. Mollusks are not segmented, but a recent discovery of a fossil form which looks more or less like a snail with segmentation reinforces the arguments of many biologists that the mollusks descended via an annelid ancestry. Until more roundworms are identified, the mollusks remain the second largest phylum, with over 100,000 species. Mollusks range in size from minute snails to the largest invertebrate animal, the giant squid, which may be over 50 feet long.

Despite external differences between chitons, snails, clams, and squids, a basic body plan is shared by all mollusks (see Figure 19.21). Every mollusk has a ventral muscular *foot*, which serves as the primary organ of locomotion; a *visceral mass* located above the foot and containing most of the internal organs; and a *mantle*, tissue which covers the visceral mass and often secretes a calcareous *shell*. Each of the five classes in this phylum demonstrates variations on this basic theme.

Chitons (class Amphineura) are the least specialized of the mollusks. They are abundant in the rocky intertidal zone along the seashore. Gills are in the mantle cavity, which circles the foot. A chiton's back is covered by eight overlapping plates, and below them lies the visceral mass.

Tooth shells (class Scaphopoda) are the least common of the mollusks but are found partly buried in sand or mud bottoms of some bays. The body is greatly elongated dorsally so that the animal has the overall shape of a tube. The shell, which covers the visceral mass, is a tube open at both ends with a foot extending from the hole at the lower end and gills at the upper end.

Snails (class Gastropoda) are similar to chitons but have a distinct head with tentacles and eyes. The shell is usually coiled, and the head and foot can be withdrawn into it. Snails breathe with gills located in the mantle cavity under the rim of the shell. In many land snails, gills have been lost and replaced with a primitive form of lung. Their digestive tract is U-shaped with the anus exiting dorsally, just under the front rim of the shell.

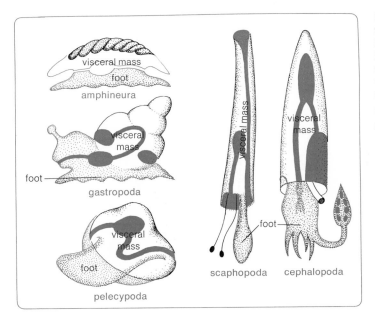

FIGURE 19.21 The body plan of the five classes of mollusks. A basic structure is common to all. Shells are in dark gray; the foot is stippled. (*Adapted from Paul B. Weisz, Elements of Biology, 3rd ed. Copyright McGraw-Hill Book Company, 1969. Used by permission.*)

Clams (class Pelecypoda) have adapted to a life of burrowing in sand or mud by becoming flattened from side to side (see Figure 19.22). Locomotion is accomplished by moving the hatchet-shaped foot forward, swelling up the end of the foot as an anchor, and contracting the foot to pull the body toward the anchor. The mantle secretes two shells, hinged on the dorsal side. The mantle, which lines the shells, forms two openings, the *siphons*, at the posterior end. Beating of cilia covering the inside of the clam makes water move in one siphon and out the other, passing through the gills (organs which hang down into the mantle cavity and serve both for breathing and for filtering microscopic food out of the water). The gills are covered with cilia, which carry trapped food to the mouth forward, between the gills, in the visceral mass. The digestive tract lies in the visceral mass and discharges through the anus into the current of water leaving through the outgoing siphon. There is very little nervous system and no head. Many members of this class, such as oysters, are permanently attached to the bottom. Other members, such as mussels, are attached to rocks with threads secreted by glands in the foot. To move its location, a mussel can extend its foot and exert enough force to break the threads, move to a new location, and secrete new threads.

Squids and octopuses (class Cephalopoda) (see Figure 19.23) are considered the most highly developed of the mollusks and the most intelligent of the invertebrate animals. The octopus lacks a shell, but squids have a horny shell within the mantle, which serves for attachment of muscles and is actually a form of internal skeleton. Other skeletal elements, consisting of cartilage, form a braincase similar to a skull. The foot is specialized into tentacles with suckers. The visceral mass, surrounded by

FIGURE 19.22 The internal structure of a clam. In this model, most of the gill flap is cut away to expose the organs of the visceral mass. Water enters via the incurrent siphon and passes over the gills, where food particles are strained out and conducted to the mouth, hidden under a flap of tissue. Water and elimination products of all kinds leave the clam via the excurrent siphon. The two adductor muscles control the closing of the valve shells. (*Courtesy of The American Museum of Natural History.*)

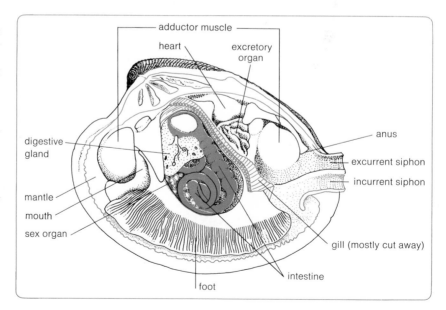

FIGURE 19.23 (a) Young octopus and (b) squid. ((a) *Carolina
Biological Supply Co.*); (b) *Courtesy of Robert C. Hermes from National Audubon Society.*)

A

B

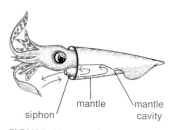

siphon   mantle   mantle
                      cavity

FIGURE 19.24. The jet principle
of locomotion in a squid. Note the
external mantle, the mantle cavity
(with arrows), and the siphon
through which water is squirted
out, propelling the squid in the
opposite direction.

the mantle, makes up the body. At the source of the tentacles is a head with a brain and large eyes similar to those of vertebrates. Horny jaws mark the opening to the digestive tract, which is U-shaped and empties into the mantle cavity. Squid can move through the water by filling their conical mantle with water and then expelling it through a siphon (see Figure 19.24). The direction of movement is determined by the direction in which the siphon is pointed. Typically, they move with the point of the mantle forward and the siphon pointed aft like a squirting water hose. Much of their movement is due, however, to flapping action of flaps on two sides of their mantles.

Mollusks are represented in fresh water by only two classes, the gastropods and the pelecypods, or, as they are more commonly known, the snails and slugs and the clams and mussels (Figure 19.25). Snails are found in almost every conceivable freshwater habitat creeping about on submerged surfaces. Almost all freshwater snails have a coiled shell which results from an asymmetry in early embryonic development (see Figure 19.26). Snails breathe either with gills, which are specialized folds of the mantle in contact with water, or they breathe by an exchange of gases between the mantle and an air-filled cavity or "lung" in the mantle under the shell. Air-breathing aquatic snails are believed to have evolved on land and reentered the water, where they are forced periodically to return to the surface and trap some air under the shell. Most snails are vegetarians and eat algae, but some eat dead animal material. Plant food is cut off and ingested with the sharp jaw and chewed by rubbing the radula, a tonguelike rasp, against the roof of the mouth. As the radula wears away, it is replaced in a manner analogous to the replacement of our fingernails. Most snails are limited in distribution to waters high in calcium car-

FIGURE 19.25 Mussel. (*Carolina Biological Supply Co.*)

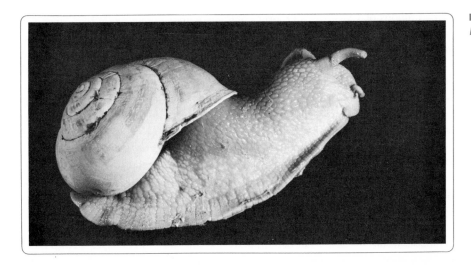

FIGURE 19.26 Snail. (*Carolina Biological Supply Co.*)

bonate since this is what their shells are made of. Oxygen is another vital factor for which snails have a narrow range of tolerance, and snails are not usually found in polluted waters. The only mollusks which have invaded the land are the gastropod snails and slugs which have become modified to be able to breathe air.

None of the clams and mussels are terrestrial, but they are found in nearly all types of freshwater and saltwater habitats, most successfully in large rivers. They usually lie partially or completely submerged in the bottom, where they siphon water through their gills and filter plankton and organic matter from the current. Methods of reproduction differ drastically between the marine and freshwater mussels. Marine mussels have ciliated free-swimming larvae, but American freshwater mussels release *glochidia,* which are really microscopic versions of adults. The glochidia must attach to gills or surfaces of fish to complete their development. They drop to the bottom after release from the mussel, and a fish must brush against them or take them into the mouth by stirring up the bottom while feeding to allow them to continue developing. During the 10 to 30 days of parasitism the glochidia change into juveniles, which break out of their cysts and drop to the bottom, where they take up adult life. Usually, the fish hosts are not harmed by the parasitic glochidia. Mussels are important in the ecology of fresh water as a source of food for many fishes, mammals, turtles, and some amphibians. They serve man as a source of food, buttons, and natural freshwater pearls. Freshwater clams and mussels live in all types of unpolluted water but occur in the greatest numbers in large rivers, especially in the shallows. They do best where there is a stable nonshifting gravel or sand bottom supplied with plenty of oxygen and food. To escape from cold temperatures most clams and mussels move deeper into the bottom with cold weather and enter into a state of dormancy. Pollution and silting of rivers have drastically cut down the numbers of mussels in American waters.

THE ECHINODERM-
CHORDATE LINE OF
EVOLUTION

Many millions of years ago a group of animals with a unique body plan diverged away from the *annelid line* of evolution to begin the second great line of evolution in animals, the *echinoderm-chordate line*.   The basic differences from the annelid line can be seen in embryonic development.   In the early embryos of echinoderms and chordates the mesoderm arises from outpocketings of endoderm to form pouches, which grow out to fill the space between ectoderm and endoderm.   Mesodermal pouches separate from the endoderm, and the cavities of the pouches become the coelom.   An additional difference is evident in the character of embryological development: In the echinoderm-chordate line of evolution the embryonic *blastopore* (see Chapter 10) becomes the anus, but in the annelid line it becomes the mouth.   The only *major* phylum related to the chordates, of which we are examples, is the phylum *Echinodermata*.

ECHINODERMS

Echinoderms are the spiny-skinned animals, the starfishes, brittle stars, sea urchins, sea cucumbers, and sea lilies.   The larvae are bilaterally symmetrical, but the adults have a type of radial symmetry which is suited for their sedentary, sluggish, bottom-dwelling way of life.   Echinoderms have a strange form of locomotion which is accomplished by means of thousands of movable suction cups called *tube feet* on the lower side (see Figure 19.27).   The suction cups are extended forward, attached,

FIGURE 19.27   (a) Sea urchin; note the tube feet (movable suction cups); (b) starfish; (c) brittle stars. (*Courtesy of Robert C. Hermes, Ron Curbow,* and *Hal H. Harrison, respectively, all of The National Audubon Society.*)

A

B

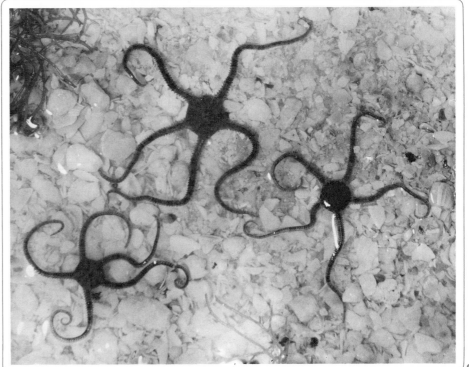

C

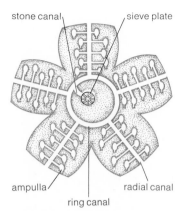

stone canal sieve plate

ampulla radial canal

ring canal

FIGURE 19.28 The components and the internal arrangement of the water-vascular system in a starfish. Water enters and leaves the system through the sievelike sieve plate at the upper side.

contracted, and detached by action of muscles and water pressure from a unique *water-vascular system* (see Figure 19.28). This plumbing system connects all the tube feet and has an external opening on the dorsal side, the sieve plate. The tube feet are used for locomotion or for holding prey, usually mussels, snails, or other mollusks, while eating. The starfish extends its stomach out of its mouth on the lower ventral side and into the prey, which is digested on the spot until it can be absorbed for final digestion in the starfish.

The body wall of an echinoderm has thin areas called *skin gills* through which an exchange of gases takes place between the water and the coelom (see Figure 19.29). The body wall contains *calcareous plates* of various sizes and shapes, depending upon the group. The common starfish has plates so close together that it can swing its arms only very slowly. Brittle stars have plates which are smaller and farther apart. Its arms are much more flexible and may break off. Sea urchins have plates fused tightly together and having projections which make it look like a pincushion. Sand dollars are basically sea urchins which have become flattened. Sea cucumbers have very small plates which are far apart and allow greater flexibility.

Starfish have a very simple nervous system and lack a brain. The circulatory system is greatly reduced, and excretion is accomplished either by direct diffusion into the seawater or by migrating ameboid cells, which carry the wastes to the exterior.

The body plan of echinoderms is based on a general plan of five major divisions. These divisions appear in the starfish as arms, in other forms as rows of tube feet, and in the sea urchin as five teeth arranged in a circle inside the mouth and called Aristotle's lantern.

THE EVOLUTION OF INVERTEBRATES

Within the invertebrate group of animals we have seen several obvious evolutionary trends which have allowed some animals of this group to become dominant both in absolute numbers and in numbers of species. One of these is a trend toward increased complexity of the *nervous system,* with concentration of control functions in a brain located in a well-defined head. Evidently this has happened in evolution several times independently, for instance among both the mollusks and the chordates. As our discussion of animals moves into the vertebrate group, we shall see this trend continued, with the production of an extremely complex and highly effective nervous coordination of the total activities of the animal. Development of a *complex musculature* accompanied the increased specialization of the nervous system, allowing faster and more precise movements in response to the increased integration of nervous control. No muscles exist in the porifera; the coelenterates, although capable of coordinated body movements, have few muscles; a single layer of longitudinal muscles appears in the nematode worms; several layers of muscle in the annelid worms, some of which run longitudinally and some of which encircle the body; and in the arthropods, which may be taken as an example of a highly evolved musculature, there exists a fantastically complex system of hundreds or even thousands of small and large muscles. These allow precise control of each body part. *Skeletal parts* also show an equivalent line of evolution; absent in sponges, coelenterates, and worms, except for supportive elements which depend on hydrostatic pressure within cavities in the body, the skeletal parts in the arthropods approximate the musculature in complexity. Among the mollusks, as we have seen, the most highly developed forms, the squids and octopuses, have also evolved skeletal elements located internally, in contrast to the primarily external system of arthropods. While not found in all higher invertebrates, a trend toward *segmentation* can be seen in one major evolutionary line, the annelid-arthropod line, with specialization of nerves, muscles, and appendages associated with the separate segments.

Increase in size, adaptation to a terrestrial environment, and intensified activity all impose special requirements for the transport of nutrients and the removal of waste materials from the cells of the body. Adaptations in the circulatory, respiratory, and excretory systems in the course of the evolution of the higher invertebrates have provided greater specialization and efficiency in meeting these requirements. No special *circulatory system* exists in the sponges or coelenterates, flatworms, or nematodes. Diffusion of nutrients and oxygen takes care of these requirements. The work required to move nutrients and oxygen from the exterior to the interior is accomplished by individual cells rather than by specialized tissues or organ systems. As a result, the body must be thin-walled, that is, no more than a few cells in thickness. Removal of carbon dioxide is similarly accomplished in the basis of diffusion through individual cells to the exterior. In many ways, these forms might be said to have an external circulatory system, this being simply the water medium surrounding the animal. All the higher animal phyla have internal circulatory systems, with vessels to carry nutrients to, and wastes away from, cells lying on the interior of the body. This evolutionary invention permits thick masses of cells to be aggregated into specialized structures (organs).

Development of the *excretory system* has been similar to that of the circulatory system. In the simplest forms, excretion is on a cellular basis, with diffusion of wastes to the external environment. In the flatworms, a specialized excretory system exists, consisting, as we have seen, of ciliated tubules, into which waste materials and water from the tissues move. In more highly evolved animals, the excretory system is tied closely to the circulatory system, and removes wastes from blood and other body fluids.

Sponges have no special *digestive system*. The system of coelenterates and flatworms has only one opening, serving both as mouth and anus. Higher animal systems have two openings, one specialized for the intake of food and one for the release of indigestible material. Increasing specialization is evident as the grade

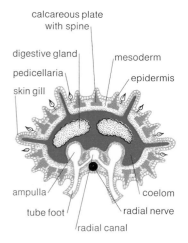

calcareous plate with spine

digestive gland

mesoderm

pedicellaria

epidermis

skin gill

ampulla

coelom

tube foot

radial nerve

radial canal

FIGURE 19.29 Diagrammatic cross section through the arm of a starfish.

of organization rises in the accessory digestive organs which supply enzymes and emulsifiers to the digestive process.

In developing these specialized organ systems, animals evolved from the condition found in the sponges, in which no distinct tissues occur, to a tissue level of organization. Thus in the coelenterates, two layers are found, with some degree of specialization and separation of the various processes of the animal between the two layers. All other phyla have three distinct embryonic layers, and it is the organ systems derived from these layers which carry out the processes we have just reviewed.

CHORDATES   The trends of evolution discussed in this chapter are continued in the chordate group, taken up in the next chapter. This phylum is probably the one of greatest interest to you since it claims you as a member.

REVIEW QUESTIONS   1   Describe the body plan and alternation of generations in coelenterates.
2   List three unique characteristics for each of the following groups of animals: sponges, coelenterates, flatworms, roundworms, segmented worms, arthropods, mollusks, echinoderms, and chordates.
3   What is meant by the annelid line of evolution?
4   Why are insects so successful?
5   What is the echinoderm-chordate line of evolution?

SUGGESTIONS FOR
FURTHER READING
* Available in paperback.

Buchsbaum, R.: *Animals without Backbones,* The University of Chicago Press, Chicago, 1948. A beautifully illustrated book with an elementary and clear description of invertebrate animals; recommended.

Buchsbaum, R., and L. J. Milne: *The Lower Animals,* Doubleday & Company, Inc., Garden City, N.Y., 1961. Written by two experts on invertebrate animals and beautifully illustrated; highly recommended.

Rounds, H. D.: *Invertebrates,* Reinhold Book Corporation, New York, 1968. Briefly but adequately discusses the structure, function, and evolution of the invertebrates.

Russell-Hunter, W. D.: *A Biology of Lower Invertebrates,* The Macmillan Company, New York, 1968. Discusses the less complex animals without backbones.

Atlantic green turtle. (*Courtesy of Gordon Smith from The National Audubon Society.*)

Chapter 20

Patterns of Diversity in Animals with Backbones

. . . lo, the winter is past,
The rain is over and gone;
The flowers appear on the earth;
The time of the singing of birds is come;
And the voice of the turtle is heard in our land.

The Song of Solomon

After discussing some of the many forms of life, with their strange names and activities, we have finally arrived at the phylum that includes *us,* the phylum Chordata. A phylum includes a broad range of organisms, however, and some of our chordate cousins seem so distant that it may be hard to think of them as evolutionary relatives of ourselves, particularly in comparison to such closer relations as monkeys, dogs, or cats.

WHAT ARE CHORDATES?

Chordates are believed to have evolved from primitive organisms which also gave rise to the echinoderms. This may seem strange, since the adult forms of these two groups look so different. Certain similarities between chordates and echinoderms strongly support the idea that these diverse groups share a common ancestry. Similarities appear in early embryonic development which sharply distinguish the echinoderm-chordate group from the annelid-arthropod group, for example, similarities in formation of the coelom as cavities in the mesoderm, formation of the anus rather than the mouth from the embryonic opening of the blastula (blastopore), and a form of cell division or cleavage of the fertilized egg in which under certain circumstances the first few cells formed are capable of forming complete new individuals if separated. This phenomenon, which explains the occurrence of identical twins, does not occur in any animal phyla outside the echinoderm-chordate group.

Further clues pointing toward a common ancestry for the echinoderms and chordates can be found in a curious group of marine organisms which exists as a "missing link" between these phyla. These organisms, commonly called acorn worms (Figure 20.1), have a swimming larva with a pattern of cilia like that of the echinoderms, and this pattern is found in no other phyla of the animal kingdom. On the other hand, two chordate characteristics, the presence of *gill slits* communicating between the anterior region of the digestive tube (pharynx) and the outside world and a *dorsal nerve cord*, link acorn worms to the chordates.

These characteristics are the basis for the hypothesis which links the echinoderms and chordates to a common primitive ancestor. All chordates possess a hollow *dorsal nerve cord, paired gill slits,* and a *notochord,* a dorsally located rod formed from embryonic mesoderm which contributes rigidity to the organism. In early embryonic development, the dorsal nerve cord arises from ectoderm lying above mesodermal cells which will later give rise to the notochord. The gill slits are openings which form between the external environment and the digestive tract in the region of the throat or pharynx. Water can be taken into the mouth and expelled through these slits. As the water passes through the slits, exchange of gases can occur between the water and blood, which flows through vessels in the walls of the slits. Through proliferation of blood-filled tissue lining the slits, *gills* are formed in these regions. The sievelike nature of the slitted pharynx also acts to trap particles of food from the matter passing through the slits. Oxygenated blood from the gill slits is pumped by a *ventral heart* to all regions of the body through a *closed circulatory system* in chordates.

FIGURE 20.1 Drawing of an acorn worm, dorsal view, showing proboscis, collar, and row of paired gill slits along forward part of trunk.

PROTOCHORDATES:
INVERTEBRATE CHORDATES

Protochordates are animals which have the definitive chordate structures just listed but lack true backbones or vertebral columns. This group includes the *tunicates* and the *lancelets*. The tunicates, or sea squirts, look like sacs attached to rocks or pilings (see Figures 20.2 and 20.3). It came as a shock to investigators when they found that

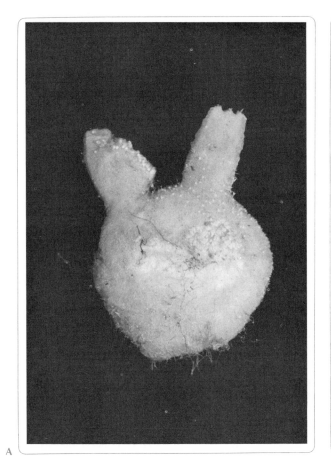

A

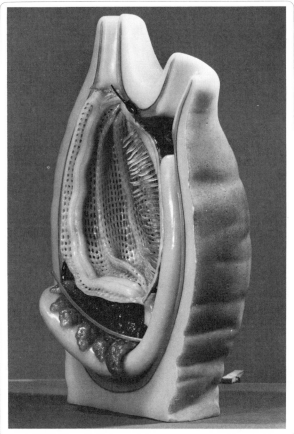

B

FIGURE 20.2 Two sea squirts, or
tunicates: (a) *Molgula* (*Carolina
Biological Supply Co.*) and (b) glass
model section of adult sea squirt.
(*Courtesy of The American
Museum of Natural History.*)

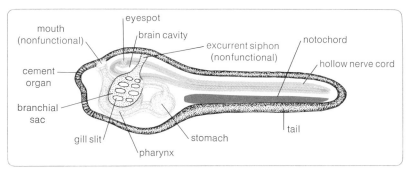

FIGURE 20.3 Cutaway model of
an adult tunicate tadpole.
Food-bearing water is drawn into
the pharynx through the incurrent
opening. Food passes into the
U-shaped alimentary tract, and
water emerges through the gill slits
and the excurrent opening to the
outside. (*Courtesy of The American Museum of Natural History.*)

these animals pass through a larval stage which possesses a notochord, dorsal nerve cord, and gill slits. A tunicate larva swims for a time and then attaches itself to a solid surface by its head region. The tail and notochord are lost, and the nervous system is reduced to a single ganglion. The pharynx, however, enlarges until it occupies most of the saclike body. The mouth leading into the pharynx shifts so that the digestive tract is U-shaped and the mouth and the anus are nearby. Water is carried into the saclike outer covering of the tunicate through the incurrent siphon, where it passes through the mouth and into the pharynx. The water then filters through the many gill slits in the wall of the pharynx, and leaves the animal through the excurrent siphon, also shared by the anus. The outer covering of the body, the *tunic,* has only two openings, the incurrent and excurrent siphons. The tunic contains a polysaccharide closely related to the cellulose found in plants.

The larval stage of the tunicates resembles a tadpole, and like a tadpole it swims through the water by moving its tail muscles. Although the use of a tail in swimming is similar to tail movements in swimming arthropod larvae, this does not constitute a case for a common ancestry between arthropods and chordates, in view of the striking embryonic similarities to be found between the echinoderms and chordates. Because of the primitive development of chordate characteristics in the tunicates, many biologists have proposed that organisms similar to existing tunicate larvae may have been the earliest chordates.

The *lancelet,* also called *amphioxus,* is a small slender fish-shaped animal which burrows in the sand along some shores (see Figure 20.4). Their notochord persists throughout life and provides a rigid axis on which the muscles can pull in locomotion. The tubular nerve cord is dorsal, but there is neither brain nor head. The pharynx has sixty or more gill slits. Ciliary action causes water to move through a mouth into the pharynx, out through the gills, and into an atrium, which empties ventrally in front of the anus. Lancelets have developed a segmented pattern of muscles and nerves independently of the segmentation which developed in the annelid line of evolution. The lancelet pattern of segmentation is also present in their close relatives, the vertebrates.

FIGURE 20.4 Lancelet, or amphioxus. Notochord and nerve cord are the dark rods above the gill slits running from front to back. (*Adapted from Carolina Biological Supply* Co.)

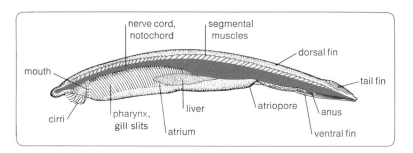

Vertebrates are chordates in which the notochord is replaced by a segmented vertebral column made of cartilage or bone. Muscles and nerves are also segmented, but in the adult the pattern of segmentation becomes somewhat obscured (see Table 20.1). Vertebrates have a dorsal nerve cord which is enlarged at the front end to form a brain enclosed in a braincase. There is a well-developed head containing pairs of sense organs. Gills in the pharynx are retained throughout life by fishes, but in terrestrial vertebrates, the embryonic gill slits disappear or are converted into other structures, such as the eustachean tube, which communicates between the pharynx and middle ear. Gas exchange is accomplished instead by means of lungs, which are secondary pouches arising from the pharyngeal region. Seven classes of vertebrates are living today. Of these, three are fishes which live exclusively in water, and four are four-legged invaders of the land.

VERTEBRATES: CHORDATES
WITH BACKBONES

Many people assume that anything in water must be a fish—crayfish, shellfish, etc.—even though the animal in question is an arthropod, mollusk, or whatever. Fishes,

THE FISHES

TABLE 20.1 Some diagnostic features of vertebrates

SUPER-CLASS	CLASS	SKIN	SKELETON	APPEND-AGES	BREATHING	HEART CHAMBERS	FERTILIZATION	DEVELOPMENT	OTHER CHARACTERISTICS
Pisces (fish)	Agnatha	Smooth	Permanent notochord plus cartilage skeleton	Without paired fins	Gills	Two	External	In water	Without jaws; cold-blooded; without neck; without lungs
	Chondrich-thyes	Denticles	Embryonic notochord; cartilaginous skeleton in adult	Paired fins	Gills	Two	External	In water	With jaws; cold-blooded; without neck; without lungs
	Osteich-thyes	Scales	Embryonic notochord; bony skeleton in adult	Paired fins	Gills; lungs in some	Two	External	In water	Swim bladder in most; cold-blooded without neck
Tetrapoda (four-legged animals)	Amphibia	Smooth, glandular	Embryonic notochord; bony skeleton in adult	Two pairs of legs	Gills and lungs	Three	External and internal	In water	Cold-blooded; without neck
	Reptilia	Scales	Embryonic notochord; bony skeleton in adult	Two pairs of legs	Lungs	Four	Internal	On land	With neck; cold-blooded
	Aves	Feathers	Embryonic notochord; bony skeleton in adult	Legs and wings	Lungs	Four	Internal	On land	With neck; warm-blooded
	Mammalia	Hair	Embryonic notochord; bony skeleton in adult	Two pairs of legs	Lungs	Four	Internal	Mostly inside female	Warm-blooded; nurse young; nonnucleated red blood cells

properly designated, are vertebrates of the classes Agnatha, Chondrichthyes, and Osteichthyes.

Agnatha includes lampreys and hagfish. They resemble eels but lack scales, fins, and jaws (hence the name). These predatory jawless animals attach to fishes with their suckerlike mouth and rasp away tissue with a barbed tongue. The notochord persists in the adult, and segmented cartilaginous vertebral parts are formed around it. There are seven pairs of gills, each opening independently to the outside. The heart is ventral and is composed of two chambers, the auricle and the ventricle. Many lampreys are marine but migrate into freshwater streams to reproduce.

Chondrichthyes includes the cartilaginous fishes, such as sharks, skates, and rays. The notochord exists only in the embryo and is replaced completely in the adult by a vertebral column. In contrast to higher fishes, the Chondricthyes have a skeleton entirely composed of cartilage. The skin is covered with tiny, pointed scales called *denticles*, since they resemble teeth (see Figure 20.5), and there are five to seven pairs of gills which open independently to the outside. Two sets of paired fins and some single fins are used to steer by as the animals propel themselves actively through the water. Cartilaginous fishes do not have a swim bladder (see the Osteichthyes below) and therefore cannot change their bouyancy. As a result they tend to inhabit a narrow range of depths. Sharks feed on the surface, and skates and rays feed on the bottom; the activities of these organisms are limited primarily to the levels on which they feed. The cartilaginous fishes are a divergent line projecting to the side from the main line of evolution leading from agnathans to the next group.

Osteichthyes. Over half of the vertebrate species are bony fishes, the osteichthyes. As the name implies, the cartilage is replaced by bone in the adult. Bony fishes usually have scaly skin, two sets of paired fins, and gill openings covered by a hinged bony plate, the operculum. In most bony fishes, a saclike organ filled with gas, the *swim bladder,* functions to adjust the bouyancy of the fish to match the bouyancy of the water surrounding it. This structure probably first evolved in freshwater fishes as an accessory breathing organ or lung located ventral to the digestive system and connected ventrally to the pharynx. In the evolution of the swim bladder, the lung assumed a position dorsal to the digestive system and gradually lost the pharyngeal connection. A dorsal sac, connected ventrally to the pharynx and functioning as a lung, still exists today in the *lungfishes*. With a swim bladder, a body fish can remain motionless in the water, but cartilaginous fish, lacking a swim bladder, must constantly swim to avoid sinking (see Figure 20.6).

Osteichthyes have come to dominate both freshwater and saltwater habitats in the world today. Few sharks live in fresh water; while lampreys have invaded freshwater habitats, osteichthyes have remained most important here. Predominantly, the fish which graze on the plankton of fresh water are the members of the minnow family, daces, chubs, shiners, and minnows. These are very important in

FIGURE 20.5 Drawing of a sharkskin (magnified), showing toothlike quality of denticles.

FIGURE 20.6 Anterior portion of a black sea bass, a member of the class of bony fishes. Note scales and the operculum, a bony plate behind the eyes which covers the gills and lets water out at its rear edge. (*Courtesy of A. W. Ambler from The National Audubon Society.*)

food chains since they serve as the primary source of food for predatory fishes. Predators of cold rivers are trout and salmon, and around the Great Lakes region, pikes must be added to the list of the hunters. In warm ponds and lakes across the United States sunfishes such as bluegills and bass are the dominant predators and in certain parts of the country gars are also active.

Early in their evolutionary history the bony fishes diverged into two main lines of evolution. One line led to the form of fish dominant today, those with fins consisting of webs of skin supported by horny rays. These, the *ray-finned fishes*, are the more important of modern fishes (see Figure 20.7). In an evolutionary sense, however, the *fleshy-finned fishes* have been of larger significance, for it was from this group that the amphibians diverged. The fleshy-finned fishes include two types, lungfish and lobe-finned fishes. The lungfishes are actually a side issue, as they are not in the direct line leading to amphibians, but their living representatives today illustrate some of the traits possessed by the fish ancestors of the first vertebrate forms to invade the land.

There are only three species of lungfish living today, one in each of the three southern continents. The African form lives in the Nile basin, the South American

FIGURE 20.7 Two ray-finned fish:
(a) the lookdown fish and (b)
spotted sea bass. (*Courtesy of
Robert C. Hermes and Jeanne
White, respectively, from The
National Audubon Society.*)

A

B

form inhabits the swamps of western Paraguay, and the Australian form is found in the rivers of the interior of that continent. All three habitats are subject to seasonal drought, in which the possession of lungs is advantageous. The Australian form has only one lung, but the other species have a pair; whether single or double, the lungs are attached to the pharynx by air tubes. Lungfish do not rely on gill breathing and must rise periodically to the surface to fill their lungs with air breathed through paired nostrils. The ray-finned fishes have nostrils, but they do not penetrate into the mouth and are simply water-filled pouches containing olfactory receptors for the sense of smell. The paired fins of lungfishes have prominent fleshy lobes and have many traits in common with the lobe-finned fishes. In their early stages of development, lungfishes are remarkably similar to the larval stages of amphibians.

The lobe-finned fishes are the group believed to resemble the ancestors of land vertebrates. They and the lungfishes were abundant in past evolutionary eras, but both groups dwindled until they are practically extinct today. Until 1939, lobe-finned fishes were thought to have been extinct for 75 million years, and then one was caught off the coast of South Africa. From the one known remaining species, and fossil evidence, it is possible to determine that the ancient lobe-fins had many of the features of the lungfish, such as internal nostrils, lungs, and the breathing tubes which characterize land forms. The lobe-fins lacked legs, of course, but the fins contained fleshy bases supported on bony skeletal frameworks with only one bone leading to the shoulder girdle. This bone led from the shoulder to a joint from which two bones led on out to a series of branching bones. The similarity of this plan to that of a land animal is obvious. Comparison of the skull and even minute details of the teeth show that lobe-fins were very much like primitive amphibians. The vital change which was necessary if the lobefins were to invade the land was an increase in the size of the fins. Primitive amphibians were essentially lobe-finned fishes in which the lobed fins had progressively become large enough to support locomotion on land. Why would lobe-finned fishes have found it advantageous to leave the water environment to which they were already adapted? Why should they have evolved larger appendages, which would present a disadvantage while swimming through the water? The answer lies in changes occurring in the climate of the geological period we are discussing, a time of seasonal droughts, when rivers ceased to flow and pools were formed of foul and stagnant water. Conditions became crowded, and with the occasional drying up of the pools selection pressure developed for larger fins, and eventually limbs, which would allow a lobe-fin to leave one pool and slither over to another pool with better conditions.

Thus adaptations toward longer and fleshier fins were a response to environmental pressures caused by increasing dryness in the habitat; fish which had strong fleshy fins were better able to *reach* water, rather than better able to leave it. As drying conditions worsened, longer trips were necessary. With greater amounts of time

FOUR-LEGGED VERTEBRATES
INVADE THE LAND

being spent out of water there was increased selection pressure for adaptations which would allow better and better success in feeding on land. In other words, land vertebrates became established as an indirect result of the changing climate.

The sequence of appearance of plants and animals on land follows the concept of the food chain. Plants made their appearance on land first, and then, when these producers of organic nutrients had become established, consumers also invaded the land; 350 million years ago land plants grew in luxuriant forests in widespread swamps. This period is called the *carboniferous age* since it was the time when the plants grew which gave rise to the vast coal deposits now releasing their stored energy to man. At that time plants were being eaten by primitive arthropods and the early insects, and the lobe-finned fishes invaded the land and added insects to their diet of fish.

Through a process of natural selection the lobe-finned fishes gave rise to primitive amphibians with fishlike tails and short stubby limbs. These limbs set a pattern, for they contained the numbers and types of bones found in the limbs of all their descendants. This form of amphibian is called a *labyrinthodont* and is the form from which the three types of amphibians and the reptile group evolved. From this basic group of amphibians evolved the land vertebrates, all of which have four legs and five digits, just like the ancestral groups in the ponds of the coal forests.

Before the carboniferous age was over, the ancestral group of amphibians had given rise to four lines of evolution which have continued to the present. One line of evolution produced the reptiles, and subsequently the mammals, and the other three produced the salamanders, the frogs and toads, and an obscure burrowing and limbless form known as caecilians. In general appearance, the salamanders resemble the ancestral amphibians, but upon closer observation it is clear that some basic changes have occurred.

In all modern amphibians, the ancestral fish scales have disappeared, and the skin is soft and moist and assists the lungs as a breathing organ. The skin also serves as a means of defense for these otherwise almost defenseless animals. Most amphibians have secretory skin glands, and in many the secretions are toxic and either deter or kill would-be predators. Many amphibians contain pigment cells in their skin which can change color and provide a degree of camouflage. Since their skin must remain damp, *salamanders* and *frogs* are restricted to water or to moist areas under logs or stones and are found primarily in the temperate regions of the Northern Hemisphere. Salamanders are missing from Africa and Australia, and only a few species are found in South America (see Figure 20.8).

The *caecilians* are found in moist tropical areas, where they live in burrows. Since they lack limbs and have very small eyes, they look like large earthworms. They are only distantly related to the other groups, and their fossil record is not known.

FIGURE 20.8 Two amphibians: (a) a cave salamander and (b) the American toad, shown here singing. (*Courtesy of The American Museum Natural History.*)

The amphibians were the first of the vertebrates to invade the land and were abundant for a while during the carboniferous period, but they are a small and insignificant group among the vertebrates today. They never did invade the land successfully; only their descendents, the reptiles, became true land animals, for the amphibians remain partially freshwater animals. The word amphibian means "both lives" and refers to the larval and the adult stages of this animal which inhabit two worlds. The larval stage is aquatic and gill-breathing, but the adult is terrestrial and lung-breathing. Even though the adults of many amphibians spend their entire lives on land, at some time during their life cycle they must return to the water to reproduce. Some forms of amphibians have evolved adaptations which allow a degree of freedom from water, but they are not strikingly successful because other forms of vertebrates can do the job better.

REPTILES The reptiles, unlike the amphibians, do not have to return to the water to reproduce, instead manufacturing their own private completely enclosed pond in which development takes place, the *reptilian egg*. Amphibian eggs and larval forms develop in direct contact with environmental water, which provides protection against mechanical injury and dehydration, furnishes oxygen (and food to the larval forms), and accepts wastes. Embryonic development of reptiles has these same basic needs, but the reptilian egg possesses adaptations which substitute for larval life in free water. The reptilian egg was one of the most important adaptations of vertebrates in their successful invasion of the land, and it has been utilized with minor changes by the birds and with major changes by the mammals. Since reptile and bird eggs are so similar, the following description of a reptilian egg applies to the bird egg as well.

The developing embryo of a reptile is almost totally enclosed by a membrane, the *amnion,* which is filled with water, the *amniotic fluid,* so that the embryo is cushioned against shocks and protected from dehydration. The digestive tract of the embryo connects on the ventral side with a source of food, the *yolk sac.* From the rear of the embryo a tube develops which becomes the *allantois,* a membranous bladder which serves as a reservoir for excretory wastes. Around the embryo and its membranes grows another membrane, the *chorion,* which becomes surrounded by a leathery *shell*. The allantois expands until it lies against the chorion and lines the egg (see Figure 20.9). The allantois becomes richly supplied with blood capillaries and, since the shell is porous, functions in a manner similar to a lung as well as a bladder. If an egg is coated with a sealing material or placed in water, the embryo will suffocate. Thus, the water-dwelling stage of embryonic growth takes place inside a small private pool within the amnion from which the reptile emerges as a fully equipped land animal.

The first reptiles are known to have been aquatic. The evolution of the land egg probably occurred when this type of egg was developed by water-dwelling reptiles

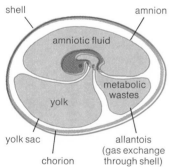

FIGURE 20.9 The extraembryonic membranes in reptile and bird eggs. Note that the yolk sac and allantois are large and functional. (*Adapted from Paul B. Weisz, Elements of Biology, 3rd ed. Copyright McGraw-Hill Book Company, 1969. Used by permission.*)

whose "amniote eggs" were successful even when the ponds in which they were deposited dried up. Though the amphibious reptiles were more successful than the amphibians in perpetuating themselves in the drying ponds, successful invasion of the surrounding dry land required some further modifications. The air bladder, which had originated in bony fishes and had expanded somewhat in the amphibians, was now greatly expanded by the reptiles. The paired limbs which were used to some advantage by the amphibians were really capitalized on by the reptiles. Limbs of the salamanderlike primitive amphibians served primarily as supports to anchor the body as it was moved in a sinuous but wobbling, splay-footed motion somewhat similar to the body motion of a fish. Legs of reptiles evolved into powerful structures capable of moving the body rapidly, almost entirely without help from the muscles of the body wall.

Primitive amphibians had scales similar to their fish ancestors, but somewhere along the evolutionary way the scales were replaced by the moist, glandular skin associated with modern amphibians. The scales retained by the reptiles render their skin almost impervious to any loss of water. This adaptation, though preventing any loss of water, presents a further problem, however, for it also precludes respiration through the skin. With added dependence upon the lungs as a sole means of gas exchange between the blood and the air, the circulatory system became more efficient. During reptilian evolution, the heart became partially divided into two halves, so that blood returning from the tissues was in part prevented from mixing with the oxygen-rich blood returning from the lungs.

Reptiles are often referred to as cold-blooded animals, but this is inaccurate since their blood is approximately the temperature of the environment, which is often quite warm (and in some cases, too warm). Also, contrary to common belief, reptiles can regulate their temperature, but they do this through behavioral means rather than by the internal control used by birds and mammals. The reptiles move from place to place in search of an environment with optimum temperature and moisture.

Since the chorion and shell are added to the egg before it is released from the mother, fertilization of the egg must take place shortly after it leaves the ovary. Internal fertilization is found in all reptiles and is accomplished by the male and female bringing their cloacas together for the transfer of sperm. The males of most living reptiles possess organs which are somewhat similar, at least in function, to the mammalian penis.

During the Age of Reptiles, which lasted for about 130 million years and ended 70 million years ago, reptiles were exceedingly numerous and occupied a great variety of the ecological niches now occupied by birds and mammals. Today, reptiles include only a few groups, such as turtles, crocodiles, lizards, and snakes, but for a span of time 100 times longer than man's existence on earth there were ichthyosaurs in the water, pterosaurs in the air, and a multitude of dinosaurs on land and in the swamps. Probably because of dramatic changes in the climate and in the types of food available, as well as the evolution of mammals which ate reptile eggs, the dinosaurs and most of the other reptiles disappeared. They were replaced by reptilian descendants, the birds and mammals.

BIRDS

The line of evolution leading to the modern birds was launched when primitive tree-living reptiles resembling large lizards evolved a variant method of producing scales in which the scales expanded into structures known as feathers (Figure 20.10). Any variation which further increased the size of these feathers and therefore the aerodynamic surface of the wings would have selective value in facilitating jumping from branch to branch. As wings evolved, the reptilian birds could glide from the treetops to the ground and perhaps feed on insects on the way down. This hypothetical story would be purely imaginary if it were not for the discovery of a feather and two fossil reptilelike birds in the mid-1800s in shale deposits in Germany. If just the skeletons of Archeornis and Archeopteryx (the names mean ''ancient bird'' and ''ancient wing'') were examined, the viewer could argue that they were merely reptiles, but their delicate entombment in shale preserved the imprint of feathers around the

FIGURE 20.10 Evolutionarily the scales of primitive reptiles have become the feathers of birds. (a) tern in flight and (b) herring gull at rest. (*Courtesy of Gordon Smith and Dade W. Thornton, respectively, from The National Audubon Society.*) (c) Snowy egret, showing mating plumage.

A

B

C

reptilian bones (see Figure 20.11). These dinosaurlike birds still had the reptilian features of a long bony tail, toothed jaws, solid bones, and clawed fingers, and they lacked the keel, or breastbone, which serves for attachment of the powerful flight muscles in modern birds. Birds may be said to be "glorified reptiles" and differ from reptiles primarily in the adaptations for flight and the maintenance of a constant body temperature.

Adaptations for flight include a skeleton which is strong but extremely light, a goal achieved through bones that are hollow and in many cases fused. Natural selection resulted in a progressively streamlined, aerodynamically effective flying machine. Appendages which interfered with flight gradually disappeared or were drastically altered. Thus, the tail is reduced to only a few vertebrae, the hand is reduced to three fingers, which are fused and serve as wing supports, the breastbone is enormous and serves as an attachment for flight muscles (the white meat in chickens), the

FIGURE 20.11 Cast of Archeopteryx. Note the imprint of feathers. (*Courtesy of The American Museum of Natural History.*)

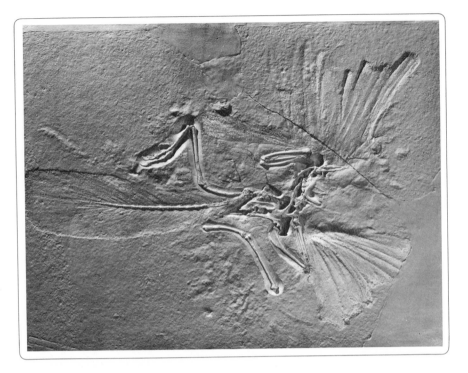

collarbones are fused into one bone (the wishbone), the pelvic bones are fused, the bones of the cranium are fused, and the ribs are jointed, thus allowing breathing. Birds breathe by pulling the breastbone, or keel, up and down and by folding the jointed ribs in a billows action to force air in and out of the lungs. While flying, this breathing movement must be in rhythm with the motion of the wings since the muscles of flight are attached to the keelbone, which in turn is attached to the breathing muscles. The very high metabolic rate of birds requires a large respiratory surface for exchange of gases. This is provided by a system of air sacs connected to the lungs, extending through the viscera and even into the hollow bones. They also surround the testes and, by means of a form of air conditioning, keep the temperature of the testes down to a range within which the sperm can live. A fairly consistent body temperature is maintained through release of metabolic heat and through evaporation of water into the air sacs.

The high metabolic rate of birds requires an efficient circulatory system which can quickly exchange gases with the lungs and air sacs and can deliver nutrients to the rapidly contracting muscles. The heart is very large, in many birds making up one-fifth of the body weight. It beats with a pulse rate which may be 120 per minute while resting, 240 while flying, and up to 1,000 when excited. The efficiency of the circulation is increased by the four-chambered construction of the heart. A four-chambered heart prevents blood that is returning from the tissues and low on oxygen from mixing with blood that is returning from the lungs and rich in oxygen. The process of excretion is almost identical to that of reptiles. Wastes are removed from the blood in the kidneys in the form of uric acid and are released from the body through the cloaca. White excretory products may be released from the cloaca along with the dark digestive wastes. In addition to being the exit for the excretory and digestive systems, the cloaca is the means by which the reproductive system releases its eggs or sperm. Since fertilization of the eggs must be internal, there must be contact of the male and female cloacas during mating so that sperm can be transferred. Only a few groups of birds (for example, river ducks in the United States) have a penis.

The brains of birds are smooth-surfaced and are distinguished by very large optic lobes and very small olfactory lobes. The relative sizes of the lobes of the brain are related to the fact that birds have the best eyesight of all animals and the poorest sense of smell. Birds have excellent hearing and rely heavily on sounds and visual signals for communication. (For nonflying birds see Plate 19.)

MAMMALS

Mammals are so much a part of the modern scene and demonstrate so many advanced characteristics that it is easy to jump to the conclusion that the origin of the mammals must have been comparatively recent. It may come as a shock to learn, however, that the mammalian line diverged from the reptile line as part of the great reptilian adaptive radiation following the invasion of the land. Primitive mammal-like reptiles were already present when the stem group of reptiles gave rise to the line of evolution which leads to the dinosaurs and birds.

The description mammal-like refers to certain characteristics discernible in the fossil record, namely, the arrangement of the teeth, skull, and limbs. These mammal-reptiles had the typical small reptilian brain. However, the roof of the mouth contained a palate, a shelf of bone separating the nasal chamber from the mouth and found only in mammals. The teeth were almost mammalian in that they were somewhat differentiated into incisors, canines, and cheek teeth which had lost the conical reptilian appearance and had surfaces containing bumps or cusps. The limbs had shifted from the reptilian positions at the side and had reached the mammalian position under the body, where they moved in a plane directly under the shoulders and hips in what was probably a more efficient means of locomotion. Since the soft parts of these mammal-like reptiles were not fossilized, it is difficult to determine whether they were warm-blooded, whether they nursed their young, and whether they had hair or scales, but the presence of the palate indicates that they fed in the way of mammals; that is, they could hold their prey in their mouth and breathe, a feat impossible for a reptile or a bird.

The mammal-like reptiles were replaced by true mammals at the beginning of the Age of Reptiles, and all during the 130 million years of the reign of the dinosaurs and other reptiles small, mouse-sized mammals were scurrying about in the shadows of the coal forests. At the end of the Age of Reptiles the mammals began their own great adaptive radiation. Three main lines of mammalian evolution can be discerned, leading to the egg-laying monotremes, the marsupials, and the placental mammals.

EGG-LAYING MAMMALS

A curious sideline of evolution, which probably diverged from the main line of mammalian evolution during the Age of Reptiles, is the group known as the monotremes (see Figure 20.12). The name refers to the presence of reptilian cloaca, only one of several features which demonstrate how little they have changed from their reptilian ancestors. The monotremes today are represented by only two species, the spiny anteater and duck-billed platypus, found in Australia and New Zealand. Reptilian characteristics include venomous spines on the legs of male platypuses, scales at various parts of their bodies, inability to regulate body temperature, and the fact that they lay eggs. These animals are nonetheless mammals since they are fur-bearing and nurse their young. When the young are hatched and leave their nest, they lick milk off the abdomen of the mother.

POUCHED MAMMALS

During the reign of the dinosaurs two types of mammals appeared which were to become the two great living groups of mammals, the marsupials and the placentals. During the last days of the dinosaurs the marsupials, or "pouched mammals," were the more abundant of the two types. Marsupials are more primitive than the placen-

FIGURE 20.12 (a) Spiny anteater and (b) duck-billed platypus, both monotreme mammals. (*Courtesy of The American Museum of Natural History.*)

A

B

tal types and represent a sort of halfway point between the complete lack of direct nutrient provision from the mother to the developing embryo in the reptiles and the placental method of attachment and complete nutrient provision.   In marsupials the embryo absorbs a milky fluid secreted by the mother's uterus, and it may bear a connection between the empty yolk sac and the mother's tissues, but neither of these routes is used for any prolonged time as a source of food.   In the opossum (Figure 20.13), the young are born only 8 days after fertilization, and in the great gray kangaroo, the largest living marsupial, only 40 days after fertilization.   The embryos in both cases are about the size of a pea, and the only parts developed to any degree are the mouth and front legs.   For the continuation of embryonic growth the embryo climbs and is pushed by the mother's tongue to the marsupium, a pouch in which it attaches itself to a nipple on a milk gland.   There it completes its embryonic growth.

The marsupials spread over the land during the beginning of the Age of Mammals. Their success was brief in most parts of the world due to the development of placental forms belonging to a line of evolution which produced the carnivores, a group characterized by a large brain and more efficient means of reproduction than the marsupials.   The marsupials lost in this competition and eventually disappeared from the land except for Australia and North and South America, which were separated from Eurasia, the home of the early carnivores, by water.   The water bar-

FIGURE 20.13 Opossum, a mar-
supial mammal (*Courtesy of The
American Museum of Natural
History.*)

rier has remained around Australia, but occasional formation of land bridges at the Bering Strait and the Isthmus of Panama allowed placental carnivores to move into the Americas and displace all marsupials except the opossum in North America and a few marsupials in South America.

THE PLACENTAL MAMMALS   The marsupials solved the problem of nourishment for the developing young by transferring them to a pouch, where they are protected and fed milk. The placentals solved this problem by a different method, which has turned out to be more effective.

In the reptilian ancestors of the mammals the egg contained a membrane, the allantois, which grew around the inside of the shell and served as a means of gas and waste exchange with the outside. In the placental mammals, the allantois comes into contact with the wall of the uterus, and tissues of the allantois, chorion, and uterus enlarge to form a structure called a *placenta* (see Figure 20.14). In the placenta, blood vessels of the mother intermingle with blood vessels of the embryo and allow transfer of foods, wastes, and gases. The embryo is attached to the placenta by the umbilical cord, a structure containing portions of the amnion and chorion, vestigial remains of the yolk sac, and arteries and veins of the embryo.

The most primitive placental mammals, chiefly insect eaters, are placed in the order Insectivora. Modern representatives of this order include the moles and shrews (see Figure 20.15). Shrews probably represent what the primitive group looked like and even show one characteristic usually considered reptilian. They have a poisonous secretion of toxin in their saliva and can kill small animals with their bite. Shrews are tiny animals, smaller than a mouse, and lose a great deal of body heat due to their small size. This problem, as well as their intense activity, means that they must eat several times their own weight each day.

The insectivores provided the basic gene pool from which the adaptive radiation of the placental mammals took place. The various lines of evolution which diverged from the insectivores include the orders of even-toed hoofed mammals, odd-toed hoofed mammals, whalelike mammals, carnivores, rodents, bats, and the primates,

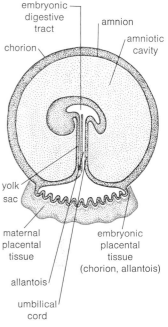

FIGURE 20.14 Diagram of the extraembryonic membranes in the placental mammals. Note that yolk sac and allantois are rudimentary and collapsed. (*Adapted from Paul B. Weisz, Elements of Biology, 3rd ed. Copyright McGraw-Hill Book Company, 1969. Used by permission.*)

FIGURE 20.15 Shrew, a placental mammal. (*Courtesy of The American Museum of Natural History.*)

the group of which we are a part. Thus, from a tiny insect-eating ancestor living at the time of the dinosaurs has arisen the variety of mammalian forms which are today the dominant land vertebrates (Figure 20.16).

FIGURE 20.16 Mammals. (a) Fruit-eating bat, (b) porpoises, and (c) hippopotamus. (*Courtesy of American Museum of Natural History.*) (d) Seals, (e) gorilla, and (f) camel. (*Courtesy of M. Chapman.*)

A

B

C

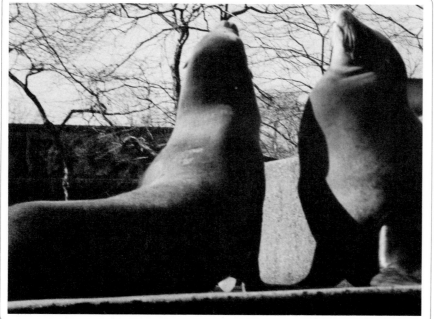

D

E

F

Current fossil evidence indicates that it was in the rain forests, the grasslands, and the savannas of Africa that man evolved from primitive apelike ancestors. The following chapters describe how man evolved and became the most widely dispersed of all vertebrates and how he used and misused the adaptations with which evolution has provided him.

1   Describe the general characteristics of vertebrate chordates.
2   Contrast the three types of fishes.
3   Give the highpoints of the invasion of land by descendants of lobe-finned fishes.
4   Why may the reptilian egg be considered the primary reason for the success of reptiles in becoming widely distributed on land?
5   How is a bird adapted for flight?
6   Contrast the methods of reproduction in egg-laying mammals, pouched mammals, and placental mammals.

Bellairs, A.: *Reptiles: Life History, Evolution, and Structure, Harper Torchbooks 520, Harper & Row, Publishers, Incorporated, New York, 1960. A somewhat technical account of the evolution of reptiles.

Bourlière, F.: The Natural History of Animals, Alfred A. Knopf, Inc., New York, 1956. A unique summary of the ecology, physiology, and behavior of mammals.

McCoy, C. J., Jr.: *Vertebrates, Reinhold Book Corporation, New York, 1968. Briefly describes each class of vertebrate.

Noble, G. K.:*The Biology of the Amphibia, Dover Publications, Inc., New York, 1954. Originally published in 1931, this is a classic account of the amphibians.

Romer, A. S.: The Vertebrate Story, The University of Chicago Press, Chicago, 1962. A highly readable account of the fossil and modern vertebrates and their evolution.

Welty, J. C.: The Life of Birds, W. B. Saunders Company, Philadelphia, 1962. A widely used text; excellent.

Yapp, W. B.: Vertebrates: Their Structures and Life, Oxford University Press, New York, 1965. A somewhat technical text.

Highly recommended is the World of Nature Series published in 1961 by Doubleday & Company, Garden City, N.Y. It includes The Lower Animals, by Ralph Buchsbaum and Lorus J. Milne; Living Fishes of the World, by Earl S. Herald; Living Insects of the World, by Alexander B. Klots and Elsie B. Klots; Living Reptiles of the World, by Karl P. Schmidt and Robert F. Inger; Living Birds of the World, by E. Thomas Gilliard; Living Mammals of the World, by Ivan T. Sanderson.

Part 6
Man in Nature

To understand the adaptations of modern man we must understand his primate ancestors who lived in trees and those who descended to the ground. A large brain, excellent vision, erect posture, and grasping hands were some of the traits which early man exploited. Selection for improvement of these traits increased. With a larger brain, tools and social hunting evolved, and the image of modern man began to form. Then, man began to control and grow *apart from nature*. Natural ecosystems were converted and simplified so that only a few crops were produced. Man established a temporary control over his environment, and his numbers began to increase at such a rate that neither his ecosystem nor the natural ecosystems that now remain will be able to continue to exist unless it is accepted that man is *a part of nature*.

Gorilla. (*Courtesy of
M. Chapman.*)

Chapter 21
Evolution of Man

Must we suppose that the picture of the original man has disappeared just as much as that of the originals of domestic animals?

Ludwig

Man is an animal, and, more specifically, he is a primate. An understanding of how modern man evolved places man and his recurrent difficulties with such problems as racism, nationalism, aggression, neuroses, and psychoses into an evolutionary perspective. All the basic facets of man's structure, function, and behavior have their roots in his evolutionary background. If empathy and compassion for fellow man is one of the attributes of a civilized person, then surely an understanding of his origins is a vital component in the cultivation of this attitude.

To place man in the proper historical context, we must look at the evolution of primates in general before concentrating on the evolution of man in detail.

PRIMATES
A fossil record of evolutionary patterns of divergence among primates has direct application and interest to man, and a knowledge of how his own family tree arose should interest every man. Unfortunately, the evolutionary pedigree of many other animals such as horses, elephants, camels, and dogs is much better known. Fossil remains of primates are difficult to find, for reasons that are clear. Fossils of vertebrates are formed when mud and silt settle over the corpse. This not only requires muddy and sandy bodies of water and but also that the dead animal lie in the water. Primates, however, dwelt primarily in *tropical forests,* where the likelihood is small that a monkey, for example, will die and fall into a pit of deep mud. Most likely is that it will fall to the forest floor and be eaten by predators or be destroyed quickly by decay. The most prevalent fossils of land vertebrates represent animals that lived on plains, where their bodies were washed into gullies and ditches and sediment was quickly deposited. Most fossils of early man were formed when the creatures were buried or preserved in caves.

The living primates are of two major groups, the prosimian (meaning "before monkey") primates and the anthropoid (meaning "similar to man") primates. *Prosimians* include the tree shrews of India and Southeast Asia, the lemurs of Madagascar, the lorises of Africa and Asia, and the tarsiers of Madagascar. Tree shrews and lemurs resemble squirrels, tarsiers look like hopping rats, and lorises resemble only lorises.

Anthropoid primates resemble man and include New World monkeys, Old World monkeys, man, and the great apes (gibbon, orangutan, chimpanzee, and gorilla). Primates are highly diverse (see Figure 21.1). Their definitive characteristics are (1) collarbones, or *clavicles,* (2) *nails* instead of claws, (3) incisor, canine, premolar, and molar teeth, (4) at least one pair of grasping extremities, and (5) rings of bone, or *orbits,* around the eyes. The primates are an ancient group which diverged early from the ancestral placental mammals, the insectivores. The insectivore stock from which all placental mammals descended is believed to have lived in the trees, and primate evolution began with the development of new and better adaptations for arboreal life.

PRIMATE ADAPTATIONS: SUCCESS
OF LIFE IN THE TREES
All primates living today except man, the gorilla, the baboon, and a few other monkeys such as the macaques spend much if not all of their lives in the trees. The traits unique to primates all confer on their bearers selective advantage for a life spent in the trees. Some of the more important adaptations of primates are discussed in the following paragraphs.

Adaptation of Limbs for
Grasping and Exploring
Highly specialized mammals such as cows, sheep, horses, and the like, can move their limbs only in a plane parallel to the body. Such restricted movement would never permit a cow to make progress through the branches in the three-dimensional world of a tree. To be successful in moving in and between trees there must be a

FIGURE 21.1 An assortment of primates. (*Courtesy of James Welgos and A. W. Ambler from The National Audubon Society and The American Museum of Natural History.*)

great flexibility in the joints so that limbs can be extended in almost any direction to grasp a branch.   Squirrels, the tree-climbing rodents, climb trees by digging claws into bark, but primates climb by *grasping* branches.   Instead of claws the primates have *flat nails,* which protect the fingers and toes as they are being extended.

Locomotion by grasping has selected for greater *flexibility* of fingers and toes with the thumb and big toe being *opposable* to the other digits.   In most lemurs, monkeys, and apes the big toe is opposable while the thumb is more inflexible or is reduced or

even absent. In these forms the hands are used as hooks as they swing from branch to branch, while the feet are used to grasp limbs upon which they rest. Here a thumb would be a hindrance and would get in the way. Man, with his erect posture, has a fairly inflexible big toe but a very flexible and opposable thumb with enormous selective value in permitting him to handle tools. It is interesting that other primates which have become adapted to life on the ground, the baboons and macaques, also possess a more highly developed hand, capable of great precision of movement.

Locomotion by grasping has also selected for *bigger hands and feet,* with pads covered with roughened skin. This allows a greater expanse of contact (more friction) with the surfaces being grasped and is the evolutionary origin of the skin whorls we record as fingerprints and toeprints.

The New World monkeys (Central and South America) have an additional device for grasping limbs. Their tails are *prehensile,* which means they can be used to grasp objects. Old World monkeys do not have prehensile tails and use them primarily to balance with. In the great apes and man the tail has been lost altogether.

To make progress through the complex and irregular environment in the trees primates must be able to investigate the surrounding habitat for hazards, foods, and shelter. The forelimbs of primates serve not only in locomotion and support but also as extendable sensing devices. Since the hands can grasp, they can also convey food to the mouth and eliminate the need for a long neck or snout.

Adaptation of Digestive Systems for an Omnivorous Diet

Primates were originally insectivorous, but today most are omnivorous or herbivorous. The food supply in tropical forests consists chiefly of plant foods and insects. Accordingly, primates are primarily eaters of fruits, leaves, and available animals. The digestive tracts of most primates are similar and differ most at the lower end, in the arrangement of the large intestine. All primates, however, have a blind pouch, the *caecum,* projecting from the large intestine. This is presumably an area where bacteria help digest foods, though its exact function remains unclear. In apes and man, a *vermiform appendix* projects from the caecum and can cause appendicitis. The appendix contains a great deal of lymphoid tissue, but its function is not yet known.

The herbivorous and omnivorous diets of primates determined the nature of *primate teeth.* The insectivore ancestors of the primates had fifty teeth, all similar in construction. Primates have fewer teeth, thirty-six in prosimians and thirty-two in Old World monkeys, apes, and man. Not only is the number of teeth reduced, but the shapes of the teeth vary, so that incisors, canines, premolars, and molars have become specialized, though not to the degree found in most mammal groups. Incisors cut food, the long canine teeth serve in defense and in aggression, and the premolars and molars are useful in grinding. The relation between diet and tooth form can be seen in the comparison between pig and primate teeth. The diet of pigs is quite similar to that of the primates, and accordingly the teeth of these two groups are also similar. This similarity led to the belief that a fossil pig discovered in Nebraska in the last century was a manlike American ape or a biblical figure drowned in the Flood.

Adaptation of Senses

At least some ground-dwelling mammals depend primarily on a sense of smell for information about their external environment. The sense of vision is poor in some ground-dwelling species, and at least some are color-blind. Watching a dog with his nose to the ground on a forest floor, you may wish you could join in experiencing that exciting world of odors (but maybe if you had you'd wish you hadn't). A sense of smell, however, cannot be an effective source of information as animals move rapidly from branch to branch. Instead, vision is the sense which gains priority in the trees. Natural selection would favor any small variation in the arrangement of the eye, its retina, and its position that allowed better sight and judgment of distance. The tree shrew and some other primitive primates have eyes on the side of their heads, but tarsiers and more advanced primates have their eyes on the front of their faces, a position which allows binocular, *stereoscopic vision*. In this form of vision the fields for each eye overlap, and each eye sees a slightly different view of an object. The difference decreases with distance from the object. For example, if you stand near a tree you will see for a distance around the right side of the tree with your right eye and around the left side with your left eye. As you back away from the tree, the degree to which you can see around the trunk decreases. This is one means by which you have learned to *judge distance*. It is a vital adaptation for the determination of the distance to the next limb. Other climbing animals, such as cats, also possess stereoscopic vision. Surprisingly, however, squirrels do not.

In addition to being able to focus on the next limb, tree dwellers must be able to see it clearly. Two kinds of light-sensitive cells are found in vertebrate retinas, rods and cones. *Rods* are sensitive to very low intensities of light and are important in twilight or night vision, where their primary function is to detect movement of objects. *Cones* are stimulated by bright light and are functional in fine vision, the perception of detail. Cones are also responsible for the discrimination of color. Most prosimian primates are nocturnal and possess only rods, but tree shrews and all the monkeys (except the night monkey), apes, and man have rods in the periphery of the retina and cones concentrated in a depression at the point on the retina where the image falls. This pit is called a *fovea*, and the mass of concentrated cones is called a *macula lutea*, or yellow spot. The cones are arranged in a grid pattern, and an image focused on the grid stimulates those cone cells upon which the light falls. Each cone cell has its own nerve fiber which can feed impulses along the optic nerve to the brain for interpretation. Visual acuity, the ability to perceive fine detail, is directly related to the number of cones and their relative distance apart.

The great development of the sense of vision in primates has been accompanied by a marked decrease in the sense of smell. No other terrestrial placental mammal has such a reduced sense of smell as apes and man.

Evolution of grasping, exploring hands and a keen sense of sight was accompanied by adaptations of the brain and nervous system, allowing finely coordinated movements of the body to be made in response to external stimuli.

Adaptation of the Brain for Coordination

Adaptations of the Skull

The shape of the skull is affected by changes in dentition, sense organs, and size and shape of the brain. Fewer teeth mean smaller jaws, a decreased sense of smell is related to a very small or absent snout, and a larger brain requires a larger braincase. The large eyes of primates are protected by a solid and sometimes massive shield of bone between eye and temple. Monkeys, apes, and man are the only mammals that have this shield. Aside from protection, the *orbital* bone probably provides better support and attachment for the eyes and prevents the jaw muscles in the changed alignment of the primate head from pressing inward on the eyes.

Primates have a habit of sitting on their haunches or otherwise holding their trunks erect while exploring the environment visually and tactually with extended hands. This behavior has selected for the positioning of primate skulls in which the anterior-posterior axis of the skull is at right angles to the vertebral column. The spinal cord leaves through the floor of the braincase rather than through the rear, as in mammals which walk on all four feet. A related change is that in all nonprimate mammals the face is a continuation of the braincase, while in primates the face is partially positioned under the brain.

Adaptations in Litter Size

Hazards associated with life in the trees select for small litter sizes since the care of infants is difficult in trees and only a few offspring can be tended by a parent. This has had profound effects since it allows primate parents to concentrate their attention on one or a few offspring for a prolonged time. The result is the possibility of a long learning period and hence of a great deal of complex learned behavior.

HUMAN EVOLUTION: PRIMATE ADAPTATIONS FOR GROUND LIFE

With an understanding of the primate forms in our ancient family tree, we can discuss how man became different from his ancestors and his contemporary relatives. We shall find that the evolution of hominid (manlike) forms followed the descent of his anthropoid ancestors from the trees.

FOSSIL POPULATIONS

For many years the fossil evidence available for the study of the origins of man and his ancestors was very scanty. The researcher had to be content with an occasional tooth, jaw, or other fragment of a skeleton. Provided with such limited evidence, the anthropological detectives were unable to choose between conflicting, thinly supported hypotheses. Usually each fragment of fossil evidence was given a new species name and often a new genus and family. The basic error in this practice lay in the failure to take into account the variations to be expected among the individuals of a variant population.

In recent years, many more fossils have been unearthed, and the picture has changed. A piece of fossil remains is now regarded as a *sample* from a population existing at a particular point in time. In many cases, variations between many fossils formerly assigned different genus and species categories are now regarded as being of no greater degree than the variations found within any population, and such variations do not warrant assignment to separate species. As a result, the number of scientific names applied to fossil evidence of primate evolution has been drastically reduced. With this shift in emphasis from individual to population the biological basis of human evolution can be better understood. It is populations which evolve, not individuals!

It often used to be stated that man descended from the apes, but this is not true, except insofar as it refers to apes now extinct which were the precursors of the hominids. Man could not have evolved from apes living today since the differences between these apes and men have required millions of years to develop, and neither the living apes nor man have possessed their present distinctive forms and functions for even *one* million years. Some fossils resemble man and some are more apelike, but as the fossils get older in geologic time, the similarities between the ape and human lines of evolution become greater. Thus the great apes of today and man share a *common ancestry;* man did not descend from modern apes, but man and the modern apes did descend from a common anthropoid ancestor. If we saw this primate in a zoo, we would undoubtedly classify him as some kind of ape.

The rocks of eastern Africa have yielded many specimens of extinct apelike forms that lived 20 to 30 million years ago, but there is little evidence relevant to the forms that existed between that period and about 2 million years ago. An apelike form called *Dryopithecus* (including the animal previously called *Proconsul*) existed 20 to 30 million years ago, and it is fairly well accepted that the dryopithecines or similar forms gave rise to the divergent lines leading to the modern great apes. The line leading to the Hominidae, the human family, either descends from the same stock of dryopithecines or diverged somewhat earlier. In the latter case *Dryopithecus* would be the ancestor of the gorilla and chimpanzee and another ape contemporary with *Dryopithecus* would be the ancestor of man. The diagram of Figure 21.2 is constructed on the assumption that *Dryopithecus* was indeed the common ancestor of both gorilla and man.

There is some disagreement about the time and nature of divergence between the ape and human lines of evolution. With the scarcity of fossil evidence it is very difficult to form a clear picture of the sequence and relationships of forms which have been extinct for millions of years. Fortunately, some clues are offered by the work of Morris Goodman, who compared protein molecules from the blood of living primates in an attempt to determine their degrees of relationship. His studies show that man's closest living relatives are the chimpanzee and gorilla with the chimpanzee being the closest. The blood proteins of the gorilla, chimpanzee, and man differ from that of the orangutan and gibbon to a degree sufficient to suggest that the orangutan and gibbon line of evolution diverged from the other line long before the human line diverged from the line leading to gorilla and chimpanzee.

FIGURE 21.2 A generalized scheme of evolutionary divergence among apes and man. *Dryopithecus*, or similar forms, gave rise to lines of evolution leading to modern orangutans, gorillas, chimpanzees, and man. Gorillas, chimpanzees, and man are the product of a split among an unknown ancestral form that arose from *Dryopithecus*. The line beginning with *Ramapithecus* is the Hominidae, the human family. The gibbon probably diverged from a form ancestral to *Dryopithecus*. There are no known fossils of the ancestors of the orangutan.

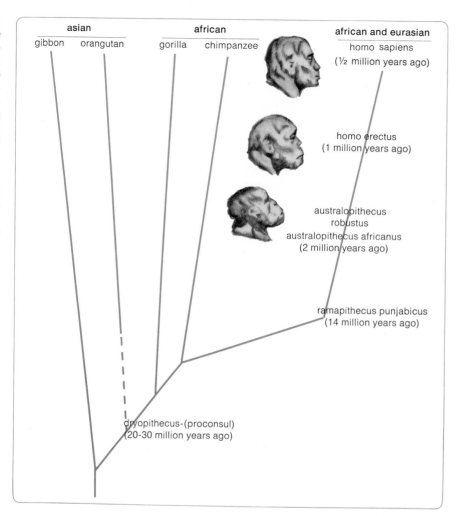

asian
gibbon   orangutan

african
gorilla   chimpanzee

african and eurasian
homo sapiens
(½ million years ago)

homo erectus
(1 million years ago)

australopithecus robustus
australopithecus africanus
(2 million years ago)

ramapithecus punjabicus
(14 million years ago)

dryopithecus-(proconsul)
(20-30 million years ago)

HOMINIDAE AND THE STAGES OF HUMAN EVOLUTION

Although some debate exists, Hominidae, the human family, consists of three genera and four species, and the sequence of their forms in the fossil record is the history of the evolution of man. The forms, and the time of their first appearance are *Ramapithecus punjabicus* (14 million years ago), *Australopithecus africanus* (2 million years ago), *Homo erectus* (1 million years ago), and *H. sapiens* (500,000 years ago).

Specimens of *R. punjabicus* have been found in rock from the Siwalik Hills in northern India and from Fort Ternan, Kenya. The fossils from India have been dated as about 12 to 15 million years old and the African forms about 14 million years old.

Only jawbones and teeth are known, but they provide a glimpse of how these primates ate, what they ate, the shape of the face, and the position of the head on the neck. They provide enough evidence to allow *Ramapithecus* to be considered as the earliest form of the family of man. It is interesting to note that this species had roughly the same distribution as its proposed ancestor, *Dryopithecus,* whose fossils date from a period over 6 million years earlier.

A great deal more fossil evidence is needed before the story of the early evolution of the Hominidae will be fully known, but some parts of the story can already be inferred. *Ramapithecus,* or another as yet unknown early hominid, left the tropical forest, became bipedal (walked on hind legs), and used tools. There is evidence that an important change in climate took place in Africa 15 to 20 million years ago, reducing the total area of forest. The changing conditions as well as the pressure on any species to compete and to invade as much of the available habitat as possible probably led the primitive hominids to spend more and more time on the forest floor and on the adjoining plains.

Because of their adaptations for life in the trees, the early hominids already possessed several traits which proved advantageous on the open plains. They were able to stand erect for varying periods of time and with their excellent vision could detect both predators and prey. With their grasping hands they could carry and use objects as tools or throw and wield objects as weapons. *Ramapithecus* had canine teeth shaped more like those of a modern man than the large canines of apes and monkeys. Since apes and monkeys use their canines for defense, it is accepted that small canines indicate a dependence upon tools for defense and procuring food. Commitment to the use of tools signaled a significant turning point in human evolution and introduced new pressures of natural selection. Selection pressures would now favor increasingly more dexterous *hands,* a larger *brain* specialized for coordination of the hands, better *vision* to use while shaping and using tools, and a more effective *upright posture* allowing the hands to be freed for toolmaking and use. Any new advantageous variation in any one of these four factors—brain, hand, vision, or bipedalism—would exert new selection pressures on the other three. A new factor endowing these primitive hominids with an enormous advantage was the extent of social behavior and social structure of which they were (or became) capable. Social interaction was necessary for protection of the group and for group hunting in the new habitat of the plain or forest floor. Given the value of social interaction, it is easy to understand the source of selective pressure in favor of adaptations leading to the development of oral communication and speech sounds. With the commitment to the use of tools, the requirement for social organization, and the onset of evolution of language, a set of novel selective restrictions and biases was established. Selection for smaller teeth and more flexible jaws to allow the formation of distinct sounds and for a brain which could deal with verbalized signals indicating objects and thoughts followed. The origin of the ability for abstract thinking and reasoning can be traced to these evolutionary processes. This new direction in evolution, the evolution of the hominid mind, probably began about 14 million years ago. Fossil evidence suggests that brains of the size and complexity of those possessed by modern man did not appear until the development of the genus *Homo,* more than 13 million years later.

Since only teeth and parts of jaws from *Ramapithecus* have been found, we do not know whether he actually made tools and we know nothing of his brain size, gait, or vision. The fossil record of man's history is then interrupted by a long gap about which we have no information. Our story resumes again about 2 million years ago, when *Australopithecus* arrived.

Australopithecus was first discovered when the fossilized skull of a female child was found in 1924 in South Africa (see Figure 21.3). Its name indicates this place of discovery, since Austral means "southern" and pithecus means "ape." Since that time, various pieces of over 100 individuals of this "southern ape man," as some chose to call it, have been found in Africa. Many of the specimens have been given different family and generic names, but they are all placed today under one of the two accepted species of the genus *Australopithecus, A. africanus* and *A. robustus.* The specimens ranged from 4 to 5 feet in height and had a brain size averaging 500 cubic centimeters, about the size of the brain of a gorilla. Backbone, pelvis, and limbs were quite human, and their arms were shorter than those of apes. They were bipedal, and unlike apes their fossils reveal that they lived away from forests, in dry open country. Their teeth were essentially human and were arranged in a curving row rather than in three sides of a rectangle, as in apes. Their canines were no bigger than their incisors and did not project above the other teeth like tusks. *Australopithecus* exhibited certain features considered apelike and others more human. The braincase and large jaws were apelike, but the teeth and the rest of the body were human in form (see Figure 21.4).

The two species of *Australopithecus* occupied different ecological niches. *A. robustus* was the larger of the two, about 5 feet tall, and had large teeth and massive jaws. An analysis of the fossil evidence indicates that *A. robustus* was a herbivore who ground seeds, nuts, and other plant food with his large teeth and jaws. It has been suggested that *A. robustus* remained on the forest floor and did not venture into the savanna plains. From such evidence it is possible to suggest that modern man's ancestor was not *A. robustus* but *A. africanus,* a small form about 4 feet tall with small teeth and light jaws, probably an omnivore. Both species of *Australopithecus* used tools.

A. africanus was a predator who hunted in groups. It is believed that he also ate plants, but there is no evidence to support the idea directly. There is, however, a great deal of fossil evidence of the animals he ate and the tools he used to kill the animals. Some of his tools were pebbles, and some were thighbones of antelopes. *A. africanus* was primarily a carnivore, and his adaptations must have been successful because his fossils are found throughout at least 1 million years of geologic history, from 2 to 1 million years ago.

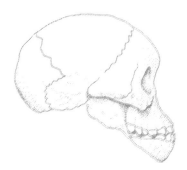

FIGURE 21.3 Drawing of skull of *Australopithecus africanus. (After Dart, The American Museum of Natural History.)*

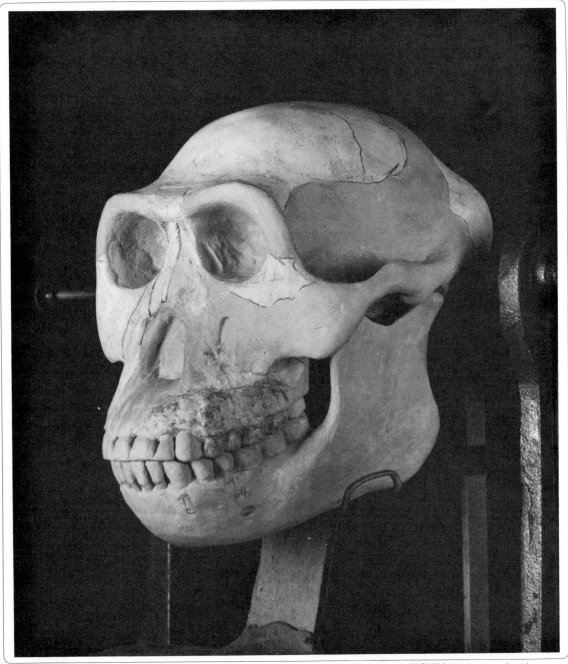

FIGURE 21.4 *Australopithecus robustus* (*Plesianthropus*), South African man-ape. (*Courtesy of The American Museum of Natural History.*)

By the end of this million years of evolution, the descendants of *A. africanus* had changed quite considerably under the accelerating pressure of natural selection described earlier. His brain size had doubled to an average of 1,000 cubic centimeters, he existed in organized social groups, he made much more refined stone tools, and he had learned to use fire. These are such distinctive changes from the traits which characterize *Australopithecus* that it is appropriate that this stage in evolution be known by a different scientific name, one which portrays the development of some clearly human traits. The name assigned to this stage in human evolution is *Homo erectus,* the genus name *Homo* placing these organisms in the human genus.

The famous German evolutionist and embryologist Ernst Haekel proposed in 1866 that the so-called missing link between man and the apes should be named *Pithecanthropus* (ape, man). In 1891, Eugene Dubois announced that he was going to discover the missing link and left for Java, where he thought he would find it. Within a few weeks he found what he was looking for, the top of a skull, some teeth, and a thighbone. We know today that there is no such thing as a single missing link. There are, instead, many links forming each of the human and ape lines of evolution leading back to the ancestral population from which the two lines diverged. Dubois named his find *Pithecanthropus erectus,* "erect ape-man," but it became commonly known as Java man. In 1937 a second more complete skull of the same species was

FIGURE 21.5 Reconstruction of head and skull of a *Homo erectus pekinensis* (*Sinanthropus*) woman. (*Courtesy of The American Museum of Natural History.*)

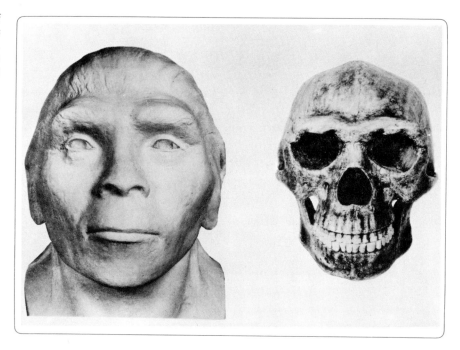

found. It revealed a brain volume of 775 to 1,000 cubic centimeters but a face that was apelike compared to that of modern man, with great overhanging browridges. Java man was found to be 700,000 years old.

In 1927, excavations in cave deposits 30 miles out of Peking, China, revealed forty specimens of men, women, and children of a fossil type which was named *Sinanthropus* (China, man) commonly known as Peking man (see Figure 21.5). The six incomplete skulls found there had brain volumes ranging from 1,000 to 1,300 cubic centimeters. Analysis of the animal bones and pollen found with the bones indicated the Peking man lived about 400,000 years ago. He lived in caves, was primarily a hunter of deer, used tools of quartz and other hard stones, and ate a cherrylike fruit. Remains of ashes indicate that he used fire.

Today Java man and Peking man are regarded as two races, or subspecies, of *Homo erectus*. Java man was a southern race called *H. erectus erectus,* and Peking man was a northern race called *H. erectus pekinensis.* It is believed that other races of this species were distributed over Asia, Europe, and Africa. Since many names of fossil finds appear in social science textbooks and the press, you may be interested in seeing how such authorities as Bernard Campbell and William Howells have placed these fossil finds as subspecies within the species *H. erectus,* though we shall not take the time to discuss them all (Table 21.1).

As shown in Table 21.1, *H. erectus* was very successful and was able to extend his distribution over Asia, Europe, and Africa. Almost all the fossils of *Australopithecus,* the gene pool from which *H. erectus* developed, have been found in Africa. *H. erectus* had a brain twice as large as *Australopithecus* and practiced social hunting with more advanced weapons. He was successful in hunting the large mammals so abundant throughout the tropical regions of Eurasia and Africa. The early forms such as Java man had arms, legs, and torso very much like modern man, but they had

GRADE	EUROPE	NORTH AFRICA	EAST AFRICA	SOUTH AFRICA	EAST ASIA	SOUTHEAST ASIA
5	H. sapiens (Verteszöllös)‡					
4						(H. erectus soloensis)†
3	H. erectus heidelbergensis*	H. erectus mauritanicus*	H. erectus leakeyi*		H. erectus pekinensis*	
2						H. erectus erectus*
1			H. erectus habilis*	H. erectus capensis*	(H. erectus lantianensis)*	H. erectus modjokertensis*

TABLE 21.1 Eight (starred) subspecies of *Homo erectus* as placed in order of appearance and geographical location by Bernard Campbell and William Howells. From William H. Howells, ''Homo Erectus.'' Copyright © 1966 by Scientific American, Inc. All rights reserved.

* The grade 1 forms lived about 1 million years ago and grade 3 about 0.5 million years ago.
† Solo man of Southeast Asia lived only 20,000 years ago, and there is much controversy over its placement as a late *H. erectus* of a long-lived form of an early *H. sapiens.*
‡ Verteszöllös Man is a form recently uncovered in Hungary and has been placed by its discoverer within the species of modern man.

somewhat smaller brains, about 700 cubic centimeters, heavy browridges, and massive jaws and teeth. The later forms of *H. erectus* such as Peking man and Heidelberg man had brains of 1,000 cubic centimeters and over but still retained the heavy browridges and massive jaws. It should be noted here that brain size is not a simple index of intelligence. Modern man varies in brain size from 850 to 1,700 cubic centimeters with no clear correlation between size and intelligence. Furthermore the body size was smaller in earlier forms, so that the brain-size-to-body ratio may have approximated that in modern man.

Peking man and Heidelberg man occupied areas more northerly than the tropics and lived in caves warmed with fires. There is no proof, but they probably wore skins from the animals they killed to keep warm. Their culture was becoming more complex and more successful.

It is accepted by many investigators that fossils discovered at Swanscombe, England, and Steinheim, Germany, represent the earliest *Homo sapiens*. The skulls are believed to be between 100,000 and 400,000 years old, which would indicate a blank period of over 100,000 years between *H. erectus* and these early forms of *H. sapiens*. During this time the average adult brain size increased from about 1,100 to 1,300 cubic centimeters, and if the location of the fossils is indicative, the early *sapiens* had gone even farther away from the tropics of their ancestors and had spread across the grassy plains of northern Europe during a warm interval between glaciations. Large grazing mammals of the deer family were abundant and were actively hunted by these people.

The Steinheim-Swanscombe population in northern Europe was diminished by an extensive climate change brought about by the advance of another glacial age. By the end of that glacial age, the former population had been replaced by a new one, Neanderthal man. Neanderthal man may have descended from the Steinheim-Swanscombe group, but he differed from them in having more massive jaws and teeth more like those of *H. erectus* than those of the Steinheim-Swanscombe group. Neanderthal man was quite successful and became distributed throughout Europe, Asia, and Africa during the years between 100,000 and 40,000 years ago. Table 21.2 lists the subspecies of *H. sapiens*.

Table 21.2 Subspecies of *Homo sapiens**

APPROXIMATE TIME SPAN IN YEARS BEFORE THE PRESENT	EUROPE	ASIA	AFRICA	SOUTHEAST ASIA
0–35,000	Modern subspecies of *H. sapiens*†			
35,000–100,000	*neanderthalensis*	*palestinus*	*rhodensis*	*soloensis*
100,000–200,000	*steinheimensis*			

* Reprinted from Bernard Campbell, *Human Evolution*, p. 351, Aldine Publishing Company, Chicago, 1966; copyright © 1966 by Bernard Grant Campbell.
† Modern man probably entered Australia and America less than 40,000 years ago.

Neanderthal man lived in northern Europe during the long and extremely harsh glacial period. From Scandinavia a sheet of ice stretched across the continent, reaching as far as northern Germany, south-central Russia, and northern England. The Alps and other European mountain ranges were heavily glaciated. Along the margins of the glaciers a region resembling arctic tundra existed. Perhaps it was the introduction of such harsh environmental pressures which selected for the body characteristics identified with the Neanderthal race. Neanderthal man was stocky, about 5 feet high, and had massive bones and a large head with prominent browridges, a receding forehead, a strong and chinless mandible, large teeth, and a high brain capacity, averaging about 1,450 cubic centimeters. He has often been described as having a stooping posture, but this description is not valid since it was based upon one fossil of a man crippled with arthritis.

Neanderthals made stone tools not only for piercing and cutting but also for scraping animal hides, probably for clothing. The hazards of the glacial times were severe, and the Neanderthals added rock shelters to their customary caves and used fire for heating their homes as well as for cooking. They hunted wild game with wooden spears and balls made of stone or hardened clay. There is evidence of religion since their dead were buried with some degree of ceremony. Culture was becoming more complex and the human family more successful.

About 40,000 years ago, the Neanderthal race of *H. sapiens* was replaced in Europe by people of an entirely modern type called *H. sapiens sapiens*. The invaders were from outside Europe, probably Southwest Asia. Their culture, quite different from the Neanderthals, is now called Aurignacian. Because the fossil evidence of this race was first uncovered at Cro-Magnon in central France in 1868, the race is often called Cro-Magnon man (see Figure 21.6). As is typical of man, they were far from uniform physically, but most of them were tall (some over 6 feet) and of what we would regard as an athletic physique. Bone measurements of their fossils seem similar to those of people living today in various parts of the world, Swedes, Basques in Spain, and Kabyles in Algeria. The fossils called Grimaldi people resemble some groups of modern African Negroes. The lesson from this is clear: Man has always been variable, and *there has never been a typical man*.

The derivation of man is not completely certain since there is not an unbroken chain of fossils linking modern man to *Australopithecus,* but new fossils are being discovered every year. Missing parts of the puzzle are rapidly being filled in and clarify the route human evolution has followed. Even though the fossil record is still very incomplete and speculation is still necessary to fill in the gaps, we know enough to reject certain erroneous ideas offered in the past and still occasionally proposed. A German named Klaatsch, for example, suggested about 50 years ago that the various races of modern man arose by parallel evolution, the white race from an ancestor similar to a chimpanzee, the black race from a gorillalike ancestor, and the yellow race from an orangutan. Obviously, such an origin would have produced three separate species, each reproductively isolated from the other.

FIGURE 21.6 Reconstruction of Cro-Magnon man, a *Homo sapiens* race present over 40,000 years ago. (*Courtesy of The American Museum of Natural History.*)

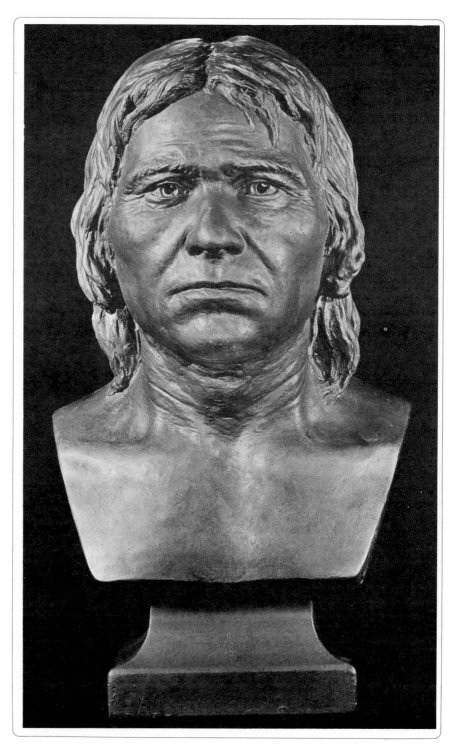

At present, an acceptable hypothesis for the evolution of man is that the human family began with *Ramapithecus punjabicus* about 14 million years ago. The gene pool present in the *Ramapithecus* population gave rise to *Australopithecus africanus* 2 to 3 million years ago, a group that walked fully erect and used tools. *A. africanus* became more and more skillful with tools—and entered into social interactions of increased complexity, with the result that greater emphasis was placed upon learned, as opposed to instinctive, behavior. As these adaptations appeared, *A. africanus* gradually evolved into a new species identifiable as *Homo erectus*. With the advantage of unparalleled physical and mental adaptations, *H. erectus* spread throughout Europe, Asia, and Africa. The gene pool of these creatures continued to change through time until it possessed the traits of modern man, *H. sapiens*.

Stanley M. Garn[1] views populations of *Homo sapiens* on three levels of complexity. He recognizes *microraces* as camps, villages, and cities; *local races* as breeding populations isolated from other local races by distance, geographical barriers, or social prohibitions; and *geographical races* as collections of local races isolated from similar groups by such major geographical barriers as oceans or mountain ranges. The following list of geographical races and their component local races is adapted from his book. (See Figure 21.7 for examples of those races marked with asterisks.)

A   European geographical race
1   *Northwest European local race: Scandinavia, northern Germany, northern France, the Low Countries, United Kingdom, and Ireland
2   *Lapp local race: arctic Scandinavia and Finland
3   *Northeast European local race: Poland, Russia, and most of the present population of Siberia
4   Alpine local race: from central France, south Germany, Switzerland, northern Italy, eastward to the shores of the Black Sea
5   *Mediterranean local race: peoples on both sides of Mediterranean from Tangier to the Dardanelles and to Arabia
6   *Iranian local race: peoples of Asiatic Turkey through to Iran and India

CLASSIFICATION OF HOMO SAPIENS INTO RACES
[1] From Stanley M. Garn, *Human Races*, 2d ed., 1969. Courtesy of Charles C Thomas, Publisher, Springfield, Ill.

FIGURE 21.7 (a) Northwest European, (b) Lapp, (c) Northeast European, (d) Mediterranean, (e) Iranian.

A

B

C

D

E

F

B African geographical race
   7 *East African local race: East Africa, Ethiopia, and part of the Sudan
   8 *Sudanese local race: most of the Sudan
   9 *Forest Negro local race: West Africa and much of the Congo
 10 *Bantu local race: South Africa and part of East Africa
 11 Bushman and Hottentot local race: aboriginal inhabitants of South Africa
 12 *African Pygmy local race: rain forests of equatorial Africa

G

H

I

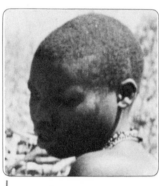

J

FIGURE 21.7 (f) East African, (g) Sudanese, (h) Forest Negro, (i) Bantu, (j) African Pygmy, (k) Hindu, (l) Extreme Mongoloid, (m) Southeast Asiatic, (n) Tibetan, (o) Dravidian, (p) Central American, (q) South American. (*Courtesy of the United Nations.*)

C Asiatic geographical race
 13 Turkic local race: Turkestan and western China
 14 *Tibetan local race: Sikkim and Tibet northward to Soviet Mongolia
 15 North Chinese local race: northern and central China and Mongolia
 16 *Extreme Mongoloid local race: Siberia, Mongolia, Korea, and Japan
 17 Ainu local race: aboriginal population of northern Japan
 18 Eskimo local race: arctic America
 19 *Southeast Asiatic local race: South China to Thailand, Burma, Malaya, and Indonesia

K

L

M

D   Indian geographical race
   20   *Hindu local race: India and Pakistan
   21   *Dravidian local race: aboriginal peoples of southern India and Ceylon

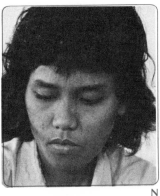

N

O

E   Australian geographical race
   22   Murrayian local race: aboriginal population of southeastern Australia
   23   Carpentarian local race: aboriginal population of northern and central Australia
F   Melanesian-Papuan geographical race
   24   Melanesian-Papuan local race: New Guinea to Fiji
G   Micronesian geographical race
   25   Micronesian local race: islands of the western Pacific
H   Polynesian geographical race
   26   Polynesian local race: islands of the central and eastern Pacific
I   Amerindian geographical race
   27   North American local race: indigenous populations of Canada and the United States
   28   *Central American local race: from southwestern United States through Central America to Bolivia
   29   Circum-Caribbean local race: southern Florida, islands of Caribbean, and lowlands of Central America
   30   *South American local race: primarily the agricultural peoples of Peru, Bolivia, and Chile
   31   Fuegian local race: nonagricultural inhabitants of southern tip of South America

P

Q

"Hybrid" local races of recent origin

32   Ladino local race: an emerging population of Central and South America formed by the interbreeding of Southern European and Central and South American local races

33   Neo-Hawaiian local race: a highly variable population formed by the mixture of northwest and southern European with Polynesian and Chinese/Japanese and Filipino peoples.

34   South African colored ("Cape Colored") local race: a population formed by the fusion of Bushmen-Hottentot, Bantu, European, Malaysian, and Indian Peoples in South Africa

35   North American colored ("American Negro") local race: a population formed by various degrees of mixture of West African and northwest European peoples in the United States, Bermuda, the West Indies, and Canada

K   In addition, a puzzling group of small populations isolated from each other but with similar appearances must be listed.

36   Pacific Negrito local race: small, dark, and frizzy-haired groups of people scattered from Philippines to the Andamans, Malaya, and New Guinea; despite their name they are not related to African Pygmies, and their relationship to each other is not known.

THE APPEARANCE OF HUMAN TRAITS

Many of the traits we consider to be characteristic of *Homo sapiens* were actually already present in *Australopithecus* 2 million years ago.   The structures and functions of modern man did not appear all at once as a package but evolved at different rates and attained a human level of development at different times.   We can use various criteria as signposts to date the appearance of human traits in the fossil record.

Foot

The big toe of chimpanzees extends somewhat to the side, and since they walk on the outside of the foot, almost none of their weight is supported by the big toe. Because apes walk on all fours, their body weight is supported by three appendages while the fourth is being extended.   Man's upright gait, however, requires balancing his body weight *on one foot* while the other is being extended.   Man accomplishes this by rotating the foot so it extends straight ahead or slightly out to the side.   Man's big toes are in line with his feet and support forty percent of his weight.   This weight is balanced and distributed over the ball of the foot and the big toe while he is walking.   Instead of using a triangle of *three legs* to support his weight like apes walking on the ground, man has a triangle of *three centers of weight on each foot,* namely, the big toe and ball, the region behind the little toe, and the heel.   Try standing on one foot to see how this triangle of weight centers operates.   The several fossil feet of *Australopithecus* known are almost identical to those of modern man; we could say that they are 99 percent like ours.   Thus, 2 million years ago an essentially human foot had evolved.

Pelvis

The *pelvis* of an ape is very long, but man's is very short.   The pelvis of *Australopithecus* is about 90 percent like ours and differs only slightly in its ball-and-socket joint, a difference which would affect the internal rotation of the leg as it is swung forward.   This slight difference in the pelvis of *Australopithecus* provided them with a less efficient walking style than that of modern man.   Perhaps they could walk only half as far in a day as we can.

The tail as an external structure is missing in all apes and men.   It can be assumed that the tail became modified at least 15 million years ago.   Prosimians and monkeys use the tail as a balancing organ, but in apes and men the tail has become so modified that it is very short and curves forward to form part of the floor of the abdomen.   Apes and man are larger animals than monkeys and spend much of their time with their chest and abdomen upright in a vertical position.   The rudimentary tail helps in supporting the weight of the contents of the pelvis.

Tail

The hands of gorillas and men differ in that the thumbs of gorillas are much shorter and stiffer than man's and have only a short muscle connected to them.   Man's thumb is much longer and more flexible than the gorilla's, and a long muscle is attached to it.   This long muscle extends from the forearm, moves the thumb about, and allows the unique contact between the fleshy portions of the thumb and fingers. The thumb and muscle of *Australopithecus* were roughly intermediate between those of gorilla and modern man.   We could say that its hand was 50 percent human.

Hand

Tools of *Australopithecus* are revealed when his campsites are excavated and animal bones and stones are found.   The bones are those of the animals which served him as food, but what of the stones?   They were all about the same size, that of the human hand.   If a group of people were told to go to a riverbank and collect stones, they would probably return with stones very similar to those found in these campsites.   There are several arguments against the objection that these were simply stones formed in that area.   The campsite region is of volcanic origin, but these were river pebbles, and the nearest river was 3 to 15 miles away.   *Australopithecus* had carried them at least that far and had used them as tools, since a fifth of them had been chipped, the flakes having apparently been used for cutting.   Pebble tools were crude: You could learn to make them in an hour, but they must have offered fossil man many advantages since tools of this kind were made and used for over 1 million years.   A more complex stone tool appears in a fossil record about 600,000 years ago, and anthropology students can duplicate them only after considerable practice. By 400,000 years ago, even more complex tools, including Acheulian hand axes, appear.   The makers of these tools clearly belonged to the genus *Homo* and evidently developed considerable skill at toolmaking.   The use of bone as tools is indicated as far back as *Australopithecus* in South Africa and was increasingly developed through the following thousands of years.   There is no way of telling when man first started using wooden tools such as spears and sticks for walking or probing, but they may have originated even earlier than *H. erectus*.   With the evolution of more complex tools there must have been an appropriate gain in the ability to learn and to communicate the elements of knowledge needed for their construction and use.

Skull The skull is shaped primarily by the brain and teeth which it houses and by the posture of the animal. A male gorilla has big canine teeth, but those of the female are small. The male's large canines are adaptations for defense of the troop. With man, tools are used for defense instead of teeth; large canines are not necessary for survival. Selection pressures, perhaps speech and its requirement for a flexible jaw, selected against the evolution of large, interlocking canines. *Ramapithecus* had smaller canines than *Dryopithecus*, and *Australopithecus* had canines almost identical to *H. sapiens*. This is perhaps an additional argument that the members of the human family have been using tools for at least 2 million years, perhaps longer. Additional inference from the skull indicating early tool use is provided by the size of the neck muscles. The gorilla has large neck muscles which undoubtedly aid in fighting with the teeth, a primary method of offense and defense in these primates. A gorilla can pick up another gorilla weighing as much as 500 pounds with his teeth. *Australopithecus*, however, had small neck muscles; it is likely that tool use in the form of weapons supplanted the offensive role of the teeth to a great extent in this early form.

Face The evolution of the face is affected by the evolution of dentition. Most of the central part of the face consists of teeth, their roots, and their supportive bone. Apes have a much larger, lower face than we have because they have much larger canines, which crowd their face forward. All our teeth are smaller than those of the apes, and we have a smaller face. This, however, causes our nose to protrude in an unapelike way. *Australopithecus* had canines almost identical to ours, but his teeth were generally larger, and he probably had a heavier, lower face. To picture how you would look if you had teeth of equivalent size, touch the end of your nose and draw a line through the air forward in an arc down to your chin. This line would circumscribe your lower face if you were an ape.

Brain Though brain size, or rather the *range* of brain sizes of a hominid species, can be used only as the crudest indicator of mental capacity, it is interesting to summarize the changes in brain size which have occurred since *Australopithecus*. The brain of *Australopithecus* was about 500 cubic centimeters, about the same size as that of a gorilla. Peking man, or *H. erectus*, had a characteristic brain size of 1,000 cubic centimeters, while modern man *averages* 1,350 to 1,400 cubic centimeters (as pointed out above, the range is 850 to 1,750 cubic centimeters in modern man). We could consider the evolutionary progression of brain sizes to be one-third, two-thirds, and three-thirds that of modern human brain size. The brain doubled in size in 1 million years and increased 50 percent during the following 500,000 years. During the past 500,000 years, the brain has increased in size less than 20 percent; the brain was almost modern in size 500,000 years ago. Size of the brain does not, of course, indicate the nature of the brain. In comparing the brains of apes and man we find that man's brain has many more neurons in the cortex, a much bigger cerebrum, more fissures, and more axons and dendrites on the neurons.   Thus, not only the *volume* but the *nature* of the brain is different in apes and man.

The sensory area and motor area concerned with receiving sensory impulses from the hand and sending motor impulses which move the hand are three times larger in man than in the ape.   From the map of the brain shown in Figure 11.8 you will recall that there is a very large area concerned with *hand skill* and with memory, planning, and speech; we have a *social brain*.   Tool use created a selective pressure for development of hand-skill areas in the brain, and social behavior promoted a selection for speech, memory, and the other mental factors important for a social existence.   Since the making of refined tools must have involved learning and communication, we can guess that such tools are to be associated with a high development of social attributes, requiring a brain of average size 1,000 cubic centimeters or more.   This is the level attained only by the genus *Homo*.

The skin and hair of man are unique since no other primate is as hairless as man or capable of sweating as much.   Several theories have been proposed to explain why man is so hairless, but the most widely accepted is that man evolved as a predator in the tropics, where his active pursuit of prey caused a high rate of metabolism.   This effort would get him food but would also tend to increase his body temperature to dangerous extremes.   It is believed that the problem of body heat selected for an increasingly greater concentration of sweat glands.   The evaporation of the sweat cools the skin and dispels the heat.   The efficiency of this system is increased as the amount of body hair present to slow down the rate of evaporation decreases.   As a result, there was selection pressure *against* body hair but *for* more sweat glands. Eyebrows direct sweat from the forehead away from the eyes, and eyelashes prevent foreign matter from getting into the eyes.

Skin and Hair

This does not explain, however, the presence of hair on the head, in the armpits, and in the pubic region.   The hair on the head may be necessary to prevent heat damage to the brain.   It has been speculated that hair in the armpits and pubic region serves both for prevention of friction and for sexual identification and attraction, but the real reasons for localized hair in the human being remains mysterious.   Most animals have marking which identify their sex.   Antlers of deer, the large canines of baboons, and the brilliant plumage of many birds are all identified with the male of the species. With human beings, the difference in body build and external reproductive structures is amplified in sexual identification by additional features.   Odors diffusing from the hair in armpit and pubic areas may have played an important part in sexual attraction in earlier evolutionary stages.   This explanation would account for the high concentration of scent glands in these areas in human beings.

Almost all other primates mate by mounting from the rear while in the trees.   The visible external features of the back side of females change during their period of

Mating

receptivity, or estrus. Man, however, is a bipedal ground-dwelling primate without periods of estrus. He usually mates from the front, a position which probably became possible with the adaptation to ground life. A major factor was undoubtedly the change in structure of the pelvis accompanying erect posture. Visual features of sexual attraction of females during human evolution have appeared on the front, rather than being confined primarily to the back of the female. Other male primates respond to a "blushing" of sexual skin on the rear of the female primates, but human males respond to features on the front as well as the back and lateral aspects of the female's body. Pubic hair, which is almost lacking in other primates, is distributed in man across the lower part of the abdomen as well as the genital region. Rounded breasts with an expanded area of sensitive skin surrounding the nipples is highly apparent in the human female but not developed in other primates. Another source of sexual attraction in the human female is her face, with its delicate features which for millenniums have been emphasized with cosmetics. It is evident that the criterion of attractiveness in mate selection has provided a powerful selective force in the evolution of what we call human beauty.

As noted above, other primates have periods of estrus corresponding to the time of ovulation. With the increase in estrogen at that time the female becomes not only receptive to males but seeks them out and stimulates them. Estrus begins a few days before ovulation and ceases a few days after. During the remainder of her estrus cycle, or if she is pregnant or nursing, the female generally does not copulate, although there are a few primate species for which this is not true. Sexual behavior of all mammals but the human is under the powerful control of hormones; the female exercises less choice. Human beings, however, have lost estrus and may be sexually active at almost any time they choose. The cerebral cortex of the brain has become dominant over the effects of the hormones, which continue their rhythmical change in level each month just as they do in all other mammals. It might seem reasonable for human females to show a greater interest in mating at the time of ovulation, but the studies of Kinsey show that the greatest interest in sex is reported by many women to be the last few days before menstruation. Since sexual drives are under conscious control, they may be influenced by social and cultural customs of the group. Because of the loss of estrus, human females do not disrupt normal social behavior with sexual mania and may maintain a relatively permanent relationship with a male without interference from other competing males. A human female may also continue to mate while pregnant and during the milk production that follows. The constant receptivity of the human female is believed to be one of the strongest forces directing the evolution of the human family.

Since other primates mount from the rear, the clitoris of the females in these animals is long enough to touch the penis during mating. The human female, however, has a very small clitoris since mounting from the front increases the stimulation of the organ and a larger size may even cause discomfort. Human females have larger labia and longer vaginas than other primates. This is believed to be an adaptation which decreases the chances for infection from sitting or lying on the ground, an activity in which early human beings probably spent a great deal of time. The longer vagina of the female accompanied selection for a longer penis in the males. As a result, the human male has a penis which is longer than that of any other primate, with the possible exception of the baboon. Some monkeys have a penis resembling that of the human, but the mighty gorilla, which weighs twice as much as man, has a penis less than 3 inches long. Monkeys and apes, however, have a small bone or cartilage called a *baculum* extending the length of the penis. The baculum stiffens the penis of monkeys and apes but has been lost during the course of human evolution. The increase in blood pressure during sexual excitement of the human male causes the penis to become sufficiently rigid for penetration of the vagina. More care and gentleness is necessary for the insertion of such a penis than with the bone-reinforced type, and the violence and speed of the ape and monkey-type mating is reduced.

The body reached human form long before the brain. To grasp this concept of the origin of most of our body in the remote past we can regard the body as consisting of three functional areas: (1) arms, shoulders, and trunk, (2) pelvis and legs, and (3) the skull.

A REVIEW OF THREE FUNCTIONAL AREAS

1   The *arms, shoulders,* and *trunk area* of apes and man are very much alike. The general plan of this area developed 8 to 10 *million years ago*. No one but a primate would have designed buses, subways, and trains with straps to hang from. No one but a primate would extend his arms to the side while stretching or rest his head on his hands or fold his hands across his chest or scratch with his hands.
2   The *pelvis* and *leg area* of man is about 2 million years old. As we have seen, *Australopithecus* had feet which were 99 percent human and a pelvis that was 90 percent human. He walked with an erect posture which allowed him to carry tools, food, and children. The face and head became essentially human in the modern sense 30,000 to 40,000 years ago at the height of the last ice age.
3   The *skull area* reflects the many effects of the development of erect posture, tool use, excellent vision, and a large brain. The evolution of erect posture was linked to the evolution of a brain which could coordinate eyes and hands in the use of tools and which would permit social interaction. Slight variations in the brain allowing improvements in these directions would have great value in natural selection. In terms of geologic time, the evolution of the brain was quite rapid once the commitment to tools and to social units became established to the degree that they were vital to survival.

In preceding chapters, it has been emphasized that structure and function are related, that structure affects function and function affects structure. This same principle

STRUCTURE AND FUNCTION, FORM AND BEHAVIOR

applies on the level of the organism. A very good example is found in the evolution of man, where behavioral adaptations resulting from the development of social organization and use of tools have caused a vast number of changes in structure of the body, including changes in posture, feet, pelvis, hands, skull, teeth, brain, and other human traits. With the evolution of a potent social brain *learned behavior became the agent exerting selective pressure on structure*. Human beings are social beings; the structural form of our ancestors evolved hand in hand with their social behavior.

ECOLOGY OF EARLY MAN

All primates were originally insectivorous, but most of them had become primarily vegetarian by modern times. Tree-dwelling primates eat not only foliage but fruits and seeds as well. This is a very nutritious diet since plants store a great deal of food in seeds. Most *H. sapiens* living today exist on plant food, but this does not mean that during his evolution man has continued the mainly vegetarian diet of his tree-dwelling ancestors. Actually, his ancestors were scavengers and predatory carnivores.

Australopithecus africanus killed and ate birds, lizards, rodents, and, according to evidence from South Africa, baboons. The fossil record reveals many baboon bones but does not indicate that he ate plants although most experts assume that he did. He probably spent much of his day foraging, as modern baboons do, pulling up grass and eating it as well as any small animals found in the grass. Leakey, the discoverer of most of the bones of this fossil man, believes that *A. africanus* were scavengers on the kills of larger predators and defended themselves as a group. The turning point in the evolution of *Australopithecus* into *Homo* is associated with the enlargement of man's diet to include the larger grazing mammals on the plains of Africa and, later, the plains of Europe and Asia. It signaled the advent of *social hunting*.

SOCIAL HUNTING

Eating large mammals provided a source of food throughout the year, even when plant foods were either dried up or frozen. Killing large mammals required man to hunt in packs in a manner superficially similar to wolves and jackals. This required cooperation, but social ventures of this kind could yield enough food for all to eat for several days. To eat the large mammals, man had to cooperate in the killing as well as in the food-sharing that followed. This change in the ecological and social habits of early man brought about profound changes in the selection pressures exerted upon evolving man. Bernard Campbell has described some of these changes.[1]

[1] Reprinted by permission from Bernard Campbell, *Human Evolution*, pp. 202–204, Aldine Publishing Company, Chicago, 1966; copyright © 1966 by Bernard Grant Campbell.

. . . *It is clear that cooperative hunting and food-sharing changed the social and physical attributes of early man in a number of very important ways.*

1   *Success in hunting required cooperation among males.*

2   *Nursing and pregnant mothers would not have the endurance to carry their young long distances, so the females would have been left together, possibly guarded by a few males, thus involving the establishment of a home base.*

3   *Travelling long distances and carrying heavy burdens put strong selective pressure on the evolution of really efficient bipedalism.*

4   *The exertions of the chase may, it has been suggested, have been responsible for the diminution of subcutaneous fat deposits, loss of body hair, and the considerable development of sweat glands (which are not found in large numbers of forest animals), all of which aid the rapid diffusion of metabolic heat.*

5   *Catching and killing large animals required ingenuity and technological skill. The earliest implements were probably stones and clubs (sometimes used by living chimpanzees). In the middle Pleistocene (1/2 million years ago) round stones are found that may have been used for throwing, possibly as a bolas, an ingenious and deadly device consisting of three stones strung together with long leather thongs. On impact the thongs will wrap around the animal and probably bring it to the ground.*

6   *The need to cut up large mammals must have stimulated the development of better chopping and cutting tools; hominid teeth were clearly unsuitable for this function.*

7   *The meat would be in sufficient quantity to be shared by all males and carried back to females. Bipedalism makes hand carrying possible and frees the mouth for speech. In the absence of a suitable alternative diet, bringing meat to the females would be strongly selected as a behavior pattern, and indeed there is evidence for it from the Middle Pleistocene, especially at Choukoutien (Peking man).*

8   *Food-sharing within a social group would certainly bring the group together in a very intimate way, a situation that probably encouraged speech, especially for planning the hunt and in accounts of what happened during the hunt. Speech was perhaps born of the need of intercourse as a result of the division of labor. For the first time, primates had something essential to communicate.*

9   *Geographical knowledge obviously became of prime importance; the locality of waterholes and herds of game must have become a vital subject for communication. Clearly, improved powers of perception, memory, and prediction were of immense value and probably evolved conjointly with speech.*

10   *The absence of males from the home base on hunting expeditions must in turn have increased the overall division of labor between the sexes. The females would have taken over all other group activities. Sexual dimorphism (different appearances of the two sexes) might have changed its character in this new way of life.*

11   *Longer periods of sexual receptivity in the females might have been selected in evolution if the males were away hunting for a considerable portion of the time.*

It would be possible to list many other important changes that might have followed the evolution of social hunting, but even from those listed it seems clear that the exploitation of the larger herbivorous mammals as a source of meat required cooperation, endurance, intelligence, foresight, and a precise means of communication. At the same time, it initiated the selection of an evolutionary trend toward further socialization with the development of speech and technology, all of central importance in our survey of human evolution.

THE USE OF FIRE   The "domestication" of fire has had profound effects upon the evolution of man. The first appearance of the use of fire in the fossil record is about 500,000 years ago at the site where Peking man was found and the newly discovered site in Hungary called Verteszöllös. Both these fossil types are *H. erectus.* Fire is also recorded at a much later date (about 50,000 years ago) in Africa. Somehow, early man learned how to trap and perpetuate fire and eventually to make his own. Some people believe that man began to use fire when he began to live as a cave dweller among the glaciers in Europe and Asia. Man probably used fire to chase cave bears and other predators out of the caves, to heat and light the caves, to cook meals, and to make toolmaking easier. With the use of fire man began using caves and other shelters as semipermanent *homes,* and he began to be less and less of a nomad.

The use of fire changed man's ecological role. He now became more of an omnivore than before. Cooking breaks down plant tissues and makes the contents digestible by man. It also makes meat easier to digest and destroys disease-causing parasites in it. By making food easier to chew cooking lessened the selection pressure for large teeth and jaws. The linguistically flexible jaw of modern man could then evolve.

SOCIAL AND
CULTURAL EVOLUTION   Man is uniquely hairless, has a flexible and opposable thumb and a straight foot, and a curiously large, domelike head lying above a small face with a big nose. Internally, his anatomy and physiology reveal traits almost identical to other primates. Our sleeping appearance offers few clues to man's phenomenal evolutionary success, but once awake our actions reveal the secret. We can use abstract symbols and reason, and we can transmit our reservoir of learned behavior from one generation to the next. Man possesses ideas. Those ideas which are transmitted from generation to generation are called *culture.* A human being raised apart from other men would demonstrate bizarre behavior. The missing element in his makeup would be culture. He would lack the ability to respond to other people properly and would recognize few concepts.

Concepts can be regarded as social "genes" in a type of evolution operating only within man, social and cultural evolution. In this type of evolution, natural selection operates through man and his acceptance or rejection of new concepts. If accepted and used, a new concept can spread rapidly throughout the culture, by analogy with the gene pool of social genes. Since it does not require transmission through sexual reproduction, social and cultural evolution occurs much more rapidly than biological evolution. New concepts can be quickly communicated around the world, where they may be accepted, abhorred, or not understood. But, unlike biological genes, concepts can be stored away in books, movies, tape recordings, and art and be retained for reinterpretation and later use.

A third dimension has been added to evolution. First, there was the physical evolution of the solar system with its chemical and physical components. This was followed by biological evolution with its diverse forms and adaptations. And, just as biological evolution was a manifestation of components of the physical world, so the third realm, the *evolution of mind,* has developed from a biological base. From physical to biological to social and cultural levels, evolution has continued on earth.

Man's rate of biological evolution may have slowed, but social and cultural evolution is proceeding at an ever quickening and sometimes terrifying pace. Where it will lead us, we cannot know. Man is unique in that he is the only animal that has guided to a large extent the course of his own evolution. The next chapter will discuss some of the decisions he must make in the very near future if his evolution is not to slip beyond his guidance and control.

> *We carry within us the wonders we seek without us: There is all Africa and her prodigies in us.*
>
> Browne

1   What are primates?
2   Describe the adaptations of primates for life in trees.
3   Describe the scheme of evolutionary divergence that gave rise to apes and man.
4   Trace the appearance of human traits in the fossil record.
5   Describe how brain, vision, hands, and bipedalism plus the commitment to tools caused the evolution of man.
6   What was the ecology of early man?
7   How did eating large mammals affect man?
8   How did the use of fire change the ecological role of man?
9   Describe social and cultural evolution and contrast it with physical and biological evolution.

Baker, P. T., and J. S. Weiner (eds.): *The Biology of Human Adaptability,* Clarendon Press, Oxford, 1966. Leading geneticists, physiologists, and anthropologists describe various needs for research on problems of man in natural environments and his adaptive responses to these problems.

Campbell, B.: *Human Evolution: An Introduction to Man's Adaptations,* Aldine Publishing Company, Chicago, 1966. Fascinating and authoritative account of man's evolution and adaptations; highly recommended.

Clark, W. E. L.: *The Antecedents of Man: An Introduction to the Evolution of the Primates,* Harper Torchbook 559, Harper & Row, Publishers, Incorporated, New York, 1963. Adaptations of fossil and modern forms of primates.

Coon, C. S.: *The Origin of Races,* Alfred A. Knopf, Inc., New York, 1963. Contains a controversial argument that the races of man diverged much longer ago than previously thought.

Dobzhansky, T.: *Mankind Evolving: The Evolution of the Human Species,* Yale University Press, New Haven, Conn., 1962. The best synthesis of human genetics, evolution, and social implications of biology in print; most highly recommended.

Harrison, G. A., J. S. Weiner, J. M. Tanner, and N. A. Barnicot: *Human Biology: An Introduction to Human Evolution, Variation, and Growth,* Oxford University Press, New York, 1964. An excellent but technical account of the biology of man in an anthropological context.

Howell, F. C., and the Editors of Time-Life Books: *Early Man,* Time-Life Books, New York, 1965. Written by an expert and beautifully illustrated; should be read.

Laughlin, W. S., and R. H. Osborne (eds.): *Human Variations and Origins: An Introduction to Human Biology and Evolution,* W. H. Freeman and Company, San Francisco, 1967. Twenty-seven articles from *Scientific American* selected and introduced by the editors.

*Calcutta street scene. (Courtesy of
Werner Bischof—Magnum.)*

Chapter 22

Man's Ecosystem: Past, Present, and Future

*Oh, Cancerous for smoggy skies, for
   pesticided grain;*
*Irradiated mountains rise above
   an asphalt plain.*

*America, America, thy birds have fled
   from thee;*
*Thy fish lie dead by poisoned streams
   from sea to fetid sea. . . .*

*America, America, thy sins prepare
   thy doom:*
*Monoxide cloud shall be thy shroud
   . . . thy cities be thy tomb.*

Crowley

Today there are over 3 billion human beings, and a typical attitude is that they have conquered nature and live their lives apart from it. In this chapter we shall examine man's ecosystem and consider whether it can continue in its present form. The pervading question is whether man will continue as a *part of nature or apart from nature.*

MAN'S POPULATION SIZE

Homeostasis in a population of plants, animals, or microbes is a result of forces pushing and pulling upon it, forces which cause the population to grow, differentiate, and maintain itself as a unit in nature. Populations can maintain themselves in a fairly constant manner because they can add new members to replace those who die, and they can disperse themselves through a variety of means. Homeostasis in populations is a result of the balance of births by deaths and migration.

Population biologists believe that man's rapid increase in numbers probably began about 8,000 years ago, when he began producing food as well as gathering it. Man began serious manipulation of the environment so that its limiting factors were less severe. There were about 5 million human beings when this shift in man's place in nature occurred, and by the time of Christ there were 250 million. These people were not evenly scattered over the earth but were found in the greatest numbers where they could enjoy their new ecological role.

Science as we know it developed mainly on the subcontinent of Europe and allowed Europeans a new role in nature. Europe, with its increasing control over nature, became the first region where man began to increase his numbers in astounding rates. Migration, however, served as a safety valve which allowed excess population to escape and prevented overcrowding. The migration of excess Europeans was an effective factor in the circumstances which led to the virtual domination of the world by peoples of European descent by the end of the nineteenth century. Around the year 1500 A.D., Europe had a population of about 100 million people, or about 20 percent of the world's population, and they lived on 7 percent of the world's land area. During the following 400 years, the European peoples seized and settled North and South America, Australia, and part of Africa and controlled Africa, India, and southern Asia. By 1900, the descendants of the European immigrants totaled 550 million, or one-third of the world's population, and either occupied or controlled five-sixths of the land area of the world.

The abuses associated with colonialism are well known, but the spread of Europeans and their culture contained a factor which resulted in great changes, the knowledge of science. With science, man had the potential of easing his burdens and lengthening his life. Through the years, disease and starvation have ceased to be limiting factors in the regulation of population growth. The death rate fell while the birth rate stayed high, and the world's population still continues to increase at the rate of over 2 percent per year, enough to double the world's population every 35 years. Table 22.1 shows the number of years required for doubling the earth's population since the year A.D. 1.

Simple arithmetic reveals that with this rate of growth the world will be populated by 50 billion people only 150 years from now. If this growth rate continues for an additional 750 years, there will be 1 billion billion people, or 120 people on each square yard of earth's surface. And the year 2900 is only as far in the future as the Norman conquest is in the past! It has been suggested that the population problem can be solved by sending people to other planets. Even if the transportation problems for

TABLE 22.1*

YEAR A.D.	POPULATION BILLIONS	NUMBER OF YEARS TO DOUBLE POPULATION
1	0.25(?)	1,650(?)
1650	0.50	200
1850	1.1	80
1930	2.0	45
1975	4.0	35
2010	8.0	?

* From H. F. Dorn, *Science*, vol. 125, pp. 283–290, 1962.

such an enterprise could be solved, it would take only a brief period, at the current growth rate, to populate Venus, Mercury, Mars, the moon, and the moons of Jupiter and Saturn to the same density as the earth.

Some people argue that there is no world population problem, that the problem exists only in certain countries of the world. It is true that the earth's resources are not a single reservoir from which all nations can draw their food and skills and that problems vary with each country. For example, the United States government strives to hold agricultural production down by paying farmers not to raise certain crops while, at the same time, in Asia and Africa, vast numbers of people are inadequately clothed and fed. Potentially, however, the results of isolated population growth will be felt in all other countries as the people in the overpopulated countries seek drastic remedies to their problems.

Growth of natural populations is held in check either by a decrease in birth rate or an increase in death rate. Man alone among the animals can decide whether births or deaths shall control his numbers. We discuss this question later in this chapter after we have examined man's food chains, habitats, and ecological niches. We can then make our decision between bombs or babies.

MAN'S FOOD CHAINS
SOCIAL HUNTING

Australopithecus, Homo erectus, and early *H. sapiens* were all predators with social structures resembling those of wolves. Man was, and still is, a small creature compared to his predators, for example, lions, wolves, and bears, and his prey, for example, mammoths and wild cows. He could compensate for his small size in two ways, however. He used *tools,* and he hunted in *groups.* As a result of social hunting, man's predators dwindled to hookworms, tapeworms, and other internal parasites, and lice, fleas, and other external parasites. His primary predator became man, and social hunting expanded to include war.

SOCIAL GATHERING

There is a property shared by all primates which we may call "monkey curiosity," an urge to touch, handle, pick up, and examine an object, and often nibble at it or take it home. Early man was probably an ardent sampler of his environment and added a variety of plant foods to his carnivorous diet. If Stone Age men living today are good indicators, early *Homo sapiens* had an extensive knowledge of the plants and animals in his environment and used them as sources of food, clothing, medicines, poisons, and religious paints. Studies of Stone Age tribes still existing in the modern world reveal a social pattern which is almost universal in groups that hunt and gather. The women typically remain in camp, supervise the children, and gather the nuts, fruits, and berries. Men of the tribes are usually off hunting or warring or are sitting around talking and sharpening spear points. This type of division of labor probably began with *Australopithecus* or even earlier. The only change in the environment caused by hunting-gathering groups would have occurred as a result of building shelters and using fire. Man's effects on his ecosystem were relatively slight during most of his history. It is only in the last 8,000 years that man has profoundly changed the face of the earth, when he began to raise food as well as gather it.

FIGURE 22.1 (a) *Llama* and (b) a Bolivian Indian plowing field with oxen. (*Courtesy of the United Nations.*)

A

B

DOMESTICATION AND
AGRICULTURE

Carl O. Sauer, in his book *Agricultural Origins and Dispersals,* argues that domestication of plants and animals did not take place as a result of necessity, as commonly believed. He argues that needy societies were so involved in satisfying day-to-day needs they lacked the leisure for reflective thought, discussion, and inventiveness. Such a privilege would be enjoyed only by persons in a fishing culture living in a mild climate near fresh water surrounded by a great variety of plants and animals. The locale for early experimentation was probably the forests, for trees would be easily removed through girdling, cutting, and burning, and troublesome weeds and grasses would not appear for a while.

Sauer and many other authorities believe that domestication took place in three isolated centers, two in the Old World and one in the New. The first center of domestication to develop was *southeast Asia,* where such familiar animals as pigs, fowl, ducks, geese, and dogs and such plants as rice, bananas, taro, and yams were cultivated. *Southwest Asia* was the site where grazing mammals and such cereal grasses as wheat, oats, and barley were domesticated. *Tropical America* provided the site of domestication of a few animals, such as llama, alpaca, and guinea pig, and several very important plants such as corn cassava, and potatoes (Figure 22.1).

The definition of domestication is somewhat arguable, but we can say that it is the *modification of plants and animals by man so that traits of the organisms are altered.* We have called domestication artificial selection in previous chapters. In *natural* selection environmental forces in an ecosystem select for increasingly better adaptations for compatability within the ecosystem. *Artificial* selection by man, however, is a selection for success in habitats created by man, and these habitats are not always in harmony with the natural ecosystems. Domesticated plants and animals may become so highly specialized for life in an ecosystem dominated by man that they cannot function in the wild. Obviously, the reverse is also true where man cannot exist on "wild" foods, but must have cultivated sources of food. It is a case of mutualistic symbiosis on a global scale.

AGRICULTURE: MAN'S ALTERATION OF ECOSYSTEMS

In earlier chapters we described the food relationships in an ecosystem and spoke of food chains and food webs and the concepts of producers, consumers, and decomposers, all functioning in such a way that energy is trapped, stored, and released in metabolic processes by a sequence of plants, herbivores, carnivores, and decomposers. We saw that ecosystems are usually complex and contain many checks and balances which perpetuate homeostasis.

During the long span of time during which man was a hunter-gatherer, man was physiologically obligated to be a carnivore except for edible nuts, fruits, and berries. The rest of the plant world remained closed to him as a source of food because he could not digest it. The discovery of how to use fire in cooking changed the entire picture of man's role as a consumer, for he could now cook plant tissues, break down their cell walls, and release the protoplasm previously available only to herbivores. The use of fire opened the path to domestication, for man could eat not only fruits, nuts, and berries, but seeds, tubers, and other parts of plants. Without fire, rice, wheat, corn, potatoes, and many other plant foods supporting various cultures today could not be digested.

When man became a vegetarian as well as a carnivore, he changed his place in the food webs of his ecosystem. Man, in fact, created his own ecosystems by planting domesticated producer organisms and feeding them to himself or to animals which he then consumed. Man's artificial ecosystems were not superimposed upon the natural ecosystems: They replaced them. It was a competition between natural ecosystems and artificial ecosystems, and, with man's cunning, it was a one-sided battle.

In complex natural ecosystems, a particular type of food may be consumed by a variety of consumers. Man, however, has traditionally not accepted any sharing of his food with other consumers. The sight of predators other than himself, even when they are not consuming his food, usually leads him to destroy them. Man's unreasonable war on such predators as coyotes, wolves, mountain lions, hawks, and eagles may be due to a feeling that they are competing with him in predation. It is interesting that he often calls carnivores "bad" and herbivores "good." Man's ecosystems are dominated by him, its producers and consumers are selected, and his selections are often too narrow.

The Koala bear of Australia eats only one food, the leaves of the blue gum eucalyptus. Since the Koala is completely dependent upon this one source of food, any decline in blue gum trees leads to a decline in Koala bears. Man has placed himself in the same predicament as the Koala in some regions of the world. Over half of the world's people live off rice, a grain that is usually raised as a single crop. Famines rage when the rice crop is poor. Ireland in the last century offers an example of the tragedy which can accompany single-crop ecosystems, in this case monoculture of potatoes.

The potato was imported into Ireland several hundred years ago and became extremely popular since it could be raised in small, single-family gardens. Ireland had a population of about 1 million people in 1670 which by 1845 had increased to 8 million. Potatoes served as the primary source of food for most of them. Over a period of 6 years, from 1848 to 1854, a type of fungus or blight destroyed every successive potato crop. More than a million Irish *starved to death* and another million emigrated, chiefly to the United States. Ireland today has a diversified agriculture, for it became evident that a food chain which depends upon a single producer organism is ecologically and economically unsound. Ecologists have become increasingly aware from their studies of natural ecosystems that complex ecosystems are much more stable than simple ones. A complex ecosystem can adjust to shifts in any of its parts when the same shifts in a simple ecosystem would destroy it. Such lessons are frightening, for most of man's ecosystems are highly simplified.

As previously mentioned, man must continually defeat his competitors if his food is to be eaten solely by him. Ironically, however, cultivation of single crops over vast areas of land creates a magnificent habitat in which such pests as insects, fungi, and weeds can flourish. The *United Nations Statistical Yearbook* reports that 20 percent of all foodstuffs in the world are lost between sowing and harvesting because of weeds, fungi, and insects and 10 percent of all foods harvested is lost during transportation and storage because of rodents, insects, and fungi. To combat this loss, man has enlisted the aid of *pesticides,* chemicals which will kill the competing pests.

Agriculture and pest-control agencies have become increasingly dependent upon chemical control over pests. The public is alarmed, but the agriculturists argue that, without the use of pesticides, insects and other pests would take over their fields. Public health experts have used pesticides, particularly insecticides, to rid much of the world of the animals which carry such dreaded human diseases as malaria (*Anopheles* mosquito), epidemic typhus (lice), yellow fever (*Aedes aegypti* mosquito), Chagas' disease (sand fly), and plague (fleas). Ten million people died of plague as recently as the period from 1896 to 1917, but only 314 cases were reported to the United Nations in 1960. Three million people died *each year* from malaria, a disease completely missing today from large areas of the Americas, the Soviet Union, Philippines, Taiwan, Ryukyu Islands, Ceylon, Thailand, plus a growing list of other countries. When we are reminded that one-third of Europe's population died of plague, the Black Death, during the Middle Ages and that millions died of typhus during the eighteenth century and World War I, we might wonder who could find fault with the use of pesticides. In 1962, Rachel Carson perceived sinister problems lurking behind the pesticide panacea and wrote a book called *Silent Spring,* eloquently voicing fears shared by many other biologists.

She dramatized several points which were not well known to the public, explaining that insects continue to harbor within their populations forms which are resistant to each barrage of pesticides and that there is widespread commercial use of chemicals which have not been thoroughly tested for *indirect* effects. Probably the most important of all, she pointed out that many chemicals persist for years and may accumulate in underground water or in body fats or may be concentrated by various organisms in a food chain. As an example, she cited the attempts to control gnats at Clear Lake, California. A relatively nontoxic compound, DDD, was tested to determine the concentrations which wildlife would tolerate. Usually 10 parts per million were used, but with a spirit of caution, only a concentration of $1/50$ part per million was sprayed on the lake. As time passed, the gnat-control program proved to be a failure, for the gnats returned after a few years. However, organisms other than gnats were affected tragically as a result of this abortive program. Hundreds of water birds died, and tests showed that they had DDD storage levels of 1,600 rather than $1/50$ parts per million! Further tests of other animals living in the lake revealed similar levels, and the high levels persisted. Algae, plankton, fish, frogs, water birds, and gulls—the lake's food web—retained high levels of the insecticide for years.

The major point of Rachel Carson's book was the ecological fact that insecticides can be accumulated by a succession of predators in a food chain. Organisms further along in a food chain may accumulate intolerable levels of toxic chemicals. She also pointed out that insecticides are used as treatments for individual problems without consideration for their effect on other parts of an ecosystem. Eventual targets of the chemical's effects are often remote and surprising. Perhaps many of the points were overstated or overdramatized, but Rachel Carson achieved one of the most important victories of the twentieth century—she opened the eyes of government, industry, and the voting public to *the workings of the ecosystems in which they lived.*

The controversies spawned by *Silent Spring* and by other ardent ecological conservationists will probably continue for many more years. There is no simple answer to the dilemma facing man. Agriculture has become completely dependent upon the use of chemical fertilizers and pesticides. Without them, food production in an already starving world would drop, but with them the present and future health of all living things is endangered. In 1963, President Kennedy set up the President's Science Advisory Committee and one of its duties was to consider the ecological role of pesticides. Their report, the *Use of Pesticides,* concludes:

The use of pesticides must be continued if we are to maintain the advantages now resulting from the work of informed food producers and those responsible for control of disease. On the other hand, it has now become clear that the proper usage is not simple and that, while they destroy harmful insects and plants, pesticides may also be toxic to beneficial plants and animals, including man. Their toxic effects in large doses are well known and precautions can be taken to see that humans are never needlessly exposed. But we must now also take measures to insure that continued exposures to small amounts of these chemicals in our environment will not be harmful over long periods of time.

They also pointed out that an average American adult carries around 100 to 200 milligrams of DDT in his body fat. Volunteers have eaten DDT until they contained twenty times the average United States level and showed no ill effects. Apparently, human beings have a very high level of resistance to any effects from DDT at least in the short run. Tests on other mammals showed results similar to those on man. Birds, fishes, and invertebrates, however, show a very high sensitivity to DDT, and there are many studies which dramatically show its effects.

The President's panel did not urge any drastic actions, but they did recommend that restrictions and controls be tightened up and that the present level of pesticides in our environment be determined and permissible levels of pesticides in our foods be established and controlled. An urgent plea was made for researchers to develop pesticides which would act only upon selected target pests and then decompose into safe residues. They also pointed out that much work remained to be done in the development of *nonchemical* methods of pest control. Predators upon pests may be searched out, such as the virus imported to decrease the rabbit population of Australia and the *Cactoblastis* insect used to wipe out thousands of acres of prickly pear cactus in Australia. Another example of biological control of pests was in Florida, where radiologically sterilized male screwworm flies were released; since the females mate only once, their sole supply of semen was sterile and the population quickly disappeared. Special international groups have been formed to study the *biological* control of pests.

Man has been the unintentional and often intentional importer of pests. Over half of the insect pests in the United States are from foreign lands. One-fourth of the aircraft inspected by the U.S. Public Health Service between 1937 and 1947 contained insects or some other type of arthropod. Man has often regretted his decision to introduce organisms such as the starling and the English sparrow, both of which have spread across the United States and are outcompeting native birds. Most of man's domesticated plants and animals, including weeds, are of European or Asian origin. Few, if any, of the ecosystems on earth have remained untouched by the meddling of man.

FIGURE 22.2 Libya: turning the tide. The desert waste is being reforested by fixing the sand dunes with live plants in a grid system. Later eucalyptus, olive, palm, and carob trees will be planted to return this region to its former fertility. (*Courtesy of the United Nations.*)

The vital role of *soil* in ecosystems in land has already been discussed. Without soil the producer organisms on land stop producing, and the dependent food chains falter and fail. Since becoming a farmer about 8,000 years ago, man has tended to ignore the basic role of soil and has proceeded with practices which have permanently removed soil from ecosystems over vast regions of the earth. Early farmers in the Middle East, about 8,000 years ago, began burning forests and raising crops in the clearings. When the soil was worn out or washed away in the clearing, they went on burning and clearing in new areas. The soil in the deserted clearings continued to be washed or blown away, and man's indelible scrawling on the face of the earth began. Deserts in Israel, northern India, and elsewhere were formed as a result of man's misuse of soil (see Figure 22.2). As civilization spread in China, around the Mediterranean, northward through Europe, and across to the New World, forests were cut down, grasslands overgrazed, and the land sculptured into vast systems of gullies whose vital soil was washed out to the lowlands and into the sea. The forests of central Europe through which Caesar's soldiers could march for 2 months have been gone for centuries, though areas in Germany and Scandinavia remain covered with forest. Similarly the vast deciduous forests of colonial eastern America are only scattered remnants today. Without the protective canopy of leaves or the branching roots of lusty grasses the soil washes away and settles out wherever the eroding current slows (see Figure 22.3). If the silt-laden water is used for irrigation, the ditches fill and cease to function. Babylon and other ancient cities were slowly choked by the closing of their irrigation canals through the accumulation of silt. The ruins of Antioch, for example, are covered by 28 feet of silt, probably produced as an indirect result of ravages of the land by the human population which dwelt there.

Deforestation is not the only cause of the ruin of the land; overgrazing and other faulty farming practices can be equally effective in causing permanent damage where forests never stood. Poor farming practices at the headwaters of the Tigris and

FIGURE 22.3 The result of water erosion.

Euphrates rivers in Armenia has caused such heavy erosion that the soil has been carried all the way to the Persian Gulf, 1,700 miles distant. The coastline there has been extended 180 miles outward from where it was during Sumerian times 4,500 years ago. In Syria, a million acres of man-made desert contain 100 dead cities, deserted since 3 to 6 feet of soil was washed from the hillsides in the seventh century.

Another malpractice was the irrigation of lands lying over a salty water table. As water was added to the land, the ground water rose and killed the plant life with its salt. Can man prevent this waste and abuse? Before you think that this story is only a tale of Europe and Asia, you should realize that by 1950 erosion had reduced 50 million acres of good American farm land to a level unfit for cultivation and that 300 million of our 400 million acres of farmland still continues to erode faster than new soil can be formed. It is a valid question to ask whether the situation is hopeless.

When the grasslands of the United States were homesteaded, the native grasses disappeared either as a result of overgrazing or replacement with wheat and other grains. Through most of the year the fields stood almost empty of plants. During the 1930s, a severe drought precipitated conditions in an area which has been called the dust bowl ever since. Clouds of topsoil swirled from state to state, laying bare subsoils in some regions and choking out crops where it fell in other areas. As a result of these conditions, the Soil Conservation Service was implemented by President Roosevelt and the Congress and farmers were alerted and informed of the tragedy that was occurring around and beneath them. Farmers were cautioned to "use the land according to its capabilities, and treat it according to its needs." An era of land stewardship had begun.

Farmers were given maps of their lands which classified it according to kind of soil, depth of soil, slope, degree of erosion, fertility, and general physical condition. Eight land classes were defined, and the farmer was encouraged to use his soil according to its capabilities—actual, not imagined.

The Soil Conservation Service attempted to convince farmers of the need to take marginal land (Class IV and V) out of cultivation and let it return to native grasses. It would also be appropriate if homes and cities were built on marginal land so that richly endowed soils could be reserved for farming, but tradition usually is the victor. Most cities are built on valley floors or flood plains so that the most fertile soils are covered by concrete, asphalt, and man's rubbish and wastes.

Americans are not faced with hunger each day like a major portion of the remainder of the world's population—at least not yet. Most of the soils which have not yet eroded away have been farmed for less than a century, and with the use of modern technology American farmers produce more food than Americans consume. We have a surplus of food in this country, but rather than having unemployed former farmers, the Congress has continued to subsidize and support this surplus commodity through price supports with federal money. In an attempt to decrease production of further surplus foods the federal government pays many farmers not to raise crops on selected portions of their lands. This plan, called the soil bank, may irk some tax-payers but it certainly helps the soil.

We have not completed the discussion of man's part in the energy relationships of his ecosystem; that is, we have not described the cycling of his biological wastes back to the producers. This, of course, involves decompostiion by bacteria and fungi and conversion of organic compounds back into the basic chemicals needed by green plants. Natural ecosystems ordinarily can decompose all the wastes produced by organisms within the system, but man's ecosystems include hugh populations living in vast cities, and his wastes overwhelm the decay organisms. Much of his wastes are never returned to the soil and, in much of the world, his dead bodies are not returned to the ecosystem but are isolated from it through embalming and burial in lead-lined caskets. When we realize that the average city dweller produces 120 gallons of sewage and 5 pounds of rubbish each day, one cannot help wondering what will be done with man's wastes when his numbers reach those forecast for the future! Overpopulation is not merely a question of food production, it is a complex problem involving all factors and processes within man's ecosystem (see Figure 22.4).

In earlier chapters we defined a habitat as an organism's home and an ecological niche as an organism's role and status. These terms can also be applied to man and his environment. Man's habitat includes all the environmental factors he can react to—his home, his place of work, his fellow human beings and other organisms. Man's ecological niche can be regarded as his specialization, his role in the division of labor in human society. Man's habitats and ecological niches have changed dramatically through the course of cultural evolution. Niches, the roles man plays in society, became more numerous and specialized as he got more involved in altering the ecosystems through agriculture and industry. Man has progressed from a society of hunter-gatherers living in temporary camps, to a society of farmers living in small villages, to an industrial society of huge sprawling cities. This story is one of increasing urbanization, with massive groups of people cooperatively controlling the limiting factors of nature so that habitat pressures more and more become those created by man. Today, 70 percent of Americans live in urban areas covering only 0.7 percent of the land, and most readers of this book participate in these gigantic man-made ecosystems. We had better turn to the ecology of cities.

The first cities, built about 5,500 years ago, were primarily trading centers for the surrounding rural areas. This role remained unchanged until the nineteenth century, when industrialization began and ecological niches were drastically expanded. In Europe around 1600, cities of over 100,000 people contained only 1.6 percent of the total European population. By 1700 the figure was 1.9 percent and by 1800 2.2 percent. By 1900, however, 40 percent of the people in England, where the industrial revolution began, were living in cities of over 100,000. Today, all industrial nations

MAN'S HABITATS
AND NICHES

FIGURE 22.4 A contemporary
woodland scene. (*Courtesy of
Dave Repp from The National
Audubon Society.*)

are highly urbanized, and the tendency toward urbanization is rapidly accelerating.
It is predicted that more than half of the world's population will live in cities of over
100,000 by 1990. As neighboring cities enlarge, their boundaries fuse, and giant
megalopolises are formed, many with fantastically high densities of people. The
average number of people per square mile in New York City, for example, is 25,000.
Since an almost continuous megalopolis already extends from Boston to Washington

D.C. and cannot expand to the east, the 37 million people living in it are going to find themselves increasingly crowded. Some effects of industrialization and urban crowding are already becoming dramatically clear.

Man's habitat must supply a source of food, fuel, clothing, durable goods, construction materials, electric energy, water, and air. Only two of these factors have become limiting in the United States, water and air.

Water presents three potential problems: Too much means *flooding,* too little means *drought,* and the water we have may be *polluted.* Millions of dollars are spent each year on flood-control and flood-prevention dams and irrigation projects. Some dams built to trap and store water have lost more water through evaporation from their vast surfaces than they have saved. Properly husbanded, water should not become scarce in American cities for several hundred years. This may be disputed by residents of New York City, where a drought caused rationing of water in the 1960s, but experts on water resources claim that the United States contains a supply that will be ample if water systems are designed to make greater use of water presently lost to the sea. Salt can be removed from seawater with atomic energy, but so far the cost is beyond what most consumers can afford; this, however, will probably change.

Most experts would rather make better use of existing water supplies. Some proposals for better use of present sources of water seem spectacular, but they may have merit, for example, a suggestion to connect all the rivers in Texas with one canal or to pipe water from the Great Lakes to the Southwest. It has been suggested that water be carried along the valleys of the Rocky Mountains from Alaska to the Southwest and California. In California itself, a majority of the voters elected to divert much of the Sacramento River to where most of the state's voters live in the parched cities in the southern region. Los Angeles, already over built in the opinion of many ecologists, has depended for years on water from the Colorado River and now, while growing even larger, must bring in water from the northern part of the state. There is plenty of water in the United States, but its *distribution* is not appropriate for man's urbanization and agriculture. Millions of acres of arable land could be farmed profitably through irrigation projects or, in some cases, drainage of flooded lands. This will no doubt be done in the near future.

Water pollution is a much greater problem than water scarcity, for although 150 million Americans are served by public waterworks, only 120 million are served by sewers. Backyard cesspools and septic tanks, which receive the wastes of almost 70 million Americans in suburbs and small towns, present no problems if properly designed and not overloaded, but neither of these criteria is met in many regions of the United States.

A principal cause of water pollution is inadequate treatment of sewage. In 1962 the wastes of 15 million Americans were collected by sewers and released into rivers and lakes without treatment. The wastes of only 61 million people received truly adequate treatment before being released. Since 100 million Americans are using water that has already been used once by other citizens, it is vitally important for our continuing health that treatment plants for sewage disposal and water supplies be adequate for the job.

Human biological wastes are not the only wastes released by the activities of man. Industrial wastes and carelessness (see Figure 22.5) pose a critical problem because of their diverse nature and their drastic destructive affects on living things. Decomposers can degrade the biological products of man but usually have little effect upon the chemicals discharged by industrial plants. Dilution seems to be the most common treatment for industrial wastes, but this obviously cannot continue with success since the number of factories using water is increasing.

Lake Erie, serving as the main water supply for 10 million city dwellers and many huge industries along its 300 miles of shoreline, testifies to this dilemma. Sewage and industrial wastes have been released into the lake for many years, and its natural ecosystem has been destroyed. Lake Erie is the fourth largest of the five Great Lakes but ranks first in degree of pollution. Of the five, Lake Erie is the warmest, most southern, and oldest and therefore most shallow. Being so shallow, it is the first of the Lakes to become drastically polluted. The Great Lakes contain 20 percent of the earth's fresh water and form the world's largest reservoir of fresh water. Nevertheless, with current "progress," it will not be long before the entire chain is as polluted as Lake Erie.

FIGURE 22.5 Oil-soaked gannet, the victim of oil spilling into the sea from an offshore drilling rig. The damage to this gannet is too gross for it to survive. (*Courtesy of George Komorowski from The National Audubon Society.*)

Every day 4.7 billion gallons of water are drawn out of Lake Erie by industries and 619 million gallons for use by over 3 million people who depend upon it for drinking water. The water is returned to the lake as inadequately treated sewage or as chemical solutions from the industries. The five states bordering the lake recently consulted with the U.S. Public Health Service and embarked on a program of pollution abatement. Preliminary studies revealed that the primary cause of the drastic changes in the lake has been phosphates, which compose up to 70 percent of household detergents. Phosphates are familiar to farmers, because they make up part of the fertilizing chemicals which are added to fields annually. It is no surprise, then, to find that the millions of pounds of waste detergent flowing into Lake Erie each year will support a vast growth of *Cladophora*, algae which in excess quantities apparently disrupt the ecosystem. A foul smell emanates from dead *Cladophora*, killed by noxious pollutants in the lake. Furthermore, the shading and clogging effects of the alga, which prevent photosynthesis and oxygen circulation, plus the effects of oxygen-absorbing chemicals accumulating for many years in the lake, have reduced the level of oxygen to a level unbearable by animals. A 2,600-square-mile area in the center of the lake, one-fourth of the lake's total area, is almost completely devoid of oxygen in the bottom 10 feet of water. The bottom of the remaining three-fourths of the lake has lost the mayflies which previously served as food for small fish and has gained pollution-tolerant sludgeworms, bloodworms, and fingernail clams. Whitefish and pike, which once supported a multimillion-dollar fishing industry, have disappeared and have been replaced by carp, which tolerate low oxygen levels and higher temperatures. The urgency of the problem is at last becoming evident to residents of the Great Lakes area, and action is being demanded. Millions, if not billions, of dollars will have to be spent to reverse the disastrous trend of pollution in these once beautiful waters. Many other municipalities across the United States have become awakened to the changes in their own water supplies and are taking action, but many more have displayed an incredible lack of comprehension of the problems they are facing and have done nothing.

Air pollution is even more complex than water pollution because more agents add their wastes to the air than flow into water and they are a great deal harder to control. Every house, apartment, automobile, truck, bus, factory, and power plant discharges its wastes directly into the air. As a result, many larger cities are choked with smog, a word combining smoke and fog (see Figure 22.6 and Plates 21 and 22), and the effects of this noxious gas are just beginning to be understood. In 1952 London had a formidable type of air pollution called a black fog which caused 4,000 deaths. Similar episodes occurred in Donora, Pennsylvania; Poza Rico, Mexico; and the Meuse Valley in Belgium, where dozens of people suffocated.

Los Angeles is shrouded with smog about 100 days a year. Los Angeles smog is a type of air-pollution problem found in other metropolitan areas as well. An eye-irritating yellowish-brown cloud with a chlorinelike odor may hover over a city for days, particularly if there are no winds. As a result, farmers complain about crop

FIGURE 22.6 To produce steel, coke is burned; result: smog. (*Courtesy of Henry M. Mayer from The National Audubon Society.*)

damage, and drivers complain about damage to windshield wipers and tires. Smog is an air pollutant which oxidizes, producing powerful acids and other destructive chemicals. Its effects are obvious in spinach, sugar beets, alfalfa, endive, oats, citrus fruits and pinto beans. Because of their sensitivity, these plants can be used as indicators of the spread of pollution. Much of the smog is ozone, a strongly oxidizing chemical responsible for the cracking of rubber exposed to smog. Oxidation of organic materials in the atmosphere forms peroxides and many other poisonous substances, all of which may irritate the eyes and damage plants. There is some medical evidence indicating that smog increases the incidence of respiratory diseases such as emphysema.

There are at least three ways to get rid of the air pollution problem: (1) A switch to fuels producing fewer undesirable combustion products would help to clear the skies. (2) A switch from oil and gas to atomic energy as a source of power would eliminate carbon compounds from the air but might substitute radioactive materials in their place. Which is worse? (3) The undesirable combustion products could be removed from the vents leading from the factories, plants, autos, and so on. Smog-control devices, though of questionable value, are now standard equipment on most new cars sold in the United States. The most direct approach to smog stemming from auto exhaust would be to substitute electric or other engines for internal combustion engines. A persistant problem, however, which the air pollution officials find difficult to control, is the thousands of private residences continuing to pour wastes into the atmosphere from furnaces, barbecues, and trash burners.

Aldo Leopold states in his *Sand County Almanac* that man refuses to try to understand any system he did not design himself. Nonetheless, frantic efforts are now being made to understand and control the causes of food shortage, water shortage, water pollution, and air pollution. Man, or at least *some* men, have realized that the systems man created are going awry. With the urging of President Johnson, the Congress passed the Clean Air Act and the Water Pollution Control Act. The preamble to the Clean Air Act states that "Federal financial assistance and leadership is essential for the development of cooperative Federal, state, regional and local programs designed to prevent and control air pollution." In both laws, the Public Health Service is empowered to enter into interstate pollution problems and call a conference of state and local agencies. As a second step they may call a public hearing, and if that does not get action, they are empowered to bring action against the polluting offenders. Perhaps man will soon begin to understand the role of soil, water, and air in his ecosystem.

Values may be defined as bases for decision making, a process not shared by organisms lower than man. Decisions determining responses to cultural pressures are based upon ideas called values, ideas with differing degrees of assigned

MAN'S VALUES

relevance. Values determine the course of human cultural evolution, and *they change through time.*

Man as a hunter and gatherer lived in harmony with nature, and if cave paintings and studies of Stone Age tribes today are valid evidence, wildlife was assigned human identities and names by Stone Age men. Today, civilized man considers himself apart from nature and holds little concern for the plight of wildlife, the organisms which he has not domesticated. Since the time of Christ, over 100 species of birds and over 100 species of mammals have become extinct as a result of man's activities. Hundreds of species are on the verge of extinction today, and experts believe that, in this century, one bird species and one mammal species become extinct somewhere in the world every year. Current cultural values lead most people to shrug and say, "Oh well, what good are they anyway?"

What about the future of man himself: Will he become extinct, will he evolve biologically, or culturally, or both? We have already referred to the plight of man's natural resources, but what about man's human resources? What is to become of man in quality and numbers?

Francis Galton, a nineteenth-century British scientist, observed that genius seemed to occur in certain families more frequently than in others and realized to his horror that these families had fewer children than the general masses. Having no knowledge of the true nature of genetics, Galton assumed that "talent" was inherited by the same processes as any physical trait. He proposed that man's hereditary nature was rapidly going downhill and needed to be controlled and directed. Galton stated in 1865:

Every animal, before it is of an age to bear offspring, has to undergo frequent stern examinations before the board of nature, under the law of natural selection. . . . [But] one of the effects of civilization is to diminish the rigour of the application of the law of natural selection. It preserves weak lives, that would have perished in barbarous lands.

Galton coined the term *eugenics* and proposed that the deterioration of the human genetic endowment could be stopped by *positive eugenics,* in which members of the upper levels of society would be encouraged to have more offspring, and *negative eugenics,* in which poor people would be discouraged from having children. One outstanding fallacy in Galton's idea was the means of determining who was superior and who was inferior. Naturally, Galton believed that he and the fellow members of his Victorian society were the models toward which all mankind should move. Similar attitudes were put into tragic practice by the Nazis, who killed millions and sterilized thousands who did not fit into their stereotype of Nordic supermen. Galton himself would have been shocked at such practices, for he believed in positive eugenics as the preferable choice. Ironically, he himself died childless.

Galton said, "It is a fact that more intelligent people are found among the rich than among the poor, but this is because their environments are much richer and conducive towards scholarly studies." The poor people to whom Galton condescended were lucky to own books. It was a condition quite similar to that found among minority groups in the United States today.

During the first part of this century investigators conducted studies which seemed to show that people with low intelligence have more children that those with high intelligence. They studied several generations in families with mentally defective children and found that the number of children produced in each generation was higher than that produced by people with higher IQs. Recently, Sheldon Reed has shown that these studies were based on faulty experimental design. In each generation in their studies the investigators had ignored the childless brothers and sisters of the parents. When their lack of children is added in with the numbers of children produced by the remainder of the same generation, the number of children produced by low-IQ people falls considerably below that of the average. Reed states:[1]

[1] Sheldon C. Reed, "Genetic Change in a Stable Physical Environment," in John D. Roslansky (ed.), *Genetics and the Future of Man,* Appleton-Century-Crofts, New York, copyright 1966 by North-Holland Publishing Company, Amsterdam, by permission.

The Minnesota and Michigan studies show clearly that if we take all the persons in one generation and arrange them according to their I.Q. values, then the average number of children for the persons with I.Q. values of 70 and below is only 2.09 while the average number of children for all persons with an I.Q. of 131 and above was 2.98. The retarded then produced only 2.09 children on the average when all of the childless ones were included, while all of the persons of 131 and above had 2.98 children. Thus, when the experimental design is correct, there is no excess of children produced by the mentally retarded. Indeed, the data . . . give some hope that the evolution of higher intelligence may be still continuing.

There is therefore no proof that man's IQ is falling, but the next question is: Can we raise man's average IQ higher than it is now? The late Hermann J. Muller proposed a plan which he believed would improve man's genetic reservoir. First, all people who know that they have "bad" genes should have only one or two offspring while those persons who know that they are bearers of "good" genes should have as many offspring as they can afford. He pleaded for reproductive responsibility as a necessary part of moral responsibility. Second, he suggested that couples which were childless due to sterility of the male could have a child with excellent genes through artificial insemination of the female with sperm from a sperm bank in which gonadal cells from geniuses had been stored. Muller believed that no woman would refuse to become the mother of a child of Einstein, Pasteur, Descartes, da Vinci, or Lincoln and that married couples with children could add a gifted child to their family through this method.

Even if it would work biologically, which is extremely doubtful, would any such program be of advantage to humanity? Human diversity has after all been the primary reason for man's spectacular evolutionary success. Besides, one can argue that no program to raise the level of intelligence and talent should be instituted as long as we remain ignorant of how these traits are developed. What good are the genes of a genius if certain features of the environment actually are the key factors in developing genius? After all, Beethoven's father was a habitual drunkard, and his mother died of consumption. Most men and women who have contributed a great deal to the progress of mankind had parents of relatively little distinction. Heredi-tarians and environmentalists may debate to their heart's content, but they cannot describe with any validity the means by which genius, talent, compassion, creativity, and all the human traits we treasure are germinated. Eugenic schemes do not take variability due to recombination into account. Perhaps the main argument at the present time comes from various studies showing that the nature of interpersonal in-teractions during childhood can make the difference between a moron and a college student. These studies began with the work of a psychologist named Skeels, who divided orphans in a midwest institution into two groups. The control group con-sisted of orphans who were allowed to remain in the cabins where they had always been kept in this institution. The other group was exposed to the attention of foster mothers drawn from a nearby mental institution. Even though the foster mothers were considered retarded, the effects of their maternal attention on the orphans were dramatic. These orphans developed into people of a normal range of intelligence, while the control group developed with a high incidence of subnormal, moron-level mentality. From this and a number of subsequent studies it appears that man already has the ability to facilitate the expression of the complex genetic system which provides his mental machinery, by ensuring appropriate environmental circum-stances.

MAN'S VALUES AND MAN'S SURVIVAL

This chapter has discussed important problems facing man, problems which, if man makes the wrong decisions, *may lead to his extinction*. We hope you have learned that man's ecosystems consist of homeostatic systems on a global scale, systems which are regulated through man's conscious decisions. Earlier chapters considered homeostasis within an organism at the level of molecules and cellular systems and dealt with the maintenance of a steady state in population level as a result of interac-tions between organisms. Homeostasis within man's ecosystems, however, is governed largely by *decisions* made by man using *values* from his culture as criteria for his actions. Judging from the current condition of his ecosystems, we can conclude that the cultural values man has applied to his own ecology have been grossly inappropriate.

Of all the problems facing man, the most basic is that of overpopulation, since most of the other problems hinge upon human population growth. Controlled for many thousands of years by natural checks and balances, man's population growth is not regulated *at the present time* by the pressures of war, famine, or disease. What of the future? Will man provide adequate food and eliminate the wastes of the exploding human population without resorting to the Stone Age tactic called war?

The potential growth of modern technology should prevent raw materials and energy sources from becoming limiting factors for many decades. Food production, for example, can be increased both in quantity and quality many times over the present level. We are now using synthetic materials in industrial processes in increasing amounts, and it should not be long before nutrient foods are synthesized by an industrialized chemical agriculture from easily available precursors. These artificial foods should ease starvation in the crowded world. Some experts predict that application of present scientific knowledge to agriculture would expand food production to the point where 50 billion persons, or 20 times the present world population, could be fed.

With improvements in technology man can draw from the earth enough food, clothing, and shelter to support many billions of people, but what would be man's new world? As man's numbers grow, he will find it necessary to eliminate *all* forms of wildlife competing with him for food and space; he will flood deserts and cut down forests to construct farms, factories, houses, and roads; he will tolerate only those wild plants, animals, and scenery that serve his needs. Already, 1 percent of the surface of the United States is covered by paved roads and streets, but this amount will increase to the point that most of the landscape will be covered over with highways, factories, and houses. All natural resources, including water and air, will be tightly regulated. To preview this way of life, visit a chicken farm, where chickens spend their entire lives in a small cubicle called a battery, or drop in for a view of laboratory mice and rats.

Detectable evolution in man ceased about 50,000 years ago, and evolution since that time has been exclusively social and cultural so far as we are aware. We do not know whether recent evolution has altered the complex of genes acquired while man was evolving as a species. We do not know how man will respond to an *obliteration of all aspects of the environment which had relevance to his evolutionary origins*. Perhaps, natural selection will favor those phenotypes which adapt best to a regimented and sheltered way of life in a world consisting primarily of people and pollution.

Commitment to population control seems to be the most urgent solution, but it must indeed be a stringently applied control, for with the present death rates in the Western world, an average of only three children per family will cause the population to double every 35 years. Obviously, the urgency of the population problem dictates that men of the sciences, arts, and technologies put their minds together to answer the question asked by Sir Julian Huxley (What are people for?) and come up with ideas which will define man's optimum numbers and a means of holding them there. Will it be done through death control or birth control?

The question put at the beginning of this chapter was whether man will continue as a part of nature or apart from nature. This chapter and all those which preceded it have presented proof that man is a biological part of nature, that he evolved through natural selection just like any other creature, that he is part of food chains and ecosystems, and that homeostatic order is possible only if there is a system of control. The control mechanisms in man-dominated ecosystems have increasingly been based upon man's conscious decisions. Man, however, has abused his ecosystems to such a degree that he is now losing this control, and many systems are tending toward disorder. Will man make the correct homeostatic decisions? *Will man prevail?*

> *Life can only be understood backward but it must be lived forward. . . .*
>
> Kierkegaard

(Courtesy of Paul Caponigro)

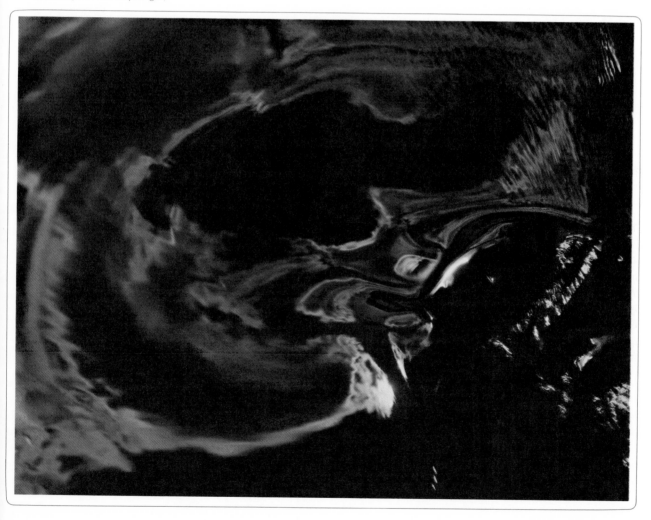

1   Why do we have a population problem?

2   How has social hunting changed recently?

3   Describe the history of domestication and agriculture.

4   What is wrong with simple ecosystems?

5   Why is there a dilemma concerning the use of pesticides?

6   Why must remains of ancient civilizations be dug up?

7   Are man's ecosystems in balance?

8   How have man's habitats and ecological niches changed?

9   Should water shortages be a problem in the United States?

10   How can we prevent water pollution?

11   What is smog?

12   How can air pollution be prevented?

13   What are values?

14   What was the fallacy in Galton's plan of eugenics?

15   What was the fallacy in the studies that showed a decline in IQ in this country?

16   Describe and discuss Muller's plan for raising the general IQ of the world's people.

17   Why is overpopulation the most important problem facing modern man?

18   Are people a part of nature or apart from nature?

SUGGESTIONS FOR
FURTHER READING
* Available in paperback.

Baker, H. G.: *Plants and Civilization,* Wadsworth Publishing Company, Inc., Belmont, Calif., 1965.   The role of plants in the ecosystem of man; exceptionally well written.

Bates, M.: *The Forest and the Sea,* Random House, Inc., New York, 1960.   A synthesis of facts about the ecosystem of man.

Bates, M.: *Man in Nature,* 2d ed., Prentice-Hall, Inc., Englewood Cliffs, N.J., 1964. The fundamental principles of human ecology in lucid presentation.

Bresler, J. B. (ed.): *Environments of Man,* Addison-Wesley Publishing Company, Inc., Reading, Mass., 1968.   A collection of articles on man and his environment.

Bronowski, J.: *Science and Human Values,* Harper Torchbooks 505, Harper & Row, Publisher, Incorporated, New York, 1959.   The impact of science on ethics and human values and on our physical environment.

Carr, D. E.: *Death of the Sweet Waters,* Norton, New York, 1966.   An excellent book on water pollution: written for laymen.

Carr, D. E.: *The Breath of Life,* W. W. Norton & Company, Inc., New York, 1966. Deals with air pollution; a companion volume to the preceding one.

Carson, R.: *Silent Spring,* Houghton Mifflin Company, Boston, 1962.   The famous book that started the whole world thinking about what man is doing to his ecosystem.

Ehrlich, P. R.: *The Population Bomb, Ballantine Books, Inc., New York, 1968. A hard-hitting argument that action is needed to save the world; highly recommended.

Hardin, G.: *Nature and Man's Fate, Mentor Books, New American Library, Inc., New York, 1959. A fascinating synthesis of genetics, evolution, and the future of man; highly recommended.

Hardin, G.: *Population, Evolution, and Birth Control: A Collage of Controversial Ideas, 2d ed., W. H. Freeman and Company, San Francisco, 1969. Original articles on the evolution of man, his population problems, and his attempts to control it.

Huxley, J.: Knowledge, Morality, and Destiny (formerly New Bottles for New Wine), Mentor Books, New American Library, Inc., New York, 1957. A brilliant group of essays by the man who calls himself an "evolutionary humanist."

Johnson, C. E. (ed.): *Social and Natural Biology, D. Van Nostrand Company, Inc., Princeton, N.J., 1968. A novel combination of readings from literature and science.

Roslansky, J. D. (ed.): Genetics and the Future of Man, Appleton Century Crofts, New York, 1966. Essays on the genetic future of man by Nobel Prize winners.

Sauer, C. O.: Agricultural Origins and Dispersals, The American Geographical Society, New York, 1952. A lucid discussion of the possible origins of domestication and agriculture.

Shepard, P., and D. McKinley (eds.): *The Subversive Science: Essays toward an Ecology of Man, Houghton Mifflin Company, Boston, 1969. An excellent choice of articles by men in literature, social sciences, and biology; highly recommended.

Teilhard de Chardin, P.: The Future of Man, Harper & Row, Publishers, Incorporated, New York, 1964. The famous Jesuit philosopher, astronomer, and anthropologist attempts to synthesize ideas from science and religion.

Udall, S. L.: *The Quiet Crisis, Avon Book Division, The Hearst Corporation, New York, 1963. The former Secretary of the Interior presents a sincere and well-documented concern for the future of our environment; highly recommended.

Glossary

This alphabetical list gives technical terms used more than once in the text or considered important enough to warrant explicit definition. Greek (Gr.) and Latin (L.) root words are also listed individually or in combination with an explanation of a technical term. Since a glossary is a list without illustrations and out of context, to fully understand what terms mean it is best to use the index to find the text passage where the terms appear and read examples of their normal use, with the additional support of the illustrations that accompany these discussions.

a- (Gr., not) prefix which negates part of word that follows; e.g., agnatha, no jaws

ab- (L.) away, off, opposite of *ad-*; e.g., aboral, away from mouth

abyssal zone see *zone of darkness (ocean)*

acetylcholine molecule secreted by ending of axon of one neuron that can stimulate the cell membrane of the dendrite of a second neuron

acetyl coenzyme A a molecule formed from acetate and coenzyme A during the first part of aerobic respiration; formed from glucose, amino acids, or fatty acids

acid (L. *acidus*, sour) a compound which yields hydrogen ions (H$^+$) when dissolved in water and has a pH of less than 7

acquired behavior behavior in which patterns of responses are affected by experience and learning; repetition of particular stimuli will not elicit identical responses

acro- (Gr. *akros*) end; e.g., acrosome, the tip of the head of a sperm

acrosome in animals, the structure at the tip of a sperm which comes into contact with egg during fertilization

actin a protein which, along with myosin, forms part of the contractile mechanism of the myofibrils of muscles

active transport the passage of substances through the cell membrane with the expenditure of energy

ad- (L.) toward, to, opposite of *ab-*; e.g., adrenal, next to the kidney

adaptation (L. *adaptare*, to fit) development of traits through organic evolution in a population which permit the group to survive; structural, functional, or behavioral traits which permit survival of an organism or a group of organisms in a particular environment

adaptive radiation formation of new species when descendants of a common ancestor invade new and different habitats

adenine a purine nitrogenous base which is part of either RNA or DNA

adenosine triphosphate (ATP) compound that provides the energy for work of all organisms; energy is yielded from bond broken when the third and terminal phosphate is released

aerobic (Gr. *aeros*, air) adjective describing a form of respiration that requires oxygen

afferent (L. *ad + ferre*, to carry) to lead or carry toward a given region; e.g., afferent nerves; opposite of efferent

algae (singular alga) protists capable of photosynthesis; three lines of evolution: green algae, brown algae, and red algae

alkaline adjective describing compounds which yield hydroxyl ions (OH$^-$) when dissolved in water and have a pH of more than 7; synonomous with basic

allantois (Gr. *allantoeides*, sausage-shaped) membrane which serves in breathing and excretion in reptiles and birds; present as a collapsed membranous bag in placental mammals

alleles (Gr. *allelon*, of one another) alternate forms of genes at specific regions of homologous chromosomes

ameboid movement (Gr. *amoibe*, change) motion or eating with the use of pseudopodia

amino acid an organic acid containing at least one amino group (—NH$_2$) at one end and at least one carboxylic acid group (—COOH) at the other; since the —COOH can give up the —H as an ion, it functions as an acid

amnion (Gr. *amnos*, lamb) membrane surrounding the embryos of reptiles, birds, and mammals and holds the amniotic fluid which protects the embryos; grown as an extension from the embryo

amphi- (Gr.) on both sides; e.g., amphibian, both lives or two kinds of lives

Amphibia (Gr. *amphibios*, living a double life)

class of vertebrates; larval form with gills and living in water, adult form with lungs and living primarily on land

amylase (L. *amylum,* starch) enzyme accelerating the hydrolysis of starch into component glucose sugars

an- (Gr.) not; like a- but used before vowel or h; e.g., anhydrous, without water

ana- (Gr.) up, throughout, again, back; e.g., anaphase, in which chromosomes are pulled back; anatomy, to cut up

anaerobic adjective describing a form of respiration that does not require oxygen

anaphase third stage of cell division; chromosomes are pulled to poles of spindles

anatomy the study of structure, primarily on level visible to the unaided eye

Angiosperm (Gr. *angeion,* a vessel, + *sperma,* seed) phylum of flowering plants; seeds enclosed by matured ovary with an expanded wall called a fruit

angstrom one ten-thousandth of a micron; one ten-millionth of a millimeter

Animalia the kingdom comprising the animals

animals (L. *animus,* vital) members of the kingdom Animalia; most are capable of locomotion, but none can manufacture their own food

Annelida (L. *anellus,* a ring) phylum of segmented worms

anterior (L. *ante,* before, in front of) front end of organism

anther (Gr. *antheros,* flowery) structure in which pollen is produced in flowering plants

antho- (Gr. *anthos*) flower, e.g., anther, part of flower

anthocyanin water-soluble plant pigment that is usually red, purple, or blue

anthropo- (Gr. *anthropos*) man, human; e.g., anthropology, the study of man

antibody protein produced by an organism which renders harmless foreign proteins (antigens) entering the organism

antigen foreign substance, usually protein, which causes an organism it enters to produce antibodies against it

apical (L. *apex,* tip) located at or near a tip; e.g., apical meristem, the embryonic tissue at tips of roots and stems

Arachnida (Gr. *arachne,* spider) class of arthropods bearing chelicera; includes spiders, scorpions, mites, and ticks

arboreal (L. *arbor,* tree) tree-dwelling

arch- (Gr. *archos*) chief, first, or main; e.g., archenteron, early gut in embryo

archenteron cavity in a vertebrate embryo which will become digestive tract

arthro- (Gr. *arthron*) joint; e.g., arthropod, an animal with jointed legs

Arthropoda phylum of invertebrates with jointed legs, chitinous exoskeleton, and compound eyes

artificial selection greater reproductive success of forms favored by man and maintained in habitats altered by man

association neurons neurons that connect motor and sensory neurons; they form complex pathways up and down and in the spinal cord and brain and constitute most of their bulk

aster (Gr. star) a pair of centrioles with fibers radiating from them during cell division; found only in animal cells

atom (Gr. *atomos,* indivisible) an extremely dense nucleus with electrons vibrating around it; smallest unit of a chemical element with the properties of the element

ATP see *adenosine triphosphate*

auto- (Gr.) same, self; e.g., autotroph, a self-feeding organism

autonomic nervous system subdivision of nervous system primarily responsible for internal homeostasis; includes unconscious control over smooth muscles; controlled by cerebrum and cerebellum

autosome chromosome other than X or Y chromosome

Aves (L. *avis*, bird) class of vertebrates comprising the birds

axo- (Gr. *axon*) axis; e.g., axon, the fiber leading nerve impulses away from a neuron

axon (Gr. *axon*, axis) an extension of a neuron (nerve cell) that carries nerve impulses away from the cell body

bacillus (L. *baculum*, rod) a rod-shaped bacterium

bacteriophage (L. *bacterium* + Gr. *phagein*, to eat) a virus that is a parasite in bacteria

bacterium (Gr. *baktron*, staff) smallest of cells; lacks nucleus and internal membranes; genes contained in single strand of DNA; member of kingdom Monera

baculum small bone or cartilage that stiffens the penis of monkeys and apes

base a compound which yields hydroxyl ions (OH⁻) when dissolved in water and has a pH of more than 7 (see *alkaline*)

benthic organisms (Gr. *benthos*, depth of the sea) bottom-dwelling organisms that attach, rest, or burrow into the sediments

bi- (L. *bis*) twice, double, two; e.g., bilateral, having two sides

bilateral symmetry body plan of animals in which two sides of only one plane through longitudinal axis will be similar in appearance

bio- (Gr. *bios*) life; e.g., biology, the study of life

-blast, blast-, blasto- (Gr. *blastos*) embryo; e.g., blastopore, opening in embryo through which cells move inside

blastocyst mammalian form of blastula

blastula an animal embryo following cleavage; usually consists of a sphere of cells with fluid in the center; precedes the formation of gastrula

blue-green algae similar to bacteria except for cover of slime and presence of cellulose in cell wall; photosynthetic; member of kingdom Monera

brachio- (L. *brachium*) arm; e.g., brachiate, to swing from branch to branch with arms

Bryophyta (Gr. *bryon*, moss, +*phyton*, plant) mosses, liverworts, and hornworts; phylum in the kingdom Plantae which lacks vascular tissue

caecum (L. *caecus*, blind) blind pouch extending from beginning of large intestine of primates

cambium (L., exchange) a very thin cylindrical sheath of embryonic cells in roots and stems of plants that gives rise to xylem on the inner side and phloem toward the outer side; responsible for an increase in diameter of a plant

carbohydrate an organic compound consisting of a chain of carbon atoms to which are attached hydrogens and oxygens in the same 2:1 ratio as in water; e.g., sugars, starches, and cellulose

cardio- (Gr. *kardia*) heart, e.g., cardiac muscle, the muscle of the heart

carnivores (L. *carnivorus*, flesh-eating) animals that eat animals

carrier molecule a mechanism of active transport in which certain molecules in the cell membrane attach to substances, carry them through the membrane, and release them on the other side

castration removal of the gonads

catalysis (Gr. *katalysis*, dissolution) process by which a substance accelerates a chemical reaction without being a final product

cell a structure enclosed in a membrane and usually including a nucleus and surrounding cytoplasm with the ability to acquire nutrients and carry on metabolism, growth, and development and respond to stimuli

cell membrane the outermost membrane of

all cells; membrane that forms boundary of cells and separates the living cell from its nonliving environment

cell sap the fluid in cells

cellulose insoluble complex of chains of glucose molecules; principal constituent of cell walls of plants and some fungi; differs from starch primarily in type of bonds between glucose units

cell wall a supportive structure secreted by bacteria, blue-green algae, algae, and plant cells; in plant cells cellulose is the chief constituent

central nervous system subdivision of nervous system primarily responsible for external homeostasis; included conscious control over skeletal muscles; controlled by cerebrum and cerebellum

centriole (L. *centrum,* center) a pair of small bundles in the cytoplasm of single-celled organisms and animal cells; they function in cytoplasm, possibly in the formation of spindle fibers

centromere (L. *centrum,* center, + Gr. *meros,* part) region on chromosome to which spindle fibers attach during mitosis and meiosis; also holds together the chromatids, the duplicate and separate strands of a chromosome

cephalo- (Gr. *kephale*) head; e.g., cephalopod, head-footed animal

Cephalopoda class of mollusks which are head-footed; squids, octopuses, nautiluses

cerebellum (L., small brain) a region of the brain behind or below the cerebrum which coordinates the activities of muscles

cerebral cortex (L., brain + bark) the outer layer of the cerebrum where most of the cell bodies of the neurons of the brain are located

cerebrum (L., brain) the largest part of the human brain; forms a domelike cap over the spinal cord; center for the reception of sensory information, associating new sensations

with old, and the dispatch of motor impulses to muscles

cervical (L. *cervix,* neck) at, near, or toward the neck

cervix portion of uterus that protrudes into the vagina

chaeto- (Gr. *chaite*) bristle, hair; e.g., polychaete, many bristles

chaparral region of shrubs and small trees with hard, thick, evergreen leaves which will withstand long periods of hot, dry weather; frequent fires

chelicera pincerlike appendages near mouths of the chelicerates

chitin (Gr. *chiton,* shell) highly resistant substance forming much of the exoskeleton of arthropods, parts of the integument of several other invertebrates, and the cell walls of fungi

chloro- (Gr. *chloros*) green; e.g., *chlorophyll,* green pigment in plants

chlorophyll (Gr. *chloros,* green +*phyllon,* leaf) the green pigments of plant cells that trap energy from light for photosynthesis

chloroplasts green organelles in the cytoplasm of algae and plants which contain chlorophyll and carry on photosynthesis

cholinesterase an enzyme secreted by ends of dendrites which destroys acetylcholine secreted by axons

Chondrichthyes fishes with a skeleton of cartilage; the sharks, skates, and rays; a class of vertebrates

chondro- (Gr. *chondros*) cartilage; e.g., Chondrichthyes, the fishes with skeletons of cartilage

-chord, chorda- (L. *chorda*) cord, string; e.g., notochord, cord along back of vertebrate embryos

Chordata phylum of animals possessing notochord, dorsal nerve cord, and pharyngeal gill slits at some time during their lives

chorion membrane surrounding the amnion and its fluid in reptiles, birds, and mammals;

grown out as an extension from the embryo; has tiny projections that grow and branch extensively in the lining of the uterus during implantation of the embryo

chorionic gonadotrophin steroid hormone produced by chorion which stimulates production of progesterone in ovary and therefore retention of the lining of the uterus and the embryo

chromatid one of the two strands of a duplicated chromosome; held together by a centromere

chromatin the darkly staining network of chromosome strands viewed while the cell is not dividing; a general term applied to the nucleoprotein of the chromosomes

-chrome, chromo-, chroma- (Gr. *chroma*) color; e.g., chromosome, threads in cell nucleus which will absorb dyes

chromosome a threadlike structure containing genes made of DNA as well as protein

chromosome map a scheme by which the relative positions of genes on a chromosome can be plotted as a result of analysis of the relative frequency of crossing-over between the genes

cilia (L., eyelid) fibrous extensions of the cell membrane which are short, numerous, and may wave back and forth like a flexible oar; this movement causes the cell to move or the surrounding fluid to move past the cell

citric acid cycle See *Krebs cycle*

class a group of closely related orders; a taxonomic rank between order and phylum

classical conditioning learning in which a new stimulus is substituted for a previous one and the same response is elicited; the stimulus and response are paired by the organism being studied

classification procedure by which organisms are assigned to categories based on degree of likeness and difference

cleavage the series of cell divisions in which a fertilized egg becomes a blastula of no greater size than the original egg

climax community a relatively stable state in an ecosystem from which there will be no further ecological succession unless it is disturbed

clitoris a small erectile organ in the upper part of the external genitalia of a female; homologous to penis of male

cloaca (L., sewer) a chamber which serves as a common exit for the digestive, excretory, and reproductive systems in reptiles, birds, and egg-laying mammals

Cnidaria (Gr. *knide*, nettle) coelenterates, the phylum possessing stinging cells (see *Coelenterata*); many biologists use name Cnidaria instead of Coelenterata for this phylum

coccus (pl. cocci) any spherical bacterium

-coel, coela-, coelo- (Gr. *koilos*) hollow cavity; e.g., coelenterate, animals with gut cavity

Coelenterata phylum of invertebrate animals possessing stinging cells and a single opening to gut cavity; sea anemones, corals, jellyfish, hydroids (see *Cnidaria*)

coelom (Gr. *koiloma*, a hollow) a body cavity formed in mesoderm and containing internal organs

collar cells flagellated cells of sponges which cause current of water and trap food

commensalism (L. *cum*, with, + *mensa*, table) a type of symbiosis in which two or more species of organisms live together in an association benefitting one organism while neither benefitting nor harming the other; e.g., the remora fish that feeds on leftovers from the shark's meals

complementary base pairing the procedure by which nitrogenous bases bond together so that a purine is always bonded to a pyrimidine, e.g., adenine with thymine, cytosine with guanine

compound (L. *componere,* to put together) atoms or ions combined in definite ratios and held together by chemical bonds

conditioning gaining a new response by classical or operant means in a laboratory (see *classical conditioning* and *operant conditioning*)

cone specialized portion of conifer which produces spores and seeds

cone cells cells in vertebrate retina sensitive to light in fine detail vision (see *rod cells*)

connective tissue animal tissue in which the cells are not in contact and the intervening spaces are filled with a product of the cells; connects, supports, or surrounds other tissues and organs

convergent evolution (L. *convergere,* to turn together) evolution of similar adaptations by different species because of living in similar habitats

copulation the act of mating

corpus luteum (pl. corpora lutea) (L., yellow body) tiny endocrine gland formed from graafian follicle after ovulation; secretes progesterone

cortex (p. cortices) (L., bark) outer layers of an organ or body part; e.g., adrenal cortex

cotyledon (Gr. *kotyledon,* a cup-shaped hollow) the one or two leaflike structures of the embryo in the seed; function as storage or absorbing organs

covalent bond a sharing of electrons in the outer shells of two atoms so that the same electrons are included in the outer-shell of both atoms

crossover exchange of segments of homologous chromosomes during meiosis

Crustacea (L. *crusta,* shell, rind) class of arthropods bearing mandibles and calcium deposits in their exoskeletons; crustaceans

cryptorchism a condition in which testes fail to descend from body cavity into scrotum

cyano- (Gr. *kyanos*) dark blue; e.g., Cyanophyta, the blue-green algae

Cyanophyta phylum of blue-green algae

cyto- (Gr. *kytos*) vessel, container; pertains to cell; e.g., cytoplasm, the part of the cell other than the nucleus

cytochrome one of a group of molecules that contain iron and carry electrons and hydrogens in the electron transport chain of aerobic respiration or photosynthesis

cytoplasm all the cell except for the nucleus

cytosine a pyrimidine nitrogenous base which may be part of either RNA or DNA

dark reaction that part of photosynthesis which does not require light but uses the ATP and NADPH as sources of energy to fix carbon dioxide molecules to other carbon compounds to form simple carbohydrates

de- (L.) away, from, off; e.g., denature, change in nature of proteins from previous state

deciduous forest region with 30 to 40 inches annual rainfall as well-spaced rains or snows; cold winters and warm summers; most trees are deciduous, i.e., drop their leaves in autumn

decomposers organisms that digest the bodies of dead organisms and return their atoms and molecules to the physical environment of an ecosystem

dehydration synthesis bonding together of compounds with the loss of water; the water is formed from the —H lost from one compound and the —OH from the other

denature a change in the folding and spiraling pattern of proteins because of changes in temperature, pH, or concentration resulting in a change in chemical role

dendrite (Gr. *dendron,* tree) an extension of a neuron (nerve cell) that carries nerve impulses toward the cell body

density number of units per area

denticle (L. *denticulus,* small tooth) toothlike scale of shark

deoxyribonucleic acid nucleic acid that contains deoxyribose sugar plus adenine, guanine, cytosine, and thymine; carries the genetic recipes that determine the traits of an organism; genes are sections of this substance; made of two strands and capable of replicating itself (see *ribonucleic acid*)

deoxyribose sugar the type of sugar found alternating with phosphate along the backbone of DNA, a nucleic acid

dermis, -derm (Gr. *derma*) skin; e.g., endoderm, inner layer in embryo; epidermis, outer layer in skin

desert region with less than 10 inches annual rainfall; temperature variable

di- (Gr.) twice, double, two; e.g., dimorphism, two body forms in a species

dia- (Gr.) through, across; e.g., the name diatom means cut in two and refers to the two halves of which the body covering of diatoms is constructed

differentiation the process in growth and development by which cells become progressively more specialized in structure and function

diffusion the movement of particles from regions of higher to regions of lower concentration

digits fingers and toes

diplo- (Gr. *diploos*) twofold; e.g., diploid, a set of chromosomes twice that of gametes

diploid a number of chromosomes twice that of gametes; each type of chromosome, except for sex chromosomes, is represented twice; i.e., all chromosomes exist in homologous pairs (see *haploid*)

dis- (L.) apart, away; e.g., dissect, to cut apart

displacement activities behavioral actions which seem out of context and without apparent cause; probably caused by presence of several conflicting drives

divergent evolution process by which one species gives rise to two or more species through time and a shift in gene frequency

diversity variety of species resulting from divergent evolution

DNA see *deoxyribonucleic acid*

dominant gene a gene that suppresses the expression of its allele, the recessive

dorsal (L. *dorsum,* back) at, near, or toward the back; opposite of ventral

double sugars (also known as disaccharides) sugars consisting of two simple sugars, e.g., sucrose, table sugar

echino- (Gr. *echinos*) spiny, bristly; e.g., echinoderms, the spiny-skinned animals

Echinodermata phylum of spiny-skinned animals: starfish, sea urchins, sea cucumbers, crinoids, and brittle stars

eco- (Gr. *oikos*) house, home; e.g., ecology, the study of interactions between organisms and their environment

ecological niche role and status of an organism within its ecosystem

ecological succession an orderly shift through time of dominant forms of plants and animals in an ecosystem, caused by the changes in the environment brought about by the life processes of the organisms in the ecosystem

ecology (Gr. *oikos,* home, + *logos,* a discourse) the study of interactions between organisms and their environment

ecosystem a self-sufficient system of interactions not only between populations of different species but between these populations and their physical environment

ecto- (Gr. *ektos*) outside; e.g., ectoderm, the outermost layer in a vertebrate embryo

ectoderm (Gr. *ektos*, outside, + *derm*, skin) the outermost layer of an animal embryo; gives rise to skin, nervous tissue, etc.

efferent (L. ex, out or away, + *ferre*, to carry) leading or carrying away from a given region; opposite of afferent; e.g., efferent nerves

egg (Norse, egg) a mature gamete from a female; contrasted with a sperm, an egg is immotile, larger, has much more cytoplasm, and varying amounts of yolk

electrolyte (Gr. *elektron*, amber) compound that dissociates into ions when in water and conducts an electric current through the water

electron particle with a negative charge moving about atomic nucleus

electron-transport chain series of molecules beginning with FAD and continuing with cytochromes; in aerobic respiration electrons are passed along these chains, and energy is harvested from the electrons and molecules of ATP formed

element one of 103 kinds of matter which, singly or in combination with others, form all the materials of the universe

embryo (Gr. *en*, in, + *bryein*, to swell) offspring in stages of development between fertilized egg and birth or release from capsule in which growth and development occured

embryonic induction see *inductive interaction*

endo- (Gr. *endon*) within; e.g., endoderm, the innermost layer in a vertebrate embryo

endoderm (Gr. *endon*, within, + *derma*, skin) the innermost layer of an animal embryo; gives rise to primitive gut

endometrium lining of uterus; richly endowed with blood capillaries; tissue to which embryo attaches in placental mammals

endoplasmic reticulum (L. *reticulum*, network) a system of double membranes forming compartments and channels that look like deflated balloons in the cytoplasm; may or may not have ribosomes attached to outer surface

endosperm nutritive tissue in seed formed from the fusion of one sperm nucleus with two polar nuclei of female gametophyte

endospore a thick-walled resistant spore formed in a bacterial cell

energy (Gr. *energos*, active) ability to do work

entero-, enteron (Gr. *enteron*) intestine; e.g., archenteron, the primitive gut cavity in vertebrate embryo

enzymatic hydrolysis the breaking apart of a molecule with the addition of water in the presence of the proper enzyme; the HOH of water contributes an —OH to one part of the molecule and an H— to the other

enzyme (Gr. *enzymos*, leavened) a protein molecule whose surface properties induce and increase the rate of the interaction of substances which collide and bind to it; since they are not consumed in the reactions, they can be used repeatedly

epi (Gr.) to, on, over, against; e.g., epidermis, the outermost layer of skin

epididymis (Gr. *didymos*, testicle) the highly coiled portion of the sperm duct next to the testis of a mammal

epithelial tissue animal tissue in which the cells are in contact; covers, lines, and protects the internal and external body surfaces

estrogen (Gr. *oistros*, frenzy + *genesis*, creation) steroid hormone produced in the ovary; causes growth of female sex organs and development of secondary sexual characteristics, e.g., decreased body hair, smaller larynx, smaller muscles; causes estrus, or "heat," in all mammals except human

ethology (Gr. *ethos,* custom, character) study of animal behavior, particularly under natural conditions in the field

eu- (Gr.) good, well, proper, true; e.g., eutherians, the true beasts

eunuch a castrated male

euphotic zone see *zone of light*

evolution (L. e-, out, + *volvers,* to roll) process by which organisms become modified through successive generations

ex-, exo-, extero- (L.) out, from, exterior; e.g., exoskeleton, an external skeleton

excretion release of metabolic wastes and excess water

FAD flavine adenine dinucleotide, the receptor molecule that accepts electrons from NAD and begins the electron-transport chain in aerobic respiration

family a group of closely related genera; a taxonomic rank between genus and order

fatty acids compounds consisting of chains of —CH_2 units with one end terminating with —COOH; the —COOH can yield a hydrogen ion and therefore function as an acid; these molecules are used in synthesis of lipids

feces (L. *faeces,* dregs) undigestible waste matter released from the digestive tract

feedback a process by which a system of regulation is itself regulated by its own effects, its output

-fer, -fera (L. *ferre*) to carry, bear; e.g., Porifera, the sponges, the pore-bearing animals

fermentation the formation of lactic acid or ethyl alcohol from pyruvic acid in respiration, synonymous with anaerobic respiration

fertilization fusion of an egg and a sperm to form a zygote

fetus (L. offspring) name applied to human embryos after the third month, when they are recognizable as being human

flagella (L. whip) fibrous extensions of the cell membrane which are long, few in number, and may wave back and forth like a whip; this movement causes the cell to move or the surrounding fluid to move past the cell

flame cells primitive excretory structures in flatworms

flower specialized region of angiosperm which produces spores and seeds

follicle see *graafian follicle*

follicle-stimulating hormone (FSH) a pituitary hormone that causes graafian follicle to enlarge and stimulates the production of estrogen by the ovary

food chain a transfer of nutrients from organism to organism in a sequence of eaters

food pyramid a pyramid-shaped graph representing the mass or numbers of organisms existing at each feeding level in an ecosystem

food web a complex network of food chains existing in an ecosystem

foreskin see *prepuce*

fovea (L. pit) pit at rear of retina of primates with a large concentration of cone cells permitting acute vision in color

fruit (L. *fructus,* fruit) a mature, ripened ovary wall in plants; contains the seed

FSH see *follicle-stimulating hormone*

fungi protists whose body consists of branching network of filaments called hyphae

gametes (Gr. wife, husband) specialized reproductive cells that must fuse with another gamete before they can develop into a new organism; fertilization required (see also *vegetative reproduction* and *spores*)

gametophyte haploid, gamete-producing plant; phase of life cycle which follows sporophyte phase in an alternation of generations in plants

gamo-, gamy (Gr. *gamein,* to marry) pertains to gametes or fertilization; e.g., autogamy, self-fertilization

ganglion (Gr., a swelling) local mass of neuron cell bodies

gastro- (Gr. *gaster*) stomach; e.g., gastric juices, the digestive fluids of the stomach

Gastropoda class of mollusks; snails, slugs, abalone

gastrula (Gr. *gaster,* stomach) stage of an animal embryo in which the blastula gives rise to a three-layered embryo containing the future gut

gemma (L. a bud) cup-shaped vegetative bud of bryophytes which in suitable conditions develops into a whole plant

-gen, -genic, geno- (Gr. *genesis*) born created; e.g., estrogen, hormone creating sexual characteristics in human female

gene (Gr. *genos,* race, stock, descent) a region of a chromosome that can be identified as having a role in the development of a trait

gene frequency the relative incidence of an allele in a population, usually expressed as percentage

gene interaction the concept that traits are formed as the result of many different genes acting in concert and affecting the expression of each other

gene pool all the alleles present in a population

genetic code the relationship between a section of DNA and the protein whose synthesis it regulates; one that allows a DNA genetic message phrased in nitrogenous bases to be translated into proteins whose words are amino acids

genetic drift random shifting of gene frequencies due to chance in small populations

genotype a set of genes believed to have caused, along with the environment, a specific trait or set of traits of an organism

genus (L. race) a group of closely related species; a taxonomic rank between species and family

gills breathing organs of aquatic animals; thin-walled projections from external surface of invertebrates; thin-walled projections from throat of vertebrates

glans the head of the penis or clitoris

gluco-, glyco- (Gr. *gleukos*) sweet, pertains to sugars; e.g., glycolysis, the breakdown of sugars

glycolysis the splitting of a six-carbon glucose molecule into two three-carbon pyruvic acid molecules in respiration

gnatho-, -gnath (Gr. *gnathos*) jaw; e.g., agnathans, the jawless fishes

golgi complex concentric layers of endoplasmic reticulum associated with secretion in a cell

gonads (Gr. *gone,* generation) organs of multicellular animals that produce gametes; ovaries and testes

graafian follicle (L. *follis,* bag) mass of cells in a mammalian ovary in which an egg forms and matures before ovulation

grassland region with intermittent rains providing an annual total of 10 to 30 inches; temperatures vary

gray matter cell bodies of neurons in brain and spinal cord

growth increase in size

guanine a purine nitrogenous base which may be part of either RNA or DNA

gymno- (Gr. *gymnos*) naked; e.g., gymnosperms, plants that form naked seeds

gymnosperms (Gr. *gymnos,* naked, +*sperma,* seed) plants with seeds not enclosed by an ovary; represented today primarily by conifers

gyn-, gyne, gyno- (Gr. *gyne*) woman; e.g., *gynecology,* the study of the physiology of the female

habitat (L. it lives) portion of an environment in which an organism lives

habituation loss of responses which have no significance; a form of forgetting

haplo (Gr. *haploos*) single; e.g., haploid, a set of chromosomes like those found in gametes

haploid a number of chromosomes characteristic of mature gametes; each type of chromosome is represented only once; i.e., only one chromosome from each homologous pair is present (see *diploid*)

Hardy-Weinberg law mathematical expression of relationship between relative frequencies of genes in a population; argues that gene frequencies stay the same in the absence of natural selection, mutation, migration, selective mating, and small population size

-helminth (Gr. *helminthos*) worm; e.g., platyhelminthes, the flatworms

hem-, hemo-, hemato- (Gr. *haima*) blood; e.g., hemoglobin, the red blood pigment

hemophilia (Gr. *haima,* blood, + *philos,* loving) hereditary disease of man in which minor wounds cause excessive bleeding

herbivore (L. *herba,* plant, + *vorare,* to devour) an animal that eats plants

hermaphrodite (Gr. *Hermes* and *Aphrodite*) organism possessing both male and female reproductive organs

hetero- (Gr. *heteros*) other, different; e.g., heterozygous, in which the pair of genes are for alternate forms of a trait; opposite of *homo-*

heterozygous a condition in which the pair of genes for a trait are alleles; i.e., they are for alternate expressions of the trait; e.g., a person who can taste PTC may be *Tt*: one gene for taster, one for nontaster

hex-, hexa- (Gr.) six; e.g., hexose, a six-carbon sugar

homeostasis (Gr. *homos,* same, + *stasis,* standing) a condition in which living systems respond to changes in their internal or external environment in ways that balance the changes and promote a relatively stable and constant condition

hominid (L. *homo,* man) a living or extinct form belonging to Hominidae, the family of man

Hominoidea a superfamily that includes Hominidae and Pongidae, the families of man and apes, respectively

homozygous a condition in which both genes for a trait are identical; e.g., a person who cannot taste PTC is said to be homozygous for this recessive trait, tt

hormone (Gr. *hormaein,* to excite) a molecule secreted, usually in very small amounts, in one part of the body having effects in other regions, to which it is carried in body fluids

hybrid as commonly used, means a heterozygous organism (see *true hybrid*)

hydro- (Gr. *hydro*) water; e.g., hydrolysis, the breaking apart of molecules with the addition of water

hymen a membrane partially covering the opening of the vagina

hyper- (Gr.) above, over; e.g., hyperthyroidism, a condition in which too much thyroid hormone is produced; opposite of *hypo-*

hypertonic a solution having less water per volume than another reference solution; if these solutions are separated by a semipermeable membrane, water will flow into the hypertonic solution by osmosis

hyphae branching filaments of fungus

hypo- (Gr.) under, less; e.g., hypothyroidism, a condition in which too little thyroid hormone is produced; opposite of *hyper-*

hypotonic a solution having more water per volume than another reference solution; if these solutions are separated by a semipermeable membrane water will flow out of the hypotonic solution by osmosis

hypothalamus (Gr. *hypo-,* under, + *thalamos,* inner room) central lower side of cerebrum where pituitary gland is attached; it and medulla oblongata are centers for autonomic nervous system and regulation of vital reflexes such as body temperature; thought to be center for such drives as hunger, thirst, sex

hypothesis (Gr. *hypo,* under, + *tithenai,* to put) a tentative explanation of causal relationships believed to exist between several interacting factors; based on accumulated facts plus an intuitive guess; must be tested for validity by experimental or descriptive means

ichthyo- (Gr. *ichthyos*) fish; e.g., Osteichthyes, the bony fishes

imprinting modification of stereotyped behavior in which a young bird or mammal learns to follow the first large object that moves

incomplete dominance a common situation in which both alleles express themselves so that the resulting phenotype is a combination of both genetic messages

induction see *inductive interaction*

inductive interaction the mechanism by which certain specialized cells induce other cells to become differentiated because of interaction between them

inorganic compounds compounds that do not contain carbon; usually called minerals

instinct behavior pattern that has not been learned

inter- (L.) between, among; e.g., interphase, the portion of the life of a cell when it is not dividing; i.e., a cell between cell divisions

interphase phase of life of a cell when it is not dividing

intertidal zone region between lowest low tide and the higher region merely splashed by the sea

intra- (L.) within; e.g., intracellular, within cells (as contrasted with intercellular, between cells)

invertebrate (L. *vertebra,* a joint) animals which never form backbones

ion (Gr. *ienai,* to go) an atom or group of atoms which have gained or lost one or more electrons and therefore have an electrical charge

ionic bond a condition in which atoms which have gained or lost electrons attract each other because of their opposite charges

ionic compounds compounds which contain ions held in ionic bonds; when dry, they are crystals, but when dissolved in water, the ions dissociate from each other and can conduct an electric current

ion pump a mechanism of active transport in cell membranes that concentrates certain ions on one side of the membrane

isolation see *reproductive isolation*

isotonic a solution which has the same amount of water per volume as a reference solution; if these solutions are separated by a semipermeable membrane, there will be no gain or loss of water by either solution by osmosis

kingdom a group of closely related phyla, the highest and most inclusive taxonomic rank

Krebs cycle a circular sequence of reactions in aerobic respiration in which acetyl coenzyme A is consumed and carbon dioxide and energy-rich electrons are produced (also known as the citric acid cycle)

labia majora the large outer folds of the female external genitalia

labia minora the small inner membranous folds of the female external genitalia

labium (pl. labia) (L. lip) any liplike structure

larva (pl. larvae) (L. mask) period in life cycle of animals between hatching and metamorphosis into adult

learning a change in behavior as a result of experience

leuco- (Gr. *leukos*) white; e.g., leucocyte, white blood cell

LH see *luteinizing hormone*

life the presence of homeostasis, growth and development, and the acquisition and metabolism of nutrients

light reaction that part of photosynthesis which requires light, chlorophyll, and water, and with the regulation by enzymes, produces energy-rich ATP and NADPH; these products can be used in the dark reaction

limiting factor factor in a habitat which will affect survival of an organism if present in too little or too great amounts

limnetic zone see *zone of open water*

linked genes genes located together on the same chromosome

lip, lipo- (Gr. *lipos*) fat; e.g., lipase, the enzyme that digests fat

lipid (Gr. *lipos,* fat) organic molecules which are fat or fatlike and insoluble in water but soluble in organic solvents such as ether, alcohol, and acetone; e.g., butter, corn oil, lard, and the lipids of cell membranes

littoral zone see *intertidal zone* and *zone of shallow water*

-logy (Gr. *logos*) study; e.g., biology, the study of living things

luteinizing hormone a pituitary hormone that causes ovulation and the conversion of the ruptured graafian follicle into a corpus luteum

-lysis, -lytic, -lyte (Gr. *lysis*) a loosening; pertains to dissolving or breaking up; e.g., hydrolysis, the breaking up of molecules with the addition of water

lysosomes bags of digestive enzymes in the cytoplasm which can digest nutrients in food vacuoles

macro- (Gr. *makros*) long, large; e.g., macroscopic, visible to unaided eye; opposite of *micro-*

major greater or larger

Mammalia class of vertebrates comprising the mammals

mammary pertaining to the breast

mantle outermost layer of body wall of mollusks; covers visceral mass with its internal organs; usually secretes a shell

marsupial (Gr. *marsypion,* little bag) a pouched mammal

medulla (L. the marrow) inner layers of an organ or body part; adrenal medulla

medulla oblongata (L. oblong shaped marrow) region of brainstem to which the spinal cord is attached; center for autonomic nervous system and the control of vital reflexes such as heartbeat, breathing, diameter of arteries, diameter of pupils of eye

medusa (after Medusa, the mythological monster with hair made of snakes) free-swimming bell-shaped stage; present in life cycle of most coelenterates; jellyfish

mega- (Gr. *megas*) large; e.g., megaspores, large spores; opposite of *micro-;* used like *macro-*

meiosis (Gr. diminution) cell division in which the daughter cells each receive only half the number of chromosomes held by the parent cell; only one chromosome from each homologous pair arrives in a daughter cell; the number of chromosomes is therefore reduced to one-half (see *mitosis*)

melanin (Gr. *melas,* black) black pigment of animals

menstruation or menses (L. *mensis,* month) sloughing off of the outermost layer of the lining of the uterus accompanied by a bloody discharge through the vagina; results from a decrease in level of progesterone

meri-, mero-, -mere, -mer (Gr. *meros*) part; e.g., meristem, part of plant with embryonic cells

meristem embryonic tissue in plants which is capable of giving rise to additional tissues

meso- (Gr. *mesos*) middle, e.g., mesoderm, the middle layer of cells in a vertebrate embryo

mesoderm (Gr. *mesos*, middle, + *derma*, skin) the middle layer of an animal embryo; situated between endoderm and ectoderm; gives rise to muscles, skeleton, circulatory system, excretory system, and most of the reproductive system

messenger RNA (mRNA) RNA which, after being formed by complementary base-pairing on a section of DNA, a gene, goes to ribosomes where it forms the template upon which amino acids are assembled to form proteins

meta (Gr.) after, behind; e.g., metaphase, the phase of cell division that follows prophase

metabolism (Gr. *metabole*, change) all the chemical changes within a living unit that result in alternation of compounds and use of energy

metamorphosis (Gr. *metamorphoun*, to transform) process by which a larva changes in structure and function and becomes an adult

metaphase second stage during cell division; chromosomes line up in a plane at right angles to axis of spindle

micro- (Gr *mikros*) small; e.g., microscopic, so small it is visible only with aid to the eyes

microbe (Gr. *mikros*, small, + *bios*, life) an organism that can be seen only with the aid of a microscope

micron one-thousandth part of a millimeter, one ten-thousandth of a centimeter

minerals inorganic compounds in the crust of the earth

minor lesser

mitochondria (Gr. *mitos*, thread, + *chondrion*, small grain) organelles in the cytoplasm in which aerobic respiration occurs

mitosis (Gr. *mitos*, thread) cell division in which each daughter cell receives a set of chromosomes identical to those of the parent cell; all chromosomes are duplicated, and duplicate sets go to each daughter cell; the number of chromosomes is therefore maintained (see *meiosis*)

molecular compound compound which contains atoms held in covalent bonds

Mollusca (L. *molluscus*, soft) phylum of soft-bodied animals with a ventral foot, visceral mass, mantle, and usually a shell but no segmentation; the snails, clams, squids, octopuses, chitons, and tooth shells

Monera (Gr. *monos*, alone) kingdom consisting of bacteria and blue-green algae

mono- (Gr. *monos*) single; e.g., monosaccharide, a single unit of sugar

-morph, morpho-, (Gr. *morphe*) form; e.g., morphology, study of structural form

morula (L. little mulberry) embryonic stage which is a solid ball of cells resulting from cleavage of fertilized egg; a solid blastula

motor neuron neuron that carries impulse out from brain or spinal cord to an effector such as a muscle or a gland

mRNA *messenger RNA*

mucus (L. *mucosus*, mucus) a thick, clear fluid secreted by cells of mucous membranes

multiple alleles the presence of more than two alternate forms of a gene in a population; e.g., there are three forms of the gene for blood types A, B, and O

multiple genes a common situation in which a trait is determined by the additive expression of more than a single pair of genes; e.g., skin color, intelligence, eye color, and hair color, each produced by more than a single pair of genes

mutation (L. *mutare,* to change) an inheritable change in hereditary material; this may be a change in DNA or in the structure or number of chromosomes (see *crossover* and *nondisjunction*)

mutualism a type of symbiosis in which two or more species or organisms live together to their mutual benefit; e.g., lichen, an association of a fungus and an alga

mycelium body of fungus consisting of many filaments called hyphae

myc-, myco- (Gr. *mykes*) mushroom; e.g., Mycophyta, the phylum of fungi

Mycophyta phylum of fungi

myelin fatty material surrounding the axons of nerve cells of the brain, spinal cord and nerves of vertebrates

myo- (Gr. *mys*) muscle; e.g., myofibril, a contractile unit in a muscle

myofibril long but extremely thin filaments which are the contractile units of muscles

myosin a protein which, along with actin, forms part of the contractile mechanism of muscles

myx-, myxo- (Gr. *myxa*) slime; e.g., Myxomycetes, the phylum of slime molds

Myxomycetes phylum of slime molds

NAD see *nicotinamide adenine dinucleotide*

natural selection the favoring of some phenotypes by the environment with the result that the favored types are more reproductively successful than the less favored; concept that some variant forms in a population are better reproducers than other variants; relative ability to produce offspring successfully

nekton (Gr. *nektos,* swimming) swimming organisms such as fishes, whales, and squid which can make their way against currents in fresh water and ocean

Nematoda phylum of roundworms

-neme, nemato- (Gr. *nema*) thread; e.g., nematodes, the threadlike roundworms

nephridia excretory organs of segmented worms

nephro- (Gr. *nephros*) kidney; e.g., nephridia, primitive kidneys found in segmented worms

nerve a group or bundle of neurons (nerve cells) surrounded by connective tissue

nerve impulse a continuing wave of depolarization along a membrane of a neuron brought about by a change in the selective permeability of the membrane

nervous system all the nerve cells possessed by an animal; specialized to receive sensory information, process it, and cause a response

neural tube a hollow rod of nerve cells in vertebrate embryos lying just above the notochord; gives rise to spinal cord and brain and the nerves extending from them

neuro- (Gr. *neuron*) nerve; e.g., neural groove, the primitive stage of the nervous system of a vertebrate

neuromuscular junction the connection between an axon and a muscle cell

neuron (Gr., nerve) a nerve cell

neuston organisms resting or swimming on the surface of fresh water or ocean

niche see *ecological niche*

nicotinamide adenine dinucleotide (NAD) the receptor molecules that carry electrons in the Krebs cycle of aerobic respiration and the light reaction of photosynthesis

nitrogenous bases the ringlike substances which together with a sugar and phosphate make up the nucleotide units that form nucleic acids

nondisjunction a change in number of chromosomes resulting from both members of a homologous pair of chromosomes going to one pole during reduction division of meiosis

noto- (Gr. *noton*) the back; e.g., notochord, cord along back of vertebrate embryos

notochord (Gr. *notos,* back, + *chorde,* string) a flexible rod extending along the length of chordate embryos on the dorsal (back) side below the neural tube; this lends support to the embryo and is replaced by a vertebral column (backbone) in vertebrates

nucleic acids organic compounds consisting of chains of nucleotides; DNA and RNA

nucleolus a darkly staining structure in the nucleus formed by chromosomes and playing a role in protein synthesis

nucleoproteins molecules which are complexes of nucleic acid and protein

nucleotides units that form nucleic acids. Each unit contains a phosphate, sugar, and nitrogenous base; these units are linked together in a sequence of sugar—phosphate—sugar—phosphate, etc.; the nitrogenous bases project to the side from the sugars and provide the genetic information of the nucleic acid

nucleus (L. kennel) organell in cells which contain chromosomes and nucleoli

nutrient (L. *nutrire,* to nourish) a substance whose matter and energy can be used in metabolism

octo- (Gr. *okto*) eight, e.g., octopus, animal with eight legs

-oid, -oida, -oidea (Gr. *eidos*) form, bearing a form similar to that of another reference organism or structure; e.g., *anthropoid,* having the form of a human being

oligo- (Gr. *oligos*) few, small; e.g., oligochaete, having few bristles

omni- (L. *omnis*) all; e.g., omnivore, an animal that eats both plants and animals

omnivores organisms that eat both plants and animals

onto- (Gr. *on*) being; e.g., paleontology, study of ancient (fossil) beings

oo- (Gr. *oion*) egg; e.g., oogenesis, the formation of eggs

operant conditioning learning in which one of a variety of responses to a stimulus is reinforced by an observer, the operator, by a reward; the stimulus and response are paired by an agent outside the organism

order a group of closely related families; a taxonomic rank between family and class

organ (Gr. *organon,* tool, instrument) different tissues structurally joined and functioning cooperatively in a task characteristic of the group but not of any individual tissue

organelle a cellular structure surrounded by a membrane and specialized for a particular function

organic compounds compounds that contain carbon

organism smallest unit capable of living as an individual, whether single-celled or multicellular

organizer regions of animal embryos capable of inducing other regions to change or differentiate in a specific way, usually in reference to the dorsal lip of the blastopore of amphibian embryos

organ system different organs, usually joined structurally, functioning cooperatively in a task characteristic of the group but not of any individual organ

osmosis the diffusion of water molecules through a selectively permeable membrane toward a region with fewer molecules of water

Osteichthyes class of bony fishes

ovary the organ of animals that produces

eggs; the part of a seed plant giving rise to large spores which give rise to tissue that forms eggs

ovi-, ovo- (L. *ovum*) egg; e.g., oviduct, duct that transports egg

oviduct a tube opening next to an ovary and emptying into uterus; also called Fallopian tube

ovulation release of an egg from an ovary and entry of the egg into an oviduct

oxytocin hormone secreted by posterior pituitary gland which stimulates the contractibility of the uterus and the muscles in the mammaries that eject milk

paleo- (Gr. *palaios*) old; e.g., paleontology, study of ancient (fossil) life

para- (Gr.) beside; e.g., parapodia, footlike paddles on sides of polychaete worms

parasitism a type of symbiosis in which two or more organisms exist together in such a way that one lives at the expense of the other; e.g., tapeworms, mistletoe, and hookworms

parasympathetic nervous system subdivision of autonomic nervous system which is antagonistic to the sympathetic nervous system; effect is generally to inhibit animal (see *sympathetic nervous system*)

parthenogenesis (Gr. *parthenos*, virgin, + *genes*, born, created) growth and development of an unfertilized egg

passive transport the passage of substances through the cell membrane without the expenditure of energy

-ped, -pedia, pedi- (L. *pes*) foot; e.g., bipedal, two-footed

Pelecypoda class of the phylum Mollusca; clams, mussels, and oysters

penis external genital organ of male that is inserted into vagina of female during copulation

pent-, penta- (Gr. *pente*) five; e.g., pentose, five-carbon sugar

peptide bonds the bonds holding amino acids together; one amino acid gives up an —OH from its —COOH and another gives up an —H from its —NH₂; water is formed from the —H and —OH; the C then joins in a covalent bond with the N

peri- (Gr.) around; e.g., peristalsis, rhythmic waves of contraction along a tubular organ such as a gut

permeability (L. *permeare*, to pass through) capability of being penetrated

pH a system indicating the acidity or alkalinity of a solution in terms of the concentration of its hydrogen ions; scale is neutral at 7 and increasingly acidic below 7 to 0 and basic above 7 to 14; originally meant "power of hydrogen"

phage see *bacteriophage*

phago-, -phage (Gr.) eating; e.g., phagocytosis, mechanism by which a cell eats

phagocytosis the process by which cells take in solid food by folding in their cell membranes to form food vacuoles

pharynx the part of the food passage between mouth and esophagus; the throat

phenotype (Gr. *phanein*, to show) the traits of an organism that result from the expression of genes as affected by factors in the environment

pheromones (Gr. *pherein*. to carry + hormones) external secretions that serve as a means of communication and integration among individuals in a group

phloem (Gr. *phloos*, bark) plant vascular tissue that conducts nutrients from leaves to other regions; located inside bark in large woody plants

phoro-, -phore (Gr. *phos*) bearing, carrying; e.g., melanophore, cell bearing melanin pigment

photic zone see *zone of light*

photo-, photic (Gr. *photos*) light; e.g., photosynthesis, synthesis with energy from light

photosynthesis the process by which cells that contain chlorophyll synthesize simple carbohydrates from carbon dioxide and water with energy from light; oxygen is a by-product

phyllo-, -phyll (Gr. *phyllon*) leaf; e.g., chlorophyll, the green pigment in leaves

phylum a group of closely related orders; a taxonomic rank between class and kingdom

physiology (Gr. *physis,* nature) study of functions and processes

phyto-, -phyte (Gr. *phyton*) plant; e.g., bryophytes, the mosslike plants

phytoplankton microscopic algae suspended in fresh water or ocean

pinocytosis (Gr. *pinein,* to drink) the process by which cells take in fluid food by folding in their cell membranes to form vacuoles

pistil (L. *pistulus,* a pestle) region of flower that produces the large spore giving rise to ovules (eggs); consists of an ovary and a long style extending to a sticky end, the stigma

-pithecus (Gr. pithekos) ape; e.g., *Australopithecus,* the genus of the ancestor of modern man, means ''southern ape''

pituitary gland (L. *pituita,* phlegm) endocrine gland located below the hypothalamus of vertebrates; consists of two to three lobes, each operating independently of the others; several hormones released into blood from one of the pituitary lobes actually are synthesized in the hypotholamus

placenta (L. cake) structure formed from the lining of the uterus and tissues of embryo in which blood capillaries of embryo are bathed by blood from mother; regions where gases, wastes, and food can be exchanged between mother and embryo; present in all except pouched and egg-laying mammals

plankton (Gr. *planktos,* wandering) freely floating and drifting microscopic algae, pro-

tozoa, and small animals in fresh water and ocean

Plantae the kingdom comprising the plants

plants members of the kingdom Plantae, but often extended to include algae of kingdom Protista

-plasm, plasmo, -plant (Gr. *plasma*) form, mold; e.g., chloroplast, green body (form)

Platyhelminthes (Gr. *platys,* flat, + *helminthos,* worm) phylum of flatworms; planarians, flukes, and tapeworms

-ploid (Gr. *-ploos*) -fold, number of chromosome sets per cell; e.g., haploid, diploid

pollen (L., fine dust) small spores produced by cones or flowers which can germinate into gametophyte, the pollen tube, if they land on female region of proper cone or flower

poly- (Gr. *polys*) many; e.g., polychaete, many-bristled

polyp (Gr. *poly,* many, + *pous,* food) attached bowl-shaped stage; present in life cycle of most coelenterates; sea anemone, Hydra

polypeptide a chain of amino acids linked together by peptide bonds

polysaccharides complex sugars consisting of many simple sugars; e.g., starch and cellulose consist of chains of glucose molecules

population a group of organisms which are all members of the same species

Porifera phylum of sponges

predator an organism that feeds on another, the prey; e.g., a fox that feeds on rabbits, its prey

prehensile grasping

prepuce the skin covering the glans of the penis or clitoris; the foreskin

prey an organism that is eaten by another, its predator; e.g., a rabbit that is eaten by its predator, a fox

primate order of mammals containing prosimians, monkeys, apes, and man

pro- (Gr.) before, in front of; e.g., prophase, the first stage of cell division

profundal zone see *zone of darkness (fresh water)*

progesterone steroid hormone produced by corpus luteum of ovary after ovulation and also by placenta during pregnancy; maintains lining of uterus and inhibits ovulation

prolactin hormone secreted by anterior pituitary gland which stimulates the synthesis of milk in mammals

prophase first stage of cell division; chromosomes become distinct, nucleus and nucleolus disappear, and spindle begins to form

prostate gland a gland surrounding the neck of the bladder of human males which secretes and releases into the sperm duct part of the fluid of semen

protein an organic compound formed from one or more polypeptide chains; most of the chains consist of at least 40 to 50 amino acids and are folded and twisted

Protista kingdom consisting of protozoa, algae, fungi, and slime molds

proto- (Gr. *protos*) first; e.g., Protozoa, literally first animals

protoplasm synonomous with living matter

protozoa protistans which lack chlorophyll and must rely upon foods in their environment as sources of nutrition; usually single-celled and capable of locomotion with pseudopodia, cilia, or flagella

pseudo- (Gr. *pseudes*) false; e.g., pseudopodium, false foot

pseudopodia the streaming forth of cytoplasm to form extensions in ameboid movement

PTC phenylthiocarbamide; the ability to taste this substance is inherited as a dominant allele

puberty the age at which the reproductive organs become functional

purines double-ring nitrogenous bases such as adenine and guanine, found in DNA or RNA

pyrimidines single-ring nitrogenous bases such as cytosine found in DNA or RNA; thymine, only in DNA; and uracil, only in RNA

race see *subspecies*

radial symmetry body plan of animals in which both sides of any plane through longitudinal axis are similar in appearance

rain forest region with almost daily rains throughout the year and annual totals well over 100 inches; temperatures average 80°F and usually vary only 10° from this average

random mating condition in which any member of a population may mate with any other member of the opposite sex

range of tolerance range of degrees of expression of a limiting factor within which an organism may survive

reasoning solving problems

recessive gene (L. *recedere*, to recede) a gene that does not express itself as a trait in the presence of its allele, the dominant gene

recombination of genes production of an assortment of genes different from parents as a result of receiving one-half of the chromosomes from each parent

reflex (L. *reflectere*, to bend back) a response of a part of the body without conscious control

reflex arc a pathway linking the receptor neuron with the neuron that brought about the response

releaser stimulus which triggers sequence of acts in a pattern of instinctive behavior

reproduction the means by which an organism gives rise to another organism

reproductive isolation barriers—geographic, anatomical, structural, behavioral, or ecological—which prevent an exchange of genes between populations by sexual reproduction

Reptilia class of vertebrates which include pterosaurs, dinosaurs, snakes, lizards, alligators, crocodiles, and turtles

reptilian egg egg with yolk sac, allantois, chorion, amnion, and leathery shell; the amnion contains fluid which protects embryo from dehydration and mechanical damage

respiration (L. *respirare,* to breathe) the process by which energy is extracted from nutrient molecules and stored in the bonds holding phosphates together in ATP

reticulum (L. little net) a network of filaments, fibers, or fibrils; e.g., endoplasmic reticulum

rhizo- (Gr. *rhiza*) root; e.g., rhizoid, the rootlike extensions which anchor bryophytes in soil

rhizome (Gr. *rhizoma,* mass of roots) an underground stem

ribonucleic acid nucleic acids that contain ribose sugar as well as adenine, guanine, cytosine, and uracil; there are three principal kinds: messenger RNA (*m*RNA), transfer RNA (*t*RNA), and ribosome RNA (*r*RNA); except for RNA of viruses, RNA consists of a single strand and cannot replicate itself (see *deoxyribonucleic acid*)

ribose sugar the type of sugar found alternating with phosphates along the backbone of RNA, a nucleic acid

ribosomal RNA RNA which, after being formed by complementary base-pairing on sections of DNA, combines with protein to form ribosomes

ribosome granules in the cytoplasm which are the sites of protein synthesis

RNA see *ribonucleic acid*

rod cells cells in vertebrate retina sensitive to low levels of light; functional in night or twilight vision

rRNA see *ribosomal RNA*

salt a compound formed when an acid reacts with a base

saur-, -saur (Gr. sauros) lizard; e.g., dinosaur

savanna grassland in tropics with scattered trees, warm temperatures, long dry seasons interspersed with 40 to 60 inches of rainfall, and frequent fires

Scaphopoda (Gr. *skaphe,* boat) class of the phylum Mollusca; tooth shells

Schizophyta the phylum of bacteria

scrotum (L.) the pouch of skin containing the testes

seed an embryonic plant sporophyte surrounded by the remains of gametophyte tissue in gymnosperms or endosperm tissue in angiosperms and enclosed in a protective outer covering, the seed coat

seed plants gymnosperms and angiosperms; plants which produce spores and seeds in cones or flowers

segmentation body plan consisting of a series of regions containing similar structures

semen sperm plus the surrounding fluid produced by the male reproductive system; in mammals, most of this fluid is produced by the prostate gland and seminal vesicles

semi- (L.) half; e.g., semipermeable, partially permeable

seminal vesicle (L. *semen,* seed, + *vas,* vessel) a gland in the reproductive system of male mammals which secretes part of the fluid of semen

sense receptor specialized ending of a dendrite of a sensory neuron; changes in physical or chemical environment may stimulate them and cause a nerve impulse to flow toward cell body

sensory neuron neuron that brings a nerve

impulse in from a sense receptor to the brain or spinal cord

sequential evolution process by which species become new species through gradual shifting in frequency of genes through time

sex chromosomes a pair of chromosomes that vary in the sexes in number or shape and determine the sex of the organism; e.g., the X and Y chromosomes

sex-influenced genes genes not on the sex chromosomes but influenced in expression by hormones or other features unique to a sex

sex-linked genes genes carried on the X chromosome, such as those for color blindness and hemophilia

signals stimuli coming from other individuals in a population of animals

simple sugars also known as monosaccharides; sugars containing a chain of five or six carbon atoms; e.g., glucose and fructose

skin gills thin regions in body walls of echinoderms through which they can breathe

slime molds protists which have a life cycle alternating between ameboid cells and fruiting bodies that produce gametes

social dominance hierarchy of social rank among animals that travel as a group; based on dominance and submission

-soma, -some, somato- (Gr. soma) body; e.g., chromosome, body with color

speciation process by which new species develop by sequential or divergent evolution

species (pl. species) (L. kind, sort) group of actually or potentially interbreeding populations reproductively isolated from other such groups

-sperm, spermo-, sperma-, spermato- (Gr. sperma) seed; e.g., spermatogenesis, formation of sperm

sperm (Gr. sperma, seed) a mature gamete from a male; in contrast with an egg, a sperm is motile, small, has little cytoplasm, and no yolk

spicules (L. spiculum, little dart) tiny skeletal elements of a sponge

spirillum (L. spirilla, little coil) bacterium with a wavy, coiled, or spiral shape

spora-, spore- (Gr. spora) seed; e.g., sporophyte, spore-producing plant

spores specialized reproductive cells capable of developing under proper conditions, directly into an offspring; no fertilization involved (see *vegetative reproduction* and *gametes*)

sporophyte diploid spore-producing plant; phase of life cycle with alternates with gametophyte phase in an alternation of generations in plants

stamen (L. thread) pollen-producing structure of flower; consists of a stalk with a terminal case (anther) which produces pollen (small spores)

starch insoluble complex of chains of glucose molecules; principal form in which carbohydrates are stored in plants; differs from cellulose primarily in type of bonds between glucose units

stem cells embryonic cells forming a reservoir in specialized tissue and capable of replacing through cell division cells lost from the tissues

stereoscopic vision ability to superimpose two fields of vision; permits judging of distance

stereotyped behavior behavior consisting of repeated, highly predictable responses; repetition of particular stimuli repeatedly elicit the same responses

steroids animal hormones derived from fat precursors

stimulus (L. goad, incentive) any change in the internal or external environment that activates a sense receptor of an organism

stinging cells cells of coelenterates which can discharge poisonous or paralyzing barbs

stomata (Gr. stoma, mouth) small openings

in the outer covering of a plant which allow the exchange of gases with the environment

-stome, -stoma, -stomato (Gr. *stoma*) mouth; e.g., stomata, small openings in the outer covering of plants that resemble mouths

subspecies populations which differ in frequency of genes from other population groups in the species; synonomous with race

sym-, syn- (Gr. *syn*) together, with; e.g., symbiosis, living together

swim bladder saclike organ of bony fish that takes in or releases gases from blood so that the fish gains buoyancy and is almost weightless

symbiosis (Gr. *syn,* together, + *bioun,* to live) close relationships between organisms of different species with mutual or one-sided effects; the forms of symbiosis are mutualism, commensalism, and parasitism

sympathetic nervous system subdivision of autonomic nervous system which is antagonistic to the parasympathetic nervous system; effect is generally to excite and prepare animal for responses in a stress situation (see *parasympathetic nervous system*)

synapse (Gr. *synapsis,* a union) a region where a nerve impulse can be transferred from the axon of one neuron to a dendrite of another

synaptic cleft a very narrow space (about 200 angstroms) that separates the axon and dendrite in a synapse

synaptic knob a swelling at the end of one of the many branches at the terminal ends of axons; these form the axon portion of a synapse and secrete acetylcholine

synthesis the formation of simpler substances into a larger, more complex, substance

taiga region with long, severe winters alternating with short growing seasons limited to a few months in summer; coniferous forests distributed across northern Canada, Europe, and Siberia; often called the spruce-moose biome

taxis orientation of an animal to some factor in its environment with constant stimulation; the entire organism is involved in the response

taxo-, taxi-, -taxis (Gr. *taxis*) arrangement; e.g., taxonomy, study of arrangement of organisms into categories

taxonomy (Gr. *nomos,* law) the classification of organisms

tel-, tele-, teleo- (Gr. *telos*) end; e.g., telophase, end phase of cell division

telophase fourth and last stage of cell division; separation of cytoplasm into two halves by furrowing in animal cells and formation of cell plate in plant cells; spindle disappears, and chromosomes become indistinct, but nucleus and nucleolus reappear

template a pattern, or mold, upon which another pattern, or mold, can be made; this second set can then serve as a pattern, or mold, for the first; e.g., one strand of DNA is a template for the other, and therefore DNA replicates itself by forming single strands which act as templates for the formation of the second strands

territory geographic region defended against competing members of the same species by displays or actual fighting, usually by males

testis (pl. testes) (L. witness) sperm-producing organs in animals

testosterone steroid hormone produced in the testis; causes growth of male sex organs and development of secondary sexual characteristics, e.g., beard, large larnyx, larger muscles

tetra- (Gr.) four; e.g., tetrapods, the four-legged vertebrates

theory (Gr. *theorein,* to look at) a generalization originally presented as a hypothesis but now supported by observation and experimentation

thymine a pyrimidine nitrogenous base found in DNA but not RNA

tissue (L. *texere,* to weave) aggregate of cells of similar origin and structure cooperatively performing a common function

-tome, -tomy (Gr. *tome*) section, a cutting apart, e.g., anatomy, a study of structures which have been separated by cutting-apart

trachea (Gr. *trachys,* rough) air-conducting tube; windpipe of land vertebrates; branching system of tiny tubes in insects

Tracheophyta phylum of vascular plants; includes ferns, gymnosperms, and angiosperms

trans- (L.) across; e.g., translocation, the movement of water and its dissolved nutrients across from one region of a plant to another in phloem

transfer RNA (*t*RNA) small water-soluble molecules which carry amino acids to sections of *m*RNA where three nitrogenous bases on the *t*RNA can form complementary base pairs with three on the *m*RNA; these molecules are synthesized on sections of DNA

translocation movement of water and dissolved nutrients in phloem of plants

transpiration (L. *spirare,* to breathe) evaporation of water from leaves or other exposed plant surfaces

transport the passage of materials through the cell membrane

-troph, tropho-, (Gr. *trophos*) feeder; e.g., tropic levels, feeding levels in an ecosystem

tropical deciduous forest region of monsoon forests in tropical Asia; two seasons of year, wet and dry, are equal in length

tropical shrub forest region of thorn forests in Africa, Australia, and Brazil; two seasons, wet and dry, are equal in length

tRNA see *transfer RNA*

true hybrid an organism resulting from a cross between parents of different species; e.g., a mule, a cross between a horse and a donkey, is a true hybrid

tube feet hundreds of extendable projections from surface of echinoderms that can attach to a surface with suction and by contraction of muscles pull the animal along or pull the shells of a mollusk apart

tundra region with cold temperatures and continuous night during the winter and continuous daylight during the summer; permanently frozen permafrost only a few feet down; almost exclusively within the Arctic Circle

turgor (L. *turgere,* to swell) distention of a cell as a result of osmotic uptake of water

uracil a pyrimidine nitrogenous base found in RNA but not in DNA

urethra (Gr.) the duct which carries urine from the bladder to the exterior of the body

uterus (L. womb) a pear-shaped muscular organ of the female to which an embryo may attach and develop

vacuole (L. *vacuus,* empty) fluid-filled membranes in cytoplasm of many cells

vagina (L. sheath) the muscular tubelike organ into which the penis is placed during copulation; ends with cervix of uterus

variation condition in which members of a group are not identical

vascular (L. *vasculum,* small vessel) containing vessels which transport fluids

vegetative reproduction reproduction without spores or gametes but with body regions that break away and regenerate the parts necessary for a complete organism (see *spores* and *gametes*)

ventral (L. *venter, belly*) at, near, or toward the front; opposite of dorsal

vertebrate (L. *vertebra,* a joint) a chordate which replaces its notochord with a vertebral column or backbone

virus (L. slimy liquid, poison) a particle consisting of nucleic acid core with a protein coat which can duplicate itself only as a parasite within living cells

vulva external genitalia of a female

water vascular system system of tubes leading from tube feet of echinoderm to exterior, where a sieve plate regulates the entry and exit of water; regulates water pressure in tube feet

white matter axons and dendrites in brain and spinal cord

xantho- (Gr. *xanthos*) yellow; e.g., xanthophyll, the yellow pigment in plants

xylem (Gr. *xylon,* wood) plant vascular tissue that conducts water from roots upward; contains tracheids, vessels, and other cell types; when present in bulk, it is called wood

yolk region of egg containing stored nutrients

yolk sac membrane containing stored nutrients in reptiles and birds; present in pouched and placental mammals but contains no nutrients; grown as an extension from the embryo

zone of darkness (ocean) region beyond the shallow seas and in the deep ocean at a depth where light cannot penetrate; usually below 600 feet; technically called the aphotic zone

zone of darkness (fresh water) region of deep lakes where light cannot penetrate; technically called profundal zone

zone of light region beyond the shallow seas and in the deep ocean to a depth where light can penetrate; averages 600 feet in depth; technically called the photic zone

zone of open water region of lakes and ponds where light can penetrate but not to the bottom; technically called limnetic zone

zone of shallow seas region of sea over the continental shelves; seldom deeper than 500 feet or wider than 100 miles

zone of shallow water region of lakes and ponds where light can penetrate to the bottom; technically called littoral zone

zones geographic regions in ecosystems

zoo-, -zoa, -zoon (Gr. *zoion*) animal; e.g., zoology, the study of animals; protozoan, an animal-like protist

zooplankton microscopic protozoa and animals suspended in fresh water or ocean

zygo- (Gr. *zygon*) yoke, pair; e.g., zygote, fertilized egg formed from the pairing of egg and sperm

zygote (Gr. *zygotos,* paired together) a fertilized egg

Index